Management Handbook
for Plant Engineers

Other McGraw-Hill Handbooks of Interest

American Institute of Physics • American Institute of Physics Handbook
American Society of Mechanical Engineers • ASME Handbooks
    Engineering Tables   Metals Engineering—Processes
    Metals Engineering—Design   Metals Properties
Azad • Industrial Wastewater Management Handbook
Baumeister and Marks • Standard Handbook for Mechanical Engineers
Brater and King • Handbook of Hydraulics
Burington • Handbook of Mathematical Tables and Formulas
Burington and May • Handbook of Probability and Statistics with Tables
Callender • Time-Saver Standards for Architectural Design Data
Chow • Handbook of Applied Hydrology
Condon and Odishaw • Handbook of Physics
Conover • Grounds Maintenance Handbook
Crocker and King • Piping Handbook
Croft, Carr, and Watt • American Electricians' Handbook
Davis and Sorensen • Handbook of Applied Hydraulics
DeChiara and Callender • Time-Saver Standards for Building Types
Fink and Carroll • Standard Handbook for Electrical Engineers
Flügge • Handbook of Engineering Mechanics
Hamsher • Communication System Engineering Handbook
Harris • Handbook of Noise Control
Harris and Crede • Shock and Vibration Handbook
Hicks • Standard Handbook of Engineering Calculations
Ireson • Reliability Handbook
Juran • Quality Control Handbook
Korn and Korn • Mathematical Handbook for Scientists and Engineers
LaLonde and Janes • Concrete Engineering Handbook
LeGrand • The New American Machinist's Handbook
Lewis and Marron • Facilities and Plant Engineering Handbook
Machol • System Engineering Handbook
Mantell • Engineering Materials Handbook
Maynard • Handbook of Business Administration
Maynard • Industrial Engineering Handbook
Meites • Handbook of Analytical Chemistry
Merritt • Building Construction Handbook
Merritt • Standard Handbook for Civil Engineers
Morrow • Maintenance Engineering Handbook
O'Brien • Scheduling Handbook
Perry • Engineering Manual
Raznjevic • Handbook of Thermodynamic Tables and Charts
Rothbart • Mechanical Design and Systems Handbook
Smeaton • Switchgear and Control Handbook
Society of Manufacturing Engineers • Die Design Handbook
Society of Manufacturing Engineers • Tool and Manufacturing Engineers Handbook
Streeter • Handbook of Fluid Dynamics
Stubbs • Handbook of Heavy Construction
Truxal • Control Engineers' Handbook
Tuma • Engineering Mathematics Handbook
Tuma • Handbook of Physical Calculations
Tuma • Technology Mathematics Handbook
Urquhart • Civil Engineering Handbook
Watt and Summers • NFPA Handbook of the National Electrical Code
Woods • Highway Engineering Handbook

Management Handbook for Plant Engineers

Edited by
BERNARD T. LEWIS, P.E.
Head, Industrial Engineering Branch, Public Works Division
Naval Facilities Engineering Command
Alexandria, Virginia

McGRAW-HILL BOOK COMPANY

New York   St. Louis   San Francisco   Auckland   Bogotá
Düsseldorf   Johannesburg   London   Madrid
Mexico   Montreal   New Delhi   Panama
Paris   Saō Paulo   Singapore
Sydney   Tokyo   Toronto

Library of Congress Cataloging in Publication Data

Main entry under title:

Management handbook for plant engineers.

1. Plant engineering—Handbooks, manuals, etc.
I. Lewis, Bernard T.
TS184.M35   658'.91'62   75-12936
ISBN 0-07-037530-5

1234567890 KPKP 786543210987

The editors for this book were Harold B. Crawford and Virginia Fechtmann,
the designer was Naomi Auerbach, and the production supervisor
was Teresa F. Leaden. It was set in Gael
by The Kingsport Press.

Printed and bound by The Kingsport Press.

Contents

1942164

SECTION 10. Safeguarding the Facility

Index follows Section 10.

Contributors

S. Altman   *School of Business and Organizational Sciences, Florida International University* (SEC. 4, CHAP. 7)

Herbert L. Antzes   *Chief Engineering Instruction Division, Postal Service Training and Development Institute* (SEC. 8, CHAP. 2)

James Beatty   *President, Plant and Maintenance Consultants, Incorporated* (SEC. 4, CHAP. 5)

Eric M. Bergtraun   *Manager, Plant Engineering and Maintenance, National Semiconductor Corporation* (SEC. 7, CHAP. 5; SEC. 9, CHAP. 6)

Herbert R. Brown   *Consultant* (SEC. 9, CHAPS. 3 AND 7)

Lewis M. Buttery   *Bonner & Moore Associates, Incorporated* (SEC. 8, CHAP. 10)

Lloyd R. Calaway   *Bonner & Moore Associates, Incorporated* (SEC. 4, CHAP. 2; SEC. 6, CHAP. 1; SEC. 8, CHAP. 10)

John A. Carraro   *President, International Consultants* (SEC. 3, CHAP. 5)

Robert G. Caughey   *The H. K. Ferguson Company* (SEC. 5, CHAP. 2)

Ronald W. Chambers   *Manager, Maintenance Engineering, The Firestone Tire & Rubber Company* (SEC. 4, CHAP. 3)

Earl O. Clark   *Property Administration, Vought Aeronautics Company* (SEC. 1, CHAP. 2)

Robert C. Colling, P.E.,   *Manager, Plant Engineering and Maintenance, Xerox Corporation* (SEC. 7, CHAP. 4)

John M. Connelly   *Director of Corporate Facilities Engineering, Black and Decker Manufacturing Company* (SEC. 3, CHAP. 1)

Morris Gewirtz   *Consultant* (SEC. 9, CHAP. 1)

John C. Gorton, P.E.   *Manager, Review and Estimates, Xerox Corporation* (SEC. 3, CHAP. 7)

William P. Goudron   *Supervisor, Industrial Engineering and Design, Plant Engineering and Design, Plant Engineering Department, Airesearch Manufacturing Company* (SEC. 2, CHAP. 4)

Lee Hales   *Consulting Associate, Richard Muther & Associates, Incorporated* (SEC. 2, CHAP. 5)

Richard J. Healy   *Head, Security Department, The Aerospace Corporation* (SEC. 10, CHAP. 1)

Mahendra Jain   *Facilities Planner, Plant Engineering and Maintenance, Xerox Corporation* (SEC. 8, CHAP. 3)

J. Kilroy   *Consultant* (SEC. 5, CHAP. 5)

E. H. Kittner, P.E.   *Engineering and Maintenance Superintendent, Georgia-Pacific Corporation* (SEC. 4, CHAP. 4)

Steve Kozich   *President, Quality Audit Company* (SEC. 8, CHAP. 9)

Arthur R. Laney   *Consultant* (SEC. 9, CHAP. 2)

R. B. Leiter   *Manager of Plant Engineering, F. E. Meyers & Brothers Company* (SEC. 5, CHAP. 7)

Charles H. Ludlum, P.E.   *Manager of Engineering Reports, The Austin Company* (SEC. 2, CHAP. 6)

Raymond P. McFarland   *The Emerson Consultants, Inc.* (SEC. 4, CHAP. 1)

Robert S. Mach   *The Sherwin-Williams Company* (SEC. 9, CHAP. 5)

Richard Mathison   *Manager, Technical Services, Xerox Corporation* (SEC. 3, CHAP. 8)

T. G. Meikle   *Manager, Facilities and Plant Engineering Division, Jet Propulsion Laboratory, California Institute of Technology* (SEC. 3, CHAP. 3)

William R. Miller   *Manager, Corporate Safety Programs, Goodyear Tire & Rubber Company* (SEC. 10, CHAP. 2)

Richard Muther, P.E., CMC   *President, Richard Muther & Associates, Incorporated.* (SEC. 2, CHAPS. 1 AND 2)

Sylvestor H. O'Grince   *Director of School Buildings and Grounds, Baltimore City Public Schools* (SEC. 6, CHAP. 2)

Robert H. O'Neill   *Director of Engineering, McNeil Laboratories, Inc.* (SEC. 3, CHAP. 6)

F. J. Packard   *The H. K. Ferguson Company* (SEC. 5, CHAP. 4)

Alan J. Parker   *School of Business and Organizational Sciences, Florida International University* (SEC. 8, CHAP. 4)

R. L. Perkins   *Supervisor, Facilities Master Planning, Vought Aeronautics Company, Division of LTU Aerospace Corporation* (SEC. 2, CHAP. 3)

H. Harry Phipps, P.E.   *Energy Systems Consultants* (SEC. 5, CHAP. 8)

N. B. Post, P.E.   *Manager, Plant Engineering and Maintenance, Xerox Corporation* (SEC. 7, CHAP. 2; SEC. 8, CHAP. 3)

Robert H. Printup   *Director of General Services, University of Chicago Hospitals and Clinics* (SEC. 8, CHAP. 5)

P. S. Ridley, P.E.   *Manager, Plant Engineering, RCA* (SEC. 3, CHAP. 9)

J. Campbell Round   *Consulting Engineer* (SEC. 1, CHAP. 3)

Richard Ryan, P.E.   *Plant Engineer, Hamilton Standard Division of United Technological Corporation* (SEC. 7, CHAP. 4)

Robert R. Ruhlin   *Director, Engineering and Management Division, Syska & Hennessy, Incorporated* (SEC. 1, CHAP. 4)

Clifford R. Sayre   *Director of Technical Training, Personnel Development Incorporated* (SEC. 8, CHAP. 6)

Max Schwartz *President, Max Schwartz Consulting Engineers Incorporated* (SEC. 3, CHAP. 2)

R. D. Shaffer *Department Head, Facilities Engineering Department, Union Carbide Corporation, Nuclear Division* (SEC. 3, CHAP. 4)

Carl T. Sieg *Consultant* (SEC. 9, CHAP. 4)

Don L. Stieghan *Harvey Technical Center, Atlantic Richfield Company* (SEC. 4, CHAP. 6)

Donald E. Toone *Engineering Editor,* Maintenance Engineering *Magazine* (SEC. 8, CHAP. 1)

E. Turban *School of Business and Organizational Sciences, Florida International University* (SEC. 4, CHAP. 7; SEC. 8, CHAP. 4)

James VanKherkhove *Facilities Planner, Plant Engineering and Maintenance, Xerox Corporation* (SEC. 7, CHAP. 3)

John M. Waligora, P.E., FAIPE *Consultant* (SEC. 1, CHAP. 5)

L. T. Wassman *Plant Engineer, Sherwin-Williams Company* (SEC. 1, CHAP. 6; SEC. 5, CHAP. 6)

Edward F. Wehlage, P.E. *Edward F. Wehlage and Associated Engineers* (SEC. 5, CHAP. 1)

W. H. Weiss *Manager of Engineering and Maintenance, Chemigum Plant, Goodyear Tire & Rubber Company* (SEC. 7, CHAP. 1)

David J. Wilkie *General Superintendent, Maintenance & Services, Chrysler Corporation,* (SEC. 1, CHAP. 1)

J. R. Witmeyer *Utilities Division Staff, Naval Facilities Engineering Command* (SEC. 5, CHAPS. 1 AND 3)

Barbara H. Young *Management Analyst* (SEC. 8, CHAP. 11)

Lester F. Zerfoss *Professor of Management and Chairman of the Management Department, University of North Carolina* (SEC. 8, CHAP. 7)

Robert G. Zilly *Construction Management Department, College of Engineering and Architecture, University of Nebraska* (SEC. 8, CHAP. 8)

Foreword

Concern over management of the plant engineering function, both in industry and government, is increasing at a great rate. This concern stems from the need to reduce resources required to design, construct, operate, and maintain our facilities and equipment in order to remain competitive. It leads, inevitably, to pressure by corporate managers on plant engineers to reduce costs and optimize efficiency and effectiveness. The central question in better plant engineering management is no longer whether; it is how. The *Management Handbook for Plant Engineers* is designed to answer the question of how best to manage the plant engineering function with the latest technology. It should provide a major contribution to the dissemination of management control techniques and the encouragement of sound corporate decisions in plant engineering management. The implementation of an effective plant engineering management improvement program depends on the coordinated efforts of corporate managers and plant engineers. I am encouraged by the publication of this handbook as evidence of private industry's growing awareness of the need to improve plant engineering management practices as a contribution to sound business practice.

EDWARD J. SHERIDAN; *Formerly,*
Deputy Assistant Secretary of Defense
for Installations and Housing
Department of Defense

Preface

Plant engineering management in all sectors, public and private, is changing rapidly. High-speed computers, new mathematical and statistical tools, and data from the behavioral sciences are providing a "knowledge explosion" which is of inestimable value to the modern plant engineer.

As modern management techniques change, plant engineering management changes too. This handbook has been prepared for the express purpose of presenting to the plant engineer the latest developments in plant engineering management systems, procedures, and techniques that should prove intellectually stimulating and useful.

Chapters in the handbook, and its section organization, reflect major developments that have occurred in plant engineering management over the last decade. All chapter authors represented have contributed the results of their original thought and research plus the invaluable background and experience which is reflected in their writings.

This handbook will be of service to plant engineering managers and supervisors at all levels in any industry, institution, or government agency. It contains treatment of plant engineering *management* to an extent found nowhere else. There are 63 chapters grouped into 10 sections: Organization and Staffing; Facilities Planning and Programming; Engineering and Construction Management; Maintenance Management; Utilities Management; Materials Management; Systems and Reports; Budget and Costs; Personnel and Administration; and Safeguarding the Facility.

In editing this handbook, I have drawn upon the learning, knowledge, and skills of 59 specialists representing a wide range of disciplines and covering the gamut of plant engineering management. Without their help this handbook would not have been written.

Since we live and work in a technological society continually thrust forward by new learnings, this handbook should have relevance not only to the modern plant engineer but to other management personnel as well. I hope that the *Management Handbook for Plant Engineers* will give plant engineers new insights into their work and will help them in the performance of their jobs.

Bernard T. Lewis

Section 1

Organization and Staffing

Chapter 1

General

DAVID J. WILKIE
General Superintendent, Maintenance & Services, Chrysler Corporation

INTRODUCTION

The purpose of this chapter is to provide an understanding of the elements that comprise an organization or staff. Note the distinction: The organization and the staff are *not* one and the same. In the following pages the distinction of each of these terms will be enlarged. The premise which supports all further definition is as follows: The organization is the inflexible structure that provides authority and avenues of response to each position regardless of who holds the position. The staff then must operate within the constraints of the organization and within the capability of the weakest member. The staff is changeable by personal interactions and new talents. The organization is changeable by administrative edict.

Organizing and staffing are prime functions of every manager. Both the foreman and the president must provide themselves with the proper people and the people with the proper mode to complete work. "Proper" in this context is then "that which best suits the manager's view of productivity."

It is well to remember that changing the organization will not cure a staffing problem, nor will changing the staff solve the deficiencies of the organization.

ORGANIZING—GENERAL

The need to organize, or more commonly reorganize, is most prevalent during periods of failure. The pressures of not getting the job done or the continual need to catch up tend to drive the group manager toward the decision to either reorganize or restaff. Other reasons to consider such changes might be future expansion, new facilities, new processes or products, changes in top management with a new perspective of plant engineering, and centralization or decentralization of the management staff. In the preceding circumstances, there are two basic categories: (1) the manager's self-determination to reorganize to meet the work requirements and (2) higher levels causing lower-level organizational changes. In either case, the group manager should be the best equipped to set up the structure.

Preparing to Organize

Though there are no common rules of organization, most personnel departments have an established policy that is considered to be acceptable to the enterprise. These policies are more stringent in large corporations than in small ones, but in either case it is advisable to contact the personnel office first and discuss what the company requires. Some questions to ask are:

1. Is there a company manual on organizational policy?
2. Are there parallel structures elsewhere in the company?
3. Is there a maximum or minimum number of subordinates ("span of control") for a given grade level or title?
4. How does the company view overlapping accountabilities and split reporting? There is a tendency during this type of discussion to shift the conversation to personalities, talent, training, and other staffing-related topics. Avoid this—stick to matters of structure.

Company policy may seem inhibiting, but the rule for the first attempt at reorganizing is *Try to stay within the policy.* Company policy is a major part of the organizational makeup. The group manager who establishes an organization is in reality establishing more policy. It is hoped that the total effect of these policies will enhance the productivity of the enterprise.

ELEMENTS OF ORGANIZATIONAL POWER: AUTHORITY, ACCOUNTABILITY

The need to change implies a change for the better. This should not exclude from improvement the existing, acceptable qualities of the current structure. Rather than setting out to analyze what is wrong, analyze what is. This requires further definition of organization:

1. Organizational objectives are definable and must be determined for each position.
2. The organization vests limited power, which is called authority, in the staff.
3. These power limits are defined by policy and detailed job descriptions.
4. Organizational power, position power, authority, is available to whoever holds the position.
5. Organizational objectives equal organizational obligation.
6. Each position is accountable for acts that meet organizational obligations or objectives.

7. Accountabilities and organizational obligations are synonymous.

8. Organizational power—authority—cannot exceed organizational obligation or vice versa.

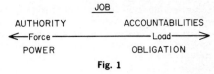

Fig. 1

The analysis of the organization is the determination of balance or imbalance between the implied organizational power and the actual organizational obligation (see Fig. 1). The given powers equal the known work content of the position.

Each position in the organization can be reviewed in terms of capability of meeting objectives. Such an analysis would take the following form:

1. Detach each position from the total organization and from the position holder.

2. Denote the prime and subobjectives of the position as they relate to the following criteria:

    a. Product
    b. Marketing
    c. Physical resources
    d. Human resources
    e. Community
    f. Profits

3. Answer the following:

    a. Is the objective accountable to the position because of job description, policy, special procedure, or is it an assumed obligation?

    b. What percentage of authority to meet objectives does the position hold?

4. Denote percentage of other major authorities regarding this objective. These authorities may be within or separate from the immediate department or division.

    a. Denote by * those authorities that are within the parent division.

See Fig. 2 for an example of analysis points 1, 2, 3, and 4. In this figure, the tool room foreman's position holds all the authority needed to ensure that tools are sharpened. Improperly maintained tools indicate a staffing problem.

The prototypes from Fig. 2 are in trouble unless the divisional manager authorizes in the procedure the accountabilities of the process engineer and the tool room foreman. Furthermore, the organization is not suited to ensure quality of tooling and fixturing.

In Fig. 3, the analysis discloses that the position of process engineer is accountable for prototype design but not for prototype manufacture; yet from Fig. 2, the tool room

Position **Tool Room Foreman**

Criteria	Job description	Policy	Procedure	Assumed	Authority				
					Job	Others	Others	Others	Others
Products Maintain fixtures and tooling to produce quality parts.				√	20%	Production 60%	Process eng'g 15%	Mat'rl cont. 5%	
Products Make prototype for preproduction evaluation.			√		45%		Process eng'g 50%	Mat'rl cont. 5%	
Products Maintain, sharpen, and repair dull tools	√		√		95%	Production 5%			
Products Make parts									

Fig. 2

foreman's position is somehow unable to assure completion. This type of gray area is not uncommon and usually results in poor performance.

Figure 3 indicates more organization gray area regarding quality capability of process tooling. The process engineer is accountable for a good process, but nothing is mentioned about providing sufficient capacity to meet production and maintenance time requirements. From these examples it appears that this organization will, however, successfully regrind and maintain tools. Note the difference in criteria—the process engineer's position is deemed more accountable to the economics of resources than it is to quality of product. This difference in perspective between engineering and maintenance could become a cause of poor performance if the staff is changed or external pressures are placed upon either quality or tool inventory. Therefore it would be wise at this time to establish priorities that define the quality and the cost implication of

POSITION ___ Process Engineer

(B-1) (C-1) (C-2) (D-1)

Criteria	Job Descript.	Policy	Procedure	Assumed	Authority				
					Job	Others,	Others	Others	Others
Products Design prototypes for preproduction evaluation			✓		95%	Mat'rl cont. 5%			
Products Provide tool routings, speeds feeds and change frequency	✓				100%				
Phy. Resources Estab. tool back up and regrind procedure to max tool life	✓				100%				
Products Design fixture	✓				100%				

Fig. 3

process tooling and build this into the job description of the tool room foreman and the process engineer.

ALIGNMENT OF ACCOUNTABILITIES

Once each position has been analyzed and reviewed, the deficiencies of each must be corrected. Then both must be rejoined into an effective work structure. In the case of fixture maintenance, cited in Figs. 2 and 3, there could be three or more plant departments all interested in getting quality parts.

From this hypothetical case, it would appear that the fixtures could not possibly be maintained; however, this need not be the case. The staff, on the basis of an interpersonal sense of responsibility, may be repairing the fixtures quite adequately. The problem with this type of operation is that if one new member with a different set of priorities is inserted into the structure, the repair of fixtures will cease. It is for this reason that the organization must contain the accountabilities that authorize the position. This, then, provides a definite basis for performance review of the position holder. In this instance, the accountabilities of the process engineer should be:

1. Design fixtures capable of producing quality parts.
2. Provide, with the aid of quality control, necessary gauges and test equipment.
3. Determine normal quality part yield per fixture, gauge, tool, etc.
4. Establish fixture, gauge, and tool part backups timebased on yield and volumes.

5. Determine operation capacity requirements, which include all lost time such as setup, maintenance, and tool change.

6. Provide ample capacity to meet production volumes.

7. Provide periodic review of fixturing and machine performance, including maintenance expense, to determine causes of failures and corrective or improved design applications.

8. Communicate all problems concerning the equipment operation that are beyond the control of the position such as:

Operator practice
Maintenance practice
Additional maintenance requirements
Additional fund requirement

9. Follow a specific (documented) procedure regarding vendor reliability.

The tool room foreman's accountabilities should then read:

1. Check stock to ensure fixture parts are on hand and report shortages to materials control.

2. Schedule fixture repair and notify production five working days in advance of start time and job duration estimate.

3. Write maintenance repair order per documented maintenance procedure.

4. Communicate all exceptions that arise during the course of work to process engineering and production.

5. Train employees as to most effective methods.

6. Evaluate performance of employees.

7. Determine practicalities of salvage methods for details removed from service and restock all salvaged parts according to documented maintenance procedure.

The accountabilities for both positions are now aligned and the plant engineering organization can now staff and expect that fixtures will be maintained, provided that production, quality control, and materials control fulfill their accountabilities.

Provide Resources and Time to Facilitate Accountabilities

In the preceding it was assumed that two positions existed and that the accountability of each had been aligned to an expected work output. The same format can be used when reorganizing or establishing a new organization. The first consideration is, then, to determine the accountabilities are or what must be achieved, controlled, processed, etc. The next consideration is what resources—money, equipment, tools, furnishings—are required to do the work. Third, how much time—frequency of events, man-hours, number of elements—is required to do the work. The element of time requirements is jointly related to staffing and to organizing. Therefore, precise values are inappropriate when the sole consideration is the organizational makeup. The base structure of any position is:

$$\text{Accountability} + \text{resources} + \text{time} = \text{authority}$$

The effective organization has well-defined authority The scope of this authority is outlined in Fig. 4.

Positional Levels

The number of management levels has often been held to be based on the total number of subordinates. In actuality, it is based on the range of accountabilities. As the enterprise expands, accountabilities begin to exceed capabilities and new positions are added. This response to growing pains is usually forced by circumstances rather than planned over the long range. Skillful organizers are mindful of the future. They align accountabilities in major categories which are divisible by two. Each position is then prepared for the eventual subdivision with a smooth transition which, once again, can meet the objectives of the enterprise. In this pyramiding process, as illustrated in Fig. 5, plant engineering is formed in about the third generation of development. The title will vary with the industry, but in general it means operations and maintenance. As the enterprise continues to expand, plant engineering will normally grow an additional five management levels. Each descending level is subdivided into more specialized fields with specialized objectives and more limiting authority. Each position level is a decision center that administers and communicates the needs of the work group. The more complex organization vests ascending amounts of authority and renumeration in each higher level of administration. In Fig. 4 the authority is not necessarily aligned with the position level; however, higher-level positions contain more authority for the administration of physical resources and profits, while the lower levels are more related to human resources and products. The accountabilities of administration are then more general-

		AUTHORITY TO (accountabilities)	POSITIONAL LEVELS (common titles)
P	C	Do physical work	Nonskilled
R	O	Plan physical work	Apprentice
O	M	Facilitate physical work	#1 Trainee
D a	M	Schedule physical work	Journeyman
U n	U	Control physical work	Leader
C d	N	Review physical work	
T	I	Report status of work	
S	T	Record events	Planner
	Y	Administer events	Detailer
			Layout
		Control attendance	#2 Clerk
	R	Schedule manpower	Designer
	E	Hire manpower	Engineer
H	S	Review performance	
U	O	Pay and compensate	
M	U	Train and motivate	Schedule
A	R	Advance or promote	#3 Foreman
N	C	Discipline or demote	Unit Supv.
	E	Organize and staff	
	S	Evaluate suggestions	
		Develop objectives	General foreman
			#4 Department head
			Assistant superintendent
P	R	Protect facilities	
H	E	Maintain facilities	
Y	S	Provide service	Superintendent
S	O	Purchase material	#5 Chief engineer
I	U	Purchase equipment	Master mechanic
C	R	Reduce loss	
A	C	Reduce usage	
L	E	Control utilities	General superintendent
	S	Improve capability	#6 Engineering manager
			Maintenance manager
M			
A	P	Elevate quality	
R	R	Promote enterprise	
K a	O	Display image	Plant engineering manager
E n	F	Improve performance	#7 Manufacturing engineering
T d	I	Reduce operating cost	manager
I	T	Preserve assets	
N	S	Prepare for future	
G			

Fig. 4

ized at higher levels than the responsibilities and staffing requirements, which are then more specific.

STAFFING

The word "staff" in the present context connotes people who cooperate in a productive effort. Staffing is, then, the forming of people into groups whose work reaps the collective benefits of each individual's training, talent, and psychological power. "Staffing" might also mean the placing of people into organizational positions. Staffing or restaffing is always done because there are vacated or open positions which, in turn, stem from any number of deliberate moves or accidental events. Of these, there are three circumstances that bear heavily on a manager's ability to staff; it is most important that they be fully understood. They are:

Hiring
Promotion
Demotion

This section is addressed to the elements of staffing primarily as they relate to these three circumstances.

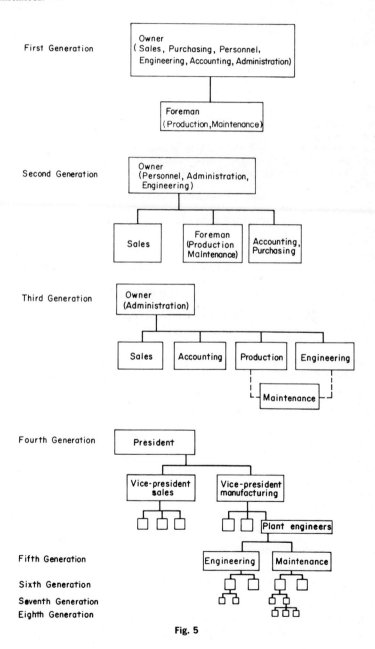

Fig. 5

ELEMENTS OF STAFF POWER: LEADERSHIP, RESPONSIBILITY, INFLUENCE, PERSONALITY

Whereas the *organization* consists of positions with accountability and authority, the *staff* is made up of people with responsibility and leadership. This parallelism coexists in every enterprise at all levels. A strong, productive operation uses its authority and leadership to achieve the objectives of accountability and the satisfaction derived from responsibility.

SATISFACTION

LEADERSHIP   RESPONSIBILITY
←Force————————————————Load→
POWER   OBLIGATION

LEADERSHIP AND RESPONSIBILITY

Fig. 6

Staff power, unlike position power, is informal, unstructured and personal rather than impersonal. It is developed within and among the individuals of the group. The unit of exchange or catalyst for this reaction is satisfaction rather than job need.

Leadership and Responsibility

The two most essential elements are leadership and responsibility. The following points identify characteristics of each:

1. People take on a leadership role by giving satisfaction to others.

2 The leader is then obligated or responsible to do what others find satisfactory.

3. The leader gives up satisfaction in other areas to achieve the power of being the leader.

4. The followers will discard the leader when he ceases to satisfy or when the need no longer exists.

5. The followers are obligated to do what the leader requires as long as they allow the situation to exist.

6. Any of the followers in one situation can concurrently hold a leadership role in another situation.

7. A person with a high capacity for responsibility has more opportunities to become the leader.

8. The leader and followers are most often not consciously aware of their respective roles.

9. Reputation for accomplishment allows more opportunity for leadership.

10. People with a broad general accomplishment have more opportunity to become leaders providing they have the capacity to assume the responsibility.

11. Capacity to accept responsibility is time-shared with accountability and is dependent on the individual's psychological ability to cope with the requirements of both.

12. Leadership does not necessarily belong to the person who holds the authority.

Influence

The third element in the interpersonal power structure is influence, which is often misinterpreted as leadership. Influence, like leadership, involves interaction between people leading to a particular accomplishment. The distinguishing characteristic of influence is that the influential person does not have to assume additional responsibility to promote an influential action. The degree of a person's influence is dependent upon the capacity of another person to accept added responsibility and for that person's acceptance of the would-be influencer.

Influence is an emotional transaction with an intellectual response. It consists of a suggestion transmission, a two-way emotional transmission, and an accomplishment. The two most prevalent forms of influence are:

1. The Need with Suggestion Influencing the Observer with Power:

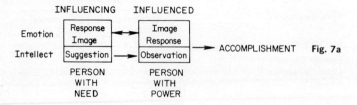

2. The Observer with Suggestion Influencing the Need with Power:

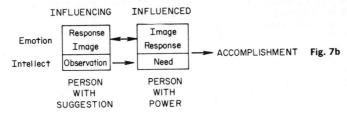

Fig. 7b

In both of these instances, there has been an established or a spontaneous emotional transaction that is recognized by the influenced as an acceptable circumstance for accomplishment. Further characteristics and description are as follows:

1. Influence is a skill.
2. Influence exists irrespective of position.
3. Influence is more discernible in peer or subordinate to superordinate relationships.
4. Superordinate to subordinate influence is dependent on the amount of authority perceived by the subordinate during the transmission of the suggestion.
5. The satisfaction derived from the accomplishment is experienced by both parties but for different reasons.

Personality

The fourth element is, for sake of definition, labeled personality. A common belief is that personality is a God-given force that renders people spellbound; that charisma, animal magnetism, love, and mystique are all rolled into one to form the perfect personality. For our purpose here, personality may be defined as the performance of a skill. The more developed a personality, the more productive the skill. The amount of personality power a person possesses increases as a person knowingly reveals more of his needs and commits himself with purpose to know more about and do more about satisfying the needs of others. The purposefulness of establishing a personality is, then, the key factor of how well the development will proceed. The productivity of the purpose is a direct result of philosophic input. The more limited, obscure, secretive philosophy will produce a less powerful personality. The philosophic base which establishes the cause to act and react with other people is the only element of a person's makeup that can be knowingly implemented and thus improved by the individual.

COMMUNICATIONS

The power of interpersonal communications lies in the ability to find the media that will transmit and receive replies with minimal interference. It is closely linked to personality. The low accomplisher transmits and receives on a narrow band. The more developed personality is the key person in a good communication system. His influence, credibility, accomplishments, leadership, and purposefulness satisfy a large segment of the group and obligate them to attentiveness, thought, and decisiveness. It then follows that the personality development process will be slow unless there is a conscious acknowledgment on the part of the individual that communications do flow to and from him and that he must become more expert as a communicator.

Elements of Communication: Noise, Quiet, Interest

People at work are seldom thought of as socializing, but work is truly a social experience, just as much as man is a social animal. Communication is the glue that holds the society —or work group—together. For the purpose of this writing, however, it is necessary to make a distinction between work and social communications. Work communication (work-comm), states specifically: "work content for the betterment of the enterprise." Social communication (so-comm) is anything other than the above. Most conversations and some writings contain both work-comm and so-comm. Both work-comm and so-comm are subject to "noise." Noise is anything that interrupts or clouds the clarity of the transmission or the reception of the transmission.

Noise Ruins Communications

Noise has many forms. A good understanding of noise is very important. Noise can manifest the following:

1. Prejudice toward the person transmitting.
2. Prejudice or disinterest about the subject matter.
3. Differing cognitive responses of value or priority.
4. Tuning out to prepare a reply.
5. Mumbled speech and poor penmanship.
6. Beating about the bush and lengthy introductions.
7. Loud sounds or background noise.
8. Poor choice or use of words.
9. Demeaning commentary.

It is entirely possible that a single conversation can contain all of the preceding, but normally it takes only one of these elements to stifle achievement. Where the enterprise is concerned, work communications should contain zero noise. Fortunately, work-comm is more objective and, therefore, more relevant than social communication, and will receive less subjective connotation. Work-comm can often be written. The work-comm writer creates far less noise than the work-comm speaker. A plus for written communication is built-in retention. Many work conversations contain social connotations that are intended to emphasize the work need. Unfortunately, this type of so-comm merely turns off the receiver. To combat this, communications should be more quiet.

Quiet is not merely the opposite of noise; it is the avoidance of noise. Where noise is conflict, quiet is the confrontation of the conflict prior to further communications. Where noise is subjective, quiet is objective. Where noise is physical, quiet is a new environment. Where noise is offensive, quiet is rapport.

People at work use their work-comm and so-comm to find a comfortable level of coexistence. An observer can sit back and easily identify both forms. The people that are predominately so-comm speakers will most likely be noise makers. People that are predominately work-comm speakers are not, however, quiet makers—just less noisy. The quiet communicator is more noticeable by his response and by that of others, than he is by what is initially transmitted. Quiet communications are always highlighted by attentiveness, comprehension, and retention. People attempting to communicate normally seek only comprehension from their addressee; consequently, they place their emphasis on description and word usage. The unfortunate part of this type of communication is that it may not be of interest to the other party. Limited interest begets limited attention, and with limited attention there is little chance for comprehension and resultant retention. The good communication is first and foremost interesting—being interested is an emotional experience. The need to know makes a communication interesting. If this need cannot be realized, the communication becomes boring and the noise level increases. The good communicator is, then, one who prepares what is transmitted or

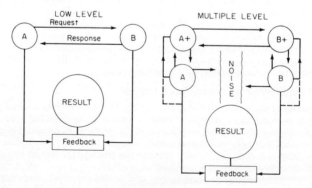

Fig. 8

received in terms of this need to know and maintains that high need level throughout the conversation.

Plant engineering is a service operation and being such, those involved receive far more work requests from peer or subordinate levels than they do from superordinate levels. This multiplicity of input forces plant engineers and maintenance people to prioritize their efforts and communicate their intent. This is a tough task for a good communicator and an impossible one for a poor communicator under the pressure of meeting heavy production schedules. As a result of inferior communications, information ceases to flow in direct peer level paths. Instead, it begins to flow up and back down the chain of command with pressures and noise added along the way. This can easily quintuple the amount of time a single low-level communication would require. Figure 8 could just as easily have shown three or four levels of involvement and with each level, the interjection of noise, perspective, and priority, but the end result could not improve on a low level communication.

ELEMENTS OF STAFF BEHAVIOR

As positions are filled, the people who hold them begin playing the roles that are deemed suitable to them. A low-level position with no subordinate structure need only be acted out in a manner that suits the boss. Higher-level roles, however, must meet not only the above criteria but must also be acceptable to the subordinates. Typically this generates, in the intermediate position role, an uncomfortable conflict. On one hand, the role player is attempting to win acceptance from the group, yet on the other, dependent upon his or her ambitions, this person seeks to be at least satisfactory to the next higher level. The identification of position is continually threatened until the role player either:

1. Gets promoted
2. Leaves the position
3. Accepts a compromised situation

The identification of the role is no pure science but is simply the most important asset of working toward the capacity of the role. The empirical data describing role playing suggest that there are three basic superordinate roles. They are:

1. Authoritarian
2. Permissive
3. Participative

It is also suggested that the former two are McGregor's theory X and the latter is theory Y;* the prime difference being that X managers do things to lazy people and Y managers do things with productive people. Further study on this issue would probably be useful, but it is well to remember that in practice the acceptance of either theory is the assumption of a role.

A manager in the process of identifying his role draws many conclusions that support his actions. The composite of these conclusions becomes what is then the act of managing people. The least explored area of these generally accepted conclusions is that the people have already decided how to act. They, therefore, do what is deemed to be acceptable when dealing with the superordinate position holder. A rat race? Not necessarily.

When the superordinate acts like an authoritarian, he expects that the subordinate will obey the command. When the actions are permissive, it is expected that the will to do will come from the demanding subordinate. When the actions of the superordinate are participative, it is expected that the response will be analytical and yet cooperative. In each case, the management role is only part of the mechanism of results. The remainder lies with the subordinate's choice of roles. The basic subordinate roles are:

1. Yes sayer and ingratiator
2. No sayer—demander
3. Questioner and participator

All plant engineering positions answer to a higher authority, and the role players at each management level are constantly engaged in a role as boss or subordinate which approximates one of these six role descriptions. Those roles that are most often played are those

---

* From D. McGregor, *The Human Side of Enterprise,* McGraw-Hill Book Company, New York, 1960, chaps. 3 and 4, pp. 33–57.

that preserve the satisfaction of the position holder's general needs. Tenure of position will eventually stabilize all responses and the personality—as well as the role played—will begin to gain identification by the group. The productivity demonstrated by the group is considered to be the most accurate gauge of the compatibility of the roles. A comfortable work existence is one that is viewed in the same way by the boss, the position holder, and the subordinates. When one of these elements is opposed in perspective, it always results in dissatisfaction.

The present author takes exception to this generalized view, however. The positions of plant engineering have a fourth element to satisfy, and that is the production customer. The role identity of the plant engineering position may be in harmony within the operation but discordant to the roles of the customer. This difference in perspective can produce a highly unsatisfactory environment. Enterprises are formed to be productive in the manufacture and distribution of their products. The roles played in the management of this activity can powerfully obscure any support group and consequently obscure their need to achieve.

CONTROLS—GENERAL

Management, historically, is the organizer, planner, motivator, and controller. At one time these functions were probably considered to be the sole prerogatives of the person who wore the corresponding hat. More recently, students of management propose that management does not depend on title and that every job must contain these elements. The titled managers of today are now finding themselves between a rock and a hard place when it comes to control. On one hand, proponents of modern management are saying, "Strip away restrictive controls." On the other, the enterprise and its system are saying, "Don't lose control." Coupled with this are the demands of labor, which seem to say, "Give us control."

This section is devoted to the understanding of various control factors, areas of control, and levels of control. Each individual, regardless of assumptions about people, needs controls if he or she is to better serve the enterprise.

FACTORS OF CONTROL

Plant engineering is predominately a long-term function. It is well to remember this on those days that are filled with emergencies that continually take precedence over any long-term activity. These daily occurrences that appear to be beyond predictability are in truth examples of poor control of long-term output.

The above could be considered a parallel function with priority override. It may be diagramed as in Figure 9. This diagram uses standard electrical symbols and demonstrates parallel inputs I–1 and I–2. The work has been arranged so as to deenergize long-term inputs at I–2–1 when short-term inputs arise, thus dropping out the long-term output. Even though the accountabilities may be well defined, the energizing factor lies in the placement of priorities.

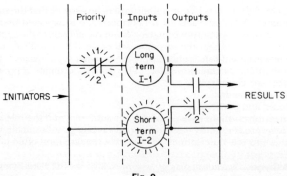

Fig. 9

The preceding points out the three prerequisites of organizational control:
1. *Input:* Assignments and accountabilities
2. *Output:* Efforts and accomplishments
3. *Priority:* Order of need, value, or timing

Though the above are mandatory factors of any control, they alone cannot control. The controllability of any system is the performance of:
4. *Initiators:* Causes and ideas
5. *Results:* Objectives and actions

This intricate control circuit, which contains inputs, outputs, and priorities, must not overload the potential. Therefore the controls must meter review and have system:
6. *Meter:* Defer or assign initiators according to value.
7. *Review:* Value of inputs versus value of results.

The control, with these seven factors considered, can now be shaped into a vehicle or:
8. *System:* Mechanism which receives, directs, or transmits actions regarding the previous seven.

AREAS OF CONTROL

Controls are considered and set into practice when situations appear to be out of control. The prime indicators of lack of control are happenings that break the laws of the land, people wasting the enterprise's money, or people violating the ethics of the administrating body. In all the above, people are the common element. Controls control the actions of people. The areas for control then must be as complex as the actions of the group. This is not as bad as might be believed. When people show up for work, they engage themselves in two functions:
1. *Working:* attempting to meet organizational objectives.
2. *Not working:* taking personal time, being on lunch breaks, goofing off, etc.

Institutional controls will always direct the actions of people engaged in work and never of those who are not working. People, whether working or not, are never controlled by rules. People are controlled by their motivations. Therefore, when people are placed in a controlled situation, it is their needs that obligate them to live within the rules. Rules are not controls, they are only constraints of the system factor of control. When people are engaged in not working, they are self-motivated and therefore self-controlled. The moment a rule affects the actions of someone who is otherwise not working, that person ceases to be not working and starts to work by obeying the rule.

PLACE ALL TRASH IN WASTE BARRELS

Fig. 10

Employees on break who place trash in the barrel are meeting a condition of employment. They are productive in the sense that someone else won't have to pick up their litter. They are, therefore, working. The employee who refuses to obey the instruction is counterproductive and therefore not working. The situation is out of control if the performance of the employee's efforts towards the proper disposal of trash is never reviewed.

The inefficiencies of a work situation are often a result of poor controls. Poor controls may possibly contain all eight factors and yet cause inefficiency. The problem with this situation is that the controls are:
1. Inhibiting   (restrictive)
2. Purposeless   (time wasting)

The inhibiting portion of a control is usually found in the system factor. The dictates of the system are inflexible to the degree that certain people must spend time doing specific things, and yet they cannot do other things that are equally productive. Job classifications, signature chains, and area support are common inhibitors. They inhibit people from working outside their areas of authority by implying unfavorable review.

The purposeless portion of a control could be found in any of the factors but is always noticed by its absence during the review. When people do things and yet never hear why they have to do them or how well they're doing, the chances are that these things do not have to be done. Purposelessness is often a product of habit. At one time, an act was considered necessary and some good was intended to be derived. Then the conditions change, the act becomes useless, and yet it still continues to be performed. Anyone who initially establishes a control must be wary of these two wasters. Flexibilities should be considered at the start, so when the control begins to take effect, and efficiency begins to improve, certain jobs may be expanded, and certain acts may be dropped.

The art of controlling people at work is always manifested in productivity improvements. Low productivity and efficiency are examples of ineffective controls. The review system that recognizes low productivity in essence has reviewed the workings of the controls.

ADMINISTRATIVE FUNCTION OF PLANT ENGINEERING

Plant engineering, regardless of the size of the enterprise, is a composite of duties that facilitate and maintain the productive capability of the enterprise, provide safety and comfort for the employees, procure and maintain utilities, and respond to the needs of the community. In larger companies, the administration of these duties is vested in one position which reports status to and receives inputs from top management. In small companies, these duties may be shared by several people, from the owner down to the handyman. Whatever the magnitude of the enterprise, the basic duties are the same.

We have chosen the word "duty" to represent the completeness of the obligation. The administration of plant engineering compels the administrator to continually develop and promote, with conviction, the view that the aims of plant engineering are good for the enterprise and are essential for continued success. The justification of this conviction is to somehow present tangible evidence of productivity.

Productivity in plant engineering is normally considered as an intrinsic value. It is something that is not necessarily measurable but nonetheless necessary. The administrator's prime reward is realized when "the necessary evil" concept of plant engineering becomes a thing of the past and plant engineering becomes a way to the future. To get this somewhat idealistic precept into perspective, consider this:

1. All the physical assets of the enterprise are at the mercy of plant engineering practices.

2. The attitudes of those employed, to a great measure, reflect the managerial regard for plant engineering practices.

3. The efficient conversion of energies and resources into product, to a great measure, depends upon the effectiveness of plant engineering practices.

4. The preponderance of all new technologies, materials, and specialities are applicable in plant engineering.

5. The continued acceptance of the enterprise by the community requires a managerial commitment to plant engineering practices.

These five points encompass the range of the obligation which then provides the grounds for actions.

Administrative Viewpoint

No two companies are structured the same What is thought of as plant engineering in one company may be quite different in another. In the broadest sense, the plant engineering functions should be aligned to coordinate and maximize the uses of the facilities.

Plant engineering manager's involvement

Process engineering	Facilities engineering	Stores	Maintenance control	Maintenance and construction

Each of the above have been identified by prime productive functions. This doesn't mean that a position should be established for each but rather that a commitment to accomplish the objectives of each should be established within the administration. To this end, let us forget about positions and numbers of people for a moment and look at objectives. Admittedly, not all plant engineering managers have all five functional fields structured within their organization. Even so plant engineering must be involved with all five if the plant is to operate smoothly. Therefore, the subdivisions of plant engineering and its administration are inherently obligated to achieve or help achieve the objectives of each function, regardless of the organizational makeup.

Plant engineering organizations   Information gathered from research indicates that the term "plant engineer" begins to appear in operations with approximately four hundred employees. Those companies with less than four hundred employees use titles such as maintenance superintendent, maintenance manager, and chief engineer. The duties of the plant engineer also seem to vary with the nature of the product. Companies that have long, continuous processes or special treatments generally include processing as part of plant engineering. Companies that have multiple products with various intermediate operations generally exclude processing from plant engineering. The most common elements in all the various connotations of "plant engineering" are maintenance of buildings and grounds, maintenance of utilities, plant layout, and material handling. It is interesting to note that only one company out of one hundred has safety administration directly affiliated with plant engineering. Several organizations have safety maintenance crews or O.S.H.A. committees, but the administration of safety was by and large considered to be a personnel or industrial relations function.

Another interesting point is the line of demarcation between "plant" and "building." When large equipment is built into the building or when the building itself somehow was part of the operation, plant engineering is most often considered to be responsible. However, functions or operations, that seem to have a less permanent flavor are often considered to be responsibilities outside the area of plant engineering. The bulk of this departure has to do with process engineering. Some consider material handling and packaging as process engineering and others consider them as separate specialties which report to either manufacturing engineering or production engineering. It is surprising to note that many plant engineers feel they have extremely limited authority.

Administrative Values

Gathering status information could easily be a full-time job, because it is safe to assume that the status of everything needs improvement and that therefore everything should be considered. This is a trap into which many administrators are drawn. They become so involved with everything that should be done that there is no time left to do anything. To avoid this, the administrator must set priorities for his actions. He must begin to consider himself as a resource and to see that the bulk of his energies go where they are most beneficial to the enterprise. Notice we used the word "bulk," not "all."

There are 30 items that pretty well isolate the obligations of the plant engineering administrator. We can each look at these items and determine our prime obligations. This is, then, the area where the *bulk* of the administrator's efforts should go. With a little more examination and a few flips of a coin, the other 29 items can be ranked. A hypothetical case might be as follows:

1. Make profit with maintenance and housekeeping.
2. Make profit with maintenance controls.
3. Provide motivation for maintenance people.
4. Conserve the resources of the facilities.
5. Make profit with the facilities engineering.
6. Make product with maintenance and housekeeping.
7. Make product with maintenance controls.
8. Make product with stores.
9. Make profit with processes.
10. Make product with processes.
11. Provide motivation for stores people.
12. Provide motivation for facilities engineering people.
13. Provide motivation for process engineering people.
14. Provide motivation for maintenance control people.
15. Respond to the community with facilities engineering.
16. Make profit with stores.
17. Make profit with process engineering.
18. Conserve resources with process engineering.
19. Conserve resources with maintenance.
20. Conserve resources with maintenance controls.
21. Respond to community with maintenance.
22. Respond to community with maintenance controls.

23. Conserve resources with stores.
24. Improve product sales with process engineering.
25. Improve product sales with maintenance.
26. Improve product sales with maintenance controls.
27. Improve product sales with facilities engineering.
28. Respond to community with process engineering.
29. Improve sales with stores.
30. Respond to the needs of the community with stores.

Some of these may seem difficult to tell apart or impossible to translate into action, but every item can be resolved. Looking at items 1 and 6, the administrator's concern for #1 is to make maintenance more profitable, which is then the administration of unfavorabilities that exist within or confront maintenance, and #6 is the administration of maintenance to produce the product purely for the sake of the product. Looking at items 4 and 5, the same kind of distinction must be made. There are benefits which reach beyond profitability when the facilities conserve resources. In Item 5, on the other hand, one recognizes the elements of profitability to be gained from using the facilities. (Remember now, this is a hypothetical case. Your situations may have entirely different rankings.) Let us continue. We have 30 windows from which to view plant engineering. We look through #1 more than we look through #30. Now, this is where the seven points of status, deficiencies, etc., can be brought into focus. To clarify this picture, the administrator needs some sort of indicator to serve as a basis of reference. It then follows that the areas of prime concern should have many indicators while areas of lesser concern may only need an occasional mention. Indicators should be relevant to the people who use them. This is often a problem in plant engineering. Indicators that are useful to the accountants are often valueless to the maintenance foreman. The pity of this is that the maintenance foreman in time learns to regard all such carrying on as a waste of time. Here, then, is where the administrator must start. Before people can reach a higher level of performance, they have to know where they are performing now, why it is considered performance, how this information is used, and how they can make use of it. The best indicators are the ones that get used often.

Production, quality control, personnel, finance, and marketing are great chart makers and indicator users, but when it comes to plant engineering, there appear to be fewer things that can be quantified and therefore fewer indicators. This is not the case, however. Much of what is happening is going on unnoticed and can be broken down in terms of informational indicators. Easily hundreds of trends or indicators can be made available simply by compounding any two or more of the following:

1. Dollars	13. Deferrals
2. Hours	14. Rework
3. Frequency of events	15. Downtime
4. Attendance	16. Overtime
5. Schedules	17. Correctives
6. Estimates	18. Causes
7. Grievances	19. Inspections
8. Usage	20. Preventive measures
9. Efficiency	21. Inventories
10. Vibration or noise	22. Quality capability
11. Accidents	23. Work elements
12. Backlog	

Measuring sticks:
1. Per unit of sales
2. Per unit of measure (square foot, pound, etc.)
3. Per unit of time
4. Per operation of department
5. Per unit of priority or value
6. Percent compliance
7. Percent accuracy
8. Per man
9. Per machine
10. Per job
11. Percent of budget

Using indicators Maintenance and plant engineering activities are too often considered as cost centers rather than profit centers. The question of whether or not this philosophy is right or wrong is quite academic and therefore should not interfere with your decisions, but it will do so if your decisions are not substantiated by accurate data. If an indicator is used to support the decision, then the inputs and the conclusions derived must be accurate. This point expressly stresses the importance of valid inputs. Even the most ill-conceived and useless indicator can be reassessed into sound information providing the inputs were correct.

The first criterion of a good indicator is that it allows for method of policing or reviewing the inputs. The second criterion of a good indicator is how often can it be used. Can it correlate other indicators? Does it help make good decisions? Does it isolate problems? The third criterion is its responsiveness to changes. Will it identify today's situation today or next month? The fourth criterion is the ease with which it can be understood.

A commonly used and usually good indicator is maintenance cost per unit sold. Let's assume that a company makes two products and sells to the consumer through a company-owned sales agency. The indicator might be laid out in a pattern similar to that shown in Figure 11. The graph indicates maintenance once cost about 55 cents per unit sold and then dropped to 35 cents. If this were the only indicator used, the administrator could quite possibly drive his company into disaster. Let us put some more information into the same graph as shown in Fig. 12. In the graphs for products "A" and "B," you see that the "A" line maintenance costs are about as high as ever, but the "B" line cost has dropped. Why? In marketing, a similar chart is used. It is called "Customer Complaints per Unit of

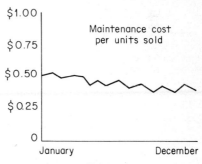

Fig. 11

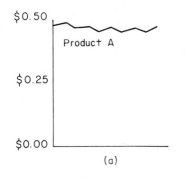

(a)   (b)

Fig. 12

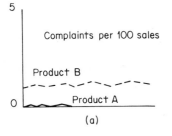

(a)

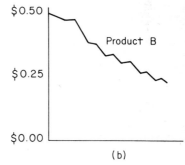

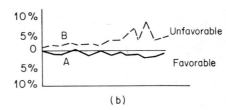

(b)

Fig. 13

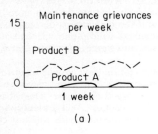

Maintenance grievances per week

(a)

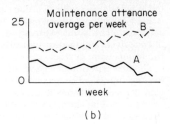

Maintenance attenance average per week

(b)

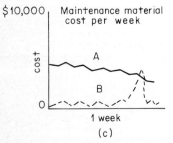

Maintenance material cost per week

(c)

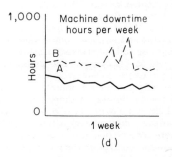

Machine downtime hours per week

(d)

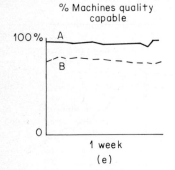

% Machines quality capable

(e)

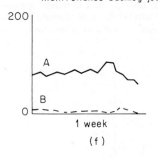

Maintenance backlog jobs

(f)

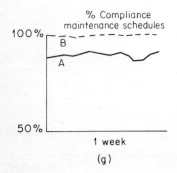

% Compliance maintenance schedules

(g)

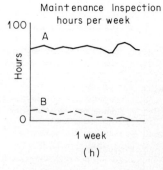

Maintenance Inspection hours per week

(h)

Fig. 14

Sales" (Fig. 13a). In production, they have a chart called "Direct Labor Performance" (standard hours per 100 units) (Fig. 13b). The picture is now beginning to take shape and a more correct assumption can now be made. This assumption is that the company is not maintaining the "B" line well enough. If this is true, the administrator still needs some basis for a decision. Other indicators are shown in Fig. 14. Fortified with all this information, the administrator's interest in maintenance to make product, maintenance to make profit, providing motivation to maintenance people, and improving sales through maintenance and others can now be converted into more accurate assumptions which will serve as a basis for further decisions. When decisions are converted into actions, the administrator should expect an improvement in certain indicators. The sum of these improvements should bring about the desired effect in one of the prime areas of concern. If the predicted effect does not occur, then the administrator should first reanalyze the assumptions. The assumptions, if untrue, are then the product of:

1. Inadequate information
2. Incorrect information
3. Illogical conclusions

If none of these appear to apply, then the error may be in the quantities expressed in the decision. Maybe a little more of this and a little less of that might move the line. If this does not seem to be the case, then it's the performance of the commitments that is inadequate. This is then a matter of getting the group to respond.

Working with other groups   The plant engineering administrator is responsible and accountable to some degree for every square inch of activity in the plant. The larger the plant, the greater the obligation. The greater number of people, the more plant engineering becomes involved with the needs of others. The administrator is remiss in his obligation if he allows plant engineering to become a "misery hole" for the entire plant. The needs of plant engineering must be communicated to the other functional areas. The administrator is equally remiss if he allows this to become an area of controversy. Progress in this area is best expressed as teamwork.

Teams have common objectives. The administrator at his positional level and the others of the staff at their levels must become more involved in the objectives of all organizational groups. Occasionally, accomplishment becomes impared because the objectives of two agencies conflict. This situation is minimal when the administrators of these organizations are working together; however, when it does happen, the lines of communication should be open so that resolution can be made. Resolving interdepartmental differences should not be a big part of administration, but uniting interdepartmental efforts should be. Here again, the value systems, priorities, and base assumptions should become more widely known. When accountabilities are interdepartmental, then the review should become more of a joint undertaking.

SUMMARY

Our theme, if summed up in three words, would be "Quantify and communicate."

When quantifying, we find it necessary to establish terms and definitions that, in turn, make the quantities more understandable to us. Communication of information related to these quantities is impossible unless these terms become part of the everyday jargon of enterprise. Therefore, it becomes necessary for members of the enterprise to first learn each other's language. We have used many such definitions, and yet they all relate to just one phase of industry.

We have said that employment requires a position and a person to fill the position. The position is part of the organization and the person is part of the staff.

We have said that both the organization and staff have power potentials. Also, we have pointed out that the potential of each can be expanded through the use of authority, leadership, objectives, influence, style, personality, controls, review priorities, etc., etc. But a perfect understanding of all this is not worth a nickle until we learn that to expand our potential is to expand our obligation.

More people, more money, or more time will not guarantee more power; the only thing that will is more accomplishment.

REFERENCES

1. Bernard T. Lewis: *Controlling Maintenance Cost,* National Foremen's Institute, Waterford, Conn., 1970.
2. Rensis Likert: *The Human Organization, Its Management and Value,* McGraw-Hill, New York, 1967.
3. Douglas McGregor: *The Human Side of Enterprise,* McGraw-Hill, New York, 1960.
4. Truett Newbrough: *Modern Maintenance Management,* McGraw-Hill, New York, 1962.
5. Arthur B. Sweney: *Response to Power Model for Integrating Superior and Subordinate People Systems,* National Academy of Management, Minneapolis, 1972.
6. Arthur B. Sweney: *Transactions of Power and Obligation for Defining Superordinate and Subordinate Relationships,* Southern Academy of Management, Washington, D.C., 1972.
7. Robert A. Sutermeister: *People and Productivity,* McGraw-Hill, New York, 1969.

Chapter **2**

Administrative Functions

EARL O. CLARK
Facilities Consultant

GENERAL

Derivation and delineation of administrative functions in a plant engineering-maintenance organization is a multifaceted task. Each individual company environment will contribute a series of different variables. The attitude of top management toward centralization or decentralization will have a strong impact on responsibilities assigned to such an organization. The size and style of the organization itself will have a strong influence on what is to be accomplished internally and what is to be done elsewhere in the company. The nature and economics of the business, in both processes and products, will contribute to methods of operation which influence administrative matters.

DEFINITIONS

In order to establish a basis to discuss administration, it is necessary that certain definitions be provided. The language of business is perhaps more complex or confusing than that used in any art or science. This is especially true when attempting to explain the differences or nuances involved in the words "organization," "management," and "administration." Each term implies a people function or relationship and a work function or relationship. The clear definition of each item relies on how the others are defined. For the purposes of this chapter, the following definitions apply.

"Organization" is construed to mean the formal structure established in a business—a structure designed to establish levels of authority, communication channels, and assignment of responsibilities to segments or individuals.

"Management" is the art or act of managing or the judicious use of means to accomplish an end. More commonly, management involves the ability to achieve objectives through the active support of others. Typically, management embraces the functions of planning, organizing, staffing, directing, controlling, and representing.

"Administration" has been defined as the function in a business which determines policy and coordinates things like finance, production, distribution, organization, and the ultimate machinery for the control of management. It has also been defined as (1) the function which includes active planning, direction, coordination, and control of the business within basic policies established by the highest elements of management or (2) the function of determining objectives, operating policies, and results. As used in this text, "administration" is interpreted to be the function that does the "grunt" work for management, or, in other words, the function that performs the staff, overhead, or indirect work in the plant engineering-maintenance organization.

"Facilities" is the term currently in vogue to describe the organization concerned with plant engineering, maintenance, and ancillary responsibilities such as property administration, specialized procurement, construction contracting, and specialized contract administration. Several more progressive companies have combined typical plant engineering and maintenance activities with industrial engineering functions in their facilities organization to provide a full, under-one-management service for other company operations. This arrangement also acts as an excellent check or balance for the usually powerful manufacturing or processing departments. "Facilities," as used in this chapter, will refer to the organization, whatever its job content.

"Facilities manager" refers to the head of the plant engineering–maintenance or facilities organization regardless of his actual title in the company. "Supervisor" means the next lower level of management. "Unit" refers to an organizational entity, whether it be a department, section, group, etc.

DERIVATION OF ADMINISTRATIVE FUNCTIONS

Each facilities organization, regardless of influencing variables, has certain common characteristics which help derive administrative functions. First, the organization should be structured as a system.

Input represents work requirements for facilities. The processor is the facilities organization which designs, schedules, routes, and performs work. Output is the completed work. Feedback relates to acceptance, complaints, and problems which occur. The system is made more effective by the addition of controls and filters.

Controls include such things as rejection or modification of input, methods and checkpoints in the processor, and quality evaluation of the output prior to, or in conjunction with, turnover of the completed work for the user. Development and implementation of control(s) can be identified as an administrative function.

Second, each facilities organization will have a specified cycle of operation. Each of the cycles represents a "present for consideration," "approve," "do work," "do it again," guidance, reporting activity, or a communication channel. If such a cycle is to be efficient, certain structuring, method development, and general arrangements must exist. These elements create administrative requirements.

Third, each facilities organization will have a typical, more detailed process model such as that shown in Fig. 1. This will suggest additional administrative functions.

Finally, each facilities organization has an underlying commonality in responsibilities which dictates a basic organizational structure, as shown in Fig. 2.

ADMINISTRATION IN THE SMALL FACILITIES ORGANIZATION

It is axiomatic that the smaller the facilities organization, the more versatile its administrative staff must be. The reasons have been pointed out—administrative functions remain relatively constant regardless of size. A typical facilities organization chart for the small company is shown in Fig. 3. Because of more informal operating conditions and quick communication, the manager of such an organization is usually responsible for all budget and expenditure activity. He is also responsible for issuing (and frequently

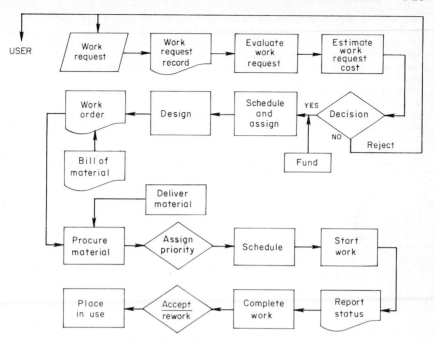

Fig. 1   Typical facilities process model.

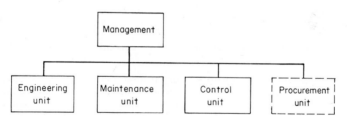

Fig. 2   Basic facilities organization.

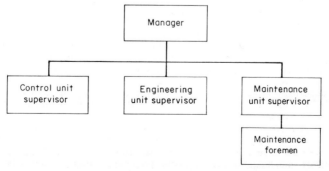

Fig. 3   Typical facilities organization—small.

authoring) all office instructions policy and procedures. He may also double in brass as the head of the engineering unit or the maintenance unit or—in the case of the very small company—both. His personal staff normally consists of one well-qualified secretary or clerk who also assists the control unit. The control unit is responsible for work request receipt or origination, evaluation, go–no-go decisions, planning priorities, and materials control—including warehousing, work-order preparation, scheduling, cost accounting, status, and completion reports. Initial staffing of the control unit in less maintenance-intensive companies can be calculated at a ratio of 1 employee for each 15 to 25 direct maintenance employees, plus 1 clerk-typist–ledger keeper for each 3 control-unit employees and 1 materials warehouseman-clerk. This unit should be considered as the fundamental administrative unit and assigned additional administrative functions and staff as organizational idiosyncrasies dictate. The ideal control-unit supervisor or planner is a junior engineer or senior draftsman with an administrative bent. With these qualifications, he can accommodate simple, routine work requests and issuance of work orders

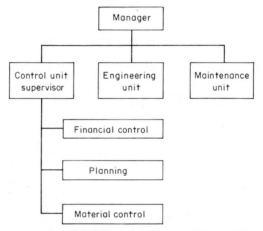

Fig. 4   Typical small facilities organization—maintenance intensive.

and instructions without burden to the engineering unit. In maintenance-intensive companies, such as continuous-process industries or high growth situations, the control unit may be more sophisticated even in the small company. All functions have less turnaround time, must be more responsive, and have a higher volume of traffic. Typical division of the organization in these circumstances is shown in Fig. 4.

Such an organization recognizes that more of the manager's time must be available to directing action rather than handling administrative details. Financial matters such as budgets, expenditures, and cost accounting can be handled by junior accounting types at a ratio of one employee for each $2 million to $3 million handled. The planner ratio may be reduced to one planner for each ten craft employees and the material control unit increased to include material expediter(s) in addition to the warehousing receipt and issue operation. No more than two expediters should be required in the small organization. Additional working supervisors or lead men should be considered at the ratio of one per each five to seven employees. Their tasks remain essentially the same as in the very small unit, but with a coordinating role added.

The engineering unit in the small organization should be assigned an absolute minimum of administrative duties. Normally, a secretary or clerk-typist for each three to five engineers is satisfactory.

Administrative duties of the maintenance unit should also be held to an absolute minimum. Typically, foremen are involved in working with the control unit on priority and schedule matters and status reporting. Clerical assistance to keep maintenance records, collect time-keeping and cost data, and handle routine trouble calls and communications can be provided at a ratio of one clerk for each three to four foremen.

ADMINISTRATION IN THE MEDIUM-SIZED FACILITIES ORGANIZATION

Increases in the size of the maintenance unit of a facilities organization creates the demand for a corresponding increase in size of the administrative staff. The reasons are fundamental. As organizations become larger, spans of control (the number of people one person can supervise) remain the same. Thus, communication lines become longer, geographical separation of activities is greater, numbers of actions increase, and a more formal organizational arrangement is necessary to maintain effectiveness. Under these conditions the facilities manager's role changes from active engagement in all areas of operation to that of a director and coordinator of effort. He has little time for engineering details or great detail of any type. This suggests that managers of medium-sized facilities organizations have more management qualifications than technical ones. It is also in this size organization that other responsibilities, such as for procurement and property administration, are usually added. A typical top chart of the organization does not materi-

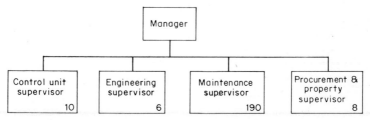

Fig. 5 Typical man loading—medium-sized facilities organization.

ally change from that shown in Figs. 2 and 3. There is an evolution in job specialties at the lower levels, as reflected in Fig. 5.

The manager's immediate staff consists of:
   1 manager
   1 administrative staff assistant
   1 secretary

The engineering unit contemplates:
   1 working supervisor engineer
   1 electrical design engineer
   1 mechanical engineer
   1 architectural/structural engineer
   2 plant layout specialists
   clerical assistance from the control unit

The procurement and property unit contains:
   1 working supervisor
   1 equipment specialist
   1 construction contract specialist
   1 property specialist
   1 property clerk-typist
   1 clerk-typist
   2 movers—office equipment

The maintenance unit is staffed with:
   1 supervisor
   9 foremen
   1 clerk-typist
   180 craft employees

The control unit utilizes:
   1 working supervisor
   4 planners/draftsmen
   2 material control clerks/expediters (including a warehouseman)
   1 budget accountant
   1 clerk typist
   1 maintenance trouble call clerk-typist

ADMINISTRATION IN THE LARGE FACILITIES ORGANIZATION

Large facilities organizations also demand a corresponding increase in administrative staff for the same reasons given for the transition from small to medium-size organizations. In addition, the large facilities organization must essentially become more self-sufficient. The primary reason for this trend is that larger companies become less centralized in their functions due to the sheer bulk of the organization. For instance, in small and medium-sized companies, both company and organizational procedure preparation may be centralized in a single company unit to provide such a service to all organizations. In large companies, such activities are restricted to overall company policies due to the inability to staff for and schedule highly variable demands from each of the many organizations.   Therefore each organization becomes responsible for its internal procedures.

Typical, or rule-of-thumb, manloading in large facilities organizations becomes much

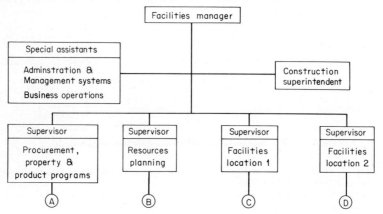

Fig. 6   Typical facilities organization—large, centralized.

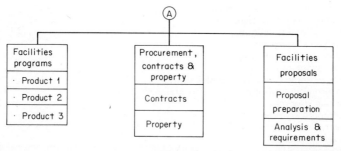

Fig. 7   Subset of Fig. 6A.

more difficult to prescribe than in the smaller organizations because influencing variables become more numerous and pronounced.   One essential guideline that seems to hold true is that manpower devoted to the administrative effort should not exceed 15 percent of the total organization manpower.

Beyond that point, most large facilities organizations follow the basic facilities functional organization structure but are severely tailored to fulfill specific charters.   Figure 6 shows a typical top chart of a large company using fairly well centralized approach to placement of administrative functions.

The subsets of this organization in Figs. 7, 8, and 9 provide further insight to the organization.

Analysis of Figs. 6, 7, 8, and 9 provides a further insight into one management philosophy.   Note that administration, systems, and business operations report to the organization head as staff members, as does the construction superintendent. These offices provide support, as suggested by their titles, to the entire facilities organization. Homogeneous grouping of functions in the subsets provides a primary coordinating agent and suggests other division of work. The final result is a reasonably well-centralized administrative effort—organizationally placed to be effective. A different, actually less

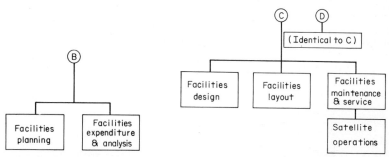

Fig. 8   Subset of Fig. 6B.   **Fig. 9**   Subset of Fig. 6C and D.

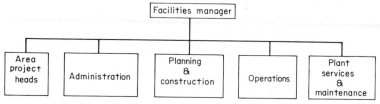

Fig. 10   Typical facilities organization—large, decentralized.

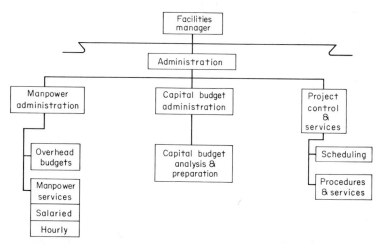

Fig. 11   Administration subset—large facilities organization, decentralized.

centralized placement of administration in a large facilities organization is shown in Fig. 10.

Area project heads are responsible for liaison, review, evaluation, and the reporting of facility requirements in a given geographical area. Functions of the administration unit are shown in Fig. 11.

Other administrative functions are interspersed with technical ones as shown in Figs. 12 and 13.

Study of the examples of the two large organizations suggest adoption of work standards for each of the administrative units as the most likely method of providing staffing information. A composite actions trend analysis is helpful in identifying workload trends.

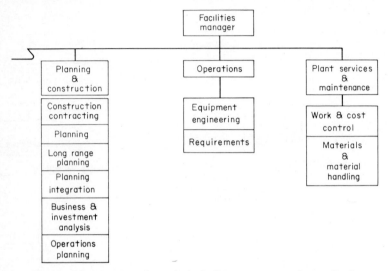

Fig. 12   Administration subsets—large facilities organization, decentralized.

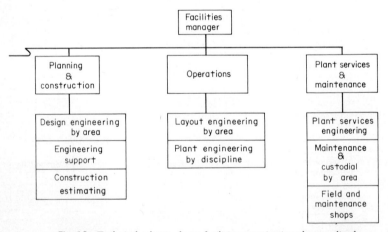

Fig. 13   Technical subsets—large facilities organization, decentralized.

ADMINISTRATIVE TASKS

Following are remarks regarding the more significant administrative tasks. An attempt is made to suggest some of the more popular methods to be used in their accomplishment and/or admonishments about what to do and what not to do.

Job descriptions   are an adjunct to a well-run facilities operation. Properly prepared, these documents provide each individual or classification of employees with information concerning duties. Fundamental responsibilities for management functions—such as planning, organizing, etc.—should be incorporated. Most modern job descriptions use conversational language, as in the following outline:

Technical accountability. What the employee is charged with doing, including a statement of responsibilities.

Currency. What the employee is required to remain abreast of, such as a state of the art, what others are doing in the same field, and innovation.

Administrative duties. Staff details such as budgets, staffing, personnel promotions, discipline, and counseling.

The "catch-all." Performs other duties as assigned.

Approvals and authorizations are delegations by management to perform certain activities such as create work orders, make purchases, and travel. They should be in writing and updated as required. This information may be contained in the policy manual, procedures, job descriptions, or in a separate document prepared at management's instruction. Any of these methods will satisfy the "authorized list" requirements, which exist in various departments in many larger companies.

Functional flowcharts are a management or administrative aid which have proven to be valuable to explain complicated relationships. These charts may relate to systems, people, paper flow, work flow, or other facilities organization functions in any combination. Briefly, they pictorially display a sequence of events or actions to accomplish some stated task or objectives. Such charts may be a part of procedures or job descriptions; they may be issued separately or posted in work areas.

Operating budgets are one of the most significant problem areas for the facilities manager. Current expenditures for maintenance in the United States approximate $24 billion. This figure represents a $6 billion increase in the past five years. Some part of that growth reflects the effects of inflation and industrial expansion. However, the major part is attributable to increasing sophistication of plants and equipment. Needless to say, more now than ever, facilities budgets are a major concern to top management because of their impact on profit.

Predominant factors used in preparation of operation of operating budgets include, but are not limited to the following:

Historical costs, temporized by growth, recession, and changed conditions. In cases of relatively stable operations they serve as a reasonably reliable departure point for projection. However, unless historical costs are carefully analyzed to make sure they express optimum cost, quality and schedule, they can lead to the perpetuation of ineffective practices.

Preplanned projects, carefully estimated and approved by management form a hard-core portion of operating budgets. Where properly described, they offer an excellent basis for addition or deletions to budgets.

Numbers of production units are reliable guides to relate facilities costs provided that, as in the case of historical costs, proper analysis has been made to assure a realistic relation.

Plant and equipment age have a direct impact on budgets. Establishment of trends relating to this factor offers a satisfactory basis for projections. Care should be taken to consider any deferred or past-due maintenance when making such projections.

Work backlogs are a frequently used device to justify budgets. Honestly presented, they reflect the current condition of operations. The value of work backlogs is directly proportional to their validity. Validity may be established by regular, scheduled review of their content. Such examination frequently exposes changed need and erroneous decision to proceed as well as the "want" or "nice to have" projects which can be eliminated.

Utility rates or costs should be a part of operating budgets. Under stable conditions, they are relatively constant. However, new equipment or processes can cause significant changes.

Work and material standards are a relatively unused but very valuable tool to be used in budget preparation. Combined with extensive preproject planning, they afford an element of reliability estimating that is not generally available through any other means.

Preparing and justifying operating budgets is easier when they relate to specific functional areas in the facilities operation. Broad breakdowns such as engineering, administration, and maintenance are satisfactory for very small organizations. Larger companies frequently establish budget cost centers or accounts for functional areas such as salaries and wages, supplies and expenses, and materials, along with various maintenance accounts covering buildings and grounds, machinery, engineering and/or production test equipment, shop equipment, office equipment, perishable and/or durable tools, and plant rearrangement. Obviously, the more sophisticated or complex systems offer an opportunity to isolate projected and actual costs for close scrutiny. The process of preparing a budget can be simplified by providing for people and their attendant costs plus materials. Depending on the type of enterprise, maintenance and materials costs can be expected to vary between 40 and 60 percent of labor costs. Major construction, rearrangement, equipment installations, and other clearly identifiable big projects should be planned and estimated separately and then overlaid on the routine base budgets.

Budgeting practices as to time periods vary from company to company, usually influenced by size. Some companies project budgets for several years, others work on a month-to-month basis. The most effective budgeting approach, regardless of company size, seems to be quarterly planning, review, and revision against an annual objective. Such practices recognize the fact that in the dynamic area of facilities operations, visibility beyond a four-month period is severely limited. More- or less-frequent budgeting appears to yield little benefit and tends to introduce either rigidity or slop into the operation.

Budget presentations to management have long been a problem to facilities managers. In the final analysis, such presentations should provide a philosophical portion which relates to agreed levels of activity and resources to support them. The psychological factor should not be ignored in preparing such presentations. Guessing games, inflation or deflation of estimates, standard management practices—such as the proverbial 10 percent reduction of any given number—must be recognized and incorporated. The physiological portion of the presentation—where facts are laid on the line—will always dictate the relative success or failure of the presentation. It is therefore wise to accumulate as much significant data as possible to make this part of the presentation effective.

Capital budgets   are more and more frequently the responsibility of the facilities organization. The most popular method of establishing capital budgets is the inquiry method. Each operating organization within the company is requested to develop and justify capital requirements for the forthcoming capital expenditure budget. Inputs are then subjected to various tests such as return on investment, present value, value added, and cost avoidance or reduction, along with technical factors and other cost factors. Following, the deletions, additions, and changes effected by these processes, a preliminary list of capital items identified as to programs, projects, or products and classified in priority may be submitted to management for review. These reviews almost invariably result in recycling the budget program until the point in time that management reaches a final decision. After management approval of the capital budget, it is common practice to move each item through a re-review and approval just prior to acquisition. As in the case of operating budgets, the better the planning, the more factual the data, and the more accurate the estimates, the more likely it is that approval may be expected.

Accounting or cost accounting   practices or routines vary in nature and scope in relationship to the size of the organization. Smaller companies have less sophisticated systems than larger companies. Regardless of size, some system of accounting or cost accounting is mandatory for successful financial operation of a facilities organization. The typical and most effective approach to establishing financial control consists of the following steps:

1. Establishing cost or account centers
2. Estimating costs
3. Charging costs incurred in the execution of projects and operations to the appropriate center
4. Measuring actuals versus estimates
5. Adjusting budgets, accounts, or operations to meet financial guidelines approved by management

Work control   in a facilities organization is second in importance only to the timely, economical completion of the work itself. The facilities organization is built around an integrated system for control of its resources. Work control includes comprehensive preplanning of workloads and tasks and a concept of control based on timely and effective performance evaluation. Therefore, an essential element in managing facilities activities is the measurement of actual performance against consistent performance standards for direct labor. If personnel are properly trained, there should normally be no wide variations in the quality of work or the amount of time expended on specific jobs. Constant measurement of direct labor expended against consistent performance standards ensures that individuals are performing to the level of their capabilities and assignments. Close evaluation of this nature will detect instances of lack of transportation, inadequate training, improper scheduling, or any of the many other factors that inhibit performance. Work or performance control, like cost accounting, does not in itself save money, solve problems, or improve operating conditions. It will, however, identify areas which should be comprehensively investigated through other techniques such as methods engineering, work simplification, and layout studies. The results of these investigations will then determine the specific actions which should be taken to correct the undesirable trends highlighted by performance factors.

Work standards   as related to production-line manufacturing can seldom be predicted accurately, motion by motion, for any particular facilities task. Variations in requirements will occur according to work location and conditions. Unpredictable job elements and variation in work methods, skill levels, and planning—plus unforeseen delays which occur on individual facilities jobs—make it very difficult to predetermine the actual time required to complete assigned facilities functions. However, work standards which are bench-mark values may be developed to implement a work control program. Development of such standards may be accomplished by:

1. Identifying repetitive work using industrial engineering techniques
2. Ranking identified work in order of most frequent occurrence
3. Estimating job content and man-hours to perform
4. Comparing actual performance data to estimates
5. Adjusting between estimates and actuals to reach a standard

Another approach can be the acquisition of base and civil engineering standards, available from the U.S. Department of Defense (U.S. Air Force and U.S. Navy) and adapting and expanding them to the local environment using methods noted above. Preventive maintenance programs are most susceptible to the application of such standards. It is axiomatic that the wider the range standards and the more accurate they are, the more effective they will be in measuring work performance and defining the management resources needed.

Work planning   is another important element of work control. The typical facilities planning operation begins with receipt or development of a work requirement. The next step should consist of an investigation to pinpoint exactly what is required. Parametric alternatives are then sought. Engineering design is completed when necessary. Operations and materials are sequenced and placed in writing—usually in the form of a work order. Standards are applied and estimates are made. The final product is an explicit statement of work to be done, who will do it, and the expected cost.

Scheduling   follows the completion of planning. A recent survey of facilities organizations indicates that all of them use some type of formalized priority system. The systems themselves are highly individualistic. Systems used by smaller organizations are usually based on a high or low priority assigned in order of receipt of the requirement. Larger companies tend to have more sophisticated systems, which contain as many as ten categories of priorities. It is apparent that most companies will seek and find the systems compatible with their environments. The important feature of all effective scheduling and priority systems is that they are subject to constant review and change.

Procurement   may be accomplished by a buyer or buyers in the facilities organization or by buyers in some other company department. In either case, the facilities organization has strong responsibilities to assure proper quality, quantity, and cost. Within the facilities organization, the procurement system should be structured to provide standardized action in the following areas:

1. Development of requirements
2. Estimating costs
3. Approval to proceed, delegated by appropriate dollar amounts or type of items to various levels in the organization hierarchy

4. Funding, including necessary approvals

5. Bids, request for quotations or requests for proposals, including minimum specifications and distribution in accord with established policy

6. Evaluation, preparation of appropriate contract documents, and award to the successful bidder

7. Follow-up to assure on schedule or timely delivery

8. Receiving, marking, and recording of the item(s)

9. Routing and transportation, including installation where necessary, to final destination

10. Payment to the seller

11. Post audit as necessary to assure proper operation, achievement of cost reductions, savings, avoidances, etc.

12. Documentation of contract/purchase order files to provide necessary information for external or internal audit

Capital item   procurement relates to acquisition of items identified as capital in nature by the Internal Revenue Service, Cost Accounting Standards Board, and company policy. It is necessary that the facilities organization be completely involved in such procurement, regardless of its role in the buying activity, for the following reasons and with the following points in mind:

1. Maintenance of items procured will normally be a facilities responsibility.

2. Commonality of new equipment with existing equipment must be optimized from a utilities service and spare parts view in order to reduce costs.

3. The facilities organization should be the residence for the expertise necessary to select suitable plant or equipment items.

4. The facilities organization is normally responsible for capital budget expenditures.

Expense item   procurement is not normally the function of a facilities organization except for the purchase of maintenance materials. Since maintenance materials inventories represent sunk costs, a major objective should be to minimize them. One way to reach this goal is to use blanket purchase orders, which effectively encourage suppliers to maintain stocks for the user. Lists of common-use items such as sheet stock, lumber, and common hardware—and estimated quantities—are placed in suppliers' hands under cover of a purchase order number used for billing purposes. Oral or written quotations are solicited from several suppliers as requirements arise. A delivery order is issued to the successful bidder. Experience has shown that suppliers will not only stock to fill delivery orders but will frequently expand their range of products handled. Periodic reviews of quotations should be made to assure proper competition. Another version of the blanket purchase order is to obtain prices, good for an extended period of time— three, six, nine, or twelve months—for listed items and establish a supplier's catalog of these prices. In this situation, delivery orders may be issued without quotation. Quantity break points may also be included. This method will generally be the most effective to establish reliable supplier inventories.

Services   procurement offers a satisfactory method of augmenting permanent facilities staff in several areas. However, contracting for architect engineer, consultant, or various maintenance services is another specialized business. As in the case of construction contracting, complete specifications and mutual understanding covering requirements are mandatory. Care should be taken to choose reputable firms to receive requests for quotations or for negotiation. There is no substitute for face-to-face discussion and necessary correction of specifications and other contract language. Most unpleasant experiences in this type of procurement can be traced to the failure to observe these two basic rules.

Contract administration   is a specialized skill necessary to the protection of the buyer. If the company conducts extensive contracting or subcontracting in the facilities area of operation, experienced contract administrators are an absolute necessity. Probably the worst choice of a contract administrator is the design or project engineer, because his vested interests are necessarily involved in such a relationship. Key activities of the contract administrator involve interpretations of the contract, communication with the contractor, file documentation for potential litigation, paralegal decisions, and unbiased communication within the company to solve problems and report status. In large companies, a successful check and balance has been introduced into the procurement system by separation of the buying function and the postcontract award administration activity.

Chapter **3**

Engineering Function

J. CAMPBELL ROUND
Consulting Engineer

1942164

RESPONSIBILITIES OF THE ENGINEER

Whoever is given charge of the engineering function must also accept some degree of responsibility within each of the seven major categories that follow, each different, but each bearing some relationship to the others with respect to the engineer's role.

Responsibilities to Production

Physical plant   The basic responsibility of engineering is to provide the manufacturing facility needed to manufacture the finished product.

The transition from theory to reality is not an easy one. From the start of a project to completion of the initial layout and budget cost estimates, the engineering staff must balance the enthusiasm of the production personnel with practical, hard-headed reasoning.

The design of the facility must incorporate all production requirements.   In-process storage space, for example, is an aspect of input by those involved in production, but it is often underestimated by designers; production input therefore, in the early stages of planning, is essential. The basic equipment layout should be examined by production personnel, who are capable of carrying out a "production run" in their own minds. It is also engineering's responsibility to obtain production's approval of specifications for major equipment before the design stage is complete.

Layout Downtime and installation delay results in financial loss. Conversely, time effectively spent on layout planning will prevent costly mistakes.

Engineering, therefore, has a responsibility to make full use of production input throughout the planning and layout stages.

Expansion allowance A long-term plan is an invaluable aid to engineering when the design for future expansion is being done. Most firms, when purchasing new property, buy more than their immediate needs dictate; the long-term plan generally shows a possible future use for the site.

Buildings may be designed in such a way as to simplify the addition of a similar structure. For instance, columns, footings, and foundations may be designed to accommodate the future bays.

Underground services such as drains and sewers can be designed to cater for future needs or, at least, they may be laid out in such a way as to avoid excavation within the building when expansion takes place.

Space for major utilities such as steam and hot water facilities, electrical substation, and tank farms should be allotted with production increase in mind.

Minimizing downtime In the event of a plant renovation, rebuild, or relocation, engineering must recognize the effect of equipment downtime on production and schedule the work accordingly.

Crash programs of this type will have to be accurate and intense. It is essential that all items be "installed" on the drawing board, so that anomalies will be avoided and a check made that all parts have been ordered.

It is vital to prepare a list of all affected services and to investigate the effect of added loading on existing services such as drains, water mains, electrical power, water treatment, compressed air, steam, ventilation, sprinkler system, monorails, conveyors, and pollution control systems.

The benefits of good preparation will be realized during the shutdown phase of the project. There is no doubt that good planning pays dividends, and it is engineering's responsibility to see that this planning includes such activities as procurement, expediting, storing, and fabrication.

Quality control The quality of equipment should be in line with or better than that existing in the factory. The aim should be to generally upgrade the facility.

Engineering, however, should make sure that this is not overdone and that any increase in plant quality is accompanied by a better-quality product and a more efficient operation.

Startup A feeling of satisfaction is experienced by everyone involved when startup of a new or rebuilt plant is accomplished satisfactorily and on time. If full production is realized right away, the feeling is almost one of anticlimax. On the other hand, if the plant has to be "run in," it is engineering's responsibility to act as "nurse" during this time.

Startup procedure is different for each facility. Some responsibilities, however, are common to all:

1. Housekeeping. Hand over a clean facility—it is worth the effort.

2. Changes made during construction should be recorded and all drawings brought up to date.

3. Tabulate all instruction manuals and nameplate data and hand over to maintenance. Indirectly, this is important to production.

4. If production staff have been helpful, put it on record and express your appreciation.

Responsibilities to Management

Cost estimates One of the major responsibilities engineering has to management is that of estimating costs. Several estimates of total cost for a project may be required, but the three basic ones are these:

1. Preliminary estimate, usually built up from cost information from previous similar projects, plus an escalation factor. Senior people with experience are valuable in estab-

lishing this estimate, as the scope may not, at this stage, be clearly defined. Management, however, is looking for a "ball park" figure to be used in long-term planning. Accuracy demanded at this stage is usually plus or minus 20 percent.

2. Layout estimate. The first detailed estimate is usually made when the design phase is complete. Plus or minus 10 percent accuracy is usually obtainable at this time.

3. Construction cost estimate. This estimate is made from completed drawings and specifications and should be within 5 percent of the final cost of construction.

There are as many different kinds of estimating aids as there are estimators. Basically, however, the aim is not to forget any part or section of the project. The estimator must have a clear knowledge of the job in detail.

Cost control In order to keep up with reality, management must be confident that the cost of a project is being "controlled." To achieve this, an accurate account of all committed spending must be kept.

PROJECT COST BUILDUP
PROJECT: Rebuild no. 4 line   PROJECT NO.: 421–7
COST CENTER: Oven rebuild   ESTIMATED COST: $36,300.00

Item	Description	PO no.†	Price	Committed
1	Supply & install pipework	3627	$14,500.71	$14,500.71
2	Special flex connection	3630	270.00	14,770.71
3	Misc. hardware	3632	220.67	14,991.38
4	Repairs to oven conveyor	3633	5,662.00	20,653.38
5	Reline burner box	3711	855.00	21,508.38
6	New control valve (NIIE)*	3720	1,650.78	23,159.16
7	Welder & mate	3768	240.00	23,399.16
16	Modify area lighting	3799	425.67	33,950.88
17	Renew sump lining (NIIE)*	3822	1,235.50	35,186.38
18	Professional inspection	3845	400.00	35,586.38
19	Modify storage bin	3855	1,560.34	37,146.72
Job Completed	TOTAL FOR THIS COST CENTER—			$37,146.72

* NIIE—Not included in estimate.
† PO—Purchase order.

Fig. 1 Project cost buildup sheet.

Figure 1 shows a typical project cost buildup. Used in conjunction with the cost estimate sheet, it can serve as a basic cost-control device. Note the following:

1. Order number includes both purchase and work orders. Where the firm's own staff will be doing work, the cost of each individual work order must be established as closely as possible for the sake of establishing a committed cost total.

2. Items not included in the original estimate show up clearly and may have to be used as a basis for requesting additional funds.

3. Only by keeping on top of committed spending can the engineering function operate confidently.

Budgets Communication between engineering and management should be constant and close. This is especially so in the case of cash flow. It is engineering's responsibility to initiate and maintain the flow of information required by management for the performance of their duties. Budgets should be carefully prepared. If a contingency or escalation factor is applied, tell management so.

Scheduling A copy of all engineering manpower schedules should be sent to management. This keeps management informed of engineering's work load and gives the feeling that, personnelwise, engineering is in control.

Secrecy   Engineering is in a position to know about new methods and products before they become fact. Secrecy is important, and the engineering manager must take positive steps to see that his staff is aware of the possible consequences of a security leak.

Reports   The basic communication between engineering and management is achieved by reports. Once the format is established, the reports should flow naturally and easily. The following should be borne in mind:

1. All written reports such as minutes of meetings, monthly progress reports, etc., should be concise and to the point, free from flowery language and verbal garbage. A difficult-to-read report is a poor report.

2. When preparing a report, put yourself in the recipient's shoes and ask yourself what information is really needed. Where the report is a long one, highlight the important points for management by summarizing the contents—and putting the summary at the beginning.

3. For technical reports, a standard form should be used.

4. Review the report forms regularly. Cut out information not being used. Simplify the method of gathering the information where possible.

Planning   It may be argued that no one plans for the present. Yet many engineering departments do their planning on a day-to-day basis. As a result, the chief engineer seldom gets the chance to step back from the mundane things of life and view the overall picture but is always being harassed by problems that demand immediate answers.

It takes real effort for an engineering supervisor to get away from the daily problems and leave them to subordinates. But only in this way can a supervisor hope to plan effectively.

An efficient engineering department will have an effective short-term plan. Short-term planning can cover anything from a month to a year and is a valuable tool in the hands of the engineer.

A short-term plan may show project timing, anticipated cost buildup, manpower requirements (in terms of man-hours or man-weeks), startup date, and estimated running-in period. These figures may also be used as a basis for monthly reports to management.

A new-product facility may take two to five years from initial discussions to startup. A long-term plan, which may cover two to twenty-five years, is an effective tool in the hands of management.

As with individuals, engineering departments of medium- and large-size organizations can establish "goals" in line with the goals of the firm as a whole. There should be, for instance, a long-term plan for plant engineering if such a plan exists for the organization as a whole. If the overall plan is prepared properly, it will include projected plant engineering facilities requirements.

There is no set format for long-term plans. The greater the number of years covered by the plan, the less accurate the forecasts will be. Periodic updating is required when long-term items become short-term, and additional items are added to the long-term schedule.

Long-term plans for a plant engineering function should include:

1. Man-weeks forecast
2. Office space requirements
3. Anticipated cash flow (salaries)
4. Anticipated cash flow (equipment and office materials)
5. Additional functions, such as the formation of a construction team within the department

Efficiency   There is no real way to measure the efficiency of an engineering department. Over an extended period of time, management will develop a feel for engineering efficiency, but seldom can this be related with accuracy to production units.

Achieving and maintaining an efficient engineering group is dependent on several conditions:

1. The standard of supervision
2. The class of technical input
3. The elimination of unnecessary methods, procedures, and recordkeeping
4. The type of employee (conscientiousness, reliability)
5. Working conditions
6. Work-load planning

Responsibilities to Maintenance

Liaison   The operation of the maintenance department relies to a large extent on how well engineering performs. Close contact must be maintained and communication between them must be unimpaired. The work interface should be clearly defined.

Maintenance, in many medium- and large-sized firms, is responsible to the production manager. This does not alter the need for close liaison between maintenance and engineering, but it does help to establish a clear definition of responsibilities.

Standards   It is not always possible to use standard equipment, but a basic foundation of standard parts and equipment is desirable.

When a set of standards is established, the fact must be accurately recorded, so that additions, modifications, and deletions may be made.

Stock items   Engineering may be responsible for adding to the list of items held in stock, but maximum and minimum quantities will be set by maintenance.

When a new facility is designed, a maintenance representative should be asked to advise on the items that should be put in stock as well as the changes that should be made in existing stock quantities because of the added facility.

New equipment   When any new major equipment is ordered, engineering should notify maintenance and, if necessary, arrange for a staff training program or course. This may mean a visit to the supplier's factory for training in the operation and maintenance procedures for the new equipment. At least one set of manufacturer's drawings, specifications, and maintenance manuals should be passed to maintenance for their reference.

Drawings and specifications   The drawings and specifications produced by engineering are invaluable to maintenance. To keep them up to date, however, requires effort, but is well worth it. The number of sets of prints kept by maintenance should be minimum. No matter how many, engineering should include them in their system updating.

Corrective and preventive maintenance procedures   Although this is basically a maintenance responsibility, engineering input to the system can be valuable.

Designers should incorporate the types of lubricating systems in use throughout the plant. Standard oils and greases should be used, even if the supplier's agreement has to be obtained. This should be obtained in writing, as it may affect the guarantee.

Access to equipment   Engineering is responsible for layout, therefore it should logically "maintain" the equipment as well as mentally construct and install it.

Conditions to be borne in mind include ambient temperatures, lighting, dust concentration, fumes—both toxic and corrosive—and hoisting facilities.

Responsibilities to Society

The design of a new facility or expansion of an existing plant must recognize the needs of society.

Water Pollution   Engineering's responsibility to society lies in the need to discharge from the plant liquid effluent acceptable to local authorities or approved by the regulating body for discharge into stream or waterway. Few types of pollution are deemed to be untreatable, although the cost of treatment may add a prohibitive amount to the cost of the finished product.

Financial help, however, is normally available from federal, state, or provincial authorities.

Air pollution   The general public is very much aware of any contamination of the air. Unfortunately, there is a tendency to observe the visible effluent and ignore the invisible. Most state and provincial authorities are aware of this and insist on discharge analysis as well as ground-level concentration estimates, especially for new facilities.

Visual pollution   This is a lesser-known type of contamination and concerns the effect of poor building and plant layout and design on the people outside the factory. A clean-looking facility creates a good impression and is important from the neighbors' viewpoint as well as being a morale booster for those working inside the plant.

Safety and health   The provision of a safe and healthy working environment is one of engineering's major responsibilities. At some time during the project design, the layout should be examined for potential fire, health, and accident hazards.

Adequate lighting, heating, and ventilation are essential for safety and health; care should be exercised by engineering when specifying the equipment to be sure that it will be suitable for the particular application.

Codes and requirements   As society matures, so the regulations dealing with what industry can do and cannot do tend to increase, in both quality and detail. In general, industry tries to abide by the requirements; as engineering has to do with physical plant, it must keep up to date on the local, state, and federal requirements.

Responsibilities to Utilities

Cooperation   As a supplier of a service to industry, the local utilities are vitally interested in a firm's future plans and schedules. Where possible, projected consumption of these services should be discussed with the utilities as soon as a ballpark figure is known, especially if the quantity presently being used is likely to increase or decrease. The utilities, in turn, have to examine their own capacity in the light of all needs for the area and, if necessary, take steps to add to their distribution systems. This, of course, takes time, so as much notice as possible must be given.

Forecasting requirements   Major changes to utility needs and effluent characteristics should be forecast as far ahead as possible. Even if engineering has no idea of their requirements for, say, a new facility, an allowance should be made and the appropriate utility notified.

Energy conservation   The realization that our present energy resources are limited has made the conservation of these resources an important part of the design of new facilities.

It is the responsibility of engineering to keep the thought of conservation before it at all times, but even more so during the design of a utility-using plant.

Existing facilities should also be examined and fuel saving innovations installed where possible.

Cost considerations   The cost of services such as coal, gas, oil, steam, and electricity should be apportioned out to the various departments. By having monthly costs brought to their notice, they become conscious of the need for conservation. The fact that these costs affect the cost per unit of production is something they can understand and grapple with.

Responsibilities to Development

Exchange of information   Both engineering and development are in touch with the outside world, therefore each is in a position to glean new ideas and information about products. To make full use of this fact, there should be regular dialogue between them.

It is not always possible to have a common library and information center, therefore engineering and development must make a conscious effort to pass on information likely to be of use to the other party.

Revision of existing products   Few products of any kind are perfect from the start of production. In fact, many products keep changing to such an extent that the latest model looks nothing like the original.

It should be remembered, however, that development had the job of bringing the product from the initial design stage to the production phase.

It is engineering's responsibility to involve development staff in a product change or revision on the premise that two heads are better than one, especially where the development "head" gave birth to the product.

Responsibilities to Engineering

Self-examination   Engineering has several major responsibilities toward itself. The engineering manager must learn to initiate and innovate. The department must never stand still. This is for the good of the whole department. Where possible, supervisors should be involved in self-examination as to their function within the department. But more than that, they should learn to stand back and view the department as a whole. Ask some questions, such as these:

1. Are we working as efficiently as possible?
2. Do we have a reliable staff?
3. Is management being realistic with us?
4. Is our work good enough?

5. Are we a credit to the company?

6. Do people like to work here? If not, why not?

Perhaps we will not like the answers we come up with, but at least we may be able to do something to improve matters before management starts asking the same questions.

Project control A well-controlled project instills confidence, not only in the person controlling it but also in management. Engineering owes it to itself to exercise good control of projects—not only the large projects but also the small ones.

Construction The transition from idea to reality is a phase which many engineering departments treat as of secondary importance. It is during this phase that a job well done in the office means an easy installation on the shop floor. Accuracy is important.

Efficiency Plant engineering is normally treated as an overhead, without a great deal of emphasis on making sure that the actual hours spent on a project remain within the estimate of man-hours for the job.

Special precautions must be taken to ensure that the engineering is done efficiently. These include:

1. Effective supervision. This calls for reliable and technically capable senior staff.

2. Good working conditions. Too often the plant engineering department is located in poor facilities in the middle of the plant. It is also often assumed that their offices need not be as comfortable as the other offices.

3. A good library. A well-organized library of reference books and catalogs can save many hours of searching and telephoning.

4. Skilled personnel. This is the backbone of an effective engineering function. If the department has a core of good people, it is well on its way to being efficient.

Accuracy must not be sacrificed for the sake of speed. All projects, of course, have a time limit, but the checking and approval of drawings and specifications must not be skimped. Errors and omissions are easily corrected at the design stage.

STAFFING CRITERIA

There are three staffing criteria to which the engineering discipline is subject:

1. Personnel: a sound personnel employment policy.

2. Power: to provide a good service, manpower must be used efficiently.

3. Projects: the staffing of a project is a major criterion.

The staffing of the engineering department of a manufacturing organization should be done in an attentive and concentrated manner. For instance, the technological aspect itself requires that a great deal of time be spent in interviewing potential engineers and technologists. School and university certificates prove only that a known educational plateau has been reached by the applicant; it does not guarantee that the applicant is a good worker or is able to work with others. General background, therefore, has to be scrutinized with great care.

Personnel Criteria

Job description It is as much a crime for a person to be employed without being told what the job will be, who will be in charge, or where that person's office, desk, or board will be as it is for that same person to lie about matters of experience.

Job descriptions are extremely useful tools in the interviewer's hands and will give the new employee confidence in dealing with what could well be one of life's major traumas. If a person knows exactly what is expected, that person is less likely to exaggerate his or her capabilities and more likely to perform well.

Supervision Poorly supervised staff are usually inefficient and, for the most part, unhappy. Good supervision pays dividends in personnel relations and work capacity.

In general, supervisors of any level can be trained. Unless the newly appointed section leader or job captain has a great deal of leadership ability built in, he or she should be sent on a leadership training course. There are several reasons for this action:

1. Authority is not automatic; the new leader must learn how to use it.

2. The new leader will be supervising educated people—a difficult chore at any time.

3. A good designer does not necessarily make a good leader. A training course will build up self-confidence.

A good supervisor

1. Is honest, sincere, and capable of generating the confidence of the team
2. Is willing to spend time with new employees, to help them become acquainted with the job, and to work closely with them as they carry out their initial assignments
3. Is able to communicate well
4. Keeps supervisees "in the picture" at all times
5. Listens to any suggestions made by his team members
6. Defines the problem or project clearly
7. Is not afraid of the job

Labor balance Management is acquainted with expressions such as "heat balance," "energy balance," "material balance," and "cash balance." In engineering, there must be a labor balance. A staff structure, for instance, which is topheavy technologically is probably using highly skilled people on work which could be done by less skilled personnel. This leads to a costly operation and discontented staff. Conversely, a technological imbalance caused by a "bottom-heavy" condition will cause inefficiency and frustration.

A core of permanent and well-tried personnel is an asset and may be used as a base on which to build an efficient department.

Working conditions Work being done in an engineering office is not routine and requires a constant input of thought and effort. To maintain this potential, office conditions should be compatible with the work being done. It is a mistake to put an engineering office in the middle of the plant—maintenance office, maybe, but not engineering. There is need for relative silence and a dust-free atmosphere, as well as for air conditioning.

Manpower Criteria

Man vs. machine. There is a limit to the amount of automation applicable to the work of an engineering office. There are, however, a large number of aids available, such as computers and calculators which greatly speed the work of designers and technologists. The slide rule has already been superseded by the pocket calculator.

The installation of a time-saving device such as a computer or calculator does not automatically guarantee that it will be fully used. Two further steps must be taken before this happens:

1. The principle must be sold to those who will be using the machine. This is more easily done today than it was 10 years ago, as college and university graduates are already sold on the principle; but still it must be done.
2. The staff must be trained to use the equipment correctly. It is not sufficient to let them read the instruction book. Actual problems of the type they are familiar with should be used in demonstration.

The major cost of an engineering assignment is labor, in the form of engineering and architectural time, drafting, inspection services, management, etc. Within a specific organization, the average cost per man-hour will vary from one project to another, but only within certain limits. If the number of man-hours can be controlled on each project, the project costs will be controlled with sufficient accuracy.

None of the operations involved in recording time and costs, accounting, or forward planning of engineering work are particularly complex. A manual system may be quite suitable for a small firm. However, for a larger firm with an increasing number of projects and departments, the manual manipulation of data becomes a monumental task. Apart from the clerical costs involved, the increase in errors and the delay in producing the control reports would soon make the system ineffective.

A computerized system also encourages clear definitions, and, generally, promotes a systematic approach and disciplined action.

Thoughtful scheduling The accuracy and usefulness of a manpower schedule will reflect the amount of thought put in to it. The title "thoughtful scheduling" is chosen in order to convey the idea that scheduling should not be done in a hurry.

Manpower may be scheduled in two ways: by project and by discipline. These two schedules are used by engineering managers to provide an overall picture of staff work load for the coming months.

Figure 2 shows part of a computer printout for an availability summary. The units in this case are man-weeks, and each trade is shown separately. The information for this summary comes from individual trade man-hour and work load reports.

MANPOWER AVAILABILITY SUMMARY

DEPARTMENT		WEEK ENDING JUL				AUG					SEP				OCT				NOV			ADD HOURS
		6	13	20	27	3	10	17	24	31	7	14	21	28	5	12	19	26	2	9	16	
STRUCTURAL	SCHEDULED MW	12	12	11	11	11	10	10	11	10	10	10	10	10	10	9	9	9	9	9	9	15960
"	AVAILABLE MW	12	12	12	11	10	11	11	13	13	13	14	15	15	15	14	15	15	15	15	15	
ELECTRICAL	SCHEDULED MW	5	5	6	6	6	5	5	5	5	5	5	4	4	4	4	4	4	4	4	4	1840
"	AVAILABLE MW	7	6	6	6	7	6	6	7	6	6	7	7	7	6	6	7	7	7	7	7	
WELDING	SCHEDULED MW	3	4	3	3	2	2	0	0	1	1	1	1	1	0	0	0	0	0	0	0	1988
"	AVAILABLE MW	2	2	2	2	2	2	2	2	2	2	2	2	2	2	2	2	2	2	2	2	
MILLWRIGHT	SCHEDULED MW	27	27	27	22	21	21	20	20	17	18	18	18	17	19	20	19	15	14	14	14	7680
"	AVAILABLE MW	24	26	26	25	25	24	26	26	23	25	25	26	27	27	27	27	27	26	27	27	
H & V	SCHEDULED MW	5	5	5	5	5	5	5	5	5	5	5	5	5	5	5	5	5	5	5	5	0
"	AVAILABLE MW	5	5	5	5	5	5	5	5	5	5	5	5	5	5	5	5	5	5	5	5	
CIVIL	SCHEDULED MW	1	1	1	1	1	1	1	1	1	1	1	1	1	1	1	1	1	1	1	1	0
"	AVAILABLE MW	1	1	1	1	1	1	1	1	1	1	1	1	1	1	1	1	1	1	1	1	
PIPING	SCHEDULED MW	3	3	3	3	3	3	3	3	3	3	3	3	3	3	3	3	3	3	3	3	0
"	AVAILABLE MW	3	3	3	3	3	3	3	3	3	3	3	3	3	3	3	3	3	3	3	3	
INSTRUMENT	SCHEDULED MW	7	7	7	7	7	7	7	7	7	7	7	7	7	7	7	7	7	7	7	7	0
"	AVAILABLE MW	7	7	7	7	7	7	7	7	7	7	7	7	7	7	7	7	7	7	7	7	

MW - MANWEEKS

Fig. 2 Manpower availability.

Plan ahead   The effective management of a plant engineering department is essential if a firm is to stay in business.   Engineering excellence alone is no guarantee that a project will be successful; there must be planning and control.

With increasingly complex engineering assignments, heavy demands are placed on project engineers and engineering managers to control the technical quality of the work output.   At the same time, tight schedules often make it necessary to work on a crash program basis, with resulting pressures and high costs.   When a large number of projects compete for the available personnel, control become increasingly difficult.   Under these circumstances, effective short- and long-term manpower planning is essential if a high staffing efficiency is to be maintained.

Most multiproject, multidiscipline plant engineering departments have well-developed systems for recording time and costs, serving accounting functions, billing on each project, project cost analysis, etc.   These systems generally provide information on past performances.

To control current operations, past performance must be related to planned current performance and expected future performance; and the facts must be reported fast enough to allow for prompt action.

The time period used for forward planning will depend on the type of engineering work done and may be on a daily, weekly, or monthly basis.   For most firms, a schedule using weekly time periods is a reasonable choice for medium-term planning.

Project Criteria

The function   Engineering's function is to design and construct facilities required for the manufacture of goods.   Normally, this is done on a project basis, each project being a different cost center.

The staffing of a project is therefore of vital importance.   With the aid of the man-hour budget and time schedules, each trade supervisor is able to allocate the men to best advantage. A glance at the total manpower needs will show each supervisor's staffing needs for, say, the next 12 months.

Compatibility The project team should be chosen with care. No two persons are alike. There should be some effort put into ensuring compatibility between team members. This is a function of leadership as well as the men themselves. A good project leader will have the enthusiasm to keep moving forward in such a way that the staff will be willing to follow.

"We," not "I" Individualists are an embarrassment to a project team. The "we" complex is desirable, as it generates good communication between team members. This, in a multidisciplined project, is essential to the job.

The Dartnell Corporation's publication on foremanship[1] suggests the following as a means of building the team spirit among the staff:

1. Make sure that everyone in the team has a good, clear understanding of the project goals and objectives.

2. Write job instructions simply and concisely and keep them up to date.

3. Review individual performance on a regular basis and let people know where they stand.

4. Keep pipelines of information and communication open so that people are not kept in the dark regarding matters that concern them.

5. Give the staff tangible, meaningful recognition when their performance is outstanding.

6. Rule out personal consideration in evaluating and rewarding individual workers.

7. Make a special and successful effort not to play favorites when it comes to job assignments.

8. Investigate all aspects of an argument or disagreement before voicing a conclusion or decision.

9. Make sure the project manager is accessible to all his people, and that he listens to their problems and gripes with an open ear and an open mind.

10. Avoid holding grudges against people, no matter how strong your personal antipathy might be.

11. Tackle people problems and face up to them promptly, so they will not fester and multiply.

12. Practice genuine equality, showing no discrimination based on religion, race, or sex.

13. Establish and maintain high standards of performance.

14. Match individuals in functional groups so that those who get along well together will work well together.

REFERENCE

1. *Foremanship*, Dartnell Corporation, Chicago.

Chapter 4

Maintenance Control Function

ROBERT R. RUHLIN

Director
Engineering Management Division, Syska & Hennessy, Inc.

INTRODUCTION

Today's maintenance forces must provide services at the most reasonable cost. Failure to cope with this responsibility on a day-to-day, year-round basis can mean the difference between financial success and failure.

Proper control systems will result in quality maintenance and reduction of waste and inefficiency. On-time job completion may be as necessary as performing work according to plan or as vital as the use of approved methods and procedures.

FUNCTION DEFINED

Maintenance control is the activity responsible for the integration, planning, and performance measurement of all maintenance work from the receipt of maintenance requirements through their completion by the crafts. This is accomplished by coordinating shop-force capabilities, manufacturing commitments, and all related resources to give the optimum of maintenance service to the entire plant. Figure 1 symbolizes the activity of the control function.

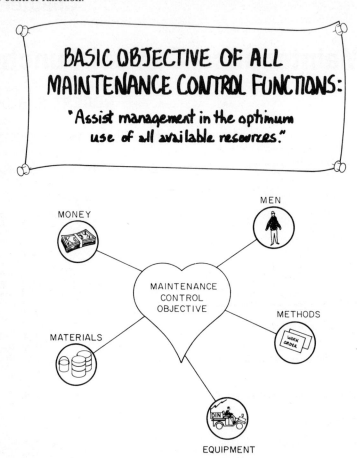

BASIC OBJECTIVE OF ALL MAINTENANCE CONTROL FUNCTIONS:
"Assist management in the optimum use of all available resources."

MEN

MONEY

MAINTENANCE CONTROL OBJECTIVE

METHODS

MATERIALS

EQUIPMENT

Fig. 1   Basic objective of all maintenance control functions.

NEED IS RECOGNIZED BY PLANT MANAGEMENT

The management and control of the plant operation and maintenance forces is a line responsibility invested in the plant engineer or facilities manager. As mentioned in previous chapters of this section, success in these endeavors will be realized only if the various key elements of maintenance management are capable of functioning in a stream-lined and authoritative organization. Today's skilled tradesmen and qualified operating technicians cannot provide their necessary services in an atmosphere of chaos. In fact, inadequate supervision, either because of improper quantity or inadequate talent, is the primary reason why so many craft and operating man-hours are nonproductive. Skilled labor is not lacking, organized management is!

On the other hand, a well-structured plant facilities department, depicted on a neatly drawn organization chart, will not guarantee that the operating and maintenance tasks will be accomplished as economically or efficiently as possible. The chart will, however, as evidenced by Fig. 2, establish a line of authority and responsibility for all functions within the department. There should be a definite split between the craft personnel responsible for performing the operating and maintenance tasks and those employed to assist supervision in controlling the work. The latter, a group of maintenance department employees commonly referred to as *maintenance control,* is a staff entity responsible for the inspection, work reception, job estimating and planning, short- and long-term scheduling, and performance analysis of all operating and maintenance tasks. The success of the facilities department can be measured in the amount of administrative and nonsupervisory work that this maintenance control group can take over from the daily activities of the operating and craft maintenance supervisors.

In order to better understand the need for such a control group, consider the following questions which relate to various areas of maintenance management. Try to present an answer for each question based upon existing conditions in your plant.

TYPICAL ORGANIZATIONAL STRUCTURES

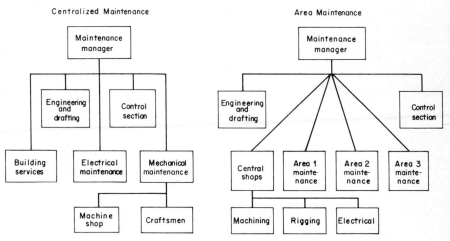

Fig. 2 Organization charts.

KEY QUESTIONS REGARDING MAINTENANCE MANAGEMENT IN YOUR PLANT

1. Why should you try to manage it? Is it not a necessary evil?
2. Who controls maintenance activities now?
3. What factors affect the maintenance forces?
4. Are specific department objectives established?
5. What are the key elements of control?
6. Who is responsible for using these controls?
7. Are present methods too costly?
8. Would all maintenance tasks be rigidly controlled?
9. Who schedules the work?
10. Is preventive maintenance planned?
11. Are the foremen ordering parts and materials?
12. How is your parts inventory controlled?
13. Do you measure your effectiveness?
14. Who coordinates interrelated shop work?
15. What is the labor productivity of your craftsmen?

Did you, like so many other readers, find that there is very little real control of the shop forces? Are you now more aware of the fact that your first-line supervisors are heavily burdened with the wrong tasks? The ultimate objective of a maintenance control group is to remove all nonsupervisory tasks from first-line members of management. A goal should be established that will allow all supervisors to spend over 85 percent of their work days guiding and directing fieldwork forces.

Are your supervisors and foremen only seeing their personnel once or twice a day?

Do your first-line supervisors spend at least 5 hours a day in the office doing "paper work"? Probably so if you do not have the necessary staff and administrative arm of a maintenance control function within your organization. Developing this type of a control group will be an initial step toward the fulfillment of a basic management concept: first-line supervisors and foremen are to be used as supervisors if labor productivity and request response is to be improved.

CONTROL DOES NOT MEAN CONSTRAINT

Maintenance personnel frequently misconstrue the word "control" as a restraint on creative ability and freedom. This can be true, but it does not have to be. There are numerous systems of work control, all of which have merit and, if properly applied, will give excellent results. A proved approach to consolidating objectives and responsibilities is through a building operations center (BOC) or maintenance operations center (MOC).

The overall objective of this concept of nerve center for a maintenance department is to identify areas of operation where improvement in methods and cost savings are possible. Problem areas are brought out in the open where they can be corrected.

Specific responsibilities and objectives of the charter for such a control group include:

- *Receipt and control:* Administration of a work request system, job planning and scheduling, material coordination, establishing job standards, and tenant coordination
- *Planned operating maintenance:* Development, monitoring, and analysis of preventive maintenance program for the facility
- *Performance measurement:* Measurement and analysis of completed work requests in relation to planned estimates of both labor and material
- *Systematic preventive maintenance:* Planning and scheduling of long-range (3 to 10 years) cyclical maintenance programs oriented to the facility
- *Material support:* Analyzing, inventorying, and reordering or job materials and spare parts for operating equipment
- *Management reports:* Developing factual, timely reports based on analysis of requirements and performance data

PURPOSE OF A STAFF CONTROL GROUP

Prior to making a commitment to establish a separate staff that will help optimize resources, a plant engineer should reflect on what "managing maintenance" means. It is simply:

1. Having direct control over the labor force
2. Taking corrective action before major repairs are required
3. Estimating repair and alteration costs
4. Providing maintenance on a timely and scheduled basis
5. Comparing actual to planned costs
6. Freeing supervision from clerical tasks

Today, maintenance line supervisors do not have the time to properly plan, estimate, and schedule work in addition to directing the efforts of their people. And increasing the number of supervisors in the maintenance department will not automatically solve this problem. However, developing a maintenance control group to process all work from inception to final cost analysis will solve a portion of the manager's problem. The specific functions that should be performed by the members of the maintenance control group includes the ability to:

1. Receive and arrange in priority all customer-generated requests for service
2. Approve and classify all operating, maintenance, and alteration work
3. Program all work for craft shops
4. Dispatch crafts for emergency jobs
5. Maintain a meaningful backlog of work for all crafts
6. Plan, schedule, and assign all operating and maintenance work to appropriate shop forces
7. Coordinate vendor services and contractors
8. Control all maintenance material activities
9. Develop preventive maintenance programs
10. Coordinate tool room and special equipment needs

11. Prepare operating and maintenance budgets
12. Evaluate the performance of all work performed by the department
13. Develop operation and maintenance manuals
14. Coordinate maintenance and customer schedules
15. Supervise maintenance-cost improvement programs

In contrast to the craft and operating groups within the maintenance department who have the responsibility to perform their tasks within defined limits of both quantity and quality of work, the primary responsibility of a maintenance control effort is to ensure that the operating and maintenance forces can perform within established limits.

MAINTENANCE CONTROL REQUIRES FORMAL ORGANIZATION

In order to operate as intended, the organizational integrity of a maintenance control group must be maintained. Two basic guidelines to be followed when establishing such a control group would be as follows:

1. The group or staff that provides the control and evaluation of the operating forces should not be supervised by those it is measuring. Entangling relationships like this often create situations where measurement and control are ineffective and meaningless.

2. The individual in charge of this group should report directly to the person who has ultimate responsibility for the overall direction of the facilities or maintenance department. If the new control group is staffed too low in the organization, it will not receive proper management attention or register adequate impact, especially when meaningful decisions are needed.

Whether the department is established on a central shop, area shop, or combination of these makes no difference to the structuring of the control group. However, a control group will perform best if all its personnel are located in a central location and away from the daily interruptions of the craft and trade shop areas. The relationship of the maintenance control function to the other functions within the various types of maintenance organizations is shown in Fig. 2 for both central and area maintenance organizations.

In light of the many service and control functions that such a control organization performs, it is commonly referred to by any of the following names:

Maintenance control center
Facilities management center
Maintenance operating center
Engineering management control
Maintenance engineering center
Work control center
Maintenance planning center

ORGANIZATION DOES NOT VARY WITH SIZE

Regardless of the physical size of the plant or of the operations and maintenance department, the role of the maintenance control group does not change. The physical makeup, number of personnel, and size of control room will be directly related to the number of personnel in the facilities or maintenance department. Staffing guides and suggested job descriptions for control center personnel are included in following paragraphs of this chapter. For ease in operation, a maintenance control group or center should be structured according to the types of tasks performed. Specifically, work elements should be established as follows:

1. Work receipt and control
2. Planning and scheduling
3. Materials and inventory control
4. Preventive maintenance inspection
5. Budget and audit

Each control center element should have its own objectives and responsibilities. A weekly staff meeting of all key personnel within the center should suffice to keep all elements working in the right direction. The task of each work element, although at times interfacing with other elements, should be clearly shown, as in Fig. 3. A summary of operations and tasks performed by the respective work elements in a typical control center group would include the following:

1. *Work receipt and control*
   a. Receive all trouble calls and requests for emergency or service work.
   b. Dispatch craft and trade personnel in response to emergency or service work.
   c. Receive all customer and maintenance department requests for repair or alterations.
   d. Control the processing of all requests for repair or alteration services until jobs are approved and ready for planning.
   e. Monitor the progress of all approved work orders and provide customers liaison as to work request status.
2. *Planning and scheduling*
   a. Classify, plan, and estimate all nonemergency repair and alteration work.
   b. Maintain a manageable backlog of work for all crafts.
   c. Specify all nonstocked materials for planned jobs. ·
   d. Provide daily, weekly, and long-term scheduling for all crafts.
   e. Coordinate the activities of service contractors who support the maintenance activities.

SKILL REQUIREMENTS FOR A TYPICAL
CONTROL CENTER

Work Receipt & Control	*Material Control*
• Planners	• Storekeepers
• Estimators	• Warehousemen
• Schedulers	• Expediters

Systems Control	*Administrative Control*
• Preventive maintenance coordinators	• Clerks
	• Budgets analysts
• Draftsmen	• Typists
• Inspectors	• Dispatcher
• Engineers	

Fig. 3 Skill requirements for a typical control center.

f. Coordinate repair, alteration, and project work with customer needs.
g. Visit work sites to monitor the progress of work.
h. Coordinate extraordinary tool and heavy equipment apparatus to support craft requirements.
i. Provide visual control and status boards to coordinate all shops and contract activities.
3. *Material and inventory control*
   a. Order all nonstock material to support planned work orders.
   b. Develop and maintain required spare parts and maintenance material inventories.
   c. Control the receipt, warehousing, and issue of all maintenance materials and spare parts.
   d. Develop materials management systems that will assist in the timely completion of all emergency and scheduled maintenance work.
   e. Provide procedures for disposing of obsolete and surplus material and equipment.
   f. Support craft productivity through the delivery of material to work sites.
   g. Prepare a maintenance material and spare parts catalog to assist department personnel using such items.
4. *Preventive maintenance inspection*
   a. Develop a comprehensive facilities identification numbering system for all assets of the plant.
   b. Maintain a building and equipment record-keeping system as a central index of all critical design, operating, maintenance, and performance data.
   c. Develop a preventive maintenance program for major and critical equipment and apparatus.

d. Prepare preventive maintenance inspection guides and procedures to be used by the crafts.

e. Coordinate preventive maintenance inspection and overhaul schedules to optimize the utilization of all resources.

f. Integrate the preventive maintenance schedule with the corrective maintenance schedule to minimize downtime.

g. Process, to the appropriate control element, work orders for corrective maintenance as generated through controlled inspection.

h. Update spare-parts inventory schemes, using machinery life expectancy and performance data.

i. Maintain a complete library of operating and maintenance catalogs and pamphlets for all buildings and apparatus.

j. Develop improved, nondestructive testing methods to be used by the maintenance forces performing preventive maintenance.

k. Prepare operations and maintenance manuals to assist the operating and maintenance forces in their daily functions.

5. *Budget and audit*

a. Measure and analyze actual labor and material performance in comparison to estimates.

b. Develop cost accounting procedures for charging of maintenance work to requesting departments.

c. Institute and monitor work sampling programs conducted by maintenance supervisors.

d. Detect abnormally repetitive maintenance trends through audit of recurring work requests.

e. Analyze and evaluate the performance of implemented preventive maintenance programs.

f. Maintain craft manpower status information for both the work control and the planning and scheduling elements.

g. Prepare and control maintenance department budgets and project allocations.

h. Develop reporting systems for management that clearly indicate the effectiveness of all the techniques and schemes used to control the entire operations and maintenance effort.

i. Perform office and clerical functions to support the other elements of the control center.

j. Assist the planning and scheduling element in the development of both labor and material job standards.

k. Provide visual media that chart performance trends for such areas as overtime, absenteeism, rework, downtime, work stoppages, and safety.

l. Direct cost-reduction programs instituted by the plant engineer.

m. Prepare information procedures and instructions to help maintenance customers prepare requests for service.

The physical size of the facility and the scope of work will determine staffing requirements. Many of the functions listed above can be grouped into position categories and performed by a relatively small number of people.

SELECTING CONTROL CENTER PERSONNEL

The personnel chosen to man the control center must have a wide range of desirable qualities. They must first have a thorough knowledge of their craft and of maintenance procedures and techniques. In addition, they must be adaptable to paper work and office routine. Since the control center is a staff function, they must have the ability to get along with others and to communicate both orally and in writing with their peers as well as with others.

In many cases, these personnel can be drawn from the ranks of the foremen. This provides another step in the overall career progression of the various trades, crafts, and operating fields and allows for promotions from within the department.

The control center manager must be qualified through both education and experience to direct the activities that are the responsibilities of the center. A technical knowledge of shop and plant operations is essential, so that the manager can effectively direct and correlate efforts in and between the various shops to best advantage. Also important is the ability to coordinate the overall work programs, such as preventive maintenance and seasonal inspection programs.

The number of planners, schedulers, and material expediters depends on the number of craftsmen in each trade on the staff. A planner can effectively plan for 20 to 25 craftsmen. If the shop is small, it may be possible to combine similar trades and put the planning under one person. Some typical combinations are carpenters and sheet metal workers, plumbers and pipefitters, electricians and instrument people, heating and air conditioning.

Too often organizations arrange to have planners cover the planning for more than 25 craftsmen. This is a foolish economy. If a thorough planning and estimating job is needed, then the planner cannot be expected to plan for too many craftsmen if, in addition, he is to help increase the overall productivity and effectiveness of the operating and maintenance forces.

JOB DESCRIPTIONS DETAIL RESPONSIBILITIES

Meaningful job descriptions should be created to delineate the many functions and responsibilities to be performed by the personnel assigned to a control center. A sampling of the key positions—adaptable large or small facilities—which are being introduced to maintenance organizations are presented below.

Control manager An individual responsible for complete administrative coordination and management control of control center, including the establishment of meaningful departmental objectives such as:

Maximization of work-force productivity

Development of maximum-minimum stores system

Development of high-efficiency, low-cost preventive maintenance system

Development of maintenance performance reporting system in order to minimize unit maintenance cost

DEVELOPS POLICY FOR:

1. Receipt of emergency service, trouble calls, and subsequent dispatching of DIN ("do it now" personnel; a unit that can respond to jobs which are incapable of being planned)

2. Receipt and flow of work requests from customer, engineering, and maintenance sources

3. Planning and estimating of both project-type and maintenance-oriented work requests

4. Daily scheduling of maintenance personnel using formal techniques

5. Preventive maintenance program, including necessary economic analyses to determine both the scope and frequency of preventive maintenance work

6. Status boards—engineering and maintenance

7. Control center for drawings, equipment manuals, overhaul procedures, equipment records, and necessary control personnel

8. Materials control and distribution

9. Work measurement program

10. Performance reporting system, including budget "charge-back" accounting and variances

Preventive maintenance coordinator An individual responsible for the complete administrative coordination of a preventive maintenance program, including predictive and functional inspections.

IMPLEMENTS OR DEVELOPS POLICY FOR:

1. Preventive maintenance record-keeping and scheduling system

2. Preventive maintenance procedure books including:

   a. Lubrication

   b. Minor adjustments and repairs of less than one-half

   c. Routine servicing

   d. Job estimates and standards

   e. Inspection procedures and routines

   f. Selection of individuals to perform preventive maintenance routines

   g. Preventive maintenance training techniques

3. Follow-up procedures

4. Economic analysis to determine frequency and scope of individual preventive maintenance routines

5. Maintains:

   a. Preventive maintenance records and files

   b. Preventive maintenance schedules

   c. Procedure books

   d. Training library

Planner/scheduler   An individual responsible for providing both complete job task analyses and daily manpower scheduling in order to minimize job delays and, consequently, maximize maintenance personnel productivity.

IMPLEMENTS:

1. Job planning for both maintenance and project-type work requests, including manpower estimating and sequencing, general scope analysis, tool and material lists and purchase orders, and sketches and prints

2. Formal daily scheduling of maintenance manpower

3. Status boards—operations and maintenance

4. Coordination of work measurement program including analysis of work sampling data and development of repetitive job standards

5. Work simplification program

6. Maintenance standard procedure books

7. Interfacing procedures with originators and/or approvers of all work requests with regards to:

   a. Priorities

   b. Completion dates

   c. Reconciliation of complaints

   d. Job progress

   e. Job completions

   f. Specific job definition

Dispatcher   Individual responsible for receipt and flow of work requests and maintenance of control center paper work and records.

IMPLEMENTS:

1. Receipt and logging of emergency service calls and dispatching of appropriate DIN personnel or maintenance groups

2. Receipt and logging of nonemergency maintenance and project work

3. Participation in establishment of work priority system, including definition of emergency and nonemergency tasks

4. Maintenance of:

   a. Work request log books

   b. Equipment records including historical work request entries

   c. Completed work request files

   d. Complete daily and weekly schedule files

   e. Pertinent statistical files as required by control center manager

5. Departmental clerical work including printing of daily schedule, monthly performance reports, and other pertinent departmental dispatches

SPACE AND LAYOUT REQUIREMENTS AFFECT CENTER'S EFFECTIVENESS

The usual center requires sufficient office space for its staff, the maintenance manager, and the subordinate craft and operating supervisors. To be most effective, these adjoining areas should be accessible to the maintenance shops and have communication lines to the operating spaces. A typical layout is displayed in Fig. 4. The average control center will require about 2,000 square feet of floor space, with the control room occupying approximately 900 square feet. The control room needs about 120 linear feet of wall space for charts and planning boards.

The control room is the hub of the center's operation. It must be provided with direct communication contact with the various shops and work centers, including radio communications with service, DIN trucks, and preventive maintenance crews. Proposed work programs and requests for work and services are received here, processed for approval, and included in the scheme of visual displays maintained in the control room.

A control center combines the skills of many people with modern management tools and techniques.   Figure 5 shows the physical makeup of a center.

Displays include various charts and status boards showing the current status of all work proposed and underway.   These provide the means for a continuous review of all work from the authorization and planning phases, through scheduling to the shops and finally

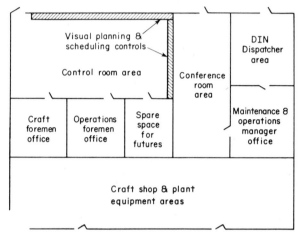

Fig. 4   Control center layout.

to completion. Other charts and graphic displays reflect availability of essential resources such as manpower, supplies, transportation, vehicles and equipment; status of contracts; and trends in utilities operations and preventive care programs.

Enough telephone in the center should be installed for efficient functioning and a maximum reduction in waiting time on both incoming and outcoming calls.   This is

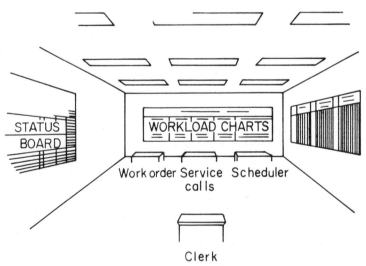

Fig. 5   Control room. Size and physical layout of each control center is dependent upon workload, staff, and degree of planning and scheduling desired by management.

especially important in the control room where incoming requests for work and services are funneled and telephone contact must be made with the shops and other offices in the facility concerning jobs and work assignments.

UNDERSTANDING THE SYSTEM IS ESSENTIAL

In addition to space requirements, a predetermined flow of customer-generated work is essential to the center's success. Figure 6 depicts an effective and systematic approach to the funneling of requests for service to respective work areas while also maintaining proper craft labor and material control.

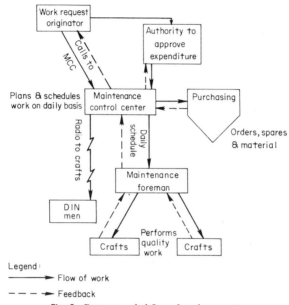

Fig. 6 Recommended flow-of-work requests.

The control room must have direct communication contact with various shops and radio communications with emergency service, DIN personnel, and preventive maintenance crews. Proposed work programs and requests for work and services are received here, processed for approval, and included in the scheme of visual displays maintained in the control room.

PERFORMANCE INDICATORS

Underlying the thought that there is merit in establishing a central control group is the idea that the data collected, analyzed, and evaluated will be developed into useful reporting procedures and applied by the various management levels in the facilities department. The many various types of reports, charts, and performance media distributed by as many control centers makes it possible to list all of the operation and financial data that a group could generate. However, as with any family of management reports, there is always a nucleus that will provide to management a greater advantage.

The results of a cost-analysis report may not be evident for a few reporting periods. In order to reflect trends, it is suggested that three months' activity be included in each monthly performance report. Three-month results should be plotted on control charts;

then trends will be more readily detected. Where cyclic and seasonal conditions may have a direct bearing on performance, it may be necessary to chart moving monthly average performance data for an entire year in order to include all cyclic factors.

A sampling of performance indicators prepared by a Center are shown in Fig. 7.

BASIC MANAGEMENT REPORTS PREPARED BY
A CONTROL CENTER

Daily
Emergency/service work activity analysis
Status of critical equipment
Listing of delayed jobs and projects
Craft schedule for succeeding day's work

Weekly
Backlog for all crafts
Equipment downtime report
Combined priority listing of maintenance and project work
Status of ordered material
Manpower availability analysis

Monthly
Work order cost analysis by customer or process area
Cost analysis of service provided
Shops' comparative performance report

Fig. 7   Basic management reports prepared by a control center.

BENEFITS OF MAINTENANCE CONTROL

In a broad sense, the benefit derived from establishing a central planning and control function is the removal of all nonsupervisory tasks from line management in its daily administration of the plant operating and maintenance forces. In specific terms, this means that one single administrative group will be maintaining records, suggesting methods, providing information, determining equipment replacement schedules, and developing preventive maintenance schemes for reducing cost and improving efficiencies. Because benefits will accrue to varying degrees based upon plant and company management philosophies, it is best to list them in terms of the nonoperational and operational benefits resulting from establishing a control group:

Operational Benefits

1. Improved reliability of equipment and utility services
2. Improved productivity of all company employees
3. Closer approximation of the life expectancy of the buildings and equipment
4. Pinpointing of repetitive repair work that may lend itself to preventive maintenance techniques
5. Identification of items that have a history of high maintenance costs and that disrupt production scheduling effects

Nonoperational Benefits

1. Decreased capital investment and replacement costs
2. Improved morale among all employees
3. Improved job satisfaction of many maintenance employees through job enrichment
4. Collection of maintenance costs that can be of help in the preparation of tax returns
5. Provision of reporting of more reflective costs in reports to creditors, investors, government agencies, and the general public
6. Assignment of proper responsibility for cost, especially as between those maintenance personnel who do the work and those who cause the work to be done

EVALUATE MAINTENANCE PERFORMANCE

Once a control center, DIN group, and other support elements are in operation, it is time to evaluate performance. The question constantly raised is: "How many people are needed to maintain the equipment in my facility?"

An accurate basis for determining personnel needs can be developed by the maintenance manager who faithfully schedules preventive maintenance. Craft hours expended to accomplish all repairs, inspection, and lubrication will provide the manager with necessary data. Combining these facts with such techniques as learning curves, repair-cost to replacement-value ratios, and short- and long-term planning will permit the manager to develop a suggested backlog of 20 days' work for each craftsman. The DIN crew should represent 20 percent of the maintenance staff.

Weekly reports to management, comparing the department's past performance, will assist the maintenance manager in determining backlog and manpower needs. Such a report will also facilitate a comparison of costs against national averages furnished by leading organization analysis reports.

If the backlog becomes too great a burden for the craftsmen, the overload situation can be relieved by subcontracting, use of overtime, or increase in shop forces.

Proper planning to raise maintenance efficiency is the most neglected phase of maintenance management. As a result, improved planning methods usually bring the largest and most immediate payoff when management shows interest in implementing change.

There seems to be a common feeling among maintenance personnel that work cannot be planned in advance with any assurance that the plan will be carried out. The principal argument has always been that rush jobs and breakdowns continuously interfere with any attempt at planning ahead, thereby wasting the effort. When this argument is advanced you can be pretty sure that (1) the preventive maintenance program is falling down, allowing too many breakdowns; (2) there is no DIN system in existence, (3) too detailed planning and scheduling of work is being attempted, or (4) planning procedures have been misguided somewhere along the way and lack the requisite flexibility. Maintenance planning that can anticipate 80 percent or more of the work a day ahead is good.

Where does one start with a basic plan for improvement after a control center has been established? Such a plan should start with a sound program of work receipt, planning, scheduling, and work measurement. From this basis, other programs can be built to encompass the entire field of maintenance improvement.

Chapter 5

Maintenance Function

JOHN M. WALIGORA, P.E., F.A.I.P.E.

RESPONSIBILITIES

Equipment Maintenance

This is probably the most important of all the responsibilities of the maintenance function. This means keeping the plant equipment in proper operating condition for accomplishing its mission, whether it be producing the product, transporting materials, research, or plant services. This must be done to optimize the cost of operating equipment, taking into account all the factors which have a bearing on operating costs. The following is a list of some of these factors:

Impact of an interruption in the operation of a piece of equipment on plant operations

Cost of replacing the equipment

Time to replace

Obsolescence

Cost of downtime

Effect on quality and quantity of output

Cost of spare parts

Impact on other operations

An example of a case in which little maintenance is required would be that of a small motor which is quickly replaced and readily available. On the other hand, a large crusher or costly machine tool or fractionating tower would be another matter. Here downtime would seriously affect subsequent operations, involving a large number of people who would be made idle, and the cost of stocking or procuring of replacement parts is high. Such an item would justify a high degree of maintenance. When a number of production machines are maintained, an additional unit can sometimes be justified to provide maintenance forces with the ability to properly handle their responsibilities.

Building Maintenance

This involves not only the physical structure such as the roofs, floors, walls, and partitions but also the building service equipment such as plumbing, heating, ventilating, air-conditioning equipment, and utilities required in the plant.

This includes repairs to correct roof leaks and defective flashing as well as anticipating the need for major repairs or replacement. Floors must be kept in good condition for safety of personnel as well as for the smooth movement of material handling trucks and equipment. Provision must be made for having on hand proper patching materials so that rapid repairs can be made to all floor surfaces, whether wood, concrete, tile, terrazzo, or anything else.

Walls require periodic inspection of brickwork to prevent leakage, corrosion of metal skins or structural parts, and other damage which could cause loss of heat or conditioned air or pose a danger to personnel and equipment. Caulking on windows, walls, and other building appurtenances must be checked and replaced when necessary.

Exterior equipment such as ladders and exposed structural steel dust collectors must be inspected and repainted to prevent corrosion and deterioration.

The degree of maintenance is dictated by the nature of the operations for which the building is used. In a drug plant, for example, a very high degree of cleanliness and maintenance is required. By comparison, for a food packaging plant such requirements may be less strict, but they would be far higher than those for, say, a cement plant.

Grounds Maintenance

This includes the patching and repair of plant roads, care of sidewalks, lawn care, weed control, maintenance of security fences, and pruning and spraying of shrubbery and trees. In addition, there is policing of plant grounds for paper and other debris, snow removal in the wintertime, salting of icy surfaces, keeping storm drains clear, etc. In plants where storm runoff goes directly to public streams, this involves control of runoff so that spills are controlled and contamination of public waterways is avoided.

New Equipment Installation

Maintenance departments that are familiar with the location of utilities and plant operations generally install most new equipment, particularly that placed in areas where operations must continue. In cases where complicated equipment requires the manufacturer's erection services, the maintenance forces may be required to help out in the installation or to become familiar with the equipment so that they will be better able to adjust, maintain, and repair it when it goes into operation.

Minor Construction and Rearrangements

Much of this work can be done by maintenance forces more quickly and with a minimum of disturbance to other operations because of their knowledge of the plant and operating requirements. This work can also serve to help iron out the peaks and valleys in the maintenance work load when it is desirable to have adequate manpower on hand to handle breakdowns and emergencies.

It should be pointed out that caution must be exercised to avoid taking on construction work at the expense of needed maintenance and repair. Many craftsmen prefer working with new materials in construction rather than on maintenance, with its exposure to dirty and sometimes unpleasant jobs. The primary mission of a maintenance force is maintenance, and this must be emphasized before its efforts are diluted with construction work.

Inspections

Inspections of equipment, buildings, and grounds uncover need for repairs and maintenance before breakdowns occur—breakdowns that can cause serious interruptions or damage to equipment or create hazards to personnel. The frequency of inspections will vary depending on the nature of the item being inspected. As an example, boilers are opened up and inspected annually; roofs may be inspected semiannually; heating, ventilating, and air-conditioning equipment is looked at daily or more often. These inspections should be made by inspectors who have the ability to detect undue wear and tear and pinpoint malperformance before a breakdown occurs. These inspections are best performed by skilled mechanics who can recognize the abnormal sounds, vibrations, smells, etc., that may signify impending problems or breakdowns. Inspection of equipment sometimes is combined with the responsibilities for lubrication, because the latter may involve the same tours as are required for inspection.

Preventive Maintenance

Preventive maintenance is, again, carried on in varying degrees depending on the importance of a piece of equipment or a facility. Its purpose is to detect the need for repairs or corrective action before a breakdown occurs, so that the necessary work can be scheduled without interrupting essential operations. This includes items such as replacement of bearings when they approach their normal life expectancy, cleaning of coils in heat exchangers, replacement of parts which cause vibrations, or noise pollution and out-of-tolerance parts that affect the quality of the product, etc.

Lubrication

This involves the determination of the frequency of lubrication and the kind of lubricants to be used as well as the actual lubrication. It involves making sure that adequate lubricants are on hand, that they are properly stored, and that equipment is on hand for readily and efficiently applying of the lubricant.

Maintenance Stores

The quantities of supplies and spare parts to be kept on reserve in any maintenance department will vary depending on the location of the plant in relation to sources of supply as well as the time necessary for securing materials and parts. This involves determining how much of any material should be kept on hand, when it should be reordered, and what the reordering quantity should be. Controls must be maintained for assuring that optimum inventories are maintained, obsolescent parts are discarded, and prompt replacement is done as required. An important part of storage keeping is the ability to find materials and parts readily when needed. Proper storage must be maintained so that the materials and parts are readily usable when needed. When mill supply houses are in close proximity to the plant, the quantities of supplies stocked in house can be significantly reduced.

Emergency Planning

This involves development of a plan to take care of emergencies that invariably involve maintenance forces. This could include such things as fires, floods, storm damage, malicious mischief, and vandalism as well as fire prevention and control. A plan for action in varying kinds of emergencies needs to be developed and periodically updated. Periodic testing of the plan and drills must be held.

Fire protection equipment must be maintained on hand and periodically inspected to assure that it is readily available when fire strikes. In larger plants, this could include the establishment of a fire brigade with necessary fire trucks and equipment to respond rapidly before public fire companies can respond. It involves testing of sprinkler systems, flow alarms, emergency pumps, and other alarms and signals.

Training of all plant personnel in the use of fire extinguishers is valuable in controlling small fires before they can get out of hand.

Communications

The maintenance function should communicate with other parts of the plant to highlight maintenance problems that are occurring, so that production operations can schedule maintenance. Thus new equipment procurement can benefit from the maintenance experience with in-plant equipment. Also, degrees of standardization can thus be established. Finally, good communications can help to minimize inventories of spare parts and to anticipate repair jobs.

Profit Improvement

Maintenance of plant and equipment can run as high as 10 percent of the plant investment and therefore has a substantial effect on the profits of any enterprise. The maintenance function has the responsibility of contributing to profit improvement through finding ways to minimize its costs and otherwise contribute to the profits of the enterprise.

Labor Relations

This involves administering the labor force in keeping with any collective bargaining agreements, handling grievances, and motivating the work force for maximum productivity.

OSHA

The Occupational Safety and Health Act (OSHA) puts considerable responsibility on the maintenance function to assure conformance to the Act. Certain regular inspections of equipment must be made and properly recorded to assure performance. Violations of the Act must be corrected promptly to assure safe operating conditions and to avoid possible penalties as well as adverse employee and public relations.

Housekeeping and Sanitation

In extremely large plants, separate organizational units may handle housekeeping and sanitation; but frequently this is a part of the maintenance function. This includes such simple tasks as sweeping floors, vacuuming carpets, waxing and polishing resilient tile floors, dusting equipment, washing walls, and mopping where required.

An important part of housekeeping is within the control of operating people, and this should be clearly spelled out in any organization. A sloppy worker in the operating group can create enough mess to keep an additional housekeeping worker busy. The operating department should be responsible for keeping its machinery clean and the operating area in good order, so that the housekeeping function can better perform the necessary cleaning jobs.

This operation may include the periodic stocking of paper towels, soap, and toilet tissues in toilet rooms as well as the periodic cleanup necessary in these areas.

STAFFING CRITERIA

Organization

There is no one set organization which can be applied to all maintenance requirements. Even in two plants of the same size making the same product, there could be differences of organization. These would depend on the overall organizational setup at the site as well as proximity to large urban centers where many services are available for contract work, materials, supplies, and spare parts, etc. Furthermore, one plant site may have a research organization independent of the manufacturing organization or other divisions, each of which requires its own set of priorities and services.

There are certain basic elements of organization used in industry which can be combined in many different ways to tailor an organization to the specific requirements of any single plant.

Craft shops   Organization of maintenance shops by craft has much to be said for it. It makes it possible to achieve a higher degree of competence among the craftsmen working together with others doing the same kind of work. Thus one person learns from the other and eventually many become better craftsmen than they would working alone. Furthermore, in a craft shop, it is the usual practice to have a supervisor from that same craft.

Craft shops lend themselves better to the establishment of apprentice programs because craft supervisors are better able to assure assignments that are necessary for the successful completion of apprentice training. Furthermore, having the expertise in a particular craft allows the supervisor to better assist in developing a training program, not only for apprentices but for upgrading and keeping the journeymen craftsmen up

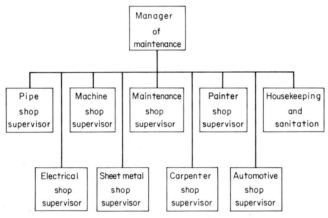

Fig. 1   Craft shop organization.

to date on new developments.   Craft shops also have the advantage of being able to justify more and better equipment, because equipment will be used more hours than would be the case with a lesser number of craftsmen assigned to an area shop.   Figure 1 shows a typical craft organization.   When the number of mechanics is small, several crafts can be combined under one supervisor.

Area shops   In a small industrial plant serving an area of approximately 100,000 square feet, one maintenance shop would very well be adequate.   It could encompass all the craft trades required for maintenance in that particular plant.   As the plant grows larger in size, the travel time of mechanics from one shop also becomes greater; and, in addition to the high cost of travel time, the response time becomes significant.   In these cases it may become necessary to create an additional area shop.   There is no set size of plant which determines when an additional area shop is needed, though a million-square-foot plant has been quoted by many authorities on maintenance as the point where multiple area maintenance shops become a necessity.   This figure may be substantially lower in the case of single-story plant facilities as compared to a multistory, compact operation.

Area shops are organized to handle the specific requirements of the operations or areas they serve.   It may sometimes be necessary to service an irregular area in order to conform to the organizational unit being served.   An example might be a plant which combines manufacturing and research operations, each of which reports to a different managerial organization. The manufacturing management has its own set of priorities; these cannot be subordinated to the priorities of a research organization. An area shop, therefore, would serve the manufacturing organization, and another might be created to serve the research organization exclusively. In other plants, there may be two or more separate manufacturing divisions, each with its own organization having its own area shop.

Area shops generally are complete unto themselves, providing the facilities for all the crafts within them, though there may be exceptions when the requirements of a given craft are insufficient to justify separate shop facilities. In this instance, the requirements of some crafts might be provided from either a central maintenance shop or from a neighboring area organization. As an example, in one organization one area shop has a complete machine shop because it serves a manufacturing division involving many

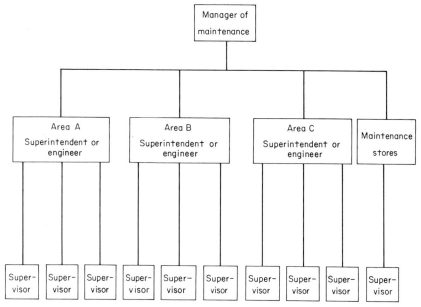

Fig. 2 Area maintenance organization.

expensive automatic machines, repairs to which may require a great deal of machine work. The other area shops in this plant do not require much machine work; therefore their requirements can be met by calling on the one area shop that has the machine-shop facilities. On the other hand, another area shop in the same plant has a complete carpenter shop and sheet-metal facilities. It serves its own area but may provide some of these craft services to the neighboring areas. Figure 2 is a typical organization chart for an area maintenance type of organization.

Centralized shop with area mechanics In this type of organization, mechanics work out of a central shop but are permanently assigned to a production department. Examples of such an arrangement would be electricians assigned to a packaging department to be immediately available for troubleshooting on a packaging line when operation is interrupted by electrical problems. Setup mechanics who make machine setups as well as doing minor maintenance are often a part of a centralized maintenance shop. This type of organization allows the mechanics assigned to an area to become more familiar with the equipment. Thus they are able to respond more readily not only from a timing angle but because of being able to capitalize on their previous experience with the equipment in a given area. An added advantage of this arrangement is that the production supervision is able to call on a mechanic immediately and to be more understanding and tolerant when the demands for maintenance exceed the manpower available.

Other combinations   There are an almost infinite number of combinations of area craft shops and area mechanics which are tailored to the specific needs of given plants. Figure 3 is an example of one such, which combines an area shop with a centralized group of craft shops. Other combinations might provide for certain types of maintenance to be fully subcontracted, as when the needs of the plant cannot be efficiently and readily met by an in-plant crew. Examples of this would be in a refinery where periodic overhaul must be concentrated in a very short period of time, requiring a mass effort to get the job done. Other examples would be the care of large-size air-conditioning chillers or elevators.

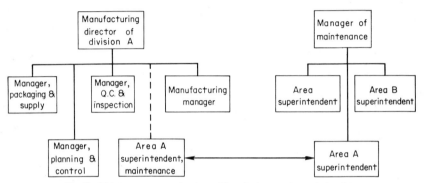

Fig. 3   Maintenance organization with a dual reporting relationship.

Dual reporting   In some organizations the maintenance requirements in an area covered by an operating department may be so closely interwoven with the operations of that group that the maintenance superintendent or area engineer works best as a member of the operating manager's staff. This can be managed by instituting a dual reporting relationship, as shown in Fig. 3. In this type of organizational setup, the area engineer reports to the manager of maintenance for overall guidance in how to do the job of manning, budgeting, and so on. The area engineer reports to the operating manager for the establishment of priorities, sequencing and timing of jobs, and many requirements that dovetail with the operating group. This type of relationship does not violate the basic organizational need for having one boss, because each of the two reporting relationships covers a specific aspect of the job. The area superintendent can call on the manager of maintenance for additional manpower when peaking requirements demand it and can thus take advantage of the know-how and the training that is available in the central organization. At the same time, the area superintendent can respond to the immediate needs of the operating manager and participate in the staff meetings (if such are held), thus being in a better position to carry out the maintenance work because of the close contact that is maintained.

With this type of organization (see Fig. 3), the superintendent or area engineer will report to the manager (dotted line) of the area served as well as the manager (solid line) of maintenance.

Staffing

First-line supervisors   The foremen or first-line supervisors are best recruited from the ranks of craftsmen who have demonstrated not only high proficiency in their particular craft but who also have leadership abilities. They should have demonstrated ability to deal with people. This applies to dealing with the management and supervision of the areas served by the maintenance force as well as with the workers supervised. It is easier to select foremen for supervising a craft shop because the source of supervisors is largely limited to the people in that particular shop, and leadership abilities are easy to recognize.

Area shop supervisors have to be selected from those who have a working knowledge of more than one craft and have demonstrated their ability to coordinate jobs involving several crafts. It is also important to have people who can oversee a number of jobs running concurrently.

Superintendents When maintenance shops approach staffs of 100, the need for a second level of supervision starts to develop. In this case, a superintendent having knowledge of all the crafts is desirable. A most common source of candidates for a superintendent's position is the group of first-line maintenance supervisors. A superintendent who has risen from the ranks has a good understanding of overall maintenance problems as well as labor relations. In difficult technical situations, it is extremely desirable that such a person have access to consulting service from engineers in the plant.

Graduate engineers make good supervisors; in many plants, all levels of maintenance supervision are recruited from among graduate engineers. Working as maintenance supervisors, they are able to contribute engineering expertise to the solution of many problems; in working with maintenance mechanics, they develop themselves as engineers. Unfortunately, in many cases, the ambitions of engineers go beyond maintenance supervision; unless some promotional opportunities are apparent, engineers are reluctant to accept these jobs. In an organization that provides for area maintenance, it is frequent practice to give an area engineer the responsibility for a given area. This person's duties encompass those normally done by a superintendent, but they also include the solution of minor engineering problems associated with the maintenance in the assigned area.

The number of craftsmen per supervisor will vary depending on many factors, including the size of the area served, the number of different crafts supervised, and the complexity of operations maintained. The guideline that will apply to most plants is generally 12 to 15 workers per supervisor. These figures could be increased in the case of workers in a craft shop, such as a machine shop, where the work is done in a relatively small area. On the other hand, an instrument shop supervisor whose people cover a large area of the plant site would have fewer workers to supervise.

Group leaders or working foremen or lead men In some plants it is practical to have people who can direct a job as well as do the work of their trade. Where such working foremen are used, the span of control for the foreman or supervisor can be much higher, running as high as 40 to 50 people.

Supervisory and Staff Training

An important part of good staffing is to provide for necessary orientation training and development. A craftsman promoted to the ranks of supervision should undergo a period of training to acquire a knowledge of company policies, labor relations, safety, cost control, etc. While much of this can be gotten on the job, it is exceedingly important that each new supervisor be given certain fundamentals before moving into the actual job of supervision. This not only helps the supervisor do a better job but also makes for better acceptance from the people supervised. These staff people should have the opportunity to attend outside seminars and conferences applying to their jobs. They should have the opportunity to attend exhibits and meetings within a reasonable distance of their plant. This gives them an opportunity to keep up to date on their jobs as well as to develop improvements through association with other people in similar jobs.

Examples of such outside exhibits are the annual plant engineering and maintenance shows and conferences, foremens' clubs, as well as technical groups such as the American Institute of Plant Engineers, the American Maintenance Institute, and others.

Programmed instruction in many aspects of supervision is available from the American Management Association as well as from organizations dealing with maintenance educational materials.

Tables

The following tables delineate the roles and functions of various levels of supervisory personnel.

TABLE 1   Manager of Maintenance

MANAGER ACCOUNTABILITY

Directs and controls the maintenance department. This includes responsibility for establishing optimum levels of maintenance dependent on the nature of the operations being done. The manager of maintenance is responsible for developing and implementing programs to carry out such maintenance. This includes responsibility for all buildings, building services, and equipment as well as assigned manufacturing and in-process equipment. Maintenance is also responsible for minor construction projects assigned to it. The manager operates within a budget of approximately $____ per year and is accountable for capital expenditures of $____ to $____ annually.

DUTIES AND RESPONSIBILITIES

1. Through subordinates, supervises the maintenance function at the plant on all three shifts. This includes preventive maintenance, emergency repairs, routine maintenance, and construction projects assigned to the maintenance forces.
2. Establishes and controls budget for department.
3. Provides for compliance with insurance and governmental regulations covering maintenance operations.
4. Maintains fire brigade and fire prevention and training programs.
5. Determines need for maintenance facilities and recommends facilities required.
6. Seeks methods of optimizing costs, quality of services performed, and improved reliability, safety, and response time consistent with the economics and the needs of the plant operations.
7. Handles contacts with local government officials for activities supervised.
8. Communicate the activities of the department with other managers and subordinates to achieve maximum overall effectiveness of the department in meeting its stated goals. Informs supervisors about the company matters which affect their operations and responsibilities.
9. Is responsible for developing and administering a program for training craftsmen.
10. Is responsible for the training and development of salaried and hourly personnel to keep abreast of new developments and techniques.
11. Responsible for deciding when maintenance work should be contracted.
12. Responsible for the maintenance of sound employee relations.
13. Responsible for housekeeping and safety in all areas assigned to or worked in by maintenance personnel.
14. Recommends the stocking of maintenance materials and tools and of spare parts for plant equipment.

TABLE 2   Area Superintendent

GENERAL ACCOUNTABILITY

Responsible for maintenance in an assigned area of the plant

DUTIES AND RESPONSIBILITIES

1. Plans and carries out programs for optimum maintenance in area
2. Responsible for quality and quantity of work performed by subordinates
3. Responsible for budgeting and controlling costs of operations
4. Responsible for inspection of facilities in area
5. Seeks improvements in methods, supplies and equipment used in area
6. Responsible for good labor relations
7. Responsible for safety of men and correction of hazards in area or on jobs
8. Communicate with management in area the need and timing of maintenance

TABLE 3 Foreman or Supervisor of Housekeeping and Sanitation

MAJOR ACCOUNTABILITY

Responsible for housekeeping and sanitation of the plant

DUTIES AND RESPONSIBILITIES

1. Prepares and carries unit work schedules covering housekeeping and sanitation
2. Supervises the employees assigned to this function
3. Responsible for upkeep of all equipment used by housekeeping and sanitation personnel
4. Responsible for good labor relations with workers supervised, hearing and resolving grievances
5. Responsible for safety of workers supervised
6. Responsible for controlling costs of the operations carried out
7. Responsible for specifying supplies needed
8. Responsible for seeking improvements in methods, supplies, and equipment

TABLE 4 Supervisor of Material Stores

GENERAL ACCOUNTABILITY

Responsible for maintaining adequate supplies, materials and spare parts and for dispensing same

DUTIES AND RESPONSIBILITIES

1. Determines, maintains, and controls inventory levels of materials supplies and spare parts used by the maintenance forces
2. Supervises stores attendants in their duties which include:
    a. dispensing materials and parts
    b. ordering, receiving and stocking
    c. identification and location of items stocked
3. Cataloging of location and availability of materials and parts
4. Maintaining good labor relations and hearing and resolving grievances
5. Responsible for housekeeping in area
6. Responsible for safety of workers and elimination of hazards in area
7. Responsible for improving operations to optimize inventories and speed up service to mechanics
8. Responsible for taking inventories and arranging for discard or sale of obsolete materials or parts

TABLE 5 Craft Foremen

MAJOR ACCOUNTABILITY

Responsible for all work performed by craftsmen

DUTIES AND RESPONSIBILITIES

1. Analyzes work orders and requests and estimates time and material requirements
2. Schedules and assigns manpower according to requirements of the job and the availability of materials
3. Supervises jobs to assure quality and prompt and efficient completion
4. Administers good labor relations within group and hears and settles grievances
5. Cooperates with other craft supervisors in getting jobs done and coordinates all work on jobs assigned to the foreman as coordinator
6. Responsible for training of workers supervised, including apprentices
7. Recommends methods and new equipment to improve operations
8. Responsible for safety of workers and elimination of hazards in area and on jobs
9. Responsible for housekeeping in area and on jobs performed

TABLE 6   Area Foreman or Supervisor

<table>
<tr><td colspan="1" align="center">GENERAL ACCOUNTABILITY</td></tr>
</table>

Responsible for all work performed by craftsmen assigned to group

<table>
<tr><td colspan="1" align="center">DUTIES AND RESPONSIBILITIES</td></tr>
</table>

1. Analyzes work orders and requests and estimates time and material requirements
2. Schedules and assigns work according to requirements of the job and material availability
3. Supervises jobs to assure quality and prompt and efficient completion
4. Responsible for training workers supervised
5. Recommends methods and new equipment to improve operations
6. Administers good labor relations in group and hears and settles grievances
7. Responsible for safety of workers and elimination of hazards in area and in jobs
8. Responsible for housekeeping in area and on jobs performed

Chapter 6

Utilities Function

L. T. WASSMAN
Plant Engineer, Sherwin-Williams Company

INTRODUCTION

As is true generally for the plant engineering function as a whole, the utilities area of responsibility in a modern plant engineering department is a dynamic, fast-moving activity. Consequently, today's responsibilities and organization in this area of activity will not necessarily be next year's or even next month's. A constant review of the responsibilities and of the functions is necessary to keep pace with the many changes that affect this phase of a plant engineering function. Changing functions necessitate a changing organization to accomplish the work that must be done.

The title "utilities manager" will be used in this chapter to refer to the individual who has the responsiblity for utilities in a plant or facility. The job may carry other titles and is often held by the plant engineer, depending on the organization and the size of the plant engineering department.

RESPONSIBILITIES FOR UTILITIES

Variation because of Utilities Source

The source of the utilities determines the kind of responsibility that the plant engineering department has. If the utility is purchased from outside the plant, from a public utility or private company, the responsibility is largely limited to metering, rates, and construction and maintenance of a distribution system. If the utility is generated within the plant or facility, the responsibility is broadened to include the construction and operation of the generating plant in addition to the responsibilities connected with purchased utilities.

Variation because of Complexity of Facility

The size and number of operations at the facility served varies the responsibility largely only by degree. The larger the facility served, the more complex are the distribution systems within it. The type of operation will determine what utilities are necessary. The older the facility, the more likely it is that information on distribution systems is lacking, making it difficult to administer. The more complex a facility, the more difficult it is to manage the distribution of utilities, control cost, etc.

Variation because of Personnel

The capabilities of and the number of personnel available to the utilities manager also determines what the responsibilities of this position are. Theoretically, certain responsibilities are assigned to the utilities manager, who then staffs to carry out these responsibilities. Actually, however, the responsibilities of a competent manager and staff tend to increase and, conversely, responsibilities of a poor manager with an incompetent staff tend to decrease. An inadequate (as far as number of personnel) staff to fulfill the responsibilities will have the same effect as an incompetent staff, and responsibilities will decline or the utilities manager will be replaced. The section of this chapter on staffing covers this more completely.

Management Responsibilities

Basic knowledge   As a manager, the utilities manager not only must direct the activities of subordinate personnel but also has staff responsibilities to superiors and to the consumers of the utilities. To fulfill these obligations, a basic knowledge of the total subject of utilities is necessary. Basic knowledge includes natural laws, the characteristics of each utility, how each is generated, how each is transmitted, etc. This knowledge is generally acquired by formal education and by a continuing education thereafter. Continuing education is very important because new developments in the field of utilities can result in increased efficiency of operation or in conservation of utilities. The subject of continuing education is discussed under "Engineering Responsibilities," in the second half of this chapter.

In addition to a well-rounded technical background, some knowledge of law and legal requirements and restrictions is also a necessity. This includes a knowledge of any licensing requirements for operators; code requirements that apply to piping, wiring, boilers, etc.; and pollution-control ordinances. Some knowledge of legal procedures, such as variance procedures, is also helpful. The utilities manager must at least be able to recognize that the facility is in violation of the law or may soon be in violation as a result of new legislation, so that legal aid may be obtained. If any possibility of violations exists, legal aid should be obtained immediately, before a crisis occurs. Knowledge of legal requirements is obtained by studying the ordinances that apply to the facility. Most ordinances will be local, but certain state and federal ordinances will also apply and all that apply must be considered.

A utilities manager will almost certainly become involved with environmental enforcement personnel from those agencies that have jurisdiction over the facility or plant. Sometimes contact will not be by choice, as when an inspection officer comes to inspect the premises of the facility or plant. The relationship between a utilities manager and enforcement personnel is peculiar and delicate. The utilities manager has an obligation to the employer to do what he can to avoid problems. On the other hand, the manager has an obligation as a law-abiding citizen to obey the law. The manager may feel that the law is unfair and oppressive, but this does not excuse noncompliance. Every effort must be made to comply. The utilities manager will be asked for information about the operation of the plant. It is at this point that a decision as to what can and should be revealed must be made. Under no circumstances should information be falsified. The manager may decide to refuse to give out information until a consultation with counsel can be held. A courteous refusal will be understood by enforcement personnel, since they are well aware of the fact that their activity may be a prelude to a violation suit.

A utilities manager should do everything possible to cooperate with enforcement officials. Obviously, enforcement personnel have a responsibility to enforce the law. If no violations exist in the plant for which the manager is responsible, there is nothing to hide. If a violation does exist, the manager should be working to correct it. It will be of value to a utilities manager to make an effort to get to know enforcement personnel, especially those at the administrative level. Such contacts can be made at various seminars, at luncheons, at public hearings, and at other meetings where pollution control is the subject for discussion and where enforcement administrative personnel are likely to attend or may be on the program. An open, cooperative relationship with enforcement personnel is preferable to an antagonistic one.

Utilities conservation Rapidly increasing utilities costs and the shortage of energy make it imperative that consumption of utilities be reduced to the bare minimum. This involves eliminating unnecessary use of utilities, maximizing efficiency where use is necessary, fully utilizing all energy available, and recycling. Of these various ways to reduce consumption, the potential of the full utilization of available energy is the one that is recognized the least. For example, steam and various gases are compressed to reduce their volume for economical transmission. They are often not used at the pressure to which they are compressed. Pressure is reduced at the use point with a pressure reducing station. This results in a waste of energy which might be recovered by reducing the pressure through a turbine to obtain usable power.

While the utilities manager cannot, alone, successfully accomplish the objective that utilities consumption be held to a bare minimum, the manager does have a major responsibility in any such program. A utilities conservation program must be established for all levels of personnel. All levels of personnel must be educated to the need to conserve utilities and told how this can be done. The utilities manager will have a direct responsibility to maximize efficiency of utilities use, such as ensuring that there will be a minimum amount of excess air consumed in any combustion process. The manager will also be directly involved in conservation by recycling, such as the use of cooling towers to reduce water consumption. It should be recognized that the ability of a utilities manager to contribute to a utilities conservation program will be limited by the time that can be devoted to this activity, to the manager's experience in this area of activity, and to the amount of imagination the manager can bring to the detection of potential methods of conserving. It may be desirable to employ a consultant experienced in utilities conservation for recommendations. A consultant will solve the lack-of-time problem and, if chosen carefully, will have the experience and imagination to do a better job than most utilities managers can do.

Utility rates Monitoring utility rates is a major management responsibility. Utility companies generally have more than one rate for the utility sold. Homeowners, for example, pay a different rate than commercial or industrial consumers, but there is often more than one rate available for the same commercial or industrial facility. Historically, large consumers have been charged less per unit of utility than small consumers. Often, there also are special lower rates for off-peak or off-season consumption. Rates are frequently complicated by additional charges for widely varying loads. The demand charge added to electric utility bills is an example of this. Fuel cost adjustments are fuel costs that may be passed on to consumers of electric power through the utility company's rate structure. Similarly, a cost adjustment on purchased gas may be part of a gas company's rate structure to pass on the cost of their gas purchases. Fuel adjustments and purchased gas adjustments are variable costs added to bills, and they may vary rapidly; therefore the net rates will vary each month.

The utilities manager must be familiar with all variations and with base rates currently being paid by a facility and must also periodically review available rates to effect any possible savings. This review is necessary because rates change, and conditions within a facility—which may allow a lower rate—also change. Since these rates are for purchased utilities, the best way to conduct a review of rates is to contact sales personnel from the utility being reviewed. These sales personnel are thoroughly familiar with available rates and with what special conditions, if any, must be in existence in a facility to take advantage of lower rates.

Familiarity with utility contracts Aside from rates, the utilities manager must also be familiar with the terms of the various contracts with respective utility companies. He should know the answer to such questions as "Is the utility subject to deliberate interruption or curtailment?" "What is the utility company liability in case of an emergency?"

The answers to these and other questions may mean the difference between having the facility that is served either running or down, since planning can be done in advance in anticipation of possible problems.

Cost distribution Determining where utilities are consumed within a facility is a responsibility covered under "Operations Responsibilities." A management responsibility, however, is to assist the accounting department in equitably distributing the costs of various utilities to consumers during each accounting period (generally once a month). This may not be necessary in a facility which does not produce a product or where only one product is produced. For those facilities producing multiple products, however, cost distribution is necessary to obtain product costs. The utilities manager can distribute utility costs better than the accounting department, particularly if estimates are necessary to break down a lump-sum figure.

ENGINEERING RESPONSIBILITIES

Distribution system planning Planning utilities generating and/or distribution systems is a major engineering responsibility. Whether long-range planning for an existing

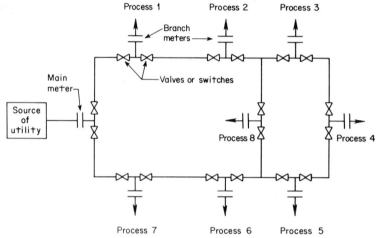

Fig. 1   Distribution of utilities.

system is being done or whether a new system is being planned, the same growth and decline factors that are taken into account by public utilities in planning their systems must also be taken into account when generation and distribution systems within a particular facility are being projected. Therefore projections must be made for future increases or decreases of utility loads and a program set up to expand the systems as required.

A second phase in planning the systems calls for building as much flexibility into the systems as possible for dependability of supply. Flexibility is provided in generation facilities by installing two smaller units in preference to one large unit. Two smaller units allow at least partial operation when one is down. The principle of two small rather than one large unit is desireable not only for units such as boilers but also for auxiliary equipment such as feed pumps, etc. Additions to an existing plant often result in this flexibility, since the new unit is generally installed in parallel to an existing unit. Flexibility in the distribution system can be provided by a "loop" system of the pipes or cables transmitting the utility. A typical loop system is shown in Fig. 1. The valve or switch arrangement shown provides the most flexibility in the event of a break in the system. A small facility can be designed with a single loop for each utility, while a large facility should have multiple loops. The physical arrangement of the plant or facility is the starting point for laying out the distribution system.

Metering utilities The quantities of utilities consumed by each process should be known. This is necessary in order to equitably distribute the cost of the utilities, so that cost of products can be accurately determined. Knowing quantities of utilities involves metering or estimating or both. Figure 1 shows an ideal metering arrangement. Line losses in the system result in inaccuracies when adding the sum of branch meters and comparing with the main meter, but the system shown allows reasonably close correlation. Metering of some utilities, such as water, is relatively simple when compared with the metering of a compressible fluid, such as steam or air. Meter calculations for orifice-type meters are complicated; their calculation requires engineering talent. Suppliers of the metering equipment will furnish calculations, but these are based on estimated flows in the various lines, hence estimates of flows must be given to the meter supplier so that calculations can be made.

In lieu of meters, estimates of utilities usage can be made. Estimates are worthless, however, if they are not accurate. Some estimates are relatively easy to make accurately, such as steam or gas required to heat buildings. Process loads are generally difficult to estimate, especially for batch processes where there is an irregular cycle of operation. Often, production personnel have more than one cost center within a process. It is recommended that plant engineering maintain one branch meter to each process and let production break down the consumption beyond that point. Maintenance of meters is important to ensure accuracy and is discussed further under "Operational Responsibilities."

Economic studies Economic studies of existing or proposed utilities-generating equipment is another important engineering function. Attention must be directed to generation capacity versus loads, alternate sources of energy to reduce costs, utilities conservation by consumers, and alternatives available when additional generation capacity is needed. When it is necessary to apply for approval from top management for funds for a particular project, information must be presented clearly and concisely and backed up with facts. It must be shown that every reasonable alternative has been considered. Empathy is an important factor when trying to convince higher management that a project is necessary and that the proposal presented shows the best of the alternatives.

STAFFING TO CARRY OUT RESPONSIBILITIES

General A study of various existing organizations that administer the utilities function of a plant engineering department reveals wide variations. Some of the variations are a result of variation in the sizes of the facilities served, but there are also wide variations in facilities of similar size and complexity.

The ideal organization will be set up to carry out the various functions without regard to the knowledge and the ability of personnel, and then personnel will be assigned who have the necessary qualifications to do the work. In an actual organization, adjustments are made, and the more competent individuals assume the duties requiring more knowledge and ability. The shift of duties within the organization may be so gradual that it will not be noticed by a casual observer.

Typical organizations are shown in Figs. 2 and 3. The dotted lines in these diagrams indicate major liaison and communication between groups and departments. Solid lines show lines of responsibility. Figure 2 is typical of an organization for a large, complex

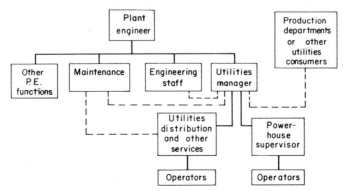

Fig. 2 Organization for large, complex facility.

facility and Fig. 3 shows a typical organization for a small facility. The broader the responsibility of the utilities manager, the more personnel will be needed to do the work. Organizations shown assume that the position of utilities manager is at the local level and that his duties are as outlined under "Responsibilities." There may be an individual at a corporate level whose prime responsibility is utilities, but generally the function of utilities at the corporate level is a part of general engineering duties. The energy conservation part of utilities is a responsibility often administered at the corporate level as a separate function. The reason for this is that the energy shortage that has developed necessitates particular attention to this subject. This is an example of how changing circumstances require changes in plant engineering functions.

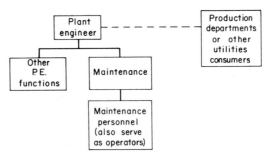

Fig. 3   Organization for small facility.

Cost orientation   Generally, a utilities manager who fulfills the requirements for the management responsibilities will have an interest in utilities costs. This manager will study accounting cost reports and will formulate the reports that are needed to get the job done. To do this, the manager must be well organized and plan work in relation to deadlines. Necessary information must be organized and file systems established if they do not exist. Common-sense responsibilities such as housekeeping inspections of utilities generating facilities are also part of the job.

Staff personnel   Personnel for the utilities manager's staff, if the job is large enough to warrant a staff, should be capable of performing the duties of the utilities manager. It is common to have an engineering staff available which can be used to assist in cost-analysis work. Cost-analysis work, strictly speaking, is accounting work and not engineering. Accounting groups can assist and are also used in the cost-analysis functions.

Staffing for Engineering Responsibilities

Large projects   Engineering study work such as distribution planning and load studies is often begun by the utilities manager personally. At some point in a project of any size, it becomes necessary to delegate the work to either the engineering staff in the plant engineering department, to a corporate engineering group, or to an engineering consultant. If consultants are necessary or desirable, the choice should be a company experienced in utilities work. Utilities is a specialized field and a good job requires someone experienced in the field. The decision whether to employ consultants depends on the size, ability, and work load of the plant engineering staff or the corporate engineering group. Increasing the staff to handle a single project is generally not warranted unless the project is of such a size that this can be done economically. The disciplines required to do the work must also be considered. Most large projects require at least electrical, civil, and mechanical disciplines and may require others such as chemical. Instrumentation requires a specialist in this field. Also, temporary office space is needed when the decision is made to increase the staff for a large project.

Engineering staff   Qualifications of an engineering staff to do project work generally are the same as for the utilities manager, although there should be less emphasis on utilities cost in an engineering staff. The reason for less emphasis is that it is the utilities manager's responsibility to decide what cost information is needed and how to get the information. It is this manager's job to make recommendations, and the engineering staff then need only engineer the project in line with recommendations.

It is impossible to give guidelines regarding the size of an engineering staff for day-to-day operation of a utilities generating operation. Most facilities are not large enough to warrant any staff, particularly if the utilities manager has an engineering background. A large steel plant might require the utilities manager to have a staff, but the decision whether a staff is needed must be based on the amount of work and the number of responsibilities that the manager already has. As already stated, there is often an engineering group available that the utilities manager can use when the need arises.

Staffing for Operational Responsibilities

Operator's qualifications The qualifications of the people who turn the valves, light the boilers, run the air conditioners, etc., range from those required for average maintenance personnel to those of the highly trained, licensed stationary engineers who run steam generation plants. Most states and cities do not require licensing or round-the-clock attendance of low-pressure (approximately 15 psig) boilers. Higher-pressure boilers generally require licensed operators and round-the-clock attendance. Other considerations, such as type of fuel, might also dictate how much of the time a utilities generating plant is attended if applicable ordinances do not require full-time attendance.

Obtaining licensed operators If licensed operators are required to operate a utilities plant for a facility, they must be hired for a new facility if none are already on the payroll. After the utilities plant is in operation, providing on-the-job training supplemented with home-study courses for likely candidates is often a good way of replacing the licensed personnel lost by attrition. Licensed operators may be hired, but these also require additional training to learn about the generating plant, since each plant is different. Obviously, unlicensed trainees would need to take and pass the licensing tests when training is completed to be elegible for the promotion to licensed stationary engineer.

If a new plant is being staffed, it is wise to find out how other plants in the area get their personnel. Operators of conditioning (heating, cooling, humidifying, dehumidifying, etc.) equipment for air may also require special training. Steam-absorption cooling equipment is an example of this. Sometimes a qualified operator for specialized equipment can be hired. Often, the supplier of the equipment will provide some training service during startup of the equipment. Supplemented with instruction manuals which can be studied, this is often adequate training.

Number of operators needed Round-the-clock attendance of boilers and other equipment requires a minimum of four people if all 21 shifts per week are to be covered. Even with four people, one shift must be covered on overtime, since each individual will stand only five shifts per week on straight time (based on a 5-day work week). A large industrial power plant may need two or more people in attendance at all times as a necessity for handling emergencies. If the plant is running normally, even one worker may sometimes be idle, but manpower needs must be based on what must be done during an emergency, such as when a momentary power interruption trips out certain equipment or trips out the entire powerhouse. It is easier to add personnel at a later date if circumstances warrant it than to start with too much manpower and then try to cut back.

Since operators will have some time to do other things when the generating plant is running smoothly, they can be assigned maintenance duties to keep them gainfully employed. It is not wise to assign them major overhaul work on equipment because then the work force may become larger than that which is needed to operate the plant. Lubrication of equipment and minor repairs should be assigned to operators. Receiving fuel and getting it to the boilers is another duty for operators. Housekeeping is also a duty that might be assigned to operators.

It is a necessity to have manpower to keep a powerhouse clean. If this is not done by operators, one or two people on the day shift can generally do the work. The number of personnel needed for this should be determined by the amount of work required to keep the plant clean. A coal plant requires someone to operate the ash system also. If a plant requires round-the-clock manning, operators will generally not be able to leave the powerhouse. Consequently work outside the powerhouse, such as operating valves and switches to direct utilities, must be done by others than the operators. Personnel from the maintenance force generally do this work. It is not a full-time job; therefore it works out well to have maintenance personnel do this work. Maintenance personnel must be trained to know the distribution systems, valve and switch locations, what to do in emergencies, how to activate distribution systems (heating a steam system slowly, etc.), and so on. Utility manuals which show all valves and switches in the various utility distribution systems in the facility served are invaluable during emergencies.

Section 2

Facilities Planning and Programming

Chapter **1**

Determination of Requirements

RICHARD MUTHER, P.E., C.M.C.
President, Richard Muther & Associates, Inc.

FACILITIES AND RESOURCES

By "facilities" we mean the
- Land or property
- Buildings or structures
- Stationary or built-in equipment, usually related to utilities and including piping, wiring, ducts, and so on
- Process machinery and support equipment

Usually the term facilities refers to those tangible or physical assets which are considered capital investments, as compared to items treated as expenses such as perishable tools, materials handling containers, expendable fixtures, or furnishing. Buildings, machinery, or equipment which are leased are considered to be facilities, for they are assets capitalized by the actual owner.

But facilities are only part of the total "physical resources" in the operation of a business or institution. The physical resources include:
- Products (and materials)
- Customers (and suppliers)

- People (managers and other employees)
- Money (investment and operating funds)
- Plant (physical facilities)

In this chapter, we are concerned with ways of determining the physical facilities required, rather than the total physical resources.

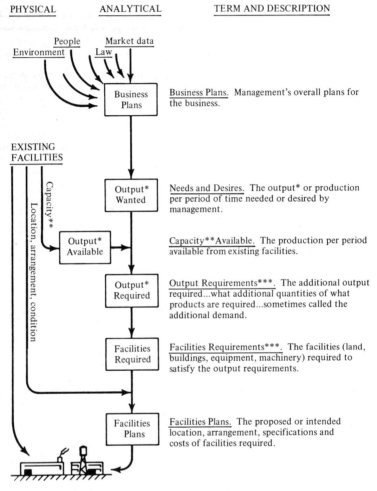

PHYSICAL   ANALYTICAL   TERM AND DESCRIPTION

Business Plans. Management's overall plans for the business.

Needs and Desires. The output* or production per period of time needed or desired by management.

CapacityAvailable.** The production per period available from existing facilities.

Output Requirements*.** The additional output required...what additional quantities of what products are required...sometimes called the additional demand.

Facilities Requirements*.** The facilities (land, buildings, equipment, machinery) required to satisfy the output requirements.

Facilities Plans. The proposed or intended location, arrangement, specifications and costs of facilities required.

* Output = The quantity of product per period of time produced or converted.
** Capacity = The maximum output--theoretical or practical.
*** Requirements = A statement of necessities to be provided--in terms of either output or equivalent facilities.

Fig. 1   General sequence of determining and using requirements. *(Courtesy of Richard Muther & Associates. All rights reserved.)*

In order to determine the physical facilities required, the planner must relate to the overall business plans of the organization. These business plans establish the needs or desires of the management. To meet them, the facilities planner must develop the output requirements, the facilities requirements, and then—usually after some preliminary cost requirements—make the facilities plan(s). See Fig. 1.

From Fig. 1, we see that determining requirements (first output and then facilities) stands squarely between the business plans (which express the business's product output needs or desires) and the facilities plans (which express the physical arrangement of facilities to produce the output needed or desired). On this basis, requirements should closely reflect the business plans of the organization. But experience shows that most managements still have a difficult time doing a good job of business planning. Especially, they generally do not fully appreciate that planning a facility with a service life of 10 to 50 years takes a different attitude, perspective, and procedure than short-range planning of operations and conventional return-on-investment justification.

MANAGEMENT PREPLANNING

Determining requirements usually does not encompass the development of management policies, long-range company strategies, or the business goals that affect facilities and on which the planning of them should be based. But these upstream, often soul-searching decisions are so important to successful facilities planning and are so directly related to it that they must be recognized and dealt with by the planner.

This involves the entire problem of establishing whether a facility is needed at all and, if so, what general requirements should precede the actual planning. Some call this preplanning; others use the term forward or front-end planning, or phase zero. Regardless of terminology, the clarifying of general needs and desires is basic to the determining of requirements. Essentially this is the *demand,* the acutal output of the facilities being the supply.

Needs and Desires

The needs and desires expressed by management include three concerns for the facilities planning manager:

1. Output of product(s) wanted
2. Conditions under which the output can be provided
3. The importance of attaining the output wanted (relative to the costs, efforts, and time delays restricting the practicality of attainment)

Output as the typical target need or desire of management's business plans is usually expressed in terms of quantity of pieces (units) per year, per month, or per week; number of tons (kilograms or pounds) per year; number of gallons (liters or cubic centimeters) per year; or simply money value of products to be produced per year. This is an expression of *how much* is wanted.

But output must also express *what* is wanted in terms of product—what items, models, styles, formulations, mixes, sizes, catalog numbers, and so on. And in order to be meaningful, the output needs and desires for *each item* or family of items should be stated.

Usually the facilities planner wants a statement of output needs and desires (or demand) for various times in the future—this year, next year, year after next, five years ahead. Such a statement is typically referred to as a forecast.

As for *conditions* under which the output can be provided, management's business plans should state or imply:

● Basic objectives or goals of the company: position in the market, growth objectives, profit goals, return on investment expected, etc.

● External practices the company intends to follow: trade practices, branch plants, high versus low investment policy, quality, support policy, manpower and distribution practices, etc.

● Operating strategies that will affect facilities required: make-buy, centralize-decentralize, own-lease, size-of-plant consideration, leader-follower, inventory-balance and production scheduling policy, overbuild or underbuild, etc.

● Recognized external constraints: community desires, legal and sociological restrictions, city codes, dedicated plant mission(s), etc.

Regarding *importance of attaining the output wanted,* management and/or its business plans should give the planner its thoughts and inclinations. For example, there are situations when growth at modest financial return is called for; other situations call for maximum return. Sometimes, a company will forego sales and/or revenue by intent when obsolete or nonprofitable product lines do not justify new plant or rehabilitated facilities. The needs and desires sometimes can be met only by making very costly investments, by a crash program timewise, by marginal reliability of product design or process, or by expecting too large a share of the market. Point: there is a relative degree of importance in attaining the output wanted, and the planner should have or strive to get this information as part of the statement of needs and desires.

As a general rule, the degree of preplanning and, indeed, the extent of effort put into determining sound requirements is a function of a company's total amount of investment in fixed assets.

Available Capacity and Requirements

The facilities planner can meet management's needs and desires in several ways:
- By purchasing the output of products, components, materials, or special process work from some other producer or converter
- From existing, already available facilities—either owned or leased

---

HOW TO DETERMINE CAPACITY OF EXISTING PLANT FACILITIES

1. Clarify your meaning of "capacity" (maximum output per period of time). Get agreement on which combination of a or b and c or d (below) you will use as "capacity":
   a. Total (or potential) capacity—output per period for 100 percent of the calendar hours available
   b. Operating (or working) capacity—output for a specified number of working hours per day, week, or year
   c. Theoretical (or ideal) capacity—output per period for theoretically ideal conditions
   d. Practical (or realistic) capacity—output per period expected for day-to-day working conditions
2. Clarify whether the capacity you are determining is:
   a. For currently existing conditions, or
   b. For future changed conditions
3. Determine what actual measure(s) of output per period of time will be used:
   a. Money value of output, production or conversion cost, value added . . . per period
   b. Quantity or number of units (pieces, containers full, truckloads . . .) per period
   c. Weight (tons, kilograms, pounds . . .) per period of time
   d. Size, cubic volume, running length . . . per period of time
4. Establish ground rules or criteria against which the output per period will be measured:
   a. What hours the plant (or each work center) will operate?
   b. What machinery, process equipment, and working methods?
   c. What products and what materials?
   d. What product mix(es)—distribution of quantities for each product or product group?
   e. What yield (or scrap loss, shrinkage, reject rate)?
   f. What extent of buy outside (purchase and/or subcontract)?
   g. What supporting utilities and plant services?
   h. What condition of building, of equipment and machinery maintenance, and any significant trend therein?
   i. What level of worker skill, effort, attitude, work conditions?
   j. What level or condition of production planning and control?
   k. What policy on level-loading of plant vs. irregular demand and related inventory-building practice?
5. If the capacity is of existing facilities but for changed future conditions (relocation to new site, planned improvement program, realignment of management methods . . .), then added definitions may be needed.
   a. Is there a learning curve for new employees?
   b. Is there a change in organization, staffing, ratio of indirect labor or supervisory upgrading?
   c. What worker performance or labor efficiency is anticipated?
   d. What machine utilization is anticipated?
   e. What degree of methods change or process rationalization is anticipated?
   f. What extent of materials handling, storing, scheduling, and dispatching improvements are planned?
   g. What anticipated batch size, order quantities, frequencies of material receiving and product shipping?
6. Estimate how accurate your measure of capacity will be based on the above. Note: Precision is not needed here. Rather, the bases on which the capacity is calculated become the practical considerations.
7. Calculate the capacity of the existing facilities for the particular bases selected above, and identify the bottleneck or limiting operation(s) and/or facilities.

Fig. 2 Procedure for determining capacity of existing plant facilities.

• From additional facilities to be provided—either constructed, renovated, purchased, or leased

• From a combination of all three

The demand less that which is purchased outside and that which can be produced in existing facilities is the amount of additional output required.

The available capacity of existing facilities is dependent on:

1. Identifying the existing facilities available
2. Determining their capacity

Identification of existing facilities owned is usually found in the records of property, buildings and structures, equipment and machinery and is obtainable from those responsible for company real estate, installation and maintenance of plant equipment, or planning and procuring machinery. A common source is the asset record in the accounting department.

Determining the capacity of existing facilities is another problem; it is independent of the demand (needs and desires). Figure 2 sets forth a form of checkpoint procedure for determining the capacity of existing plant facilities.

The capacity or capacities of the existing facilities, together with the portion of the demand met by outside purchases, can then be subtracted from management's needs and desires to determine the additional output required. However, the condition and location of the existing facilities, as well as their capacity, will be important to the planner. For example, output may be adequate but the facility producing it may be too far away, in a dilapidated or inefficient building, or not up to legal regulations on safety, waste treatment, noise, or pollution. So, from a practical standpoint, condition and location of the existing facilities must be appraised, and it is good to do this when determining the existing capacity available.

Inventory of Existing Facilities

To make the above kinds of determinations, the facilities planner or plant engineer should have a comprehensive record of existing facilities. Actually, this inventory of facilities is not dissimilar to those maintained as asset records from which depreciation charges are made and which are used by facilities planners, layout planners, materials handling analysts, manufacturing planners, and/or maintenance engineers. Sometimes a value appraisal of assets provides a good listing of existing facilities. However, the planner may have to put together his own inventory of existing facilities from the records of others. As for evaluating the condition of existing facilities, this will have to be done primarily by direct observation of the facilities themselves.

A typical inventory record of a plant building would include much of the following:

1. Site (location)
2. Building number
3. Name of building
4. Facility or asset number
5. Year constructed (date completed)
6. Type of construction
7. Initial cost of construction
    a. Site preparation, clearing, demolition, landscaping
    b. General structure
    c. Plumbing, drainage, tanks, etc.
    d. Heating, ventilating, air conditioning
    e. Electrical
8. Date(s) of major renovation
9. Cost of major renovation(s)
10. Number of floors (stories)
11. Area of floor space
    a. Gross building area (ground level)
    b. Net floor space (all levels)
12. Further details of construction
    a. Roof
    b. Walls
    c. Floors

      d. Ceiling heights
      e. Floor loading
      f. Column spacing
      g. Doors, docks, and windows
      h. Built-in elevators, cranes, etc.
      i. Toilets/washrooms
      j. Power and/or lighting
      k. Process steam
      l. Compressed air
    m. Transformer, load center
      n. Special pits or foundations
      o. Special fire, fume, waste facilities
      p. Special plumbing, electrification, ventilation

Stated Needs and Facilities Requirements*

Usually management plans to expand (or contract) its output in order to *balance sales demand(s)*. But companies may need added facilities for other reasons:
- To reduce operating costs
- To produce a new or different product
- To lower costs of freight or distribution
- To meet new governmental regulations
- To reduce costs of maintenance
- To reduce costs of utilities
- To meet conditions of new process
- To obtain short-supply materials or energy

    Therefore management should be more explicit than the simple statement of so much output of such-and-such products. The planner almost always has a problem of obtaining and/or developing specific input data in the form in which it can be used—especially if management needs and desires are expressed in dollars only. Sales projections in dollars—even if divided into product groups—are of little use to the planner until converted into specific product and quantity requirements. Additionally, the value or worth of money changes with time, especially in times of inflation, so conversion of actual, current dollar figures to inflation-adjusted "constant dollars" is an important step.

    Industrial plants should be designed around five basic elements:

    1. *Products* (or materials or services—their nature, physical characteristics, or properties). *What* is the facility to produce?

    2. *Quantities* (or sales volume or contract quantity of the items to be produced, handled, or serviced). *How much* is the facility to produce?

    3. *Routings or processes* (the operations necessary, their sequence, and their machinery or equipment). *How* will the facility produce them?

    4. *Supporting services* (including plant service and utilities, personnel services and amenities, and material services like production dispatching, test laboratory, scrap baler, or paint reclaim). *With what support* will the facility produce?

    5. *Timing* (operating hours, seasonal considerations, urgency, product life, etc.). *When and how long* will the facility produce?

    These five elements are the key input data a planner should have in order to plan a specific facility. But basically, more often than not, it will be necessary to start with something less than this and to determine or derive these or equivalent data from which to plan.

Determining Machinery Required

Selecting the process and the equipment to perform each operation in the process rests on many factors. These include first of all (1) the products (or materials) and (2) the demand or quantities of each item to be produced. Additionally, several other factors are suggested: (3) risk of obsolescence; (4) competitive advantage; (5) technological development; (6) quality of product or materials; (7) similarity to existing available equipment; (8) skills and availability of labor; (9) reliability of the process and the specific equipment;

---

* This portion of this chapter is from the forthcoming book by Richard Muther entitled *Systematic Planning of Industrial Facilities,* Management & Industrial Research Publications, Kansas City, Mo.

(10) the capability in quality and capacity of the equipment; (11) availability of process (if licensed or in development) and of specific equipment (if long lead time for procurement); (12) conformance of process and equipment to meeting national or municipal constraints; (13) the cost of the equipment, including freight-in, installation, and projected maintenance; (14) the operating economics of the process and/or equipment; (15) cost and availability of capital funds.

In *selecting* the process required, the sequence generally followed is as follows:

1. Analyze the specifications of each product and the materials or components to make it, together with the anticipated demand, from the standpoint of the intrinsic characteristics and likely costs of production.

2. Coordinate, consolidate, and consult with product planners, product designers, or formulation engineers as to prospective product improvements and the extent of design freeze and/or approval.

3. List the basic operations, and the alternative basic operations, required to produce the product.

4. Evaluate and determine the basic operations that are best—usually in terms of the various tangible and intangible considerations listed in the section above.

5. Determine the most effective way to integrate, combine, and sequence the operations, including the chief methods of handling, storing, and controlling. That is, check the availability, suitability, and compatibility of the entire process.

6. Draw process and/or equipment specifications preparatory to:

    a. Obtaining sources of specific equipment, machinery, and "attachments"

    b. Comparing prices, delivery, quality, and service

    c. Determining whether to build, lease, or buy the equipment

    d. Submitting a request for appropriation of capital investment funds

In *calculating* the actual number of machines or pieces of equipment required, the following general guide may be used:

$$\text{Number of machines required} = \frac{\text{pieces per hour to meet production requirements}}{\text{pieces per hour from machine in question}} = \frac{\text{operating time per piece for machine in question}}{\text{time per piece to meet production requirements}}$$

Suppose a schedule calls for 2,000 pieces per week. The first machine turns out 10 pieces per hour and the plant operates 40 hours a week. How many machines will be needed?

$$2,000 \text{ pieces per week} \div 40 \text{ hours per week} =$$
$$50 \text{ pieces per hour required}$$
$$1 \div 50 \text{ pieces per hour} = 0.02 \text{ hour per piece}$$
$$\text{(balancing factor)}$$
$$1 \div 10 \text{ pieces per hour} = 0.10 \text{ hour per piece}$$

$$\text{Number of machines required} = \frac{50 \text{ pieces per hour required}}{10 \text{ pieces per hour per machine}} = 5 \text{ machines}$$

$$= \frac{0.10 \text{ hour per piece per machine}}{0.02 \text{ hour per piece required}} = 5 \text{ machines required}$$

This answer assumes no defective work and 100 percent machine utilization, and we should make some allowance for these factors in determining the number of machines. Capacity-reducing delays include: (1) operator delays (personal time, idle time, avoidable delay, rest to overcome fatigue, below-standard skill or effort, and miscellaneous unavoidable delays) and (2) machine delays (changeovers or setups, tool changes, repairs due to breakdown or wear, oiling, greasing, and cleaning, failure of utilities such as power, air, water, etc.; miscellaneous interferences; imperfect dispatching or shop loading; and the like). Machine or equipment delays should be considered and compensated for on an individual machine basis, entirely separate from operator delays.

In the case of exceptionally costly, automatic, continuous-cycle equipment or bottleneck machinery, it is of prime importance that "utilization factors" (that is, 100 percent minus the percent of machine idleness) be accurately known. For nonimportant machines, estimated factors based on experience and judgment will suffice.

Reject allowances also depend on the machinery and the material. To be correct, the planner should determine these allowance figures for each type of machine and/or product (or material). In practice, we sometimes take a shortcut and use an overall reject-and-percent-of-capacity allowance.

Check the problem given above: 2,000 pieces per week, 40 hours per week, and theoretically 10 pieces per hour per machine. Use a factor of 5 percent rejects and 90 percent utilization. How many machines will be needed?

$$\frac{2,000 + (2,000 \times 0.05)}{40} \div (10 \times 0.90) = 5.86 \text{ machines}$$

Obviously we cannot purchase less than a whole machine; so we shall need six machines. Here, theoretically, we will have a little extra machine capacity.

In most cases, the calculations may not come out so close. Suppose we have 5.15 machines; would we need 5 or 6? This will depend on several factors including workplace layout, better tooling and other methods improvement, possibilities of overtime, whether other operations in the plant are dependent on exact output of these machines, or if we can use alternate though less efficient machinery to do the work.

The planner may have to plan for peak, seasonal loads. However, we should not overlook the possibility of reducing the machinery requirements, say by smoothing out any irregular demands on production. Note that it is easier to make 5 machines do the work of 5.50 (through overtime, extra shifts, and reduced idleness) than to make 1 machine do the work of 1.25. In the first case, the additional work amounts to but 10 percent overload for each machine.

Supporting Service Requirements

Establishing what supporting services are needed cannot be as precise a process as calculating machine requirements. First, there is the question of what services to provide. Second is the question of how much of each service to provide. A checklist of possible supporting services is shown in Fig. 3. This kind of facility services check sheet provides reminders for identifying needed services, rating the importance of each in a particular project, evaluating the condition of existing services, compiling space requirements, and the like.

As for how much of each service to provide, this can be arrived at in several ways. The facilities planner may use all of them in any particular project.

1. *Calculating.* Mathematically matching the proposed demand for the service (or throughput of material or utility) with the capacity or capability of the service in question.

2. *Converting.* Adjusting present capability of the service to required capability by index value or percentage change—that is, from what you now have to what you require for the proposed demand.

3. *Comparing.* Comparing the capability or capacity of the service in question with those of other similar departments, plants, or companies and selecting the new capability or capacity for the proposed demand.

4. *Test model.* Setting up a physical model or pilot operation and experimenting with the levels of capability of various services. This is typically combined with testing a new process or method of operation.

5. *Ratios.* Developing ratios of service capability to producing capability—usually for several past periods or for different departments, plants, or companies, especially if there is a legally designated ratio—and establishing the new service requirements by ratio to the producing capability for the proposed demand.

SUPPORTING SERVICES CHECK SHEET

PLANT AND UTILITY SERVICES

Power generation, distribution
Electrical distribution.
transformers, sub-station
Heat generation, distribution
Lighting distribution, fixtures

Ventilating equipt.
Air conditioning, cooling
Air cleaning, smoke, fumes, dust, dirt, odors
Cooling pond, tower
Air compressors
Vacuum pumps

Process steam
Process water
Water, tower, tanks, well, pump house, mains
Fire protection incl. sprinkler system
Potable water

Sanitary sewage
Storm drainage equipment, dams, holding lagoon, flood sump
Settling basin

Noise control, abatement facilities
Plant protection, security
Gas generation

Gas stand-by storage
Fuel storage
Vehicle storage, repair

PERSONNEL OR EMPLOYEE SERVICES

Stairways
Personnel elevators
Telephone, communication equipment
Mail parcel room

Wash rooms, showers
Toilets
Lockers
Smoking lounges, areas
Drinking fountains
Telephones (personal)

Germicidal, decontamination room
First aid room(s)
Medical, health facilities

Food Service:
Kitchen
Dining
Cafeteria
Vending Machines

Credit union
Counselors, payroll adjustment
Recreation facilities
Library

Highway turn-off, access, egress
Car parking
Personnel entrance
Pick-up waiting room

Time clock, time cards
Bulletin board(s)

Fire doors, escape
Fire extinguishers, hose house
Storm, fall-out shelter
Music equipment
Public address, paging equipt.

PRODUCTION OR CONVERTING SERVICES

Rail spur, siding
Highway turn-off, access, egress
Highway vehicle parking
Canal, turning basin
Heliport

Freight elevators
Weigh scale(s)
Off-site storage, staging

Maintenance:
Electrical
Mechanical
Carpenter
Handling equip't.
Highway vehicles
Spare parts storage

Tool making, pattern ship, tool maintenance
Tool crib, die storage
Machinery repair
Old tool, pattern, maching morgue

Stockroom
Supplies. Warehouse
Box, crate, lumber storage
Packing materials
Idle containers, pallets

Scrap collection, sorting, storage
Materials Reclaim, rework, salvage
Baler, grinder, chopper
Trash collection, storage
Dump
Incinerator

Process waste treatment
Waste disposal
Paint, acid, caustic storage
Lubrication, cutting oil storage
Oil or collant recirculation, pumps. filters, reclaim
Cylinder gas storage, distribution

Process control equip't., room
Quality control, test facilities
Sample, formulation room
Contaminants treatment
Clean rooms

OTHER OR MISCELLANEOUS SERVICES

Office areas (perhaps already considered)
Conference room(s)
Visitor reception
Switchboard
Chapel, meditation room

Customer service
Training center
Display room

Computer room(s)

Stationery storage
Special storage, vault
Confidential
Clean
Conditioned
Duplicate prints
Files, old files storage

Copy, reproduction center
Printing shop, drak room
R & D, experimental, test facilities
Model shop
Calibration, standards room

Grounds keeping equipment
Janitor, custodial facilities
Gatehouse
Fire marshall
Safety director
Plant sign(s)
Flag pole(s)

Notation		
References	a	c
	b	d

NOTES: _____

Fig. 3 Supporting service check sheet.

In reality, most facilities planning projects involve a combination of these ways. See Fig. 4.

When determining requirements for utilities and plant services, it is particularly important to consider future demand. For example, installing a transformer, water tower, boilers, or waste treatment plant is the kind of thing you do not want to do each year or with each change in demand. Therefore, the planner should extend these require-

---

1. List all major plant activity-areas for existing plant. (These are the left-hand columns in example below.)

2. Determine present floor space for each of these major activity-areas.

3. Modify the amount of floor space for each activity-area depending upon whether it is judged to be tight or loose, to arrive at comparably equivalent base areas for present occupancies.

4. Add up all the modified amounts of floor space(base areas)for all activity-areas and calculate their percentages of total floor space. (Third column of example below.)

5. Determine (through projections and calculations) the <u>Equipment</u> requirements (number of machines) for the PRIMARY manufacturing operations--then convert these to floor space needs. (18,000 sq.ft. in example below.)

6. Relate the floor space needs for primary manufacturing operations to its previously calculated percentage of total floor space (9.0% in example below).

7. Then, calculate the total projected floor space (100 x 18,000 ÷ 9), and allocate the floor space for each of the other activity-areas according to its percentage of the total floor space.

EXAMPLE

Activity-Area Number	Major Activity-Area to Support Primary Manufacturing Operations	% of Total Plant	Projected Floor Space (Sq.Ft.)
1	Raw Wire Storage	5.5	11,000
2	Wire Cleaning & Spheroidizing	6.0	12,000
3	Wire Drawing & Cut-off	5.5	11,000
4	Primary Manufacturing Operations: Bolt Headers, Boltmakers, Rod Headers, Part Formers...	9.0 - - -	18,000*
5	Secondary Equipment--Threaders Trimmers, Slotters, Tappers...	10.0	20,000
6	Washing & Heat Treatment	8.0	16,000
7	Galvanize, Plate, Finish	7.0	14,000
8	In-Process Storage	6.5	13,000
9	Packing	5.0	10,000
10	Finished Goods Warehouse	24.0	48,000
11	Support Services	10.0	20,000
12	Offices	3.5	7,000
		100.0	200,000 Total

* 18,000 sq. ft. is the area requirement calculated to meet the output needed (demand).

Fig. 4 Total plant floor area requirements determined from calculated space needs of primary manufacturing operations. *(Courtesy of Richard Muther & Associates. All rights reserved.)*

ments so that construction need be done at one time only, with resulting lower cost over the life of the expanding facility. In other words, there is an overprovision of service capability so that expensive, highly fixed facilities do not have to be reengineered and replaced or modified periodically.

A similar overprovision is common in the acquistion of land. Real estate is usually far less costly per acre or square meter than either the building or the equipment and machinery placed on it. Yet enormous costs—in administrative involvement and purchased services—accrue whenever it becomes necessary to acquire new land, to demolish or modify adjacent property, and/or to abandon a good-but-too-small existing site prematurely. A general rule to guide the planner is this: The greater the fixed investment cost per square foot, the more insurance in overprovision is required.

Projecting Long-Range Requirements

A statement of specific input-data requirements is not possible with any degree of reliability in long-range planning projects. Still, to the extent possible, it is important for planners to project the anticipated changes in the basic criteria to which they plan their facilities in the short range. After all, the planners will have to make some assumptions about future products, processes, services, and timing considerations. A form of long-range recording of anticipated changes in processes is shown in Fig. 5.

FORECAST SUMMARY

☐ Product Characteristics -P
☐ Sales/Production Quantities -Q
■ Process/Routing Changes -R
☐ Supporting Services/Utilities -S
☐ Time/Timing Changes -T

Plant: Houston Wks   Project: 7829
Prepared By: L.R. Plympton   With: Task Team
Date: 9 Oct.   Sheet: 4   of: 6

Entries this sheet cover _____ Pump Division _____

Process	Now	+ 1 Year	+ 2 Years	+ 5 Years	+ 10 Years
Heat Treat	All done here by stnd. or spl. Product H.T. Depts.	Same	Same, plus larger H.T. furnace for under-water items	Possible duplication of H.T. facils at 2nd site	Same
Stress Relief	All stress relief done in Weld Shop	In-line vibration equipt for hi-vol, small size items	Same	Extension of vibration eqpt. to larger items	Localized vibrators (?)
Welding	Centralized Weld Shop; wide variety of equip. & techniques	Introduction of E-Beam	Same	Extend use of E-Beam (tied-in with vibration stress relief)	Major use of E-Beam &/or Laser-Weld techniques
Painting	Central booth; large parts out-doors or sent out. Convetnl eqpt.	2 decentralized booths in product areas; conventional equipment	Add airless spary equipment	Begin conversation to electrostatic or spray plating	Further use of electro-static or spray plating
Machining	Mostly conventnl equipment; some tape; some auto-matic. Av. age 18 yrs.	2 new tape mchs; 1 heavy H.P. mch.	More tape and heavy H.P. mchs	Machine replace-ment program 50% complete (fewer old machines)	Eliminate all old machs except specials. Trend to larger & heavier
Cutting Tools	75% throw-away tips 15% brazed tips 10% hi speed T.S.	Same, but intro-duce ceramic tips	80% throw-away 15% brazed tips 5% hi speed T.S. 10% T.A. Ceramic	Same, but 25% ceramic	Primarily throw-away tips and ceramics

Fig. 5 Ten-year forecast summary (projection of process changes). *(Courtesy of Richard Muther & Associates.)*

Thus, for limited or short-range projects,* planners convert management's statement of its business plans and output needs and desires plus their own records of existing facilities into specific input data projected into the future.

Selecting from among the significant basic input data and projecting them can be done in several ways. One may, for example, draw on the following:

1. Simple estimates of informed individuals
2. The judgments of several people
3. Salesmen surveys, customer inquiries, market studies
4. Projections of historical trends (eyeball extension, mathematical extrapolation, high-low range squeezing)

* "Short-range" is generally considered anything less than 3 years ahead. "Long-range" is therefore anything that projects 3 years or longer. A more definitive scale is this: "immediate," up to a year; "short-range," 1 to 3 years; "medium-range," 3 to 5 years; "long-range," 6 to 10 years; "extra long-range," more than 11 years.

5. Organized involvement projections (structured discussions, organized brainstorming, Delphi method, or a modification of these)

6. Correlation with predictable and/or publicly issued indicators (gross national product, trade association data, standard industrial codes, etc.)

Long-range projects   For broad or long-range projects, planners, even though they should continue to project basic input data directly, should supplement that technique with other methods of projecting requirements.   Indeed, for extra-long-range projections, planners almost always rely on other, less finite inputs.   Some of these include:

1. Comparative index numbers
2. Planning ratios
3. Type-of-facility proportions
4. Related determinants
5. Land-to-building relations
6. Ranges of projected estimates
7. Life-cycle considerations
8. Combinations of several of the above

Comparative index numbers   Index numbers put all current values at 100 and projections are made in number values related to the current index of 100.   This allows planners

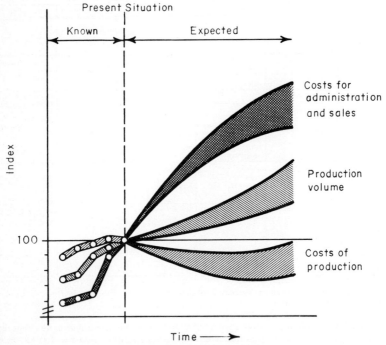

Fig. 6   Projecting with index numbers.

to compare the extent of changes in various products, markets, processes, and the like. Figure 6 illustrates projecting with index values.   Also note that projections are expressed in ranges of future values.

Planning ratios   Mathematicians tell us that ratios are more stable than either their numerators or denominators.   By projecting a ratio into the future, the numerator can be calculated for a given denominator.

For example, if an office area will need a projected 140 square feet gross per employee 10 years from now, 100 employees anticipated at that time will require 14,000 square feet of space.

This technique is generally termed *ratio trend and projections*. It is an excellent device for determining long-range requirements.

Figure 7 illustrates the ratio trend and projection method of forecasting. The ratio square meters per thousand dollars of manufacturing cost (inflation adjusted to constant money) is calculated from historical records for selected past years. The ratio is plotted as shown and the trend line extended. Target ratios are projected for the future. Fu-

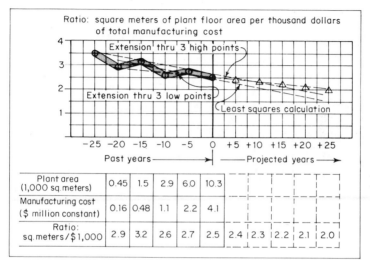

Fig. 7   Ratio trend and projection.

ture plant area requirements can be forecast from the target ratios and various estimates of future manufacturing costs.

Type-of-facility proportions   Facilities can be classified. Records and projections of requirements can then be made in general classes of facility rather than precise detail. Type-of-space projections, both for under-roof and open-yard land, are especially valuable in projecting long-range space requirements for site planning.

Related determinants   By relating one factor to another known factor of reasonable reliability, the first factor can be determined. This is basically the technique of correlation, but related determinants are usually internal. The number of workers per shift related to the number of toilet facilities per 100 employees (male and female) related to the male-female proportion anticipated determines the number of toilets required.

Land-to-building relations   Land-to-building ratio is a special type of determinant or ratio that has general as well as specific company use. Planners should be alert to several similar but different ratios. For instance, "land" is sometimes open land or yard land; at other times it may represent the entire site. Building may be land under roof or total floor space available on all floor levels.

Ranges   A range of projected values establishes a high and low for the requirements. "Plan-for" ranges are not unlike a tolerance on a mechanical dimension. The approximate requirements are set as a pair of high and low output values, and planners convert to high and low anticipated facilities requirements to cover the range.

Life-cycle considerations   Everything ages or passes through its life cycle. This is true of styles, product designs, types of processes, buildings, and even companies or businesses. A historical trend of sales volume which shows a compound growth rate cannot continue

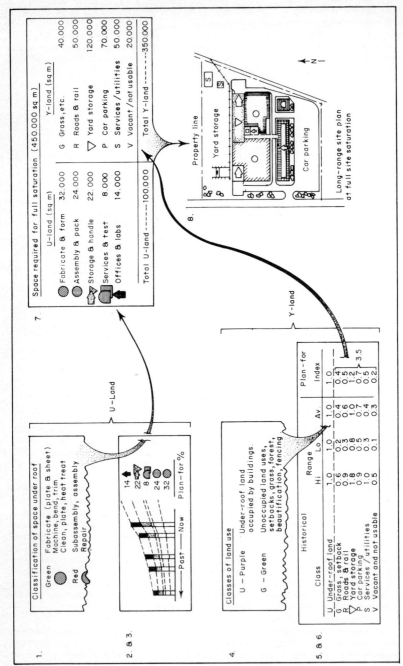

Fig. 8 Combination of projecting techniques. *(Courtesy of Richard Muther & Associates. All rights reserved.)*

forever. The concept is true; finding your position on the plotted curve(s) is not easily done until some time after the fact.

Combinations of several projecting techniques As often as not, a long-range projection of requirements employs several of these techniques in combination. Indeed, some are so similar that they could be said to be variations of each other. See Fig. 8 for a pictorial description of establishing long-range space requirements using a combination of classifying and projecting methods.

In projecting requirements related to money figures, it is usually better to use annual manufacturing (or producing) costs than annual net sales, in order to eliminate pricing policy and sales allowance considerations. Also, when working with money figures for historical records and projected ratios, be sure to adjust actual money figures to inflation adjusted (or constant) money. Both of these "corrective adjustments" have been used in Fig. 7.

Converting long-range output requirements into facilities requirements The planner must convert management's long-range needs or output requirements into plan-for facilities requirements. This involves determining the requirements for five physical components of a facility:

1. *Space.* The size, type, and any mandatory or preferred shape of the physical area to be planned, usually derived from the process and support equipment that will occupy that space
2. *Handling.* The transportation requirements to, from, and within the area
3. *Communications.* Any special facilities for communications and/or circulation of people to, from, and within the area
4. *Utilities.* The kind and amount of utilities required, including emanating wastes, effluents, and auxiliary service amenities
5. *Building.* The structural and environmental requirements of the area to be planned

Converting output requirements to facilities requirements is essentially a matching process. But the matching is complicated by several things:

- The need to match by type and subtypes of facility
- The sequence in which requirements may arise
- The adjustments for change in operating conditions—working hours, manpower or machine utilization, maintenance, etc.
- The efficiency allowance for a new facility because of its more orderly handling, storing, dispatching, and general housekeeping
- The consolidation or division (and duplication) of individual facilities and/or their support services
- Variations in product mix, lot size, yield or reject rate
- The general operating attitude of employees as related to the size of the whole plant, the posture of management, and the stance of labor unions
- Company policy on over- or underbuilding of requirements
- The practical amount of facility to provide in order to maintain column spacing, to make an economical construction project size, or to provide consistent continuity of crane rails, utility runs, etc.
- The customer service level or degree of out-of-stock permitted before another unit of automated warehouse or another whole duplicate processing line is called for and under what conditions an entire unit or line may economically be added
- The extent of leasing versus owning plant space
- The policy on single versus multiple sites, single versus multiple buildings on the site, and/or single versus multiple floor levels

In any case, a set of specifications which basically *size* or dimension the facility or facilities required should be the end result of the planner's work of determining the facilities requirements.

FACILITIES REQUIREMENTS SUMMARY

After matching output requirements to facility requirements, a summary of facilities requirements is called for. Figure 9 indicates such a summary for a short-range project

ACTIVITIES AREA & FEATURES SHEET — Physical Features Required

Plant __Tool fab.works__
Project __Prod.dept. layout__
By __H. Nelson__ with ____
Date __5-5__ Page __1__ of __1__

Requirements for shape or configuration of area (space)

Relative importance of features
A – Absolutely necessary
E – Especially important
I – Important
O – Ordinary importance
- Not important

Enter requirements for shape or configuration *and* reasons therefor

Enter unit and required amount under each

Physical features (column headers): O'Head clearance, Max overhead support load, Max floor loading, Min column spacing, Water & drains, Steam, Compressed air, Foundations - or pits, Fire or explosion hazard, Special ventilation, Special electrification

Column notations: Existing clearance OK | Not applicable | 250 lb per sq. ft. | No columns required

No.	Name	Area in sq. ft.	Water & drains	Steam	Compressed air	Foundations	Fire/expl.	Special vent.	Special elec.	Requirements for shape or configuration
	Production department	2585								
1.	Punch press	550	–	–	I	–	–	–	–	
	Auxiliary punch press	200	–	–	I	–	–	–	–	
2.	Drilling	250	–	–	E	–	–	–	–	
3.	Grinding	250	E	–	E	–	–	–	–	
4.	General fabrication	400	–	–	O	–	–	–	–	
5.	Wet tumble	100	A	–	–	–	–	–	–	Min. 10 X 6 feet
6.	Special production	360	I	–	E	ⓑ	–	–	–	
7.	Raw M-H storage	ⓐ 0								
8.	In-process storage	400	–	–	–	–	–	–	–	Provide setdown space 4 feet wide; plus aisle ⓒ
9.	Assembly	ⓐ 0								
10.	Shop toilet	75	A	–	–	–	–	–	–	
11.	Shop office & tool room	ⓐ 0								

Notation References

a — Not part of the area involved in the layout – no space requirement.
b — Machine #17 requires special foundation.
c — Permits stacking two rows of 2' X 2' or one row of 3' X 3' containers with access to each.

No. ____ Activity ____ Sheet ____ of ____

Fig. 9 Space specifications for manufacturing plant. *(Courtesy of Richard Muther & Associates. All rights reserved.)*

Facility	Process steam lb/hr	Heating steam lb/hr	Comprsd air scfm	Process gas scf/day	Heating gas mcf/day	Oxygen T/day	Propane gph	Fuel gas gpm	Electrical distribution Switch	Duct	Mill water gpm	Potable water gpm
Melt shop	--	1,000	1,500	800	--	--	--	--	34.5kV	13.8kV	16,500	30
Bar mill	5,000	--	2,000	400	12,500	--	--	3,600	13.8kV	13.8kV	5,000	10
Maintenance shop	--	3,000	1,000	1,350	750	0.2	--	--	1500kVA	480Vac	850	5
Office & lab areas	--	12,000	--	--	--	--	--	--	750kVA	250Vac	--	5
Other	22,000	5,000	--	1,000	550	0.6	—	200	1500kVA	480Vac	850	50

Fig. 10 Summary of utility requirements for a steel mill.

for a manufacturing firm. It shows for each area the amount of space, physical features required, and any mandatory shape or configuration. Note that the physical features required are related to their importance in planning the actual facilities rather than specified in anticipated load. This allows the planner to move ahead faster where physical features are not of primary importance.

When the business involves a high degree of process equipment and therefore a major investment in utilities, these service loads have to be spelled out more specifically. See Fig. 10.

FINANCIAL REQUIREMENTS

Before actually planning the arrangement and schedule for providing facilities—indeed, before approval of any summary of facilities requirements—there has to be a financial check. Estimates must be made of costs to provide for or meet the facilities requirements, and these costs must be reviewed for economic justification, availability of funds, and timing of such expenditures.

The best way to do this is to tie in the facility requirements with the company's capital investment budget (as opposed to the current operating expense budget). Capital investment budgets set forth the money anticipated for facilities and usually do this by quarter year and/or by year for several years ahead. Thus, the capital budget forces planners to set their requirements into a priority of need compatible with a sequence of available funds.

If a company has significant investments in plant and equipment and is not operating with a capital investment budget, the facilities planner or plant engineer can provide a real service to the company by working with the financial officer to set up such a program. In any event, because facilities are by their nature long-lead-time items, the planner should be sure to project facilities requirements over several periods ahead. Certainly any facilities program that reflects long-range planning must develop intermediate stages of site development geared to anticipated plant capacity and then correlated to money available and to periods of time ahead.

ORGANIZING FOR FACILITIES REQUIREMENTS

To deal successfully with long-range requirements, the planner should seek consistent and pertinent historical data on which to base his projections. It is true that products, company policies, and industry practices can change suddenly or radically; but effective past records converted into projected requirements in general terms are one of the best bases on which to make long-range plans. Properly done, this gives the facilities planner an opportunity to think big and project ahead without depending on the sales forecasts that are traditionally designed for relatively short-range consumption.

A facilities planning record-and-requirement book is a helpful device. Such a book can take various forms, but that described in Fig. 11 has proved highly practical. It provides a means of organizing both long-range historical and projected data. The numbered features are

    1. Loose-sheet record-and-requirements book

    2. White divider for indexing and clear back-up sheet

    3. Historical data plotted as *permanent* record on graph tracing paper (or vellum)

    4. Overlay of clear tracing paper for *current* trending and projecting of base data, ratios, and/or requirements.

The features of this book have been developed over many projects in many industries.

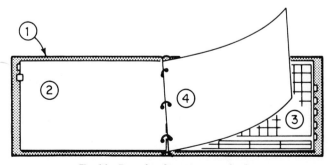

Fig. 11   Record and requirements book.

The permanent data record sheets can provide room for 30 years of past records and 30 years of future postings. However, planners frequently prefer to begin their books by setting their "now point" with only 10 or 20 years of historical records, so they will still have 30 years of projections 10 years from the current time. Moreover, extensive historical data are often not available.

A facilities planning data book has several benefits. It allows the planner

• To keep his facilities records, output or capacity data, and requirements projections in a single identifiable location

• To organize historical records in a permanent, definitive, and consistent way

• To make projections and derived requirements in an easily understood and efficient manner that is both portable and readily reproducible

• To document in an adequate way the historical or permanent data and yet to do as much projecting as often as desired on separate overlay sheets

Semilogarithmic paper (log scale vertically and a linear time scale horizontally) may be used instead of the regular graph grid. It has the advantage of showing constant percentage change as a straight line.

REVIEWS AND REVISIONS

It almost goes without saying that requirements will change. As the economy, business success, management attitude toward risk, profit, and return alter, the facilities requirements will change too. Additionally, there are frequent improvements in products or formula specifications, processes, services available, employee expectations, and so on, and of course existing facilities wear out and break down.

All this means that facility plans will have to change. And when facilities plans change, it is a logical time to review and revise facilities requirements, output requirements, and so to go back to management's needs and desires.

Most plants should set up regular, scheduled-in-advance times to review requirements and facilities plans. Short-term planning should probably be reviewed each quarter year; long-term planning reviews should be annual. An established sequence of events should be integrated with these reviews. For example, one typical long-range facilities planning review schedule follows this sequence:

• Management restatement of policy, preferences, and business plans—needs and desires: 6 months before decision

• Product planning (marketing and product engineering) response with statement of products, physical specifications, quantities, mix—output requirements: 5 months

• Process engineering selection and determination of machinery and equipment requirements: 4 months

• Plant engineering selection and determination of plant and service requirements together with facilities plans: 3 months

• Financing review and adjustment(s): 2 months

• Joint recommendation(s) to management: 1 month

• Management decision: D day

Obviously, this timing is not nearly fast enough for short-range reviews or for sudden changes in conditions. A general rule is that the shorter the time until the facilities are to be on stream or in operation and the more fluctuating the economy or market condition, the more frequently all the above parties must consider the entire sequence of needs statement, output requirements, facilities requirements, financial requirements, facilities plans, management approval, and implementation.

Chapter 2

Evaluation of Existing Space Organization

RICHARD MUTHER, P.E., C.M.C.
President, Richard Muther & Associates, Inc.

There are several interpretations and applications of the term "space." The word is used to refer to distance, area, volume, or just plain openness. Facilities planners typically mean the area occupied by something or enclosed or used for some purpose; therefore they are concerned with the kind of occupancy, its physical features, its location, the effects of external constraints on the space, and the like. Industrial space is usually sized in terms of area (square feet, square meters, acres, etc.). It can be cubic in dimensions; however, when so intended, the user will generally clarify that he means cubic or volumetric space.

LAND AND FLOOR SPACE

The facilities manager is generally interested in total amounts of space, tending to equate it to available output. The facilities planner is concerned in addition with the breakdown of existing space into subdivided amounts, and—for each—its kind, condition, shape, arrangement, supporting services, and capability to produce or perform.

Space is typically divided into *outdoor* (site land) and *indoor* (under-roof) space. Each can be further divided, just as regional or city planners might classify or zone areas into heavy industrial, light manufacturing, commercial, residential, and so on.

Land (out-of-doors site space) is frequently divided as:

1. Buildings, built-upon land, or land under-roof—sometimes designated by plant (or production) buildings, offices, and service buildings

2. Production or open land used for outdoor work—where the intrinsic characteristics of materials are changed or converted

3. Service or plant and production services—cooling pond, transformer, chip collection, scrap storage, test track, drainage ditch, etc.

4. Storage (for raw, in-process, finished materials, and so on), including yard or outdoor receiving, loading, and shipping

5. Roads, railroads, barge canal—including turning area, truck parking, railcar hold area, etc.

6. Parking for employees' and visitors' vehicles—including personnel roads and sometimes including recreation fields

7. Set back, greenbelt, landscaped areas—including fencing strips and cared-for land

8. Vacant or undeveloped but usable land—land not yet developed that may be unused or used for some other interim purpose

9. Waste, lost, and unusable land—land not practically usable because of sheer steepness, all rock, river, dedicated to highway, etc.

Easements, rights of way, land dedicated for flood overflow only, and the like create problems of classifying land into specific categories.

Floor space or building (indoor or land under-roof) is frequently classed as:

1. Forming, fabrication, treating, or converting space—sometimes considered space for primary operations

2. Assembly, subassembly, disassembly, packing—sometimes considered space for secondary operations

3. Storage and handling or transport-related space—including receiving, shipping, and warehousing

4. Supporting service or inspection space—for areas serving plant, production and personnel, including production test, customer service repairs, baler, air compressor room, etc.

5. Offices and office-type laboratories—drafting rooms, reception, display room, conference areas, meeting room, etc.

Aisles or gangways may be held out as a separate class, perhaps along with elevators and stairways. Sheds that are roofed but open on the sides, unheated buildings, covered walkways, and minor outbuildings create problems of classification. More significant is the consideration of floor space for multilevel buildings, especially when determining the amounts, usage, and utilization thereof.

LAND-TO-BUILDING RATIO

A basic concept for space planning is the land-to-building ratio. It may serve as a guide for relating total site to anticipated or existing buildings thereon; or it may be a measure comparing the land areas needed to support the under-roof space in use.

"Land" may be considered as (1) open land (Y or yard land) or (2) total site. "Building" may be considered as (1) land built upon (U or under-roof land) or (2) floor space on all levels.

In the first instance, $Y + U =$ total site; in the second condition (site to floor space) the ratio is $Y + U$ to the floor space considered. The planner should be aware that terminology here can be misleading—especially when making utilization comparisons. Heavy industry prefers the former; multistory buildings will use the second.

The ratio wanted or desired at any particular time varies significantly. From one industry to another, there are many extremes. For a rented warehouse, $Y{:}U$ of 1:1 may be fine; for a light manufacturing company with growth of 10 percent per year, $Y{:}U$ of 4:1 or 7:1 would be more adequate, depending on extent of car parking, yard storage, outdoor services, and so on.

LAND UTILIZATION

Land for industry usually has a value of less than one-tenth the value of the building, machinery, and equipment to be set on the land. On the other hand, the cost to relocate a plant because it has run out of expansion land can be extremely high. As a result, measuring the utilization of land tends to be less significant, for high utilization can have negative as well as positive meaning.

Evaluating land for planning purposes, on the other hand, is highly significant. Beside the location of the land, its access and egress capabilities for transport vehicles, personnel, utilities, drainage, and communication are important physical considerations or constraints. Additionally, for effective utilization of the land, it should have harmony, regularity, and consistency. That is, the physical land itself will have various limits of utilization that vary with the slope or contour, the shape, and the vertical regularity of soil and subsoil conditions and their consistency throughout the site. Restrictive easements, zoning limitations, unsympathetic neighbors, and flooding or wetlands seriously affect a site's utilization.

An irregular, sloping, interrupted, or odd-angled site can be difficult to utilize. Normally, one parallels or squares the facilities with the major expanse of property line. This will increase the utilization of land. Also, planners try to plan rectangular-shaped buildings, rather than build angular or curved walls that may occupy more of the site but call for more expensive construction and usually contribute to lowering the utilization of floor space inside the building.

Keep the odd-angled corners of the site for car parking, yard storage, and miscellaneous small outbuildings or structures.

Railroad trackage and even roadways can eat up a lot of space. Rail curves should be carefully planned. Space can be saved if truck and personnel vehicle uses the same roadways, though this is likely to create problems of congestion, safety, and security.

Utility lines and utility service equipment (water tower, transformer, pump house, fuel oil storage, etc.) can be costly to relocate, so they should be planned ahead of time for ease of expansion. This means dedicating strips of site for future utilities, tying in the utility runs with dedicated roadways, and planning the distribution of utilities vertically (underground especially), so both the necessary slope and crossings or intersections are possible. A well-planned infrastructure for a site may commit land initially, but it can significantly improve space utilization when the land becomes more densely occupied, purely aside from the later savings in maintenance, rehabilitation or construction.

FLOOR SPACE UTILIZATION

The utilization of plant floor space is important. Actually, like finished goods inventories, too much or too little is costly. So facilities managers should target for the right kind of space of the right amount in the right place at the right time and for the right cost. This is seldom achieved, for the minute you attain it—if indeed you ever can—conditions will change, so that you will be out of balance.

Actually, the problem is magnified by subdividing, both dividing physically and in terms of use or occupancy.

If we divide 10,000 square feet into two 5,000-square-foot areas (in two buildings or two floor levels, or merely by building a wall between the two), we now have the problem of attaining a good space utilization in each area as well as for the total. The more divided, split, or honeycombed each area is, the more space is lost because of inability to divide practically the use of occupancy of the space in the same divisions. This idle space to balance divided areas frequently runs 5 percent of the total. This leads to overcrowding and underutilization of the various areas.

Large open spaces tend to improve the utilization of space. So do large column spacings, consistency of floor levels, and freedom from obstructions of every kind.

Straight aisles improve space utilization except under very special local conditions. Stay away from dead ends, doglegs, and diagonals. Aisles against walls cost space, for they serve only one side. Aisles against columns usually save space—except when the space along the column lines can be used effectively for built-in conveyors, storage of tools, or instrument panels, and they are better protected if backed out of the way against the column line. This exception applies particularly when overhead traveling cranes are involved.

CUBIC SPACE UTILIZATION EFFICIENCY

$$\text{SPACE UTILIZATION EFFICIENCY} = \frac{\text{Cubic Feet Usefully Occupied}}{\text{Net Usable Cube}}$$

DEFINITION: S.U.E. measures how effectively your enclosed space is being utilized (manufacturing and warehousing).

PROCEDURE:

1. Calculate the "net usable cube" by:

   a. multiplying the width times the length times height of the building (interior dimensions), and

   b. by deducting the cubic feet lost because of obstacles or factors beyond your control. For example: trusses and columns; required clearances for fire sprinklers, utility pipes and enclosures; stairwells, elevators, docks, doorways, and clearances in front of them; office space or services not related to the operations in question. (Do *not* deduct for factors that can be controled, like aisles, inspector's work area, battery charging area, etc.)

2. Calculate "cubic feet usefully occupied." This is done by measuring the base area(s) given to materials, machinery and equipment, processes, and operator working areas for *useful, productive* purposes, excluding aisles. Then multiply this by the height. (Averages may be used.)

3. Divide #1 into #2 to get S.U.E., expressed in percent.

SAMPLE WORK SHEET:

1. TOTAL AVAILABLE CUBIC FEET (interior length × width × height) .... _____ cu ft

   LESS SPACE LOST DUE TO OBSTACLES:

   a. columns & trusses   _____   g. dock areas   _____
   b. sprinkler clearance   _____   h. elevators, stairwells   _____
   c. pipes/ducts/outlets   _____   j. clearance for doors   _____
   d. office(s), enclosures   _____   k. _____   _____
   e. transformer/comprsr.   _____   m. _____   _____
   f. washrooms/toilets   _____   n. _____ . _____ cu ft

                                                      NET USABLE CUBE (1) .... _____ cu ft

2. SPACE IN ACTUAL USE

   a. warehouse/stores   _____   d. working areas like
   b. forming/treating   _____   inspctn., maint.,
   c. assembly/sub-assembly/   vehicle storage,
      disassembly/packing   _____   in-proc. materials   _____

                                                      CUBIC FEET USEFULLY OCCUPIED (2) .... _____ cu ft

$$\frac{\text{Cubic Feet Usefully Occupied (2)}}{\text{Net Usable Cube (1)}} = \underline{\qquad} = \underline{\qquad} \% \begin{array}{l}\text{Space Utilization} \\ \text{Efficiency}\end{array}$$

Fig. 1 Cubic space utilization efficiency—an explanation and sample work sheet. *(Developed from data in Management Guide to Productivity by James A. Bright, 1961. Limited edition by Yale Material Handling Division.)*

CUBIC SPACE

Cubic space is often of more interest than land or floor area. This is especially so in storing gases or liquids, but it is also true in storing bulk solids and many standardized boxes, containers, or unit loads.

Figure 1 shows a way of determining cubic space utilization efficiency.

MEASURING FLOOR SPACE

For control of space utilization, we need a target (or standard) and a measurement of actual occupancy.

There may be some confusion over the meaning and intent of *measurement* of floor space occupied. The planner or manager of space must distinguish between gross area (the entire area of the building including exterior walls) and net area (the assignable floor space that can be used for the functions to be housed). Net area, or net assignable area, excludes the exterior walls as well as such building services as general corridors, stairwells, elevators, rest rooms, machinery rooms, and the like.

The *accuracy* of space measurements is of concern. Most managers are not interested in great precision. Rather, meaningful control and/or use of the space is the chief objective.

Planners all too frequently measure space available to the last square foot. The end number is often the result of some calculation in which the base numbers are paced off or scaled from a print. Or, for forecasting space needs, the space requirement is derived from an estimated percent or a projection of sales and/or capacities. Very accurate numbers under these conditions are "precisely wrong." They violate the accuracy-of-values theory; they are deceptive by implying a correctness of data which is not really there; and they take longer to write, to read, and to add.

This is not saying that detailed designs need not be accurate. Rather, it is saying that when determining utilization or planning (as distinguished from design), space measurements are better rounded off, usually to the closest round number representing about the third significant digit.

BUILDING OCCUPANCY REPORTS

Large companies, especially those with government contracts or government-owned facilities, periodically make reports of building occupancy. Such a report usually:

1. Identifies the various sites and buildings thereon
2. Defines the classes or categories of occupancy
3. Reports the area occupied at the time of reporting by each class or category of space in each building
4. Summarizes these into various recaps by class of space, building, site, and total company

Sometimes the number of employees is also reported for the same space. This provides data on personnel as well as space and allows ratios (of square feet per person) and comparisons between areas to be made.

Figure 2 shows a section of a building occupancy report.

REPORTING SPACE UTILIZATION

Occupancy reports aim at identifying what departments or functional activities occupy what space and vice versa. But for reporting utilization—the extent or degree to which the space available is being used—other types of measuring and reporting are more meaningful. Usually, these are combined with, or an extension of, the occupancy report, having columns for the space standard and the target (or allowed) space.

Sometimes these utilization reports are plotted in graphical form when time is significant or in bar-chart (or profile) form when comparing plant to plant or area to area. In all comparisons or utilization data, be sure the figures are comparable. You might have good utilization on a net basis but poor utilization on a gross basis.

SPACE AND PERSONNEL SUMMARY

BUILDING NUMBER	DESK & BOARD SQ FT	%	MANUF. SQ FT	%	LAB. SQ FT	%	SPECIALIZED SQ FT	%	WAREHOUSE & STORES SQ FT	%	VACANT ALLOCATED SQ FT	%	VACANT UNALLOCATED SQ FT	%	NET SQ FT	%	SINGLE PURPOSE SQ FT	%	GROSS SQ FT	PERSONS
FACILITY 2																				
201	26,390	49			616	1			10,962	20					37,968	74	15,934	30	53,902	285
202	6,959	14	494	1	26,684	53	3,145	6							37,282	74	13,157	26	50,439	117
203	2,917	19	100		5,066	33	1,514	10	789	5					10,386	67	5,138	33	15,524	45
204	14,851	29	220		22,521	45	320	1	595	1					38,507	76	11,932	24	50,439	153
205	13,486	25	6,451	12	18,896	35	2,259	4	3,087	6					44,179	82	9,585	18	53,764	206
206									345	1					345	1	20,155	99	10,500	
207					2,031	100									2,031	100			2,031	
208			200	100											200	100			200	
209					400	100									400	100			400	
213					580	51									580	51	443	49	1,023	
220																	1,380	100	1,380	
221																	1,200	100	1,200	
FACILITY 2 TOTALS	64,603	27	7,465	3	76,794	32	18,200	8	4,816	2					171,878	72	68,924	28	240,802	806
FACILITY 4																				
401	20,605	41	1,229	2	5,048	10	5,730	11	1,192	2	610	1	1,606	3	36,020	71	14,380	29	50,400	248
461			320	12	2,016	76			320	12					2,656	100			2,656	4
FACILITY 4 TOTALS	20,605	39	1,549	3	7,064	13	5,730	11	1,512	2	610	1	1,606	3	38,676	73	14,380	27	53,056	252

Fig. 2 Building occupancy report showing for each building the total space and personnel, and a division of the space into various functions with the percent of total area for each function.

PROGRAM OF SPACE UTILIZATION

A. What do we want?
   1. What will we use the space for?
   2. What kind do we want?
   3. How much do we want?
   4. Where should it be located?

B. What do we have now?
   1. How much space?
   2. What do we use it for?
   3. Where is each use?
   4. What is its condition?

C. What do we need?
   1. At what rate should we provide it?
   2. What use(s) provided when?
   3. What use(s) provided where?

D. How do we get the space we need (or divest ourselves of what we do not need)?
   1. What will we provide for each use?
   2. Where?
   3. When?
   4. By whom?

E. Feedback
   1. Were we right in retrospect?
   2. If so, why?
   3. If not, why?
   4. If not, how do we correct?

Fig. 3 Program of space utilization.

GENERAL PROGRAM OF SPACE UTILIZATION

For planning and managing the utilization of space, a general concept or comprehensive program can be helpful. Such a basic program is outlined in Fig. 3.

SPACE CONTROL

Space utilization efficiencies and space occupancy reports serve as a means of knowing what you have. They allow comparisons to be made from period to period and building to building. They serve as an aid to space planning and control. But for better and more finite control, especially at the more specific level, a method of establishing *space standards* is needed.

Space standards can be developed in several ways:

1. by simple historical record
2. by calculation for planned occupancies
3. by conversion from existing occupancy
4. by deriviation from standard space data
5. by trending past ratios (square feet per ton shipped per year, for instance) and deriving space from the projected ratio.

The last of these is suited to long-range facilities planning and to control of the planners, as compared to control of existing space utilization.

A procedure for developing space standards is as follows:

Phase I   Establish orientation and definition:

1. Determine the purpose(s) of establishing the standards and what they will be used for.
2. Establish what areas or types of space will be involved.
3. Check the feasibility (time, money, and capability available).
4. Obtain management concurrence.

Phase II   Plan how to classify space and how to determine standards therefor (solution in principle):

1. Describe or name each of the various "individual items" and/or "activities" (departments or functional subareas) in the areas involved.
2. Establish basis for the standards (square feet per individual item, per unit of product produced, per person, and so forth).

Phase III   Classify activities and develop standards for them, using synthetic data and/or past, existing, or planned-for-future plans (solution in detail):

1. Classify each "activity-area" by type of space.
2. Determine the number and type of "individual items" in each activity area.
3. Determine the average number of square feet per "individual item."
4. Determine the average number of square feet per activity area for its type of space.
5. Document the standards established.
6. Verify, test, or compare the standards established.
7. Obtain management approval of the standards.

Phase IV   Put to use:

1. Assign space based on the standards established.
2. Follow up to determine actual space utilized; compare against the standard; and take action to control.
3. Use for preplanning.

Figure 4 shows the development and use of space standards in diagrammatic form.

SPACE UTILIZATION IN CHANGING CONDITIONS

It is often difficult to utilize space as your demands for space increase. Space standards are especially useful when conditions are changing. A standard of 140 square feet gross of space per "office sitter" directly relates the area requirements to number of employees allocated, approved, or required. Similarly, 5 square meters of plant space per ton of product per month produced can be readily converted to target space for given or planned levels of output.

It should be noted that:

1. Space standards are only applicable when the conditions on which they are based prevail. Example: 300 square feet (approximately 30 square meters) per automobile for car parking gross may be realistic for large American cars when the parking area is shaped to accommodate a large number of cars, but it would not hold for smaller European cars for restricted parking space.
2. Space standards themselves may vary with quantity. Example: 90 square feet gross per office employee might be suitable for 25 persons in a general office area, but the standard could well drop to 80 or 75 square feet per employee if 200 or 300 office employees were to be housed in a large general office area.

3. Space standards will change with time as the conditions on which they are based change. Example: 132 square meters per unit shipped per 8-hour shift may be adequate for today's product mix, but with a miniaturization-of-product program, the standard will creep toward a much lower level.

When changes occur, as of course they always will, the planning of space to be utilized

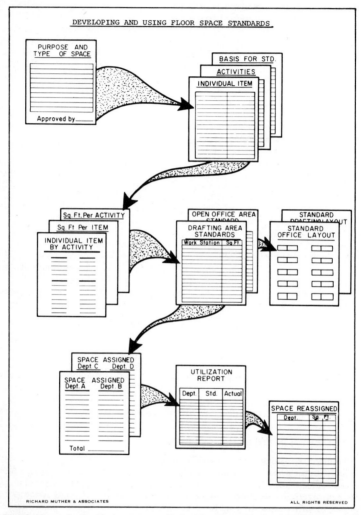

Fig. 4 Developing and using floor space standards. *(Courtesy of Richard Muther & Associates. All rights reserved.)*

in the future actually affects its utilization. One can hardly provide or adjust space in very small amounts; leases must be signed for a period of time; buildings must be constructed in amounts that are economic. So projections of space needs should be compatible with what actually happens—to the extent this is possible. To allow for some anticipated errors, managers usually provide enough to carry them from the current expansion through to some projected requirement in the future. This means space is added (or deleted) rather abruptly even though the density of its occupancy or use changes more slowly or more smoothly.

Figure 5 shows a projection of planned space that is synchronized with a theoretical plan for release of space and a practical plan tied in with leases, removals, and/or sale of buildings.

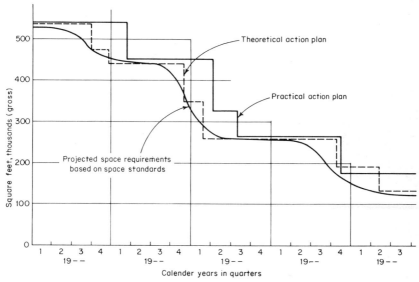

Fig. 5   Space planning for practical utilization. This plan shows phasing-out of office and laboratory space in a multibuilding complex. Note the variations in projected space requirements, theoretical release of space plan, and practical action plan.

USING OVERSUPPLY OF FACILITIES UNTIL NEEDED

We cannot practically build a square foot at a time. Nor can we economically buy an acre of land every time we need more. So we normally supply more than we need at the moment. How to use the idle land or floor space is worthy of consideration.

Land can be used until needed by:

1. Retaining it in rough condition for beautification or environmental pleasantness
2. Partially developing it for recreational uses
3. Leasing it as farmland
4. Establishing a mobile home park (approximately 10 years payback)
5. Establishing an office park (with temporary buildings or buildings you can convert later to offices, laboratories, and supporting services)
6. Building and leasing the structure or its floor space until needed.

Floor space can be used until needed by:

1. Building more than needed and leasing part (especially suitable for multistory office buildings)
2. Using it for storage, light assembly, and/or packing by another division of the company
3. Only partially finishing the building and storing materials there until production operations need the space
4. Storing materials under roof that could go outdoors
5. Using space for offices, simple laboratories, and/or personnel services and relocating them to other building(s) later.

CONDITION OF SPACE

The condition of existing space is important to managers. In addition to the amount of space, three other evaluations may be involved. These include:

    1. Actual age
    2. General condition (as though considered for resale)
    3. Suitability for a specific contemplated purpose.

More often than not, cost figures or actual numbers are unavailable or unsuited to appraising the usefulness of facilities. A synthethic scale for auditing and apprasing is usually more meaningful.

A rating scale built around a vowel-letter sequence can be used effectively. This way, rating letters are applied to particular facilities for each of several factors or criteria.

FACTORS • Actual age • General condition • Suitability (particular use)	P-8	P-10	P-11	P-12	T-1
Age in years	46	37	31	21	12
Impact of age on physical condition	U	O	I	E	E
Annual cost of maintenance	O	I	I-	E	I
Structural soundness including foundations	A	I	I	E	A-
Utilities and ancillary equipment	I	X	O	E	E
Safe, convenient, clean, comfortable . . .	I				T
Other . . . _General appearance_	C				
Suitability of facility 1) for: _Assembly and packing_	E				
2) for: _Finished goods storage & shipping_	C				

Evaluating description	Letter/Value
Almost perfect results (excellent)	A/4
Especially good results (very good)	E/3
Important results (good)	I/2
Ordinary results (fair)	O/1
Unimportant results (poor)	U/0
Not acceptable results (not satisfactory)	X/?

Fig. 6 Evaluating the age, condition, and suitability for two proposed uses of several buildings on a site. *(From Richard Muther, Systematic Planning of Industrial Facilities, Management and Industrial Research Publication, 1976.)*

Figure 6 shows a way of recording the condition of existing space from all three standpoints (age, condition, suitability).

Additionally, by weighting the importance of each factor, converting the vowel-letter ratings to number equivalents, and extending the weight times the rating number, a quantified total can be put on each building or facility for comparative purposes.

Frequently, more specific information is needed about particular space. In this case an activities area and features sheet, as discussed in Section 2, Chapter 1, may be helpful.

Or a floor space evaluation worksheet like the form shown in Fig. 7 may be used to advantage. The ratings of dynamic considerations (in lower right of the figure) can be extended by a weighting (or relative importance of the consideration) to develop a comparative rated-weighted value.

FLOOR SPACE EVALUATION

Plant _____   Project _____
By _____   With _____
Date _____   Sheet _____ of _____

Identification and description of space being evaluated:
   No. _____   Name _____
   Location _____

A) Amount or Size:

B) Form, Shape, Togetherness:

C) Building Features:
   Structure type _____
   Floor strength(s) _____
   Max. ceiling/roof load _____
   No. of floor levels _____
   Other _____
   Age _____
   Condition _____
   Condition _____
   Condition _____
   Column spacing _____

D) Services Features:
   Heating _____
   Ventilat'g _____
   Air condtg _____
   Toilets _____
   Sanitary sewage _____
   Storm drainage _____
   Floor drainage _____
   Other _____
   Electrical power _____
   Lighting _____
   Process steam _____
   Process gas(es) _____
   Process water _____
   Potable water _____

E) Access and Egress
   Materials _____
   Supplies _____
   Productn workers _____
   Support wkrs, suprvsn, visitrs

F) Dynamic Considerations:

	Rating: best to worst						Wt.	Val.
	A	E	I	O	U	X		
1. Effectiveness of space arrangement: Flow_____ Handling_____ Layout_____ Storing_____ Man/mch. util._____ Other_____								
2. Density of present occupancy Tight, heavy_____ Loose, light_____								
3. Cost to move per unit of floor area incl. utils. Fixed_____ Mobile_____								
4. Constrainedness (limits on growth/expansion at present location)_____								
5. Worth of present location–extent of meeting necessary or important relationships_____								
6. Extent of need to change present occupancy Expand_____ Rearrange_____ Contract_____ Upgrade_____								
7. Other_____								
Total ⟶								

Fig. 7 Floor space evaluation work sheet. *(Courtesy of Richard Muther & Associates. All rights reserved.)*

REQUESTING SPACE

In large corporations and government agencies, requests for space must be made in a formal way and supported by backup information. Typically, this space is divided into several classes:
    1. General-purpose space
       a. Office space
       b. Storage space

c. Particular space requiring special expenditures to construct, maintain, and/or operate

2. Special-purpose space (space wholly or predominantly utilized for the special purposes of the occupying group, function, office, or agency and not generally suitable for use by others)

In requesting space, the following general outline may be used as covering most points to be considered:

1. Date request initiated
2. Initial, renewal, or supplementary request
3. Office/department/plant requesting
4. Location
5. Occupant(s)
6. Term or period of anticipated occupancy
7. Type(s) of space needed (see classifications of land and floor space)
8. Breakdown of space requirements
   a. Value of occupying machinery and equipment (for each area or functional activity area)
   b. Number of occupying personnel (for each area)
   c. Special building requirements (floor load, ceiling heights, column spacing, etc.)
   d. Interior construction required
   e. Need for contiguity of space (one floor or several, one building or several, etc.)
   f. Particular floor level
   g. Doors and docks, number and type
   h. Elevators, cranes, built-in equipment
   i. Utilities—heat, vent, air, special electric, gas, water, etc.
   j. Lighting
   k. Telephone and other communications
   l. Sprinkler, fire protection, alarm
   m. Guard service for security
   n. Flooring, special maintenance or custodial services
9. Have funds been made available or budgeted for construction, renovation, rent, services?
10. Justification of space requested.

From the viewpoint of controlling space utilization, most space planners agree that the time to provide for proper space utilization is when the space requests are initially considered. It is very difficult to reestablish space allocated or assigned after the occupying group or function is installed. Charging space costs to particular plant and/or department budgets or comparing similar occupants' efficiencies of space utilization will tend to help overcome this practical problem of cutting down on space needs.

From an overall standpoint, management should clarify its polic(ies) on space utilization. In rapidly growing plants, it is often wise to overprovide space. This reduces the frequency of building projects, the disruption to operations, and the likelihood of having to give up an opportunity to accept a large order or major contract. And of course, empty plant space puts a certain pressure on the marketing department to provide sales orders that will fully utilize the plant's capacity.

On the other hand, conservative managers and treasurers find there is less risk when the company seldom if ever provides more space than it really needs, in spite of the fact it may take, say, 2 years to provide additional space. This way, the space tends to be densely occupied, with resulting reduced costs for space and presumably lower overall operating costs.

Chapter **3**

Evaluation of Existing Equipment Utilization

R. L. PERKINS

Supervisor, Facilities Master Planning, Vought Aeronautics Company, Division of LTV Aerospace Corporation

GENERAL

The evaluation of existing equipment utilization is dependent on the point of view of the person making the evaluation. Someone in production will analyze the equipment in terms of system performance as well as productive time. A person in maintenance will analyze the equipment in terms of maintenance costs and downtime. Management's point of view concerns mainly the profit generated by the equipment and its future for generating new business. The plant engineer is normally considered by management to be the authority on machinery and equipment and is usually given the task of final approval of new equipment or major machinery refurbishment prior to general management's approval. The plant engineer must be aware of the viewpoints of production, maintenance, and management in order to make an accurate evaluation and to offer recommendations that will maximize overall company benefits.

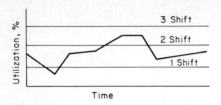

Fig. 1   Typical equipment utilization chart.

DEFINITION

Equipment utilization is gauged by dividing productive time by available time. Productive time normally includes running time, setup time, and regularly scheduled maintenance time. Available time is the time planned for the equipment to be operating on a one-, two-, or three-shift basis and normally includes planned overtime. Figure 1 is a typical utilization chart.

EQUIPMENT UTILIZATION FROM THE PRODUCTION VIEWPOINT

Purpose

Production personnel view equipment utilization evaluation as one of their primary control tools. The following is a representative list of production uses for equipment utilization analysis:

1. *Maximize productive time.* An analysis of the basic equipment utilization chart will reveal inequities in machine loading. As an example, if the chart indicates a need for overtime or a partial second shift operation, an evaluation should be made to shift the load to a less efficient load group, subcontract the overload, upgrade the available equipment, or purchase additional machinery. This type of evaluation must carefully consider the criticalness of the parts, the future potential of the type of equipment, and the company's future plans and strategy.

2. *Minimize costs.* This is closely related to item 1 and is covered in the same type of evaluation. It should be noted at this point that it is important to bring the controller's organization into the analysis cycle to make sure that the short-range costs and long-range potential gains coincide with the company's tax structure, future plans, and strategy.

3. *Optimize scheduling.* The equipment utilization chart offers an excellent opportunity to optimize scheduling by making available a tool with which the scheduler can readily evaluate the load of every load group and the history of any specific critical piece of equipment.

4. *Optimize production planning.* This relates directly to item 3, "optimize scheduling," and eliminates unnecessary machine-group overload by making load data and equipment history available.

5. *Evaluate manufacturing supervision.* One of the most common uses and the most controversial (to the person evaluated) is using equipment utilization evaluation to evaluate the efficiency of manufacturing supervision. Two separate techniques are used, depending on a number of variables:

   a. Standards method. The standards method is used to rank each foreman against every other foreman. Some companies extend this rating method to general foreman, superintendents, general superintendents, and director levels. The basic principle in this system is that the time standard used must be correct and equitable in all cases. It is evident that inaccurate or incorrectly applied standards would bias the entire system.

   b. Target method. This method establishes a calculated or arbitrary utilization target for each unit, group, or section. This relegates time standards to a less critical role than in method *a*, since the relative improvement in utilization and the relationship to the target are the measuring tools.

6. *Develop standards for forecasting and estimating.* The history developed by the equipment utilization charts can be reduced to a set of factors or standards to be used in forecasting new business or estimating new jobs. The most common use of these factors in today's industry is to refine previous data in order to follow the trends as the equipment either deteriorates or is rebuilt to new standards.

7. *Develop data for proposals.* The data developed to maximize time and to develop standards for forecasting and estimating should be used to develop data for proposals. This is the most current data available and will assist the company management to accurately assess the probability of winning a contract.

8. *Develop data for equipment replacement analysis.* Evaluation of equipment utilization is one of the basic means to determine the timing for replacement. This replacement may be due to deterioration of equipment efficiency, obsolescence, or incorporation of new materials or methods.

9. *Develop data for sourcing analysis.* Equipment utilization analysis develops the data necessary to make the economic decision to produce a product or subcontract it. The factors used are overall machine load, efficiency, and machine downtime history.

Methods

Equipment utilization evaluation from the production standpoint is normally one of the tasks of the industrial engineer in a staff position, as a member of a manufacturing team, or as a part of an industrial engineering department.

Equipment utilization charts are usually maintained for production machinery only. Equipment under the control of facilities, engineering, quality, or R&D is justified and maintained for its capability. Utilization is not normally a factor. Sophistication of the equipment utilization analysis varies according to the size of the operation.

1. *Small company.* In a small company the staff industrial engineer develops the standards for each machine or load group by time study or previously prepared data. The utilization report is then manually prepared, using the data from the machine operators time cards.

2. *Large company.* In a large company the industrial engineering department normally prepares equipment utilization reports. An industrial engineer estimator analyzes the planning paper from the manufacturing planning department and estimates the individual work elements by means of predeveloped standards. If a new or unique operation is encountered, a request is made to the time-study section to develop a standard for that particular operation. These data are usually computerized for later comparison to the actual data from the operation. This method has the advantages of automated printout to any level desired; automatic, accurate, and timely computations; and a feedback system of actuals to standards to continuously update the standard estimating data.

It should be noted that although the methods of obtaining equipment utilization vary depending on the resources of the individual company, the formula, information, and uses are basically the same.

Production Equipment Utilization Evaluation—Illustrations

Figure 2, a production equipment utilization chart, is a typical example of a utilization chart reflecting several manufacturing decisions added by evaluation of this data.

This equipment evaluation chart indicates a poor machine utilization percentage due to, in this case by definition, equipment deterioration from age. At point 1, the decision was made to refurbish the equipment. A major point in this determination was the evaluation of the productive time lost. This is represented by area "A," and the time to recover the lost time is represented by equal area "B." Point 2 reflects the position that the equipment is beginning to meet its projected utilization target after refurbishment and starting the cycle over again. Additional manufacturing information that would be used during an evaluation of this type would be projected shop loads, schedule, tolerance levels, substitute equipment availability, and cost of refurbishment.

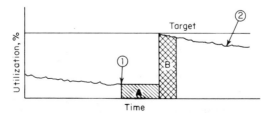

Fig. 2   Production equipment utilization chart.

EQUIPMENT UTILIZATION FROM THE MAINTENANCE VIEWPOINT

Maintenance personnel view equipment utilization as a vehicle to assist Production in achieving their objectives as well as a tool for leveling and minimizing maintenance costs.

Purpose

Maximize "up" time An evaluation of the equipment utilization chart gives maintenance the data to develop craft schedules for maintenance and to develop the degree of maintenance necessary for a specific piece of equipment.

In Fig. 3 the ordinate is in terms of percent utilization. The abscissa indicates time. The utilization target is that level at which the machine is considered to be working at the maximum expected efficiency. This target on an industrywide basis averages about 85 percent. Point 1 shows the expected utilization of a new piece of equipment. Points 2 and 3 indicate the expected drop in utilization and the recovery after a planned maintenance cycle. Points 4 and 5 depict the situation as the utilization percentage drops off faster as the equipment ages. It also indicates that even after the maintenance cycle, the machinery utilization does not return to the target line. Point 6 shows either a complete machine breakdown, a rebuild cycle, or an equipment replacement cycle.

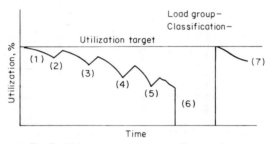

Fig. 3 Maintenance equipment utilization chart.

Point 7 depicts the start of a new cycle, with the equipment utilization equaling the utilization target. The following data can be gleamed from this illustration:

1. Actual vs. theoretical utilization of a new piece of equipment
2. Maintenance cycle
3. Changes to maintenance cycle as system deteriorates
4. Decision point in time to:
   a. Rebuild
   b. Replace
   c. Subcontract
   d. Investigate new machinery and/or methods

Minimize maintenance trade time The various types of equipment maintenance have evolved from one ancestor which could be labeled the breakdown system or "don't touch it until it falls on the floor" syndrome. This system has obvious merits from a minimum maintenance standpoint; however, critical machine time tends to be excessive. On the other end of the maintenance scale, we have precautionary machine maintenance. This type of maintenance theory is predominant in the process industry where excessive downtime can be fatal. In between these two extremes of maintenance, where the loading and leveling of trade time is either nonexistent or constant, the normal condition of trying to achieve the production goals and also achieve the maintenance budgeting goals exists.

Evaluation of the machine utilization chart can assist in minimizing trade by leveling and accurate scheduling. It can be readily seen that observation of the maintenance points on the various equipment utilization charts and an analysis of the conditions that change the maintenance cycles makes the development of a maintenance schedule minimizing the various trades relatively simple. This task would assume a much different aspect of complexity however, if the analyst did not have access to the data furnished by an evaluation of the equipment utilization charts. Then any schedule or load would be "by the seat of the pants," with the inherent overruns.

Minimize waiting time   Accurate scheduling of the maintenance trades and minimizing trade overloads, two aspects of the evaluation utilization, will assure the minimum equipment waiting time.

Minimize degradation of equipment   This is a cost factor affecting both maintenance and production. If the equipment is allowed to deteriorate excessively, then the eventual cost of maintenance, machine downtime, and production is adversely affected. Conversely, excessive maintenance to virtually eliminate the degradation factor will have the same effect of excessive costs and downtime. Figure 4 indicates the results of these conditions.

An analysis of the three graphs in Fig. 4 illustrates the relationship of the equipment utilization graph, the downtime graph, and the maintenance cost graph in the evaluation cycle. The "A" curve shows the condition when equipment is allowed to deteriorate excessively. The three graphs show minimum utilization, maximum downtime, and maximum cost. The "B" curve indicates the condition when equipment is excessively maintained. It can be readily observed that utilization remains at the "new" condition; however, downtime is high, due to time for maintenance, and costs are high. The "C" curve indicates a more realistic approach. Utilization in this case will slowly deteriorate with time, downtime will be low, and maintenance costs will be minimized.

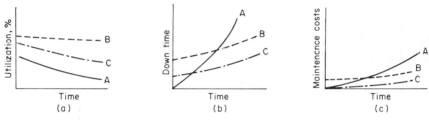

Fig. 4   Typical maintenance analysis charts.

Develop history for scheduling and maintenance manloading   Utilization of the data developed by the analysis of equipment utilization charts allows maintenance to use a technique developed and proved by production management. The history developed by the equipment charts can be reduced to a set of factors upgrading and refining the standards used for maintenance scheduling and for projecting future manloading.

Methods

Equipment utilization evaluation from the maintenance standpoint can be one of the tasks of the following personnel:

1. Industrial engineering
2. Facilities planning
3. Plant engineering
4. Maintenance staff
5. Maintenance supervision

The task assignment depends on the type of industry, the size of facility, and the organization structure.

In the majority of cases the equipment utilization charts are prepared by Industrial Engineering and provided to the maintenance organization for their analysis. In the real world the group that prepares the basic utilization chart is of no consequence. The important point is the evaluation of the equipment utilization chart, the reduction of this data, and the final analysis must be made by line supervision that have direct responsibility for the equipment. Only in this way can the direct line supervision have the insight into the problem and be able to relate to the other factors of budget, available manpower, and job priority.

EQUIPMENT UTILIZATION FROM THE MANAGEMENT VIEWPOINT

Management views equipment utilization evaluation as one of many factors affecting its primary interest: profit.

Purpose

Maximize profit   Management relates to both production and maintenance viewpoints in striving to maximize profit by balancing production and maintenance costs with equipment utilization. Figure 5, plotting costs against percent utilization, indicates the relationship between the cost of maintenance and the cost of production as related to utiliza-

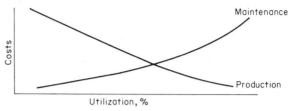

Fig. 5   Cost vs. utilization graph.

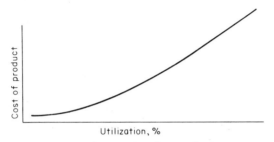

Fig. 6   Cost of product graph.

tion. The data developed from this analysis—along with other factors such as material costs, overhead costs, and fringe benefits—enable management to evaluate the cost of the product versus the percent utilization, as illustrated in Fig. 6.

Evaluation of the cost of the product in relation to utilization will develop the data to allow management to relate utilization to profit and assist in the task of maximizing profit by controlling equipment utilization factors.

Minimize cash flow   The cost of maintenance in relation to a production percent utilization figure can be used by management as one of several factors to assist in minimizing cost flow. Figure 7 is an illustration of this process.

Figure 7 has cost as the ordinate and time as the abscissa. The curve labeled "A" is the cost of maintenance, and curve "B" is the cost of substitution on less efficient equipment. Curve "C" is the cost of replacement of the original equipment. Management can use the data shown on this type of graphic presentation to decide, based on the

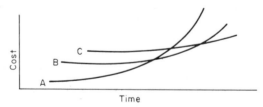

Fig. 7   Chart of management alternatives.

company's financial posture and long-range business plans, how to minimize cash flow for its individual application.

Develop data for long-range projections   Management, as previously shown for production and maintenance, can utilize data developed from equipment utilization charts to produce new standards or to modify existing standards for projecting long-range business plans. Equipment utilization evaluation can show capacities for future work, need for equipment replacement, future maintenance costs, manpower requirements related to equipment, and equipment cost trends.

Marketing tool Equipment utilization evaluation can provide sales with open capacity, downtime statistics, cost trends, and future capacity schedules.

Methods

The data from equipment utilization anaylsis are a small part of the overall data utilized by management in the decision-making process. These data are normally taken from the production-developed utilization charts and flow through the production chain of command to the various marketing, business planning, and financial organizations. Specific applications that could affect the company as a whole usually are prepared, analyzed, and presented by the industrial engineering department.

EQUIPMENT UTILIZATION FROM THE PLANT ENGINEER'S VIEWPOINT

The plant engineer, as stated at the beginning of the chapter, must be aware of the viewpoints of production, maintenance, and management to be able to evaluate all the salient points and thus to maximize the overall company benefits.

Purpose—Controlling Maintenance Costs

The plant engineer has the responsibility of controlling and minimizing maintenance costs while relating to the production goal of maximum utilization and reliability. Controlling maintenance costs effectively requires the precise development of that position which maximizes equipment reliability (as shown by the equipment utilization evaluation methods) and minimizes equipment maintenance, equipment repair, and equipment replacement costs. To achieve this goal, the various costs factors must be defined.

The factors in equipment maintenance can be broken into two major categories: those affecting costs of a maintenance organization and those affecting production.

Maintenance factors

MAINTENANCE CRAFT TIME This is the major item of costs to be considered. It consists of the electricians, mechanical trades, and plumbers and the general overhead factors of supervision, clerical services, and fringe benefits. The management of this factor will be of prime interest in the determination of the relationship between equipment maintenance costs and equipment reliability. The main variable in this factor is the logical scheduling of manpower.

MATERIALS This factor is usually considered a constant. Some degree of improvement may be possible with techniques such as kitting and a closer degree of cost control. A definite danger of increased costs looms if control reaches into the "overkill" category.

Production factors

DOWNTIME ON A MACHINE DURING MAINTENANCE Downtime on a machine during the maintenance cycle is a complete loss of resources from the production standpoint. This factor is closely tied in to the maintenance factor of trades time. The scheduling of trades is again the variable in this case.

LOST PRODUCTION TIME DURING WAITING This factor, like the previous factor, is considered by production to be a complete loss of resources. It is a variable controlled by the availability of materials and the scheduling of trades.

COST OF DEGRADED SYSTEM PERFORMANCE The degradation of systems cost is a factor affecting both maintenance and production. If the system or machine performance is allowed to deteriorate excessively, then the eventual cost of maintenance, the machine downtime, and the production from the equipment of systems is adversely affected. Conversely, excessive maintenance to virtually eliminate the degradation factor will have the same effect of excessive machine costs and downtime. The variable is the analysis of the tolerance allowable for a given task. This breakdown of equipment

maintenance costs factors gives us four major variables, each with several internal variables, and the materials factor that can generally be considered a constant.

Balancing factors   Now that we have determined those factors that determine maintenance costs, let us examine the factors that can be utilized to minimize the total
cost-vs.-reliability equation.

Shop load   The shop load is defined as that work which is scheduled or planned for
a specific machine or machine load group over a period of time.   A shop load will be
factored by the realization or performance factors developed by the particular industry.
In addition, studies made in the aerospace industry indicate a need for determining the
obsolescence factor of a particular machine and incorporating it into the overall formula.
It can be readily seen that maintaining an up time or reliability factor of 90 percent is
unnecessary and costly when the shop load is at 50 percent.   Utilization of the shop load
factor will vary in different industries, and care must be exercised in its use to minimize
critical downtime.   Figure 8 illustrates this significant point.

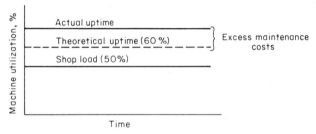

Fig. 8   Machine utilization chart.

General shop   The shop load factor seems to be most applicable in the general type
of detail shop where the load can be forecast with a reasonable degree of accuracy for
a period varying from 3 to 6 months.   In this case, it is suggested that this factor plus
an allowance of perhaps 10 percent can be used to set the needed equipment reliability
limits while minimizing the overall maintenance costs inherent in unplanned labor and
expedited material.

Job shop   The shop load factor in a job shop offers less chance for savings.   This
application requires a higher degree of reliability, since the work load cannot be determined to the same degree of accuracy or over a reasonable length of time.   One application that might prove useful is to segregate the equipment into classes of declining
criticality.   The factor could be used by varying the allowance in relation to criticality.

ACCURACY.   The second of the cost-vs.-reliability balancing factors that we will consider is the accuracy factor.   The tolerance of the work being performed on a part should
determine the condition of the equipment prior to maintenance.   This factor, like the
shop load factor, is related to the type of shop and feasibility of forecasting the type of
job to be loaded in the future.

CRITICALITY.   One last factor must be considered in this evaluation.   Certain critical
machinery in any shop must be maintained to a high degree to minimize a line shut down
condition.   This special classification of equipment may not follow the analysis that we
are developing, as the maintenance costs to achieve maximum reliability could be significant when compared to the downtime costs.

Relationship development   It is not our purpose to develop the coefficients of the
variables to show the relationship between maintenance costs and machine reliability,
since each individual company tends to vary to such a degree as to make any single
formula or program completely invalid.   Even within a company, different machinery
load groups, or in some cases singular pieces of equipment, must be handled under
different sets of conditions.   The factors must be evaluated on an individual basis by each
company.   Reviewing briefly, there are four major variables in the factory maintenance
category: maintenance trade time, machine downtime during maintenance, lost production time during waiting, and cost of degraded system performance.   In addition, the
balancing category consists of three functions: shop loading, accuracy, and sometimes
criticality.   A critical evaluation of the nine major factors and an analysis of the type of

industry must be made to determine the type and degree of control deemed most feasible.

Feedback systems To achieve maximum benefits from this system (or any similar system), a closed loop or feedback system should be established. This will trace the actions taken, measure the effectiveness of the actions, and feed it back into the maintenance formula. This, in effect, will decrease the probable error factor in decision making.

An additional technique that can be valuable is to trace the opportunities to make a decision affecting maintenance costs and feed them into the feedback system. The fact that a decision was or was not made is not important in opportunity theory, as the effect of the decision on maintenance costs can be analyzed. Then this opportunity can be used to increase the system accuracy in future decisions. This gives us a decision-making tool that is improved by good decisions, bad decisions, and lack of decisions.

Approach to cost modeling Now that the several factors that determine the cost of maintenance and that effect equipment reliability have been developed, an approach or formula can be stated. The formula equates maintenance costs to production factors as limited by the balancing factors. Utilizing the previously developed factors, the formula would be stated as follows: maintenance trade time plus material costs is equal to the downtime on a machine during maintenance and the lost production during

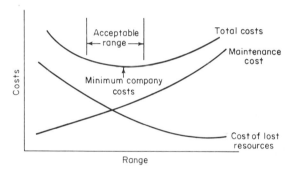

Fig. 9 Maintenance cost factors.

waiting (limited by shop load and criticality) plus the cost of degraded system performance (limited by the accuracy factor). This approach can be applied to a range of applications varying from those unsophisticated problems where empirical factors or limits can be applied to large-scale problems were regression techniques are applicable. As computation of the formula leaves the rule-of-thumb stage, it becomes a natural application for computer processing. Computerized techniques will not only find the minimum cost point but will also validate the input data and indicate the limits of confidence for the answer. By converting the formula to a simplified graphic presentation, we can illustrate the conditions previously defined. (See Fig. 9.)

Figure 9, a cost graph illustrating the maintenance cost factors, has the ordinate in dollars and the abscissa indicating range. The point on the total cost curve indicating minimum company costs is the position to strive to achieve. Under actual conditions, however, budget limitations may force movement to the left of the point; while political considerations, company image, or critical operations could force movement to the right. Evaluation of the graph readily indicates the fact that limited movement to the right or to the left of the mathematically correct minimum cost point will not effect the overall cost picture to a great extent. This allows the utilization of a range of values (control limits) instead of a single point. The control limits, when applied back to the formula, translate into practical considerations of flexibility in scheduling, manloading, and minimizing maintenance costs.

Approval Authority

The plant engineer is normally considered by management to be the company authority on machinery and equipment and is usually given the task of final approval of new equipment or major machinery refurbishment prior to general management's approval.

The plant engineer has the following techniques available for his use from the three principle areas:

Production equipment utilization evaluation
  1. Maximum production time
  2. Minimize costs
  3. Equipment replacement analysis

Maintenance equipment utilization evaluation
  1. Maximum up time
  2. Minimize maintenance trade time
  3. Minimize waiting time
  4. Minimize degraded system performance

Management equipment utilization evaluation
  1. Maximize profit
  2. Minimize cost flow

Utilizing one or a combination of these techniques gives the plant engineer the power to objectively evaluate the data and base a decision on a broad-based knowledge of total company needs, policies, and strategy.

Chapter **4**

Evaluation of Existing Utilities and Usage

WILLIAM P. GOUDRON, P.E.

Supervisor, Industrial Engineering and Design, Plant Engineering and Design, Plant Engineering Department, Airesearch Manufacturing Company

INTRODUCTION

The evaluation of existing utilities and usage is one of the prime responsibilities of the plant engineer. The knowledge of and proper usage of all utilities is a necessity to keep plant operating costs under control, meet local, federal, and OSHA requirements, and to allow manufacturing to produce at a maximum rate at the lowest cost.

The plant engineer is directly responsible for and control of the usage of the following utilities:

    Electrical power
    Heating, ventilation, and air conditioning
    Compressed air and gas
    Water (domestic and industrial)

Storm drains and sanitation sewers
Fire protection

A monitoring system should be developed to give the plant engineer an overall view of the plant and operating conditions. In addition, there should be the capability of early warning if any equipment begins to go out of control and the ability to shut down the equipment before extensive damage can be done. A successful system should monitor heat, cold, flow, pressures, vibration, temperatures, levels, and amperes on equipment; it should also have the capability to monitor the fire protection system.

ELECTRICAL POWER

The plant engineer must know the plant electrical system. An important tool and requirement to obtain a permit is the single-line diagram. It shows by single lines and standard symbols the course and parts of a circuit or system. The following items will help ensure an accurate and complete diagram.

1. Use standard symbols.
2. Approximate relative positions of components.
3. Record all known facts—never leave anything to guesswork.
4. Identify the diagram properly.
5. Show future plans if possible.

See Fig. 1.

Another important tool is the panel schedule. This is necessary to maintain proper loads and wire sizes to and enable the plant engineer to add or change load requirements and to keep the plant operating most efficiently. See Fig. 2.

There is also a need for planned maintenance of the electrical system. A breakdown in the electrical system can mean an inconvenience to production or a complete shutdown and loss of production, creating idle workers and loss of profit.

Ground Rules for an Adequate Electric Maintenance Program

1. Inspect and test protective devices regularly.
2. Inspect all motors and equipment on a planned schedule.
3. Keep rotating equipment properly lubricated.
4. Keep electrical gear well ventilated.
5. Remove dust and dirt from equipment.
6. Maintain proper grounding on all equipment.

The keeping of maintenance records allows the plant engineer to keep equipment in repair, keep the high-usage parts on hand, and know the maintenance cost of existing equipment. This, in turn, tells the engineer when it is most economical to replace or modernize equipment.

When to Update the Equipment

If a plant is operating satisfactorily, it is difficult to convince management to authorize a large expenditure for new equipment. The following criteria indicate to the plant engineer when a more up-to-date wiring system is needed.

1. Inadequate interrupting capacity. The National Electric Code requires that all current interrupting devices be capable of interrupting the available fault currents at their terminals. Where fault currents have increased above equipment ratings, the fuses and/or circuit breakers must be replaced with fuses and/or circuit breakers with adequate ratings. If this occurs, a review of the entire electrical system should be made.

2. Unsafe operation. The first and major concern of any electrical system is the safety of the employees.

3. Uncertain reliability. When service becomes doubtful because of age or obsolescence, there is the possibility of a plant shutdown and loss of production if the system is not updated.

4. Requirement for higher voltage. Added machinery can be less costly to install if higher voltages are used.

5. Installation of automated equipment. Computers and solid-state equipment require steady power to operate. This may call for an "uninterruptible power supply."

6. Excess voltage drop. Increased loads and long feeders cause voltage drop; changes should be made in the distribution system when this occurs.

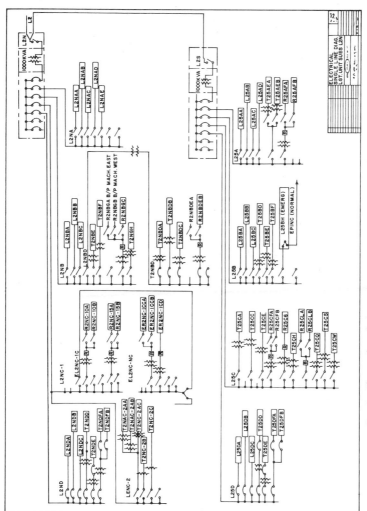

Fig. 1 Electrical single line diagram (*Courtesy The Garrett Corporation*).

INSTAL. DATE 11-10-66
REVISION 5-8-70
"PP3A-A"
FLOOR FIRST
UNIT 10   COLUMN No. BZ/CA-61

CKT No.	DESCRIPTION	EQUIP No.	H.P.	AMPS	SW	FUSE	WIRE & COND	AØ KVA	BØ KVA	CØ KVA	COL. LOCATION
A	SUMP PUMP		1.0	1.8	60	15	9#12-11/2"	.50	.50	.50	BSMT-CB-58/59
B	SUMP PUMP		1.0	1.8	60	15		.50	.50	.50	"
C	AIR COMPR.VENT FAN		25.0	32.0	60	40	3#8-1"	8.86	8.86	8.86	ROOF
D	RECEPTACLES (2)				60	50	3#6-1"	.40	.40	.40	1st FLOOR
E	SPARE				60						
F	SPARE										
G	1 KVA CONTROL X'FMER				60	5		.50	.50	.50	IN PNL.
H	SPARE				60						
J	EXITER & PUMP PNL.				200	200	3#4/0-3"	16.80	16.42	16.80	BSMT-CC-59
K	SPACE										
L	BLOWER MTR.		5.0	7.5	60	30	3#10-1"	2.10	2.10	2.10	1st FLR-CB/CC-60/6
M	EXITER			21.0	60	30	3#10-1"	5.80	5.80	5.80	1st FLR-CB-60
N	5.0 KVA X'FMER			10.4	60	20	IN PNL.	2.50	2.50	-	CONT'L PNL-CB-60
P	SPACE										
R	SPACE										
S	SPARE				60						
T	SPARE				60						
U	COOL'G TOWER FAN #1		40/10	52	200	150	6#4-2"	14.39	14.39	14.39	BM/BN-67/68
V	COOL'G TOWER PUMP #3		50	63	200	175	SEE CKT. W	17.44	17.44	17.44	BO-68/69
W	COOL'G TOWER PUMP #2		50	63	200	175	6#2-2"	17.44	17.44	17.44	BO-68/69
X	PNL. PP3AA-X				200	200	3#4/0-3"	20.49	21.49	21.49	BZ/CA-60
								107.72	107.22	105.22	TOTAL KVA / Ø
								224.41	223.37	223.37	TOTAL AMPS / Ø

PANEL DATA	
480 VOLT 3Ø 60 CYCLE	SUM OF TWO LARGEST LOADS 223.37
BUSS AMPS 600 A	447.78
MFG SQ "D"	MULTIPLIER = .9
90"X 30"X 20"	= TOTAL AMPS 403.0
	= TOTAL KVA 320.2

PANEL FEEDER DATA
BKR LOCATION PP3A   BKR LETTER A
BKR SIZE 600A
TRIP SIZE 600A
FEEDER SIZE 3 #350 MCM(EA) CONDUIT (2) 3"C
PARALLEL WITH

Fig. 2 Electrical panel schedule *(Courtesy The Garrett Corporation).*

An important consideration for an optimum electrical system is the power factor. The reasons for a good power factor are:

1. Better voltage
2. Reduced power costs
3. Increased capacity
4. Reduced system loss
5. Smaller transformer requirements

The leading piece of power factor equipment used to compensate for lagging power is the capacitor. It has high efficiency and no moving parts to wear or maintain.

The plant engineer must keep abreast with changing processes and techniques to best utilize his system. Electrical modernization must keep pace with advancing technology.

HEATING

Heating is a requirement to be met for the comfort of employees and for various processes. The comfort zone for employees is 68°F to 70°F, with a relative humidity of 50 percent. There are many heating methods available, and each situation should be analyzed to determine which is best, taking into consideration initial installation, maintenance, original cost, operating cost, and ability to meet the most severe temperatures. Occasional failure of a heating plant to maintain preselected temperatures in extremely severe weather is not critical in terms of economics. However, the control of certain processes depending on close regulation of temperatures requires a separate study, design, and heating system.

Types of Heat	*Types of Heaters*
Steam	Four-way unit heaters
Hot water	Horizontal unit heaters
Gas	Vertical unit heaters
Electric	Radiators
Oil	Infrared radiant heaters
Solar	Gas- and/or oil-fired duct heaters
	Electric ceiling panels
	Electric duct elements
	Forced-air heaters
	Gravity heaters

A building can be constructed so as to save on energy consumption in many ways. In modern construction, the trend is to a minimum amount of glass and, with proper insulation, there will be a substantial dollar savings in heating in the cold months and cooling in the hot months.

A unique system in a multistory building is to construct a core floor between two occupied floors. All heating, cooling, ventilating, generating, pumping, plumbing, piping, and electrical and communications systems would be located on the core floor, which also serves as an air-return plenum for the air-handling equipment. Being enclosed, this system reduces the maintenance on equipment and thus allows a better controlled system to service the floors below and above with all utilities. In addition, this system actually lowers the dollars-per-square-foot cost of the building.

Another system is the "total energy package." This system is run by a gas turbine engine turning an alternator to generate electricity, utilizing the exhaust to heat a waste heat boiler that generates steam for heating, hot water, and cooling.

Regularly scheduled inspection and maintenance will ensure maximum economy in operation and maintenance of the heating system with a minimum of equipment downtime. Heating elements should be cleaned when necessary. Fan blades should be cleaned regularly, as dirt can cause unbalance and vibration, resulting in noise and damage to the bearings. Motors and bearings should be properly lubricated. Belt drives should be kept in proper tension and belts replaced when they show wear. Filters must be kept clean for proper and efficient operation of air-handling equipment.

VENTILATION

Proper ventilation is required for both the safety and comfort of the employees in shop and office and to obtain the maximum output from machines, equipment, and processes.

Whenever possible, a natural flow of air should be used. This can best be done with large quantities of outside air, if the air is not too hot in relation to the humidity. The cool-air inlet should be as low as possible and the hot-air outlet as high as possible in the roof. Several types of ventilators are effective; each situation must be analyzed to determine which of the following will serve best:

1. Wind-driven turbine ventilator
2. Continuous-ridge ventilator
3. Belt-drive power roof exhauster
4. Direct-drive power roof exhauster
5. Centrifugal roof exhauster
6. Axial roof exhauster
7. Directional-type ventilator
8. Centrifugal wall ventilator
9. Axial wall ventilator

Always make certain there is an ample supply of air, so as not to starve the exhauster. Positive and negative pressures can also be controlled by adjusting the supply and exhausting of air. The limits of air velocity for the comfort of the employees ranges from 50 fpm to 200 fpm. If possible, the air should be to the front of the employees; as little air as possible should be directed to the head, neck, and back. Therefore the air system must be adjustable both in velocity and direction.

Incoming air must be filtered to remove dust and foreign particles from it. There are many effective filters, including the following:

1. Standard throwaway filters
2. Washable, reusable filters
3. Automatic roll-type filters
4. Automatic self-cleaning filters
5. Electrical filters
6. Activated charcoal filters

For an efficient ventilating system, it is mandatory that all filters be properly maintained and replaced so as not to restrict the airflow.

Just as incoming air must be filtered, exhaust air must not put contaminants into the outside air. This can be accomplished by air scrubbers or bag-type dust collectors.

AIR CONDITIONING

As the technology of modern times progresses, the need for air-conditioned facilities becomes greater and greater. These are needed to provide the proper environment for exotic processes and equipment in addition to maintaining the comfort of the employees.

There are many types of air conditioners; each situation should be analyzed by a trained professional mechanical engineer to determine which unit or system is best suited and most economical while also calling for the least maintenance in a particular situation.

In many instances modular units can be used for supplemental cooling or to individually cool the controls on numerically controlled equipment where high temperatures cannot be tolerated. Self-contained units are an economical method for cooling outlying areas. Larger areas can be serviced by single- or multizoned air-conditioning units using remote sources of refrigeration.

In large installations, the plant engineer should strive to operate the equipment as economically as possible. Normally an 80 percent makeup of ambient air is satisfactory; however, if the outside air is cooler, this ratio should be changed to utilize the cooler outside air, depending on the humidity. This will conserve energy. In a duct system, it is most important that a maintenance system be set up to keep the ducts clean, that the seals on all dampers be tight, and that the air system be properly balanced.

The following list can aid the plant engineer in maintaining the air-conditioning equipment. As a periodic inspection is made, a list should be checked off and remarks recorded. A list of needed repairs should be made, and this should be followed up by a disposition of repairs. At the time of inspection, the equipment should be oiled and minor adjustments on the units made. The following are to be checked:

1. Conditioned space: General condition, temperature, ventilation
2. Condenser (air-cooled):   General condition; lint and dirt condition; fan motor, starter, and drive
3. Condenser (water-cooled):   General condition; water regulating valve and strainer; evaporation condenser or cooling tower; drain, flush, and refill sump; float and strainer; spray nozzles; scale, corrosion, and fouling; water treatment and bleed-off; pump motor, starter, and drive; fan motor, starter, and drive
4. Compressor: General condition, noise, vibration, temperature, operating pressure, oil, suction, discharge, safety devices, cutouts, heaters, capacity controls, drives and belts, motor and starter
5. Refrigerant circuit: General condition; leaks and refrigerant charge; refrigerant controls and strainer
6. Water cooler: General condition; chilled water piping and insulation; pump motor; starter and drive
7. Air handler: General condition; fan motor, starter, and drive; filters; drip pan and drain; spray nozzles; cooling coils
8. Controls: General condition; thermostats; motorized valves and dampers
A well-maintained system should be inspected once per month.

COMPRESSED AIR AND GAS

Compressed air is one of the most useful utilities serving the plant and there is no limit to its application.   The ingenuity of the user is the limiting factor in determining the areas of usage.

Following are a few of the ways in which compressed air can be used:

Operating assembly tools	Operating screwdrivers
Operating impact wrench	Operating hoists
Operating multiple gang tools	Operating drills and reamers
Operating riveters	Operating clamps
Operating presses	Operating brakes
Spraying paints	Spraying metal
Sandblasting	Inflating tires
Transferring liquids	Operating pneumatic controls
Conveying materials	Agitating tanks
Operating jacks and lifts	Inflating tanks
Combustion for gas burners	Jet pulverizing
Operating rock drills	Air-jet cleaning
Aeration of tanks and bins	Operating paving breakers
Ejecting sewage	Operating tampers
Boring under roadways	Providing air curtains
Starting gas diesel and jet engines	Driving piles
Blowing whistles, horns, and sirens	Operating doors
Operating laboratory equipment	Chip conveying
Operating positioners	Glass bead blasting
Testing vessels for leakage	Cleaning machinery
Operating pneumatic-tube systems	Cleaning molds
Operating chipping hammers	Cleaning fixtures
Operating pneumatic cylinders	Removing liquids
Cleaning machined parts	Operating clutches
Operating motors in explosive areas	

In many applications it is beneficial and necessary to use dry air.   This is accomplished in many ways, as by using

1. Refrigerated units
2. Dessicant units
3. Filters

These units are usually placed at the compressors, while line filters can be placed just prior to the application of the compressed air.

Branch lines should always be taken off the top of the feeder lines, and blow-off lines should be at the end of each air system.

The Compressor

The original installation should be carefully planned, including all the proper associated equipment. This will make for a safer, simpler, and lower-maintenance installation. A compressor will always perform better and give longer service when installed in a building. If the compressor is air-cooled, there should be an adequate airflow supply and exhaust to properly cool the compressor. Sufficient room should always be allowed for proper and safe inspection and maintenance. Never install a compressor where the atmosphere is damp or dusty or where corrosive vapors are present.

One person should be assigned the task of maintenance, and complete records should be kept on routine inspections, maintenance, overhauls, and breakdowns. These records permit the scheduling of preventive maintenance and tell which high-usage parts should be kept on hand.

Lubricating is of the greatest importance. Only the recommended oils and quantities should be used, and a record should be kept of the running time of the compressor by means of a running hour meter. As in the electrical system, safety should always be foremost in maintenance and operation. Before attempting to work on a compressor, be certain that the power is off and the switches are tagged. Be sure there is no pressure in the unit and block the piston to prevent movement.

Safety valves should be popped manually at least once a week.

The mechanical designer should take into consideration the following items:

1. Actual cost of compressed air
2. Compressor capacity required
   a. Often it is more economical to have two smaller compressors than one large one. This allows for a backup in case of a breakdown, and often one compressor can handle the load at off-peak periods.
3. Selection of pipe size and supports
4. Proper hoses
5. Causes of low air pressure
   a. The system should continually be checked for leaks, which causes wasted energy and increased operating cost.
6. Problems caused by moisture in air
7. Specialty equipment
   a. Separators
   b. Filters
   c. Oilers
8. Foundations
9. Vibration

NATURAL GAS COMPRESSION

It is most probable that the compression of natural gas requires more power for handling than any other gas except air. Most fields of natural gas utilization and processing require compressors.

Diesel motors or gas turbines are usually the prime movers of the compressors. All types of compressors are used, but the dynamic and reciprocating units predominate.

Proper piping design is a necessity if one is to have an economical and maintenance-free system, taking into consideration the present and future conditions to be encountered. In all cases round pipe is to be used, taking into account the pipe's internal roughness.

WATER

One of the utilities most taken for granted is our water supply. It is required for sanitation and industrial facilities, drinking, cooling, processing, irrigation, heating, and fire protection.

In the initial installation of a facility, it is most important that the piping be sized and pitched correctly, not only to meet existing conditions but also to anticipate future requirements. It is mandatory that the water system be designed as a loop, with sectionalizing valves arranged so that, in case of interruptions, any one particular area can be shut off without shutting the entire system down. This is especially necessary in the fire protection system.

It is extremely important to reuse industrial water. This not only conserves energy but reduces cost and waste. The reuse of water can be set up in many areas.

1. Water from the cooling coils of vapor degreasers can be routed to rinse tanks or test tanks.

2. Water from welders can be used in rinse and test tanks.

3. If several rinse tanks are used, water can be transferred from rinse tank to rinse tank. The aeration of air in water rinse tanks will make the rinsing more effective.

4. A closed-loop system provides for the reuse of water in the cooling towers.

Timers and shut-off valves should be installed to prevent the continual running—or wasting—of water.

The water system should be continually monitored to prevent a shutdown during operating hours. Valves should be maintained and checked periodically. As corrosion and wear begin to show, corrective action or replacement should be made before a major breakdown in the water system occurs.

Backflow devices should be used whenever water lines run into tanks to prevent contamination of the water system in case of a backflow. These devices should be checked and certified once a year. Domestic and industrial water lines should never be crossed, and all lines should be properly identified, showing the direction of flow.

A water treatment plan should be put in effect to control hardness, filter out foreign particles, control algae in units such as cooling towers, boilers, and process tanks.

It is the plant engineer's responsibility to maintain an adequate water system.

STORM DRAINS

Proper drainage is of prime importance to any building site. Poor drainage can cause flooding, undermining, and erosion. Foundations can be damaged, roads may be washed away, and buildings may be flooded. This can stop production and thus cause loss of work and dollars.

The main tool to be used in designing proper drainage is the topographic map including the site where the plant is located and all adjacent areas. The map can show all the natural watercourses, whether water will flow from other parcels, and available means of drainage. The U.S. Geodetic Survey is a good source of this type of information.

The plant engineer should know the precipitation and the runoff caused by the precipitation to allow for proper drainage.

There are three general methods used to properly dispose of the runoff.

1. Sheet drainage. This is used in large areas and essentially depends on a properly graded surface to prevent gullies and erosion. Often a swale is cut to run the water to a catch basin and from there to a district storm drain.

2. Closed conduit. When underground devices are required, closed conduit is used. The more common types used are circular pipes, box drains, arches, and pipe arches. These are manufactured from corrugated metal, vitrified clay, and reinforced concrete.

3. Open channel. These can be circular, triangular, or rectangular, such as street gutters and surfaced and unsurfaced ditches. Ditches must be guarded to prevent injury and loss of life.

As additional structures are constructed, it is most important that the drainage system be reviewed and that proper corrections be made if the existing drainage system is changed in any way. It is difficult and costly to design a drainage system around buildings, therefore every effort should be made to plan for all future growth as well as present conditions.

Drainage control must also be designed for roads, paved surfaces, and roofs.

1. Roadways. Water should not be allowed to puddle or flood the roadway. It should be diverted to curb gutters or cross gutters.

2. Paved areas. Minimum slope for all paved areas should be no less than 1 percent. All walkways and paved areas should be pitched away from buildings and foundations.

3. Roof drains. Water should not be allowed to stand on the roof, and roof drains should be run to storm drains if available. Roof downspouts spilling into unpaved areas must have splash blocks to prevent erosion.

It must be noted that industrial waste can in no way be allowed to contaminate storm-water drains. Wastes should be run into clarifiers or neutralizing tanks. These should be properly maintained and pumped out regularly to remove sludge. It is of the utmost importance that records be maintained to prove that all wastes and contaminants are being controlled properly.

SANITATION SEWERS

Sanitation sewers must be sized according to local codes and the waste must be disposed of so as not to contaminate local streams, rivers, or waterways. Proper-size cleanouts must be installed for maintenance of the lines.

If septic tanks are used, they must be sized according to code. Leach lines must not contaminate underground water or neighboring property. Sludge should be pumped from the septic tank at least once a year.

FIRE PROTECTION SYSTEM

The loss of an industrial plant by fire can be tragic. Lives can be lost, equipment destroyed, products destroyed, and jobs lost. Though there may be insurance coverage, it could take anywhere from months to years to rebuild and resume production.

The proper coverage by adequate fire protection will mean reduced insurance rates, which would more than offset the cost of an adequate fire protection system. The installation of a system must meet local and state codes in addition to OSHA require-ments. No matter how small or how large a facility may be, it is important to have a company-sponsored fire brigade. The local fire department will train them in the proper handling of fire equipment. This group cannot only prevent major fires and fight smaller fires but it can also continually be checking to make sure there are no violations of the fire code, thus maintaining the safety of the buildings.

It is essential that all buildings be 100 percent sprinkled with the required number of proper extinguishers, standpipes, fire hydrants, and fire alarm boxes.

It is the plant engineer's responsibility to make certain that the equipment is always in the proper operating condition. Valves, flows, pressures, piping, and alarms should be checked and recorded monthly.

It is also advisable to have a monitoring system which detects water flow in the system automatically and notifies the local fire department if a sprinkler head is set off. This is especially important if the plant is not working 24 hours a day, 7 days a week.

Chapter **5**

Site Selection

LEE HALES
Consulting Associate
Richard Muther & Associates, Inc.

THE SITE SELECTION PROCESS
Importance of location Site selection decisions are among the most important a
company can make. Poor geographic location limits profit in many ways: through high
transport costs, high wage rates, disruptions from labor strife, bad weather, energy
shortages, local regulation, etc. A poor site can limit profit through high development
costs. It may also compromise capital investments by prohibiting expansion or use of
certain manufacturing processes, thus limiting response to market growth and change.
In some cases, the site and its location can mean the difference between profit and loss.

Few companies abandon developed sites. Selection decisions are usually irreversible
and companies must live with incorrect ones, regardless of the difficulties and costs
involved.

Scope of projects Site selection may consist of an international search for a country
in which to build a new plant. At the other extreme, selection may simply involve
deciding which adjoining property to purchase for an upcoming expansion.

The search may proceed no further than identification of a foreign country (or
community in the case of a national search). Typically, however, it will continue through
selection and procurement of property.

Projects may be undertaken for complete or partial relocation, expansion (without
relocation), or a combination of these reasons.

Four phases of site selection A project can be simplified and better managed if the
planner organizes it around the four phases shown in Fig. 1.

Phase I includes the development of overall requirements to be satisfied by the site and its geographic location. Objectives should be defined and their relative importance decided in keeping with the business plans of the firm.

Phase II involves selecting a general location. It narrows down the search to a general area and can require a series of decisions regarding the country, the region, and finally the community in which a site is to be sought.

Phase III involves selecting a specific site. A search is made for available sites within the top one or two communities chosen in Phase II. These are then evaluated and the most suitable is selected.

Phase IV consists of procuring the land by purchase, lease, option, or some other means of acquisition.

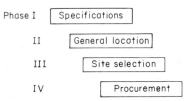

FOUR PHASES OF SITE SELECTION

Phase I   Specifications

    II   General location

    III   Site selection

    IV   Procurement

Fig. 1 Four phases of site selection. *(Courtesy of Richard Muther & Associates. All rights reserved.)*

Note that the phases overlap. The selection process will be a learning one, with feedback at various points. Finding out what differences exist among communities may lead to some adjustments in specifications. For this reason, cursory reviews of communities or regions should begin prior to the final statement of specifications. Similarly, there is no point in considering a community that contains no suitable sites. Therefore preliminary searches for specific sites should be made among promising communities toward the end of Phase II. Finally, for promising sites, initial steps toward procurement should be taken before a final selection is made. Such steps can assure that sites will indeed be available at firm, acceptable prices. An option or right of first refusal can be obtained on two or more promising sites if there are chances that the top choice might not develop as planned.

Three basic questions   No matter how many variables there are or how complex the problems may be, three basic questions are fundamental to every selection project. These are:

What is wanted?
What is available?
What is most suitable?

In keeping with the four-phase approach shown in Fig. 1, the planner will answer these questions first in Phase II, when selecting a general location, and then again in Phase III, when selecting a specific piece of property. The nature of the questions will vary in each phase and also with the purpose of the project. What is most suitable for a factory may be unacceptable for a distribution center.

Staffing the project   Site selection is never a one-man job, no matter how limited the scope of the project. The decisions involved will affect virtually all the company's operations, often in very subtle ways.

While final decision-making authority may rest with a single executive, successful experience in most companies suggests that managers of all affected operations be involved, usually as a committee or task force. Otherwise the few persons responsible will tend to overemphasize their functional concerns and overlook others of equal or greater importance.

Many planners find the best working arrangement to consist of two groups. One is a top management group responsible for setting objectives, reviewing progress, and making or approving final decisions. The other is a study group composed of operating managers or their designated representatives. This group gathers and analyzes information from outside sources and makes recommendations. Often an outside consultant, industrial realtor, or development official will provide assistance to the study group.

Ideally, the project manager will be the prospective plant manager or engineer for the new site and the study group will include those who will be planning the facilities for the site.

Role of the plant engineer   The plant engineer usually plays a key role in site selection projects. Often no other person has equal knowledge of requirements in such critical areas as water and energy supply, effluent and air pollutant treatment, historical land-to-building ratios, site development and building costs, and the like.

In addition to helping determine what is wanted, the plant engineer is well equipped to evaluate what is suitable among available sites. And in recent years, with the need to consider energy supplies and environmental controls, the plant engineer has been playing an increasingly vital role in evaluating regions and communities.

PHASE I: DETERMINING SPECIFICATIONS

Develop a business plan No search for communities or properties should begin without a reasonably firm plan setting forth the following items:

1. What products (or components thereof) will be produced in what quantities
2. What markets will be served through what distribution channels
3. What manufacturing and administrative operations will be performed
4. Which sources of supply will support the operations through what distribution channels
5. How many workers will be required in what occupational classes
6. What supporting services will be required (not only utilities but also janitorial, security, catering, etc.)
7. What wastes will be produced in what quantities
8. How much space will be required to house and support the operations (including yard space)
9. How fast will the site grow and what will be its future size and uses

Attention to operating costs Managers defining the objectives that will guide the search should be thoroughly familiar with the cost structure of the operations proposed. It is not uncommon to find location decisions made on the basis of freight rate differentials where transport represents 5 percent of total cost. Meanwhile taxes representing 10 percent are not examined. The importance attached to an economic objective must bear some relation to the portion of total cost that it represents.

Define objectives A review of the business plan and manufacturing cost relationships will reveal the objectives to be met by communities and properties in Phases II and III.

Objectives should be defined in brief explanatory terms—low distribution cost, adequate water supply, etc. Typically, they will express the desire to minimize development and operating costs while satisfying constraints regarding availability of local resources. In short, objectives constitute *policy statements* that will guide the project toward the most advantageous site. For this reason, they should be formulated and agreed upon by those who will make the selection decision.

Since objectives will vary with project scope, they will be defined once for selecting a general location in Phase II and then be redefined in Phase III for selecting a specific site.

Identify relevant factors and criteria Policy statements are fine for guidance but generally are insufficient for comparing communities and sites. They must be further *specified* for comparing sites. To accomplish this, one or more selection factors must be identified for each objective.

In Fig. 2, "high visibility" is an objective, important for public relations purposes. If visibility of sites is to be compared meaningfully, then the planner must define visibility in a way that permits measurement. This is done by establishing a selection factor and corresponding criterion, preferably at the same time the objective is defined. In the case of visibility, main frontage traffic volume is the factor. Volume is obviously to be maximized.

If the objective is low development cost, the factors might be low land cost per acre and low construction costs per square foot. The criterion would be minimization in each case.

If the objective is actually a constraint, such as adequate gas supply, and the factor is 9 million cubic feet per month, the criterion would simply be satisfaction. To discriminate further among sites having 9 million cubic feet, an additional factor could be added, such as frequency of service interruption. Minimization would be the criterion.

Planners having difficulty translating management's objectives into relevant factors

	OBJECTIVES	FACTORS	CRITERIA
PHASE II	Low labor cost	Average hourly wages (by category)	Minimize
	Adequate labor supply	Manufacturing workers in commuting radius	Maximize
	Adequate community services	Full-time fire department	Satisfy
	Mild climate	Degree days	Minimize
PHASE III	High visibility	Main frontage traffic volume	Maximize
	Adequate gas supply	9,000 mcf*/month	Satisfy
	Proximity to labor	Average commuting time from suburban communities	Minimize
	Proximity to utilities	Distance to city water	Minimize
		Distance to nearest sub-station	Minimize

* 1,000 cu ft

Fig. 2 Site specifications. *(Courtesy of Richard Muther & Associates. All rights reserved.)*

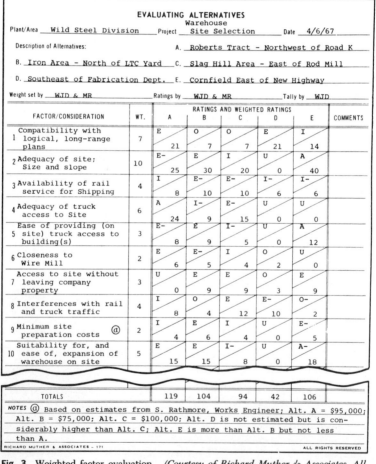

Fig. 3 Weighted factor evaluation. *(Courtesy of Richard Muther & Associates. All rights reserved.)*

should turn to published checklists of site selection factors. Two of the most comprehensive ones are listed in the references at the end of this chapter.

Economic comparisons   The most appealing approach to site selection is simply to identify the development and operating costs at each potential site and select the one with greatest return. This is easier said than done and is usually restricted to the regional or community level of analysis. Economic comparisons at the site level are often meaningless where functional characteristics (access, proximity to work force, etc.) can be far more important than tangible costs. It is not unusual even at the regional level to find little variation in total operating costs, requiring that the decision be made on the basis of functional characteristics.

Still, wherever possible, planners should address economic objectives and their factors with return-on-investment analyses or projected profit-and-loss statements. If economic justification was part of the business planning, the model used should be left intact and the search devoted to gathering appropriate cost data for each prospective site.

Cost data can be very time-consuming to generate and are subject to rapid decay. A number of detailed internal studies will be required from participating managers. The effort involved makes it all the more important to fix objectives and factors early in the project. Significant changes in plans and objectives will render cost data useless and set the project back a considerable amount of time and money.

Weighted factor comparisons   Where cost data are incomplete or unavailable and where functional characteristics are of great importance, the weighted factor method of selection can be extremely useful. An example is shown in Fig. 3. This approach is often used with a concurrent economic appraisal. The following steps are suggested for Phase II or III comparisons.

Evaluating Description	Letter	
		Value
Almost perfect results (excellent)	A	4
Especially good results (very good)	E	3
Important results (good)	I	2
Ordinary results (fair)	O	1
Unimportant results (poor)	U	0
Not acceptable results (not satisfactory)	X	?

Fig. 4 Vowel letter rating scale. *(Courtesy of Richard Muther & Associates. All rights reserved.)*

1. Develop business plan and define objectives.

2. Identify relevant factors and criteria.

3. Assign a relative importance to each factor, giving the most important one(s) a weight of 10 and weighing remaining factors on a scale of 1 to 10.

4. Obtain approval of objectives, factors, and weights from those who will make or approve the selection decision.

5. Compare contending locations and sites by rating them on each factor. Evaluate all sites on one factor at a time, using the A, E, I, O, U, X scale shown in Fig. 4.

6. After rating, convert letters to numerical values and multiply by factor weights. Total the resulting values for each site and made a numerical comparison. Because all values are relative, a clear choice should have a 20 percent advantage over its closest competition.

7. If there is no clear favorite, the top two or three may be reevaluated with other persons, with additional factors, or with different weights.

Comparisons are subjective   Use of a formal procedure and numerical values should not obscure the fact that the weighted factor method merely aids in making a series of subjective decisions. Many factors will not be quantitative, calling for little more than educated guesses on a particular site's performance.

Internal consistency   When using a large number of factors, there is a tendency to lose sight of the relative importance originally placed on the objectives. This is particularly true when using long checklists of site selection factors.

Consider, for example, proximity to labor force to be twice as important as adequate community facilities (schools, churches, etc.). If ten factors are used for measuring adequacy of facilities and only two for measuring proximity to labor, then care must be taken in assigning weights to ensure that community facilities do not overly influence the outcome.

Importance of fixed objectives   Minor changes in objectives and specifications can be accommodated and are to be expected from feedback during the search and from facility planning that may be proceeding concurrently. However, if objectives change significantly, the project will have to be terminated and begun again in a new direction.

Obviously a site suitable for a machine shop may not accommodate a foundry. If only 200 workers are needed, a large community that can supply 1,000 workers may not be as suitable as a smaller one. In short, Phase I must be completed before a community and site can be selected in Phases II and III.

PHASE II: SELECTING A GENERAL LOCATION

Common objectives   No two location projects will have exactly the same objectives or define shared ones in quite the same way. Still there are some commonly occurring objectives around which most general location searches are organized. Not surprisingly, these are primarily economic, because nearly all operating costs vary with location. Also present in every project are objectives relating to local resources, that is, specifications that must be met if the plant is to operate at all.

A few of the most commonly occurring objectives are listed below, along with typical factors for each. The list is by no means complete and order of appearance is not significant. The checklists cited in the bibliography at the end of this chapter contain exhaustive lists of selection factors for each objective.

1. *Low material supply cost.* When raw materials are expensive to transport and store or when prices vary geographically, supply costs can be critical. Typical factors include:

- Cost per unit of raw material
- Annual inbound freight costs

2. *Low distribution cost.* Unless material suppliers and the market center are in the same location, managers must balance the desire for low supply cost against the desire for low distribution cost. Typical factors include:

- Delivered cost per unit of finished product
- Annual outbound freight costs

3. *Low labor cost.* When products are labor intensive, low labor cost can be the most important project objective. No single factor is adequate to compare labor costs. Conclusions are generally based on annual labor costs or labor cost per unit, synthesized from the following:

- Wages by occupation (starting, median, top)
- Fringe benefits
- Average work week and local holidays
- Overtime compensation

4. *Adequate labor supply.* Available labor is either adequate or inadequate, with conclusions usually based on quantity available and productivity. Typical factors include (by skill or occupational group):

- Potential workers within commuting distance
- Unemployment rates
- Absenteeism
- Turnover
- Strike history and potential

5. *Adequate utility service.* Availability in desired quantities exists or does not. The quality of what is available can be evaluated by measuring the following factors:

- Interruptions in service
- Rates or charges
- For water, hardness and chemical composition
- For gas, Btu value

6. *Low taxation.* When all other costs are comparable, taxation can become the deciding variable. State income taxes can be significant and differ not only in rate but in definition of taxable income. Typical tax factors to evaluate include:

- Corporate and personal income taxes
- Sales, use, or payroll taxes
- Unemployment compensation taxes
- Workmen's compensation taxes
- Property taxes
- Franchise and other taxes and fees
- Local taxes (and inducements)

7. *Adequate community services and facilities.* These are intangibles but are often as important as operating costs. Factors to be measured are the *availability, quality, and cost* of those services and facilities needed. These might include:

- Business services
- Education facilities
- Recreation facilities
- Medical facilities
- Police and fire protection

8. *Adequate transportation service.* Aside from supply and distribution costs, certain levels of service may be essential to the operation of the plant. Factors to be measured include (by transport mode):

- Transit times to or from particular cities
- Delivery schedules
- Number of lines available
- Special services available

9. *Mild climate.* When outside space will be used to store or assemble, or when temperature and humidity must be controlled inside, mild climate is important. Typical factors include:

- Degree days by month
- Number of clear days
- Average monthly temperatures
- Average monthly humidity

10. *Freedom from regulation.* The extent to which incorporation, employment, use of the environment, and other actions are regulated varies by location and can have impact on the cost and level of activity permitted. Typical factors to consider would include:

- Right-to-work laws
- Collective bargaining laws
- Health laws
- Incorporation laws
- Cost of required pollution controls

11. *Availability of suitable sites.* While it is rare to find no suitable sites, it is wise to check contending communities before selecting the general location.

Conducting the search The value of clearly defining objectives and factors in Phase I becomes readily apparent once the search begins. Contacts with industrial development officials can generate a flood of statistics. Much of this information will be of little value in reaching a decision. With factors in hand, the analyst can proceed directly to extract only what is needed.

There are professionals ready to help at any level of search activity—state, regional, or local. Utilities, railroads, and industrial realtors also offer search assistance. It must be kept in mind, though, that each of these sources of assistance will also be trying to "sell" a particular area along with presenting facts about it.

The search process can be expedited by working "down," from assistance first at the state and regional level to assistance from local chambers of commerce and industrial realtors once the top one or two communities have been identified.

PHASE III: SELECTING A SITE

Common objectives At the site level, physical characteristics and relationships with surroundings are more important than economics. Most companies desire the same general characteristics, resulting in a fairly commonly occurring set of objectives and selection factors. The most common of these are listed below. Note the way in which objectives concerning labor, utility, local services, and others have been redefined from Phase II, for use here in selecting a specific site.

1. *Proximity to labor force.* A site may not be able to attract and retain workers if it must compete with others in locations closer to the center of the working population. A costly result can be the need for higher wages than would have been necessary in a better location. The factor typically measured is commuting time.

2. *Proximity to utility service.* The distance to the nearest lines can significantly influence site development costs and time, and time can often be measured in lost sales and market share. Delays can be lengthy if utility companies must order special equipment to extend service. Factors most commonly measured are distances and costs for each service required.

3. *Proximity to community services and facilities.* Not only is closeness important for services such as police and fire protection but also for such commercial services as motels and restaurants. Typical factors include response time (for police and fire) and driving time (for other services and facilities).

4. *Adequate site size.* One hopes that the specifications developed in Phase I will properly identify the amount of space required. All that remains in this, Phase III, is to ensure that this amount is actually available. The selection factor should be *usable area*, which will be a function of topography, soil conditions, easements, and the like.

5. *Adequate soil strength.* Where heavy construction is contemplated, adequate soil strength becomes a constraint. Even in the absence of building designs and firm load data, soil strengths should be evaluated carefully to avoid sites that may require expensive soil preparation and special footings. Soil bearing strength is the common factor for this selection objective.

6. *Adequate drainage.* Grading and special construction to ensure proper drainage can be costly, particularly where yard space is to be heavily utilized. Sites are usually compared using the cost of drainage-related improvements as a factor.

7. *Compatibility with surroundings.* With the general trend toward more restrictive land-use controls, compatibility with the immediate area of a site becomes important. This can be checked on a long-term basis by comparing the intended uses of the site with those projected for it in the community's comprehensive plan.

8. *Freedom from regulations.* While regulations cannot be avoided, their likely effects can be evaluated and compared among contending sites. The factor to be measured is the attitude (favorable or unfavorable) of each body having jurisdiction over the site and its intended use.

9. *Frequency of transport service.* Pickup and delivery frequency can vary greatly among sites within the same general area. This is particularly true for rail service and also for mass transit. Factors are usually defined in terms of pickups, deliveries or stops per day, per week, and so on.

10. *Accessibility.* Some sites may require costly and time-consuming improvements to get workers and transport equipment onto and off the site effectively. Such improvements might include grade crossings, highway access, intersection controls, and the like. The cost of needed improvements is the most commonly defined factor for accessibility.

11. *Low taxation.* Property taxes can vary greatly within a local area. These should be ascertained for each site and compared using an annual cost factor.

12. *Low site preparation cost.* Aside from improvements for drainage and soil strength, there can be varying costs for clearing a site of existing structures or vegetation. These are normally evaluated on a cost-per-acre basis.

13. *Ease of future expansion.* What is the likely future use and ownership of neighboring property? Is the site "boxed in" or expandable through future acquisitions? Sites may be compared on these issues with a factor such as future availability of neighboring property.

14. *Low land cost.* The purchase price of a site is often overemphasized in relation to total development costs. Still, it is an important variable at the local level, typically measured in dollars per acre.

Conducting the search   Search activity during Phase II—general location—will have assured that at least one site is available in the local area. If it satisfies all site objectives, there may be no need to look further. If the area selected in Phase II is small, there may be no more than one site available.

The same sources of assistance used in finding a general location can be used to find specific sites, usually with more use made of local development officials and realtors.

Once the search has been narrowed to the one or two most promising sites, top management should make visits to each. If the owner will give an option at a reasonable price, it should be taken as soon as top management reaches a decision. If not, negotiations for purchase should begin in order to ensure that the site will be available at a reasonable price.

If land price is subject to increase with the owner's knowledge of interest in it, secrecy should be maintained as long as possible. In any event, local publicity should be withheld until Phase IV—procurement—when purchase or occupancy is reasonably certain.

PHASE IV: PROCURING A SITE

Some overtures will have been made during Phase III toward purchase or lease of the most attractive site(s). These may have been in the form of options or rights of first refusal. Or perhaps contacts were merely established through a realtor and prices ascertained. In Phase IV, final negotiations will be conducted for purchase or lease of the most attractive site. Closing must be preceded by the following procurement activities:

- Final review of all restrictions on site use
- Preliminary review of plans with all permit-granting authorities
- Development of financing plans and approval by top management
- Final soil testing

An option may be retained on a second-choice site throughout this period, as insurance against unforeseen problems with the first choice.

PITFALLS IN FINDING NEW SITES

Site selection is a relatively infrequent activity for most companies. Consequently, few managers in a project will have had the benefit of prior search experience. A brief review of the common oversights and mistakes listed below can be instructive for those confronting a search project for the first time.

1. *Failure to specify what is needed.* Many planners operating on a crash program basis begin collecting information, contacting officials, and visiting communities without a specific list of needs (objectives, factors, and criteria). As a consequence, much time is wasted, and these planners are unable to make convincing recommendations to management.

2. *Misunderstanding of cost relationships.* Often occurring in Phase I, this pitfall can result in improper choice of objectives and overemphasis on unimportant variables.

3. *Misunderstanding taxation.* The ratio of business activity within a state to total national business activity plays a major role in determining state income tax payments. Comparisons based on application rates alone can be very misleading. Overlooking differences in payroll and unemployment compensation taxes can also result in costly decisions.

4. *Overestimation of labor supply.* Watch out for differences in commuting patterns, since these define the total labor market. Within the market area, those available and seeking work may not be acceptable for reasons of skill and productivity. There may also be other companies moving in or expanding nearby, competing for the available labor.

5. *Improper estimation of labor cost.* Labor cost comparisions should be based only upon the wages that will apply to the operation in question. These might be the local average for the industry involved or the dominant wage for the area regardless of industry. Fringe benefits, holidays, sick leave, and other expenses should also be added in when comparing labor costs.

6. *Failure to identify local land-use and growth patterns.* The intended use of the site should be compatible with the long-term use of the immediately surrounding area. When use is incompatible, there is a risk that regulations will restrict the future uses of the site.

7. *Purchasing too small a site.* One of the most common site selection failures is purchasing a site too small to permit unforeseen expansion of facilities. This failure can result from:

- Overlooking yard space requirements
- Underestimating plant space requirements
- Overlooking unusable portions of sites
- Failing to anticipate company growth
- Skimping because of land costs (often less than 5 percent of total investment)
- Having no idea of an ideal plant arrangement

8. *Failure to look long range.* Some companies have located in areas that soon after proved to be overindustrialized. The consequences of failing to spot this trend can be increased competition for labor, congestion in the site area, competition for utilities, and blocked expansions. On the other hand, some companies have located in relatively undeveloped areas only to find that their own long-range growth exceeded the labor supply and utility capacities.

9. *Overlooking impact of environmental regulations.* Restrictions and therefore pollution-control costs can vary greatly from site to site even within one local area. Regulations are subject to change with deterioration in air and water quality. Be sure to check the attitude of the citizenry and local activist groups regarding potential changes in regulations. Also look for any general trend toward further urbanization or industrialization that might result in future restrictions.

10. *Underestimating adequacy of support services.* Often in small communities and even in some large ones, specialized services in such areas as machining, plating, equipment repair, hardware, and parts are limited or unavailable. Inadequacies in these areas increase downtime and indirectly require greater supply storage and operating costs.

11. *Underestimating moving costs.* The costs of moving equipment, inventories, and personnel are often overlooked completely. These can vary with location and should be included in all development expense estimates.

12. *Overlooking quality of life.* In spite of the many checklists on community quality, such factors are often overlooked or given scant consideration. The result can be a site location that is unattractive to both managers and workers, hampering recruitment and long-term development of the site.

13. *Incomplete soil tests.* A common source of development cost overruns is unforeseen subsoil conditions. The cost of complete testing is insignificant in comparison with the cost of redesign and lost production through delayed construction.

14. *Looking for specific sites too soon.* The tendency on many projects is to look for sites as soon as possible, usually concurrently with the search for a general location. This tendency has a number of undesirable effects. First, it wastes valuable time and money, since many of the communities will be discarded. Second, it can create ill will and rumor by indicating more interest in a community than really exists. Third, even in the chosen location, it increases the chances of land values increasing before negotiations are opened. Finally, if the project is confidential, looking for sites too soon risks undesirable publicity early in the search.

REFERENCES

1. "Checklist of Site Selection Factors," *Site Selection Handbook,* Conway Research, Atlanta, Ga., annually.
2. "Industrial Site Selection Today," *Factory,* May 1968.
3. M. J. Newbourne and Colin Barrett: *Guide to Industrial Site Selection,* The Traffic Service Corporation, Washington, D.C., 1971.
4. "Plant Site Selection Guide," *Factory Management and Maintenance,* May 1957 (includes lengthy checklist).
5. Leonard C. Yaseen: *Plant Location,* American Research Council, Larchmont, N.Y., 1960.
6. Leonard C. Yaseen: "Site Selection," in H. B. Maynard (ed.), *Industrial Engineering Handbook,* McGraw-Hill Book Company, New York, 1971.

Time Phasing of Project Elements

CHARLES H. LUDLUM, P.E.
Manager of Engineering Reports, The Austin Company

INTRODUCTION

The many varieties of facilities planning projects handled by the plant engineer defy description. However, by far the most interesting and time-consuming is that for a new plant on a new site. All the plant engineer's talents and experience must be brought to bear on the topic. Planning must be in depth, accurate, and—many times—accomplished in an extremely efficient manner to permit plant completion at an early date. The essence of efficient execution is scheduling. Without a schedule, progress cannot be measured and resources cannot be allocated with certainty.

Whether the assignment is a new facility, an addition to an existing facility, or a renovation of an existing plant—regardless of physical size—all the project elements are present. The precise content of each element will vary with the scope of the individual project. Obviously, a renovation project would not include an analysis of a new site.

Project elements There are four well-defined elements in all projects:

1. Setting criteria. This consists of establishing the guidelines for project scope. It is a process of translating the project requirements into physical dimensions and parameters.

2. Planning. Those actions which, based upon the criteria, define the physical aspects of a project.

3. Implementation. The engineering, construction, relocation, etc., required to produce the physical aspects of a project.

4. Postmortem.   An evaluation and documentation of an entire project from initiation through completion.   This would cover completion vs. schedule, cost vs. estimates, and the like.

Each of these elements, stated above in the most general terms, contains a myriad of subelements.   These have been covered in depth elsewhere in this handbook and will be treated here only as it is necessary to establish a basis for time requirements and time phasing for a project.

Time requirements and time phasing   The four project elements are generally carried out in a sequential manner.   Except for criteria, each is dependent upon the substantial completion of the preceding.   As a part of the discussion of the element components, the time required to complete the work is assessed.   The time phasing of the components within the elements is reviewed as well as the phasing of the elements in the project.

Figure 1 shows an elemental project schedule, which indicates the total project time and the relative proportion of that time consumed by each individual element.   It indicates that the entire project will require 25 months from initiation to completion and that planning and design efforts will require at least 6 months before actual construction can start.

As each element is examined, simplified bar graphs are used to illustrate the relationships of the primary components.   They also indicate the options available to the project manager and the various conditions met in practice.

Recently, as an aid to scheduling, techniques and equipment have been developed which permit the project manager to exercise greater control than had previously been possible.   Before any of these can be adapted effectively, it is essential that the project elements and the time required for their execution be thoroughly understood.

Time (months)	1	2	3	4	5	6	7	8	9	10	11	12	13	14	15	16	17	18	19	20	21	22	23	24	25	26	27	28	29	30	31	32	33	34
Criteria																																		
Planning																																		
Implementation																																		
Post mortem																																		

Fig. 1   Elemental project schedule.

It is not possible to cover every eventuality or all types of projects in a discussion of this subject.   Each project is different and requires an analysis of its scope before an overall schedule or a detailed schedule can be prepared.

The intent of this chapter is to establish the primary elements and provide a framework which can be utilized by the project manager as a basis for consideration of his project.

For the purpose of continuity, the examples given in this chapter are based upon the development of a multimillion-dollar facility to be constructed on a new site and involving complete relocation of equipment from the existing facility.

CRITERIA

Analysis of requirements   All facilities planning projects are initiated by a need for more production capacity, improved productivity, relocated production, or a different type of production.   Frequently, combinations of these comprise the project.

The requirements as presented to the planner are often ambiguous and set forth in such terms as "units of product per unit of time" or possibly a statement that a new plant is desired for the production of specific products at a location determined by a marketing study.   Often the requirement is predicated on completion by a certain date in the future.

Operational criteria   These are well-defined dimensions and parameters for planning, not generalities.   In the instance of a new plant, on a new site, for the production of a specific volume of related products, the following must be established:

1. A table must be prepared defining the desired volume of product per unit of time by size, type, and model designation.   Preferably this should be compiled on a monthly basis.

2. A fundamental decision should be made regarding manufacturing processes.   It should be established that the existing types of machines or machine tools will be installed

or that acceptable or desired variations from current practice will be employed. As a result of these determinations, route sheets should be prepared and identified as a firm basis for production operations on prime products.

3. Generalized data should be prepared regarding utilities and other specific criteria. Estimated quantities and qualities should be outlined for each item.

4. Total personnel needs of the facility should be evaluated. Should the planning be based upon one, two, or three shifts?

5. A firm statement should be formulated regarding the disposition of existing property and buildings as well as obsolete machine tools and equipment.

Locational criteria   If a new location is a part of the project, locational criteria must be established. These will bear on markets, material sources, labor availability, communities, and the like.

This analysis can be started nearly as soon as the project is initiated. Whether prepared in house or by qualified consultants, it can range from cursory examination of potential areas to exhaustive analyses consuming great blocks of time. On the average project, one should allocate about one or two months for this purpose.

Project outline   During this step an outline should be prepared delineating the remaining elements of the project. This outline should include the clear definition of each element and should state by whom it will be accomplished.

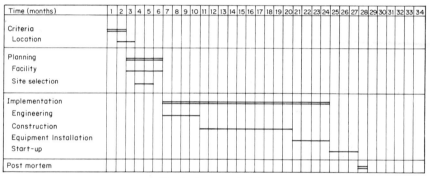

Fig. 2   Project schedule.

If personnel are not readily available within the plant engineering department, the project manager should include recommendations regarding assignment of plant personnel by name or by category, acquisition of personnel to augment the staff, or the use of consultants experienced in the performance of certain portions of the work.

Budget estimates should be generated covering all aspects of the remaining elements: planning, implementation, and postmortem.

In addition, a schedule should be prepared for the entire project. This need not be complex at this point in the project, but it must be accurate and capable of execution. A simple bar graph such as Fig. 2 will set forth each major item and the time allocated for its accomplishment.

Documentation   All the above should be prepared in written and graphic form and submitted for approval and/or comments. This documentation, when approved, will serve as a scope-of-work statement throughout the life of the project.

Time requirements   The time required for the determination of criteria will be dependent upon many factors beyond the detail work required to translate requirements into criteria. The extent of industrial engineering assistance available and the accessibility of other management representatives, such as sales and production, will certainly affect the time span. A most important factor is whether the personnel assigned to the project are able to devote full time to such work or are expected to carry out these duties along with their normal work load.

In the instance of a substantial project, it is advisable to assign individuals on a full-time basis with clear-cut responsibilities for project accomplishment. If personnel are not

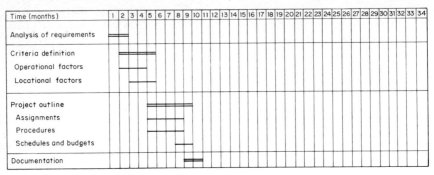

Fig. 3   Criteria determination schedule.

readily available, it would be prudent to obtain the services of a qualified consultant.

It is not unusual for the criteria determination for a large project at a new location to require several months for its accomplishment. Rarely will it be completed in less than one month. Figure 3 sets forth the relationship of the primary actions of criteria determination. It illustrates the sequence normally met in such work.

Occasionally the project manager is not required to produce the criteria, these having been established in appropriate form by management. The project manager's assignment is then limited to the preparation of the project outline.

PLANNING

Scope   As this element of the project contains both investigation and preliminary engineering, care must be taken in directing this work to establish the extent of these activities. The decisions made during planning will affect the character of the facility, its initial cost, and its effectiveness as a production tool. Clearly, this is not the time for detailed engineering, nor is it the time for "shooting from the hip."

It is extremely difficult to precisely define the magnitude of engineering which must be performed. Certain facets will require much analysis while others can be established with minimal effort.

For instance, it is essential that the production equipment be properly calculated to determine the number of machine tools required, as this affects the facility size; yet it is not necessary at this time to go beyond a general description of the building type and configuration.

It is vital that planning receive adequate consideration in the preparation of the project schedule. However, this element must be carefully supervised so that detail-minded engineers do not carry their investigation into the realm of final engineering before reaching a decision.

Collection of pertinent data   The development of a new plant for the production of related products will entail the following steps:

1. An analysis of the existing plant, department by department, covering
    a. Floor space utilization by department and function.
    b. A review of the flow of materials and sequence of operations
    c. Machine tools and equipment:
      ● Machine tools for each operation
      ● Operator data
      ● Ancillary equipment
      ● Utilities of machine or process
      ● Alternative utilities
      ● Materials handling methods and equipment
      ● Inadequacies, if any, of the existing workplace and methods

2. Examination of engineering standards and other records to permit establishment of the equipment needs for the required volumes of product

3. All data relating to the material and products handled, such as physical volume, weight, etc., at the various stages of production

4. Pertinent data relative to new processes, equipment, and machine tools likely to be considered for the new facility

5. Documentation of nonmanufacturing items like:

   a. Personnel needs and conveniences

   b. Training facilities

   c. Administrative areas

   d. R&D or experimental areas

Analysis   A preliminary evaluation of the data in relation to the criteria will, in most instances, provide an approximate number of tools, equipment, and the like. This, with the use of appropriate conversion factors, will reveal:

- Approximate facility size
- Approximate personnel needs and shifts
- Approximate utility and service needs

Based upon these, a generalized description of the required building site can be prepared, criteria established, and site studies begun.

The site studies will consist of an examination of the preferred location for suitable sites and the evaluation of each of these with respect to all the criteria.

When a specific site has been selected, it should be examined in depth, possibly during an option or escrow period. This examination should include such factors as:

- Surveys, both boundary and topographic
- Soil borings and analysis
- Easements, zoning restrictions, etc., affecting the use of the site
- Availability of utilities and services

Facility development   The second step in planning consists of in-depth industrial engineering studies, calculations, preparation of layouts, and possibly even the construction of a model. These actions define, substantiate, and delineate the project.

Alternative schemes should be prepared and examined in terms of maximum operational efficiency, flexibility, expandability, and both operational and initial cost. These systematic comparisons lead to the selection of a concept for further development.

The results of the development of the approved scheme will include:

1. A detailed floor-plan layout of the facility should indicate machines and equipment and the location of receiving, shipping, warehousing, employee conveniences, offices, and all the ancillary items needed for a complete facility.

2. Services and utility data should be complete and the location of all mains, both electrical and mechanical, should be established along with their capacity. Any special requirements should be delineated.

3. The facility should be illustrated defining the flow of materials, architectural configuration, structural considerations, and similar factors.

4. Presumably, at this point the site selection work will be completed and the facility can be presented on the site showing orientation, access, services, site coverage, parking, and the like.

5. A detailed budget estimate is essential. It should include all the expenditures necessary for the completion of the project, including:

   a. Site acquisition

   b. Engineering

   c. Building construction

   d. Equipment relocation and installation

   e. Startup

   f. Employee relocation allowances

   g. Hiring and training costs

6. Implementation of the project should be detailed and scheduled. All remaining steps to project completion should be incorporated, with recommendations or decisions regarding the procedures to be employed for their execution.

Documentation   All the above should be documented appropriately for presentation. The report may take any of several forms, depending upon the review and approval channels of the particular firm. However, it should contain the following:

1. Requirements for the project—sales projections, new product, or whatever has caused the need

2. An analysis of the space, personnel, and machines, etc., required to fulfill the requirements

   3. A review of the various alternatives considered

   4. A description of the recommended project

   5. Implementation data—schedules and costs

Time requirements   The time period for the collection of data generally falls at either of the extremes. If data are readily available in appropriate form in house, this should not take longer than a few weeks. However, if the information is not available and must be generated, several months may be needed for this effort. It is recommended, as a time-saving measure, that during the criteria development stage the appropriate people be informed of the desire for specific data. If it is not readily available, its preparation should be initiated immediately. Presuming an average condition, one should assume about a month for the collection of pertinent data.

Figure 4 illustrates the relationship of the primary elements of planning. Note that site studies were started when the site criteria could be defined, and that they were completed so that the facility could be developed on the basis of a specific site.

The time consumed by site analysis is nearly impossible to define with any degree of accuracy unless a specific situation is considered. Experience indicates that it rarely can be completed in less than 2 months.

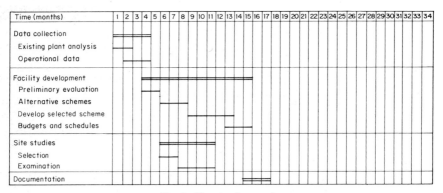

Fig. 4 Planning bar graph.

The scope of analysis and development can be very time-consuming. Usually it will require at least two or three months. Often it is a coordinating process of the efforts of consultants and/or other departments within the firm for the accomplishment of certain specialized activities.

To this point we have consumed about a month for criteria, the first element, and—say—4 months for planning, the second element: a total of about 5 months. However, the project is defined and the steps to its execution are clear.

IMPLEMENTATION

This phase covers engineering, facility construction, installation of the equipment, and startup. In essence this is the physical execution of the project.

Engineering   This includes the layouts, the calculations to size the equipment and services, the architectural and structural design of the facility, and the illustration of all of these in graphic and written form. The end product—working drawings and specifications—must be such that persons unfamiliar with the operations can fully understand the facility and be able to purchase the materials and physically construct it. The results of the engineering work may consist of up to 200 drawings, 300 to 400 pages of detailed specifications, and a carefully prepared project estimate.

The conclusions and decisions reached during the planning phase will be confirmed and quantified during engineering. Often recent marketing conditions or new equipment will modify conclusions reached during the planning work. Also, physical constraints of architecture or structure may cause deviations from previous decisions.

There must be constant reviews during engineering due to the number of persons involved in the project. The team may consist of up to four or five firms as well as representatives of other departments within the company. These reviews will maintain unanimity of purpose and assure accuracy of end product.

It is advisable to schedule at least three milestones during the performance of this work for review of the overall project budget. Preferably these are at the one-third point, the two-thirds point, and at the completion. Any deviations which may have taken place can be substantiated or adjustments can be made to keep the budget in line with previous concepts.

The engineering work may be done in house, by an organization which offers complete service, by an architectural and engineering firm, or by a group of specialized consultants. All of these require varying degrees of supervision by the project manager.

The time factor will vary considerably depending upon one's choice of procedure. If one can assume that the engineering for a substantial project can be completed in about 5 to 6 months at a normal pace, it is reasonable to believe that this might be reduced to about 3 months to permit an accelerated program.

At the conclusion of the engineering work, and based upon the construction documents and cost estimates, approval will probably be required from management. When this has been secured, construction and installation work can proceed.

Building construction   Physically this consists of the site preparation work, substructure, superstructure—the "bricks and mortar"—plus the mechanical and electrical services.

The scheduling of this work is complex, since many parties must be consulted and their work coordinated. Much has been written concerning construction scheduling and very sophisticated techniques such as CPM and PERT have been developed. It is not the purpose of this chapter to examine these techniques except as they affect the overall project phasing.

It is nearly impossible to generalize concerning the time required for building construction. A medium-sized manufacturing building will require nearly as long to build as a very large manufacturing building due to the necessity to place orders for material, schedule the various parts of the work, and such other aspects. Probably a minimum of 12 to 14 months is a practical range for most facilities, regardless of size. For the purposes of discussing time phasing, 10 months has been assumed.

Equipment installation   That part of the scheduling which directly involves the project manager is the equipment relocation and its reinstallation at the new facility. Inherent in this scheduling is the need to minimize equipment downtime and consequent loss of production. It is imperative that production control, manufacturing engineering, and management be made a part of the program and that, once a procedure is established, it be rigidly adhered to. Due to production requirements and the effort to reduce the overall effect on output, equipment relocation may consume many months.

Various procedures have been utilized to decrease production interferences. For example, it is often helpful to:
- Relocate department by department—starting with warehousing and shipping
- Relocate specific tools or equipment, retaining similar items in operation at the existing plant
- Shut down the existing plant and institute a "crash" relocation.

The choice is dependent upon the type of operation being relocated, whether or not duplicate machine tools and equipment are available, and—occasionally—upon the type of product. A seasonal product, for instance, may experience no difficulty in utilizing the crash program. As the variables are so numerous, it will be assumed that the equipment installation requires four months.

Start-up   The startup portion of the work, covering the running in of the machines, training of new personnel, implementation of the production control procedures, and the like, will follow the equipment installation. Its duration varies considerably and depends upon the complexity of operations. Some firms experience startup for as much as 6 months to a year and others can be said to be running relatively smoothly in as little as a month. An average condition might be 3 months.

Time phasing   There are a number of methods which may be utilized for the performance of the work. A general contractor may be selected by negotiation or by competitive bidding. Complete service may have been elected at an early stage. Independent contractors may be chosen for their specialities and coordinated by the project manager, or

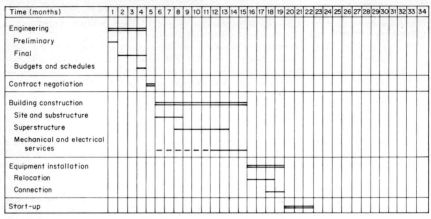

Fig. 5   Implementation bar graph.

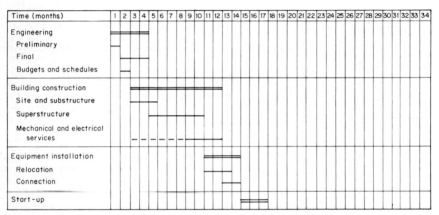

Fig. 6   Alternative implementation bar graph.

the manager may prefer to use in-house personnel for portions of the project. Often the basic building is constructed under one arrangement and another is used for equipment installation and hookup.

Figure 5 shows time phasing for the implementation element. It sets forth the various facets of the work as they might be carried out on a typical project. For comparison, Fig. 6 shows a time phasing for implementation which would be typical for a complete service or negotiated arrangement. The engineering and construction are telescoped, indicating a reduction in implementation of 5 months.

The time factor in each of those can be further improved if the equipment is new rather than relocated. If new, it can be installed concurrently with the facility construction, since the overall productive capacity, considering both plants, will not be affected by unforeseen delays in the new plant construction.

POSTMORTEM

Scope   The scope of the post mortem covers:

1. An evaluation of each step of the project with respect to effectiveness, schedule, and cost. This will include candid statements setting forth what might have been done differently. Hindsight is considerably better than foresight.

2. A realistic tabulation of all the costs associated with the project. This is particularly valuable for accounting purposes. Include the cost of in-house personnel, whose time often is not directly allocated to the project.

3. Documentation. Arrange for operating and installation manuals, in duplicate as a minimum, for all items of equipment. Be sure that all drawings have been adjusted to reflect "as-built" conditions, including any startup modifications, and obtain reproducibles for file storage and prints for day-to-day use. Take steps to see that all pertinent correspondence is identified and properly filed.

4. Prepare a completion report to management containing a recapitulation of the project evaluation and a cost tabulation, and spell out the location of the project documents.

For those frequently engaged in facilities planning, the postmortem can be extremely valuable. Many lessons will have been learned during the course of the project. If recorded, they can be a source of information for the next project.

Time requirements This phase will require a very short time and probably will be performed by a few people on a part-time basis.

The knowledge that a postmortem will be a part of the project scope will permit preparation, during the preceding phases, of the necessary information by the persons and organizations involved.

It is well to indicate at least a month for its accomplishment and to insist that it be completed within that period of time.

PROJECT TIME PHASING

Two schedules have been prepared for a typical project—assumed to be a facility of about 300,000 square feet in size—a metal working operation to be relocated from an obsolete facility. The upper portion of Fig. 7 represents the conventional consecutive method of facility planning and acquisition. The lower portion sets forth an accelerated program which is possible under negotiated or complete service agreements. Note that while a time savings of up to 6 months is possible in the overall project duration, the criteria and planning elements remain ostensibly the same.

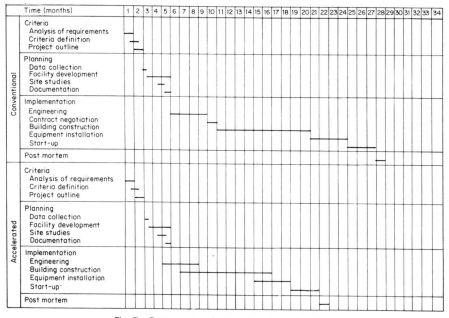

Fig. 7 Comparative schedules for a typical project.

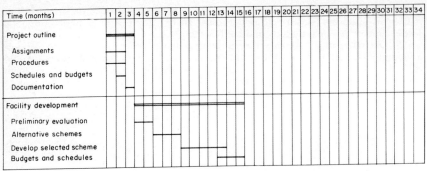

Fig. 8 Alternative criteria and planning bar graph.

Variations The overall project time phasing can and does vary from those examples discussed previously. For example, the site may have been selected prior to the initiation of the project. All investigative work may have been completed, and the project will be based upon utilization of that site.

It is also entirely possible that no existing plant is involved. The project may be based on pilot-plant data or upon an industrial engineering feasibility study. In these instances, the criteria having been established, several steps in the initial elements can be deleted. Figure 8 illustrates such a circumstance. Note that while the time needed for criteria is diminished, planning is affected only by the elimination of the data collection step.

Small projects, such as a minor addition to an existing building or a small outbuilding, will require the employment of all the project elements. Obviously, these elements will not be well defined nor will they require a great deal of time for their execution. Perhaps the time periods will be weeks or days rather than months.

It is well to consider that each facility project, no matter how small, requires the application of the procedure and documentation described in this chapter.

Section 3

Engineering and Construction Management

Chapter **1**

Defining the Scope of the Project

JOHN M. CONNELLY, P.E.
Director of Corporate Facilities Engineering, The Black and Decker Manufacturing Company

INTRODUCTION

Defining the scope of any construction project is critical to the success of that project. Stating your company's requirements in a thorough and precise fashion will result in savings in both time and money. More importantly, it will be the major factor in your receiving the facility that reflects your specific requirements. However, the author of any project description must not be guilty of "tunnel vision." A proper description will honor the requirements of all pertinent departments: personnel, production, maintenance, security, quality control, etc.

The best time to assemble the components of the scope of the project is at that stage of in-house preplanning when the 3- or 5-year production forecast for the new facility has been determined. With this knowledge, the plant engineer will be in a position to coordinate many detailed requirements. Industrial engineering, using the marketing forecast from which the design manufacturing capacity is determined, can furnish details of production equipment. A tentative plant layout can then be prepared. Bay sizes are not important at this stage, but a popular spacing should be utilized. Some common spacings are 30 × 40, 40 × 40, and 40 × 60 feet. When optimum materials handling and process flow have been determined, the plant configuration will begin to take shape. Knowing production equipment requirements is the key, not only to utilities needs but also to quantities of people. This opens the door to office and social area requirements. Outside consultants can give valuable assistance in any or all of the foregoing, and the degree of their utilization will depend upon the extent of your company's in-house capability.

The scope of the project, when completed, will be the basic information package utilized by the building design professionals in their preparation of preliminary plans and specifications. Depending upon the completeness of the package, it may be used to obtain lump-sum proposals and cost estimates from architects and engineers, design-build contractors, general contractors, or construction management firms. It may even generate firm prices for the entire project.

This chapter will discuss thorough design criteria for a typical manufacturing facility.

DESIGN CRITERIA

The purpose of the criteria must be clearly stated at the very outset. The following example is directed toward the acquisition of architectural and engineering proposals, although a similar format could also be sent to design-build firms or to any of the other construction disciplines. It should be noted immediately that requesting lump-sum proposals, based upon thorough design criteria, from design professionals is a highly ethical and accepted practice. Fees based on a percentage of construction cost are used when a project is undefined; but when the scope is well defined, the professional can estimate the construction cost and set his fee according to his professional guidelines. Fee, however, should never be a weighted factor in the selection of a design professional.

The material that follows is not intended to be a project description for every project. It does, however, cover most of the key points of the design and construction processes. Neither is it intended to be a checklist, although it may serve as a reminder. Every item mentioned deserves its own consideration and should be stated to suit the individual owner and circumstance. Where possible, it should read like a performance specification yet not be so tightly written that it inhibits any opportunity.

I. General

A. The intent of this submittal is to provide a basis for acquiring architectural-engineering proposals for the complete design of a manufacturing and office facility to be located at (city, state). Proposals developed from this project description should be sent to (owner's representative). Based upon the following guidelines, please submit this information:

    1. Lump-sum price to prepare complete working drawings and specifications

    2. Lump-sum price to supervise construction and a statement of the scope of the supervision to be provided

    3. Time required for the completion of working drawings and specifications in calendar days

    4. An estimate of the time required for the construction of this project, also stated in calendar days

    5. A cost estimate for the construction of this facility as outlined in these design criteria, with a breakdown into the following categories:

        a. Site preparation—all earth moving, cut, fill, etc.

        b. Paving:

            (1) Concrete truck aprons

            (2) Bituminous concrete drives

        c. Architectural and structural

        d. Heating, ventilating, and air conditioning

        e. Plumbing

        f. Electrical

        g. Fire protection

        h. Testing laboratories and inspection services fees

B. This booklet is to be returned with your proposal.

C. *Architectural and engineering services.* Furnish all architectural and engineering services required to properly design and prepare working drawings and specifications for the complete work described in these design criteria. All design shall be accomplished by architects and engineers registered in the state of this particular site location. Furthermore, all design shall be accomplished in accordance with the requirements of all jurisdictional governmental authorities and the insurance underwriters.

It shall be specifically noted that the owner's drawings and criteria are intended only to outline the facility and minimum standards acceptable to the owner.

All drawings and designs, including those of design development status, shall be submitted to the owner for his review, comments, and/or approval prior to their being advanced to the working drawing stage. This review and the resulting comments by the owner shall not free the designers from their responsibility of furnishing the owner with professional services complete in all details reasonably implied and meeting the requirements of jurisdictional governmental authorities and the insurance underwriters. One complete set of computations and reproducible transparencies (not sepias) shall be delivered to the owner prior to final acceptance.

D. Purpose and scope. The purpose of the design criteria is to present some general design guidelines. These specifications and the accompanying graphic illustrations describe the project in sufficient detail to establish its basic design concept, to identify major materials and methods of construction, and to describe the major mechanical and electrical systems in a manner that will allow the design professionals to provide fixed prices for the complete working drawings and specifications, responsible cost estimates, and a time of completion for the construction of this facility.

The design criteria are to be used as a guideline only, and the final construction documents shall be modified to conform with jurisdictional and performance requirements of the project while providing construction of overall economy through simplicity of design and selection of materials.

In addition, the design criteria are a basis for an accurate budget estimate.

E. Graphic illustration sheets. The following preliminary drawings shall be used as a guide in the preparation of working drawings and specifications. The drawings are intended to show basic information about the construction site and the allocation of floor space within the proposed building. The final construction documents shall be modified to conform with all governing codes, insurer's requirements, and to provide good performance with design economy.

   1. *Survey.* This topographic survey (Fig. 1) is of recent date and indicates site dimensions and existing structures and trees. It identifies elevations by contour lines.

   2. *Plot plan* (Fig. 2) suggesting the approximate location of the building and general site improvements.

   3. *Floor plans*
      a. Office portion (Fig. 3)
      b. Manufacturing portion (Fig. 4)

F. Schedule. Time is of the essence with respect to the work described within these design criteria. The time required by the designers to complete working drawings and specifications will be given special consideration when proposals are reviewed.

G. Approvals, permits, and fees. In writing the specifications, the designers shall assign the responsibility for obtaining all permits to the proper contractors. The contractor's schedule of values shall include an allowance for all such items, but the owner shall pay the actual costs as they are required.

H. Insurance. (This section should be provided to the plant engineer by his company insurance executive. In addition to stating types and limits of coverage, the name of the insurance underwriter should be given.)

I. Inspections. The designers shall assure that the contractor shall facilitate and obtain all inspections. This includes inspection services (soil, concrete, etc.) required by the specifications as well as those inspections required by governmental authorities having jurisdiction and by the insurance underwriters. Written reports of all inspections shall be delivered to the owner for his permanent files. The contractor shall be responsible for the immediate correction of any defects discovered during any inspection.

The cost of all testing laboratory and inspection services shall be paid separately by the owner, but their estimated costs are to be included in the cost estimate referred to in section I.A5 above.

The designers shall assert their, and the owner's, right to inspect the site and any and all phases of the work at any time. The contractor shall facilitate their access.

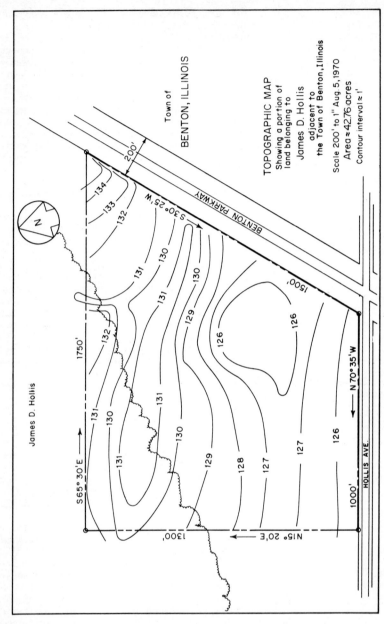

Fig. 1 Topographic map showing a portion of land belonging to James P. Hollis adjacent to the town of Benton, Illinois.

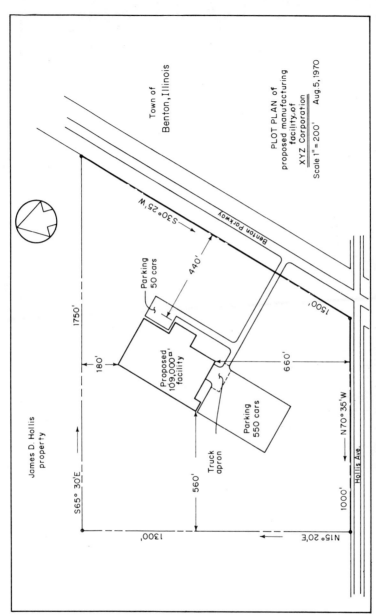

Fig. 2 Plot plan of proposed manufacturing facility for XYZ corporation.

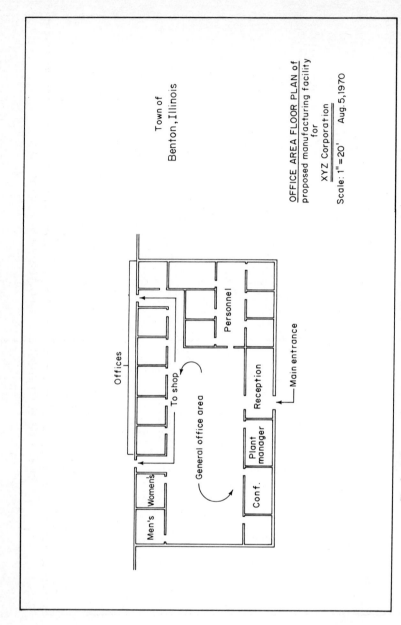

Fig. 3 Office area floor plan of proposed manufacturing facility for **XYZ** corporation.

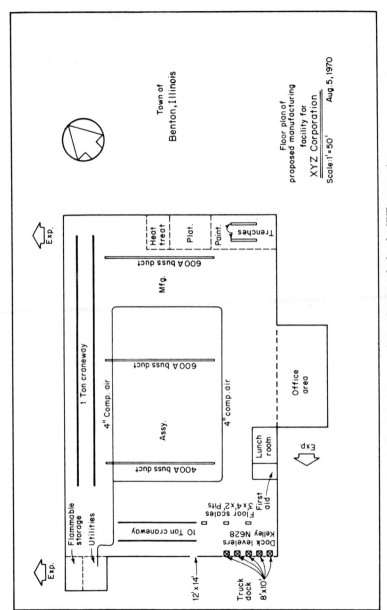

Fig. 4 Floor plan of proposed manufacturing facility for XYZ corporation.

Upon completion of the project, the contractor shall be required to obtain, and deliver to the Owner, all necessary Certificates of Occupancy required by government authorities having jurisdiction.

J. Guarantee. The construction documents shall require the contractor to guarantee all materials and workmanship to be free from defects and to be in compliance with specifications, codes and laws for a period of one year from the date of Final Acceptance by the Owner. This shall not waive longer warranties made by some manufacturers such as 5-year compressor warranties and 20-year color-fast siding.

In the event that said defects or violations are discovered, the contractor shall initiate corrective action within 24 hours of written notice to him by the Owner. The Owner reserves the right, should the contractor fail to make expeditious correction, to have the work performed by others and to charge the contractor for those direct costs plus a stated percentage for his overhead expense.

K. Operating and maintenance manuals. Prior to final payment, the contractor shall provide to the Owner two bound manuals containing the following information:

1. Names and addresses of all subcontractors and suppliers together with their respective areas of work or material supplied and the locations, in the project, of each

2. Manufacturer's recommendations for the maintenance and repair of all finished surfaces (floors, walls, etc.)

3. Complete operating instructions for each integrated equipment system

4. Complete operating, maintenance, and repair instructions for each type and model of equipment installed

5. Complete parts lists together with recommended spare parts for each type and model of equipment installed

L. "As-built" drawings. Prior to the final acceptance of the work, the contractor shall deliver to the owner reproducible transparencies (not sepias) of every construction drawing. These drawings shall show changes to the contract drawings that were made during the progress of the work, i.e., changes due to interferences, additions, deletions, etc.

M. During construction. The designers shall specify that the contractor shall provide all necessary utilities, communications, temporary toilets, heat, and maintenance during construction and the removal of same at the proper times. The contractor shall furnish and maintain office space, adjacent to the contracting site office, for the sole use of the architect's, engineer's, and owner's representatives. The contractor shall make available to the design team and the owner complete and current construction drawings, specifications, shop drawings, schedules, etc., at all times. All temporary facilities shall be removed by the contractor when required.

N. Safety. It shall be specified that the contractor shall maintain safe working practices and conditions during the progress of the work and shall adhere to safety requirements of federal, state, and local jurisdictional authorities. In addition to the reports and record keeping required by law, the contractor shall deliver to the owner a written report regarding each accident occurring in connection with the work herein described. The report shall include the following:

1. Description of incident
2. Person or persons involved
3. Property involvement
4. Extent of injuries or damages
5. Medical treatment rendered
6. Action taken to prevent recurrence

O. Cost estimates. The designers shall prepare detailed cost estimates at the submission of preliminary designs and again at the completion of drawings and specifications.

P. Renderings. The architect shall submit pencil renderings of the proposed aesthetical treatment of this facility for the review and comments of the owner. The architect shall maintain the exterior of the project so as to blend with its environs. The architect shall incorporate suggestions of the owner until the owner is satisfied with the overall effect. Only then shall a 16 × 20-inch watercolor rendering be prepared.

Q. Manufacturer's names. Throughout these criteria may be found instances where products are identified by the name and model number of a certain manufacturer. It should be noted that this has been done to denote an acceptable type and quality grade of product. The owner is open to recommendations based upon economies, lead times, etc., but reserves the right to make all final decisions in this regard.

II. Architectural and structural

A. Site grading. The owner has no special requirements in this regard, but grading shall be accomplished in such a manner as to promote the drainage of storm water away from buildings, parking areas, and roadways and to facilitate the removal of all storm water from the site.

B. Parking areas and roadways. Paved parking areas shall be provided for the numbers of automobiles indicated on the plot plan. Drives shall be bituminous and design shall be in accordance with recommended practice in that area and shall include crown, drainage consideration, generous radii for truck turning, etc. Base course for portions subject to heavy traffic shall be a minimum of 25 percent deeper than for other areas, and all material selection, placement, and compaction shall be performed under the supervision of a duly registered soils engineer.

Paved areas shall be striped with yellow traffic paint delineating each parking space and shall have traffic directional and safety signs designated by painting on said pavement with the same traffic-grade paint.

C. Bumpers and curbs. Bumpers are not a requirement of these criteria and curbs shall be installed only as necessary to facilitate storm drainage.

D. Truck apron. An adequately sized, appropriately designed concrete apron, as shown by the plot plan, is required.

E. Storm drainage. Shall be surface as much as possible, with culverts under roadways as needed to direct storm water away from site improvements. Roof leaders shall connect with an underground system within at least 100 feet of the building. Floor-level cleanouts at each leader and exterior catch basins as necessary to promote drainage and cleaning capability shall be integral with this system.

F. Excavation. Shall be in accordance with good practice and, prior to the commencement of concrete work, shall be inspected by a qualified soils engineer to ensure that suitable earth foundations have been obtained.

G. Backfill. Shall be selected, placed, and compacted under the supervision of a qualified soils engineer. Testing results, engineer's reports and recommendations shall be submitted to the owner before concrete placing operations commence.

H. Unit prices. Shall be submitted by the contractor to govern changes in the work produced by subsurface conditions not anticipated by the drawings. Prices shall include all shoring, bracing, forms, and other incidentals necessary for the performance of the work.

1. General excavation—per cubic yard
2. Piles—per lineal foot
3. Foundation excavation—per cubic yard
4. Additional footing concrete—per cubic yard in place

I. Frame and exterior walls. The manufacturing building shall be of structural steel frame construction. Clear height from finished floor to bottom of overhead structural members shall be a minimum of 20 feet. The owner is interested in bay sizes of approximately 40 × 40 feet but wishes to receive recommendations, based upon economies, on this aspect.

Wall coverings shall be insulated metal panels, the final selection of which shall be made by the owner taking into consideration the designer's recommendations based upon economy, durability, aesthetics, etc.

The attached office building shall have a minimum 9-foot ceiling height. Exterior wall to be masonry, load-bearing if economically advantageous, face brick to match that used in the approximately 5-foot-high masonry wall at base of manufacturing building.

Structural steel shall be designed for suspended sprinklers, utility piping, electrical lines, air-conditioning equipment, etc. Additional capacity for hoists and/or moving cranes shall be provided only in the bays in which they are located.

J. Roofing and roof penetrations

1. Roofing and base flashing shall consist of a 20-year built-up UL class-A rating system as manufactured by Johns-Manville, Koppers, Carey, or approved equal.
2. Roof applicator shall be approved by manufacturer furnishing materials, and

manufacturer's letter of approval shall be submitted to owner before any roofing work is started.

3. Roofing subcontractor, in his letter of transmittal of item 2 above, shall guarantee to repair the roof, should it leak because of defective workmanship or materials, for a period of 5 years from the date of final acceptance of the project by the owner.

4. Steel roof deck shall be 1½ inches of minimum gauge for economy, having a phosphatized shop coat of off-white paint. Deck in the manufacturing area shall be Inland-Ryerson type "S" Acoustideck or a similar, owner-approved deck having a minimum noise reduction coefficient of 0.75.

5. Roof construction shall include fiberglass rigid insulation as per recommendations of the mechanical engineer, but providing not less than 0.20 conductance.

6. All of the foregoing shall be applied in such a manner as to create a class 1 roof as will be approved by the insurance underwriters. Roofing subcontractor will be required to submit the underwriters' form entitled "Roof Installation Acceptance Certificate—Steel Deck," fully completed, to the owner.

K. Moisture protection

1. Flashing for roof drains shall be 6-pound lead extending 12 inches beyond drain in all directions.

2. Gravel stops to be extruded aluminum minimum 0.063 inch thick in standard mill finish.

3. Cap flashings, through-wall flashings, and others to be Hydro T, Metal 20, or equal.

4. All fasteners (screws, clips, etc.) shall be of a type and grade that discourages electrolytic or any other type of corrosion.

5. Structural expansion joint to be of design and type approved by owner.

6. All pipes, vents, etc., shall be installed through the roof deck before roofing is applied. Pipes shall be provided with sleeves and flanges of a type and size to assure waterproof seal with the built-up roof.

L. Interior partitions and ceilings

   1. *Permanent partitions*

      a. Office

      (1) Permanent partitions shall be ½-inch gypsum wallboard, recessed-edge type, with studs 24 inches on center. Boards shall be nailed or screwed at all bearings with nails spaced not to exceed 6 inches on centers. Fasteners at edge and end bearing shall not be less than ⅜ inch from edge of board. All joints between sheets shall be reinforced with perforated tape and cement. (Joint compound—"Tapers Mud").

      (2) One wall of the general manager's office and the conference room shall be faced with Formica Vertical Interior Paneling.

      (3) The designer will use Formica VIP as an accent wall in the lobby.

      b. Toilet areas, first aid, and cafeteria areas. Those areas exposed to moisture damage shall be of concrete block with vitreous finish. Provide a 6-foot-high ceramic tile wainscoat in toilet areas or as required by code. The economics of glazed structural block shall be considered in lieu of the above construction.

      c. Plant area. Shall be concrete block, 8 inches maximum (unless required otherwise by code or approved by owner).

      d. Plant Toilet Areas. Shall be concrete block with vitreous finish.

      e. Contractor shall state price per unit for addition and deletion of permanent walls according to the following schedule:

CLASS I. Gypsum Board Walls as Specified:

    ½" Gypsum Board Wall   Deduct per Lineal Ft._____

                          Add per Lineal Ft.   _____

    3′ door openings including cost of frame

    Deduct_____ Add_____

CLASS II. Concrete Block Walls as Specified:

      4″ Wall   Deduct per sq. ft. _____

                Add per sq. ft.   _____

      6″ Wall   Deduct per sq. ft. _____

                Add per sq. ft.   _____

      8″ Wall   Deduct per sq. ft. _____

Add per sq. ft.   _____
Door openings including cost of frame:
3' Door   Deduct_____ Add_____
6' Door   Deduct_____ Add_____

M. Doors and frames

1. Frames. All door frames shall be minimum 16-gauge pressed steel, bearing an appropriate UL label where required. All frames shall be shop prime painted per the manufacturer's standards.

2. Hollow metal. All interior pedestrian doors shall be 1¾ inches thick by 7 feet high flush-panel hollow metal and shall have one 10 × 10 inch light. All doors shall bear an appropriate UL label where applicable. All doors shall be shop prime painted per the manufacturer's standards.

3. Wood. Interior wood doors shall be 1¾ inches thick, flush type.

4. Doors and frames in partition walls shall be as manufactured by the partition manufacturer.

5. Overhead doors. Where and to the sizes noted on the drawings, overhead doors shall be wood overhead doors, manually operated, with the exception of the single 12 × 14 foot door, which shall be electrically operated.

N. Caulking. All perimeters of sash, door frames, metal walls, expansion and contraction joints in masonry, etc., shall be caulked utilizing compounds as manufactured and recommended by Pecora or equal.

O. Brick. All walls having brick facing shall be of cavity wall or full back buttering construction so as to preclude the penetration of water. The mortar utilized shall be nonbleeding and noneffervescing. Cavity walls shall be provided with weep holes.

The backup walls for brick facing shall be of Waylite autoclaved concrete blocks having a thickness as determined by structural design and the requirements of all jurisdictional governmental authorities.

All brick utilized shall have suitable horizontal reinforcement similar to Dur-O-Wall, spaced 24 inches vertically.

P. Block. All new exterior and interior walls and partitions to be constructed of concrete block as designated on the drawings shall be lightweight steam-cured concrete blocks of sufficient size and design to satisfy the structural and fire requirements of all jurisdictional governmental authorities and the insurance underwriters. All walls shall have horizontal reinforcement similar to Dur-O-Wall spaced vertically on 24-inch centers.

Q. Carpentry, millwork, etc.

1. Roof blocking. All the necessary wood roof blocking as required for metal fascia and gravel stop, etc. All blocking will be pressure Wolman CCA Salts treated.

2. All wood blocking, furring, framing, etc., required to properly set work of other or same trade. Such materials subject to decay from moisture shall be pressure Wolman CCA Salts treated.

3. Materials shall be new except as otherwise noted. Workmanship shall conform to applicable, commonly accepted trade practices for good construction in this class of work.

R. Hardware. All hardware shall be Russwin "Stilemaker" line. Where Russwin hardware needs to be supplemented, a commercial series of Sergeant, Corbin, or an owner-approved equal shall be utilized. All hardware to match in finish. An allowance of $2,000 shall be made for the hardware material only; labor is to be a portion of the fixed contract amount.

All door cylinders shall be Best Universal Lock Company removable-core master keyed and having three submaster systems.

S. Finishes

1. *Floors* in the cafeteria and first aid rooms are to be of vinyl asbestos 3/32-inch-thick floor covering, Classic Flexichrome or equal. Wherever resilient tile floor covering is installed, a 4-inch-high set-on vinyl base shall be installed on all walls and partitions. All colors to be as approved by the owner from recommendations to be made by the architect.

Boxed new tiles of the same factory production run in an amount equal to 5 percent of square feet of applied tile will be delivered to the owner on completion of the project.

Toilet floors shall be terrazzo or ceramic tile. In the cafeteria the area 7 feet from the vending machine wall, including the food preparation area, shall be terrazzo or quarry tile.

Lobby flooring may be slate, terrazzo, travertine, etc., depending upon architect's recommendations and cost.

All office areas will be carpeted by the owner. This contract shall provide only the concrete finish as per section II*BB*.

2. *Walls* are to be painted except where, on partitions in the office area, a factory-applied vinyl covering may be used. Toilet walls shall have ceramic tile wainscot. The exterior of the building at the main entrance to the office area shall be given a stone and/or glazed brick treatment for esthetic purposes.

Should insulated metal walls be chosen, they shall receive a factory-finish baked enamel on both sides. All concrete blocks and gypsum board walls are to receive two coats of paint.

3. *Painting.* The following surfaces are to be painted: All exterior exposed items of structural steel, all interior exposed structural steel columns, all channel bucks, miscellaneous iron, hollow metal doors and frames, all exposed partitions and doors throughout the office and personnel areas, including the exposed walls above the ceramic tile in the toilet rooms. All paint application shall be Benjamin Moore or equal per the following schedule:

    a. Exterior surfaces:

        Concrete Block: Two coats Sonoborne Hydrocide Paint

        Structural and Misc. Metal: One coat Retardo Rust Inhibitive paint
(light gray)
One coat Impervo Enamel

    b. Interior surfaces:

        Metal Trim: One coat Alkyd Enamel Underbody
          (tinted to finish coat)
        One coat Dulamel Eggshell
        All of the above is to be in addition to the shop and primer coats required.
        All finish colors are to be as approved by the occupant.

    c. Heat treating and plating areas:

        Structural steel and roof deck underside in these areas shall be painted with an acid-resistant paint.

T. Expandability. The foundation, structural framework, walls, and all affected areas of design and work shall be designed and constructed to permit expansion to the direction noted on the drawings.

U. Special pits and foundations

1. Three floor scales will require pits. Refer to floor plan for dimensions and location.

2. Five dock levelers will be required. Refer to floor plan for type and locations. Road surface to plant finished floor dimension shall be 51 inches.

3. One 250-ton-capacity press is to be installed. The designers will be provided with location and foundation requirements.

V. Production equipment. With the exception of the preceding section, process equipment to be furnished by the owner will not have separate pads, foundations, or pits but will rest on vibration isolators not secured to the floor slab.

W. Special drains. Each of the following areas require 12-inch-wide by minimum 6-inch-deep trenches, properly pitched and having removable gratings (Grip-Strut or equal). An appropriate catch basin shall be installed in the sanitary sewer line about 8 feet from each trench drain.

1. Paint washer
2. Paint stripper

Note that in each of the above areas, floors are to be pitched to the drain.

X. Overhead hoists. Lifting devices, including bridges and hoists, are specifically excluded from this contract. However, the architect shall provide structural capacity in the bays indicated and also specify that the contractor provide and install the rails and the necessary electric power to the proper location at each installation as follows:

1. Steel room area—One 10-ton-capacity bridge
2. Punch press area—One 1-ton-capacity bridge

Y. Miscellaneous metal. Provide hand and safety rails as required by code and industrial safety.   Where downspouts and walls, particularly at truck entryways, are subject to impact damage, provide appropriate guards.

Z. *Security fencing*. Fencing is not a requirement of this contract.

AA. *Landscaping*. Finish grading with stockpiled topsoil, seeding, and maintenance of fine lawn and meadow lawn through the first growing season is a requirement of these criteria. However, the furnishing and planting of trees, shrubs, etc., is *not*.

BB. *Concrete*

1. *Materials*

   a. Conform to applicable requirements of the building code of the American Concrete Institute and to the specific requirements hereinafter specified.

   b. Concrete to be 3,000-pound concrete at 28 days designed by an approved testing laboratory at contractor's expense, but shall not have less than six sacks of cement per cubic yard of concrete.

   c. Gradation and quality of aggregates shall conform to applicable requirements of ASTM. Combination of fine and coarse aggregates shall be combined in proper proportions as directed by the testing laboratory designing the mix.

   d. Cement to be approved standard brand of portland cement conforming to ASTM (C-150), type I or type II, low alkali. One brand shall be used for all work. Contractor shall deliver to owner certified mill reports of tests made at an approved testing agency, including statement of the manufacturer that the cement conforms to specifications. At contractor's expense, the contractor shall also provide for the casting and testing of concrete cylinders in order to determine the strength of the concrete delivered. A set of four concrete cylinders shall be made for each 100 cubic yards or less of each type of concrete utilized in any one day. Two concrete cylinders shall be tested for compressive strength at 7 days and two at 28 days. The compressive strength tests shall be accomplished by a reputable testing laboratory approved by the owner, and copies of each test report shall be filed with the owner within 5 calendar days of the actual date of test.

   e. An admixture of Pozzolith as manufactured by the Master Builders Company, or equal, shall be used. Quantity per sack of cement and method of use shall be per recommendations of manufacturer and laboratory furnishing the design mix.

2. *Slab thickness*

   a. Office areas and areas of light manufacturing and assembly shall have a slab of 6-inch minimum thickness.

   b. Manufacturing, assembly, and storage areas of medium weight and traffic conditions shall have a slab of 8-inch minimum thickness.

   c. Areas of heavy weight and traffic conditions shall have a slab as designed by an engineer based on specific load and soil conditions.

3. *Control joints*

   a. Expansion joints of ½ inch shall be provided for around the entire perimeter of building.

   b. Isolation joints shall also be placed around all columns.

   c. An approved elastic compound shall be used in all expansion joints.

4. *Reinforcing steel*

   a. All reinforcing steel shall be new intermediate-grade billet steel, as per ASTM A15. All bars #3 and larger shall be deformed as per ASTM A305. Mesh reinforcement shall conform to ASTM A185.

   b. All reinforcing steel shall be designed by an engineer with all slabs receiving a minimum of #6 welded wire mesh, 6 × 6 inches. In unstable earth, structural reinforcing shall be provided in lower part of slab.

5. *Vapor barrier*

   a. All floor slabs on ground shall be poured on a vapor barrier.

   b. Vapor barrier shall be polyethylene plastic having a minimum thickness of 6 mils (0.006 inch), free of pinholes and other blemishes, which shall be installed in accordance with manufacturer's requirements. All joints shall be lapped 12 inches.

6. *Concrete slab finish*

   a. Monolithic slabs shall be used throughout except for special design conditions, where alternate solutions will be submitted to owner for approval.

b. Power floating shall be used on all floor slabs after screeding and tamping or rolling, making possible the use of a stiffer mix.

c. Steel hand-troweling shall be used on all floor slabs. Apply three steel trowelings or more, as may be required to leave hard, dense, smooth-finished floor surface, burnished to produce ringing sound from trowel.

d. Accuracy of finish shall be ±⅛ inch from a theoretical plane in any 10-foot distance.

e. Sealer and hardener shall be applied to all exposed light-duty concrete floor slabs.

CC. Space allocation and planning

1. *Block area layout.* Refer to enclosed block area layout for principal planning features.

2. *Space allocation.* The enclosed block-area layout shows the general space allocations. In addition, a ¼-inch scale plan will be supplied which shows detailed space allocation and machinery locations.

3. *Modular planning.* Office areas shall be designed to a 4-foot module. The manufacturing area shall be designed to a 4-foot module unless specific process requirements dictate otherwise. Aisleways and hallways shall be arranged in straight runs, eliminating jogs and irregular partition alignment. Rooms (except for general office areas) and work areas shall not be used for through circulation, such circulation being handled by corridor or aisle areas.

4. *Utilities distribution and coordination.* Utilities and services in plant area shall be coordinated into an integrated distribution system affording maximum flexibility consistent with design economy. Lighting fixtures in office areas shall be arranged to coordinate with 4-foot module. Electrical and telephone distribution in office area shall be in slab and coordinated with 4-foot module.

DD. Employee facilities. This facility is to accommodate 612 employees, as follows:

	Office building	Manufacturing building	Totals
First shift:	177	118	405
Second shift:	177	78	195
Third shift:	10	2	12
Male/Female Ratio:	60/40		Grand total: 612

1. *Toilet rooms.* See enclosed plan for location of toilet rooms. Toilets are to be provided to satisfy all governing codes. In addition, the following minimal requirements shall be met:

a. All toilet rooms are to be provided with hot and cold running water.

b. Each toilet room shall be *mechanically exhausted,* controlled by the lighting circuit.

c. *Floor drains* are to be provided in each toilet room so that floors may be flushed readily.

d. *Toilet partitions* are to be metal flush panel and ceiling hung. Doors are to be provided with locks and gravity hinges.

e. *Toilet room doors* are to be provided with push plates and pull handles only, not knobs and lock sets.

f. *Miscellaneous fixtures.* Over each washbasin provide a 16 × 20 inch plate-glass mirror with one-piece stainless steel frame, and stainless shelf. In each women's toilet stall provide one two-roll toilet paper dispenser; on the door of each, one chrome coat hook and one stainless feminine napkin disposal with cover. Provide sanitary napkin dispenser in each women's toilet room. In each men's toilet stall provide one two-roll toilet paper dispenser and one chrome coat hook on the interior side of each door. Provide a soap dispenser for each lavatory and a towel dispenser for each two lavatories, with conveniently located surface-mounted waste receptacles, one to be located near door.

g. *Water closets* shall be china wall-hanging siphon-jet elongated bowl with 1½-inch top spud, equal to Crane Walton.

h. *Urinals* shall be vitreous china wall-hanging washout type with extended shields and wall hanger, equal to Crane Correcto.

i. Lavatories shall be vitreous china wall-hanging type with back. 54-inch Bradley Model BFB stainless steel wash fountains will also be approved when appropriate. Faucets shall *not* be of the spring-shutting type.

j. Janitor's closet with service sink to be located in each toilet area.

k. Service sinks to be 22 × 18 inches A.R. enameled cast-iron roll rim with back and rim guard.

l. Fixture ratios based upon industrial plant populations, male and female:

Water closets: 1– 9 1
10– 24 2
25– 49 3
50–100 5
Over 100: add one closet for each 30 additional persons.

m. Fixture ratios based upon industrial plant populations:

Urinals: Whenever urinals are provided for men, one water closet less than the number specified herein will be provided for each urinal, except that the number of water closets shall not be reduced to less than two-thirds of the number specified herein.

Lavatories: 1–100: one for each 10 persons. Over 100: add one lavatory for each 15 additional persons.

2. *First aid.* Provide first aid facilities as shown on floor plan, with connecting toilet room containing water closet and lavatory.

3. *Eating facilities.* Provide a lunchroom as indicated on plan. Roughed-in utilities shall be provided for future cooking facilities.

This section of the criteria should also detail the owner's requirements for vending machine locations, flagpole, door seals, and all other items having architectural or structural considerations.

Section III may be entitled "Mechanical" and could state specific needs related to heating, ventilating, and air conditioning as well as plumbing, sewage, potable water, compressed air, fire protection, and special process needs.

Section IV could be "Electrical." The designers will have to know what type of power is available from the local utility as well as the total capacity in connected load and demand load of the facility. The manufacturing area floor plan, Fig. 4, is utilized to portray the locations and extent of primary distribution. In this section the plant engineer should specify metering, buss duct type, under-floor duct, convenience receptacles, lighting methods and levels, switching, and special systems such as clocks, alarms, and signals.

Section V should be "Foundation Recommendations" and should include the soils investigation report prepared by a soils engineer.

Section VI would be "Architectural/Engineering Contract" and would consist of the actual contract that is proposed as the agreement.

The final section, of course, would be VII, "Graphic Illustration Sheets," and would consist of the drawings mentioned in Section I*E.*

Chapter **2**

Coordination with Architect/ Engineering Firms

MAX SCHWARTZ
President, Max Schwartz Consulting Engineers, Inc.

INTRODUCTION

Let us assume that management requires the design and construction of a new mill building. Since the plant engineering department is deeply involved with the selection and placement of the new equipment, it is decided that outside professional services are to be used for the design of the building. These services may be provided by a large architect/engineering firm, a consulting engineer, a contractor, or even the vendor of the equipment. (Generally, whatever the exact nature of the outside professional, such a consultant is referred to as the architect/engineer or is referred to as the A/E. Following convention, we will also refer to the outside professional as the architect/engineer, and assume that, frequently, this is an architect/engineering firm of some type.)

Coordination between management and the A/E starts with the issuance of a purchase order. The conditions, scope, and schedule of services to be performed has already been fixed by the contract between management and the A/E. Compensation, whether it is a lump sum, percentage of construction, payroll costs times a multiplier, a per diem rate, a retainer, or a combination of these has also been established by the contract or agreement.

Plant engineering has been assigned the task of coordinating all aspects of the design project. In order to properly execute this responsibility, the words and intent of the contract and purchase order must be known. The services to be provided by the A/E must be agreed upon. If any ambiguity exists concerning the scope of the services to be included under the contract, the plant engineer should devise a checklist. There should be agreement early in the project as to which of the services the A/E will furnish and which not.

Suggested checklist:
1. Preliminary report
2. Design services
3. Professional services during construction
   a. Occasional inspection
   b. On call for problems
   c. Continuous inspection on an 8-hour-per-day basis
4. Cost estimate
5. Disciplines furnished:
   a. Industrial engineering
   b. Architecture
   c. Civil engineering
   d. Structural engineering
   e. Mechanical engineering
   f. Electrical engineering
   g. Chemical or process engineering
6. Will A/E augment plant engineering design staff?
7. Will A/E take full charge of design?

Once the plant engineer and the A/E have established the exact scope of the work, both parties must take care that the scope is adhered to. As the management's representative, the plant engineer must be careful not to lead the A/E away from the scope previously established while also taking care that the A/E provides all services agreed to.

Soon after the contract is signed, the plant engineer should establish a meeting date with the A/E. At this initial meeting, the A/E should receive the building program and, if available, site condition surveys and tests, instructions, and standards documents. The starting date of the schedule for preparation of schematic, preliminary, and working drawings could be established at this meeting as well.

It is good policy to decide early how control is to be exercised over the project. It is highly recommended that a periodic review of plans and specifications be made by the plant engineer. In fact, many A/E firms will demand such reviews and approvals or corrections before proceeding with each phase of the work. An efficient method of review requires that the A/E submit three sets of plans, specifications, and cost estimates at different intervals. The first submittal should be at 10 percent completion. The second submittal should be at 50 percent completion and the third at 90 percent completion. Firm dates should be set when these submittals are to be made. It is the plant engineer's duty to establish and maintain a maximum number of "review days." The plans and specifications must be reviewed and returned to the A/E within that limit. This method of review promotes full control of progress, scope, and cost of the project.

LIAISON

Once the guidelines have been established, the actual business of liaison between organizations begins. Early in the project, one individual from the plant engineering department and one from the A/E firm should be assigned as sole representatives in all communications. These people are generally referred to as project engineers.

Each of these two persons accumulates information, requirements, questions, and other pertinent data from the various divisions in their respective companies. The plant engineer is in close contact with the representatives of management, production, maintenance, quality control, and purchasing and sees to it that the requirements of each department are integrated into the whole project. The A/E representative must supply correct data and answers to the group leaders of the architectural, civil, industrial, mechanical, structural, and electrical engineering groups.

The project engineers should encourage frequent dialogues, conferences, and communications between management and the A/E, but all such activities should be directed through the project engineers themselves.

COMMUNICATION

Once the groundwork has been laid for communication, how do the participants ensure "meaningful" exchange? How can the two parties best exchange ideas? The medium of communication most generally accepted in these circumstances is graphic representation. Such representations take the form of flow diagrams, plans, details, sketches, bar charts, and tabulations, to name a few. But here, as in any language, a dictionary or glossary is necessary, because the mutual understanding of symbols is critical. Each discipline has its own recognized symbols and nomenclature. It would behoove the plant

MAX SCHWARTZ
CONSULTING ENGINEERS, INC.
6464 Sunset Boulevard
LOS ANGELES, CALIFORNIA 90028

Phone 462-2369

LETTER OF TRANSMITTAL

DATE	JOB NO.
ATTENTION	
RE	

TO ______________________

GENTLEMEN:

WE ARE SENDING YOU ☐ Attached ☐ Under separate cover via ______________ the following items:

☐ Shop drawings ☐ Prints ☐ Plans ☐ Samples ☐ Specifications

☐ Copy of letter ☐ Change order ☐ ______________

COPIES	DATE	NO.	DESCRIPTION

THESE ARE TRANSMITTED as checked below:

☐ For approval ☐ Approved as submitted ☐ Resubmit ______ copies for approval

☐ For your use ☐ Approved as noted ☐ Submit ______ copies for distribution

☐ As requested ☐ Returned for corrections ☐ Return ______ corrected prints

☐ For review and comment ☐ ______________

☐ FOR BIDS DUE ______________ 19 ______ ☐ PRINTS RETURNED AFTER LOAN TO US

REMARKS ______________________

COPY TO ______________________

SIGNED: ______________________

Form 240-1 — New England Business Service, Inc., Townsend, Mass.

If enclosures are not as noted, kindly notify us at once.

Fig. 1 Typical letter of transmittal.

engineer to have included in the project library the standard symbols for each field of engineering, since it goes without saying that a single symbol on an engineering drawing can mean more than a paragraph of written words.

The need to transmit drawings, specifications, cost estimates, etc., between management and the A/E will arise frequently. Two types of forms, shown in Figs. 1 and 2, are available to expedite the transactions.

The letter of transmittal can be typed in three copies using coloress (NCR) paper. The original and one copy are generally sent to the recipient and one copy is kept in the sender's file. The recipient signs one one copy, with any comments noted, and returns it to the sender.

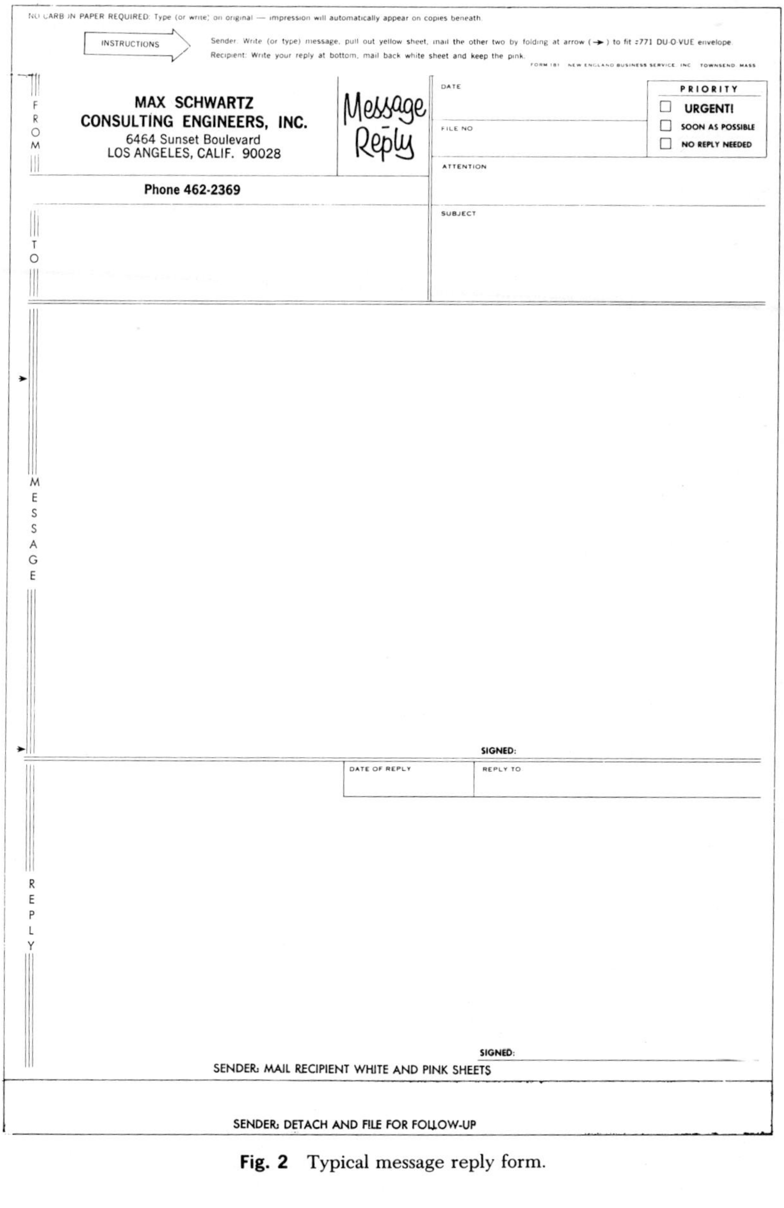
NO CARBON PAPER REQUIRED: Type (or write) on original — impression will automatically appear on copies beneath.

INSTRUCTIONS

Sender: Write (or type) message, pull out yellow sheet, mail the other two by folding at arrow (➔) to fit #771 DU-O-VUE envelope.
Recipient: Write your reply at bottom, mail back white sheet and keep the pink.

FORM 181 NEW ENGLAND BUSINESS SERVICE, INC. TOWNSEND, MASS.

FROM

MAX SCHWARTZ
CONSULTING ENGINEERS, INC.
6464 Sunset Boulevard
LOS ANGELES, CALIF. 90028

Phone 462-2369

Message Reply

DATE

FILE NO

PRIORITY
☐ URGENT!
☐ SOON AS POSSIBLE
☐ NO REPLY NEEDED

ATTENTION

SUBJECT

TO

MESSAGE

SIGNED:

DATE OF REPLY

REPLY TO

REPLY

SIGNED:

SENDER: MAIL RECIPIENT WHITE AND PINK SHEETS

SENDER: DETACH AND FILE FOR FOLLOW-UP

Fig. 2 Typical message reply form.

The message reply form is usually used for simple memos which do not require formal typed letters. These forms also make three copies, using NCR paper. Two copies are sent to the recipient and one remains with the sender. Here too, the recipient notes comments and returns one copy to the sender. In this manner a complete history of the exchange of thoughts is clearly recorded. The number of these memos used during any project is unlikely to outweigh their utility. They serve countless purposes, from confirming telephone conversations, recording questions and answers, and serving as a "tickler file" to keeping a chronological history of the project. These memos also carry legal weight in any litigation. They can establish who broadened the scope of work or who first requested a change.

There are unwritten laws governing the coordination of any project. For proper coordination, the plant engineer should be aware of these unwritten laws. One must always confirm instructions and A/E commitments in writing. It is risky to assume that the job will be done because of a verbal agreement. Many busy people have poor memories, and almost everyone will take a matter a great deal more seriously if it is in writing. On critical items, it is wise to send a copy of the memo to a third party who can serve as a witness.

EXPEDITING ACTION

In carrying out a project, it is unwise to wait for manufacturers' representatives, vendors, and others to furnish critical data. One must go after them and keep after them. Many projects progress in direct proportion to the amount of follow-up and expediting that is applied to them. Expediting includes planning, investigating, promoting, and facilitating every step of a project. Develop a technique of looking immediately for an alternate way around each obstacle encountered or for some other recourse or expedient to maintain progress without losing momentum. On the other hand, be careful about making excessive demands on the A/E for action. Too much insistence and agitation may result in antagonism instead of cooperation. Avoid all forms of vacillation in any actions. Before committing an opinion or promoting an undertaking, wait until you have had a reasonable opportunity to obtain and study the facts. Then be careful of the accuracy of your statements.

Strive for conciseness and clarity in oral and written reports and instructions. Try to keep each memo or letter confined to a single subject.

Never invade the domain of the internal organization of the A/E without the knowledge and consent of the project engineer in charge. But in all transactions, be careful to include everyone who has the right to be in. Be careful about whom you mark for copies of letters, memos, etc., when the interests of other departments are involved.

Promises, schedules, and estimates are necessary and important instruments in a well-ordered business. You have the right to insist upon having periodic estimates of the cost of phases of work from responsible representatives of the A/E.

When you are dissatisfied with the services of someone in the A/E firm, make your complaint to the project engineer.

In dealing with the A/E, remember that you represent your company, ostensibly with full responsibility and authority. Outsiders will regard you as the legal, financial, and technical agent of your company in all transactions, so be careful of your commitments.

CONFERENCES

Project conferences should not be too large or too small. Large meetings frequently dissipate the subject over a number of conflicting or irrevelent points of view in a generally superficial manner. A considerable amount of skill is required to manage a sizable meeting so as to keep it on the proper subject.

Small meetings, of three or four persons, can usually hammer out a program or dispose of knotty problems much more effectively; but then there is the possibility that all interested parties will not be represented.

CHECKLIST

The following is offered as a checklist for design and development projects:
    Define your objectives
    Plan the job by outlining the steps to be accomplished

Prepare a definite schedule
Assign definite responsibilities for each item
Make sure that each person has sufficient help and facilities
Follow up; check up on progress of work
Revise your schedule as required
Watch for "bottlenecks," "log jams," and "missing links"
Hit lagging items hard
Drive to finish on time

TECHNICAL

Before the purchase order is issued, it is determined which of the various disciplines will be included by the A/E in its services. Some of the disciplines are:
Structural engineering
Mechanical engineering
Civil engineering
Industrial engineering
Electrical engineering
Architectural design
Once the disciplines are known, the plant engineer has a better understanding of what general services will be received. The A/E firm can provide a wide range of specific services. These are, of course, examined and discussed before the purchase order is issued. The A/E firm can provide any or all of the following specific services:
Schematic and preliminary drawings, estimates, and specifications
Intermediate working drawings
Final working drawings
Assistance in preparation of bid and contract documents
Shop drawings
Supervision of construction
Interpretation of drawings and specifications during construction
Contract payment certificates
As-built drawings
Rendering and industrial illustrations
Reports
Selection of colors, textures, and finishes
Reproduction of documents during construction
Surveys
The exact meaning of each of these specific services must be fully understood by the plant engineer and the A/E.

Preliminary drawings, estimates, and specifications are documents prepared as accurately and completely as possible. They are intended solely to assist in processing and estimating the project and to resolve problems concerning construction methods, materials, and equipment early in the design. Preliminary specifications should contain statements of:
1. Scope of work—in which project is described
2. Work not included—in which a list of buildings or any other work shown on the plans but not included in the construction contract is noted
3. List of trades, with an enumeration of materials, construction methods, and mechanical systems required

The plant engineer, management's representative, should provide the A/E firm with as many company plans, calculations, and other records of relevant existing facilities as possible. The A/E should be advised that the plans must be verified in the field, but much duplicated effort will be eliminated by providing the A/E with a good set of facility plans. A set of "as built" plans allows the A/E to estimate the degree of difficulty that will be encountered while designing the new facility, thus making it possible for the A/E to plan ahead for existing interferences or interfaces.

Intermediate working drawings should be submitted to the plant engineer for approval. This will provide the plant engineer with greater control over the entire project and will keep the project on schedule. Any errors or modifications can be made before final drawings are completed.

Final working drawings, along with final specifications and estimates, are generally

CHECKLIST
The architect and engineer must conform to all local governing laws and codes. Some that should be followed are:
National Electrical Code
ACI Building Code—Building Code Requirements for Reinforced Concrete
Building code—local city, county, or state
Plumbing code
Construction safety orders
Heating, ventilating and air conditioning code
Grading regulations
API–ASME Code—Unified Pressure Vessels for Petroleum Liquids and Gases
Air pollution control rules and regulations
Uniform building codes
National fire codes
Zoning code, city, county, or state
General industrial safety orders
Code of federal regulations—OSHA regulations
American National Standards

Fig. 3 Checklist of government agencies.

submitted ready for bids. These drawings show complete design with sizes, sections, and relative locations of various members. These are usually shown as plans, elevations, and details. From the final set, the plant engineer can compile the complete construction documents or the A/E may be asked to do the preparation. A construction document package may include the following:
Working drawings
Grading plans
General conditions
Special conditions
Detailed specifications
Equipment call-outs

The construction documents, in order to be complete, should set forth the kind, type, extent, location, and method of installation of the materials, structures, finishes, specialities, electrical and mechanical systems, and any special or service-connected equipment required in the work.

Steel-shop drawings can be furnished by the A/E but are more generally furnished by the steel fabricator—a subcontractor. Shop drawings are prepared to provide the complete information necessary for the fabrication of component parts of a structure, including the location, type, size, and extent of all welds and bolts applied in the shop. In conjunction with these drawings, erection drawings are also prepared by the steel erector. These drawings show, by mark number, the final location of each member in the structure.

The A/E's role during construction is oftentimes misunderstood. This topic will be full discussed below, in the section entitled "Professional." But it is important for the plant engineer to know exactly what kind of supervision is wanted from the A/E and to recognize that the more complete the supervision, the more costly it will be. If the A/E is to have complete control and supervision over the construction of the project, the A/E must also have authority and power over the subcontractors. This authority is usually monetary.

The A/E can provide reports on any situation within the plant. In any project, the A/E must conform with all public agencies having jurisdiction over the planned work. Some of the agencies consulted are:
City planning commission
Zoning
Building setbacks
Parking requirements
City or county engineer's office
Street profiles
Curbs and walks
Storm drains
Extension of utilities

Industrial waste
Air pollution
City or county department of health
City or county fire department
Department of building and safety
Traffic department

Figure 3 is a checklist of local laws and codes to be followed.

Other services available to the plant engineer are very specific to the project. An artist's rendition or rendering of a new facility, structure, or machine is an approximation of the final appearance of the project. Often, changes brought about by monetary considerations greatly alter the final appearance.

Surveys are another service provided by the A/E firm. But the term "surveying" covers a wide variety of services. The plant engineer must be sure of the services that are being received. Classifications of surveying often required for industrial work are:

Land or property surveying
    Property and boundary survey
    Architectural surveys
    Tax maps
Engineering surveys
    Design data surveys
        Control, horizontal and vertical
        Culture and topography
        Profiles and cross sections
    Construction surveys
        Layout surveys
        Quantity and measurment surveys
        As-built surveys
        Utility surveys

In order to manage a project economically and efficiently, the plant engineer must arrange a mutually agreeable detailed schedule. Occasionally, a rough schedule of work is included with the proposals submitted by the A/E. This may include the dates of preliminary and final drawing submittals. But this type of schedule is not adequate when a very tight construction schedule is required. Long-term delivery items must be given priority. If the new work interrupts production, accurate scheduling is essential.

There are two common methods of graphically describing a design and construction schedule. The simpler one is the bar chart. Figure 4 shows a typical bar chart for a

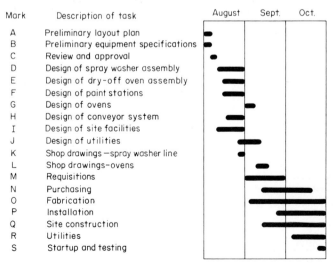

Mark	Description of task	August	Sept.	Oct.
A	Preliminary layout plan			
B	Preliminary equipment specifications			
C	Review and approval			
D	Design of spray washer assembly			
E	Design of dry-off oven assembly			
F	Design of paint stations			
G	Design of ovens			
H	Design of conveyor system			
I	Design of site facilities			
J	Design of utilities			
K	Shop drawings —spray washer line			
L	Shop drawings–ovens			
M	Requisitions			
N	Purchasing			
O	Fabrication			
P	Installation			
Q	Site construction			
R	Utilities			
S	Startup and testing			

Fig. 4   Typical bar chart for a conveyorized cleaning and painting system.

sample project. The other, more sophisticated, is the critical path method (CPM) as shown in Fig. 5.

The bar chart indicates the date of the beginning and completion of each unit of operation. These units may be labeled "preliminary design of treatment area," "shop drawings of pipe supports," or "requisition of pumps."

The project engineer of the A/E should discuss and determine all aspects of the schedule with the plant engineer. Some of the critical factors limiting a schedule include:

Marketing requirement for the product
Disruption of production
Stockpiling of products before construction
New utilities

From the A/E's point of view, some limiting aspects are:

Availability of personnel on staff
Results of testing, soil, and waste-water analysis
Availability of data

The establishment of a schedule at the beginning of the project allows the plant engineer to plan his production and allocation of funds, assign plant and administration personnel, and review the progress of the A/E and contractor. The A/E also can determine staff assignments, emphasize critical items, and coordinate other projects in the office. The schedule also tends to keep both the plant engineer and the A/E from delaying or procrastinating on decisions or actions. After reviewing the scheduling,

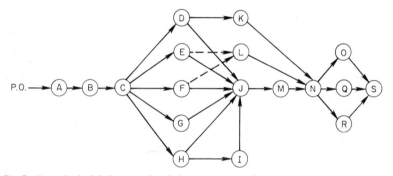

Fig. 5 Typical schedule by critical path for a conveyorized cleaning and painting system.

management can determine whether it will do part of the construction, fabrication, and installation with its own in-house force or whether it will contract the work out. On time and material A/E contracts, the plant engineer has a good tool to continuously judge if the cost of the A/E's services is remaining on plan.

Figure 5 illustrates the critical path method. The encircled letter indicates the unit of operation or decision listed on the bar chart. The number between circled tasks indicates the estimated time in days or weeks to complete each unit of operation. By adding the total elapsed time along each path from A to S, the longest path can be determined. This longest path is called the critical path. Any delay in this specific path would delay the entire project.

On complex, long-duration projects, the data of the critical path system are processed by computer. In this method, final completion dates are continuously corrected by actual elapsed time.

Whatever system is used, the plant engineer should keep in mind that the chart should be in keeping with the size and complexity of the job. It should not be too complicated, since maintenance of the chart can be a full-time job in itself. There will be many changes on each job before it is finalized.

Some project engineers use cards attached to a 2 x 3 foot board with a piece of drafting tape. Noted on the upper left corner is the start, and on the right upper corner is the completion. As the work on the project progresses, more steps, decision points, and alternatives become apparent. Shifting the cards on the board is easier than erasing and rewriting. After the net work diagram is set up, the critical path can be easily established.

As a final note on the technical aspects of the relationship between the plant engineer and the A/E firm, some mention should be made of the desire for standardized procedures. It is in this interest that some firms prefer to have all engineering drawings on their own paper and in their own format. This facilitates filing, cross-referencing, and storage. In this case, the plant engineer should furnish the A/E with vellums for drawings, calculation sheets, and stationery for specifications. In addition, the plant engineer should stipulate drafting standards, nomenclature, and special details. These special details can be trapping of steam lines, instrument hookup, color coding, and type of manufacture of valves, instruments, and other equipment.

FINANCIAL

The foundation of business is confidence, which springs from integrity, fair dealing, efficient service and mutual benefit. Mutual benefit requires that a professional contract be arranged between management and the A/E. The compensation schedule may vary depending upon the type of project and the services expected of the A/E.

On projects involving design of new facilities, where these facilities are neither too complicated nor repetitious, a payment of a percentage of the overall construction cost is usual.

Other projects that do not involve extensive construction or the risk of major complications lend themselves to a fixed lump sum.

For projects requiring extensive studies, without a defined scope, a salary cost times a multiplier plus direct nonsalary expenses defined in the contract agreement are the most equitable form of compensation.

It goes without saying that the plant engineer should not cause any meandering, detours, or extensive studies, especially when working under the first two contracts. This will justifiably cause demands for "extra compensation" or hard feelings, at the least. If the scope of the work has been changed, an addendum to the contract must be made immediately. This is in the interest of fairness, and it strengthens mutual confidence.

In view of the fact that the kind of contract written decides the method of compensation, how important are formal purchase orders? To what extent should formal purchase orders be used when there are changes, additions, or reductions in the original scope of the project? Normally a purchase order requires a substantial amount of time. Often a requisition, cost estimate, justification, and approval by top management are required before a purchase order for change of scope is approved. This is often too time-consuming for an emergency change. The plant engineer and the A/E must make verbal and nonverbal agreements to enlarge the scope of the project. After the heat of the emergency is long past, there may be a disagreement as to the amount of extra work that was done. It is essential that these changes be documented by records as soon as possible and that they be as detailed as possible.

Another financial problem is determining exactly when the obligated services of the A/E are ended. Long after the project is completed, should the A/E be expected to determine the settling rate of the floor or to rearrange room partitions when management is reshuffled? These nebulous areas of financial compensation may be sources of ill feelings between the plant engineer and the A/E.

Maintaining financial control over a continuously changing project can be a full-time job for any plant engineer. Any system that is used to record each revision will help the plant engineer. The A/E is aware that all changes must have the plant engineer's approval. The plant engineer is then alerted to the cost and consequences of a revision. Figure 6 illustrates a form designed to keep the A/E and the plant engineer aware of the ramifications of each revision.

To provide the plant engineer with better control over the project, it is helpful for the A/E to maintain a daily engineering progress report. This is especially true when the A/E has a large staff working on major projects. Figure 7 shows a typical report in which the A/E lists the number of people of each discipline involved on the project. This procedure has the advantage of informing management that a full staff is working, and it also backs up the monthly statements from the A/E.

The plant engineer's financial responsibilities with the A/E begin with the arrangement and signing of the contract. These responsibilities extend into revisions and their monetary ramifications, tabulations of engineering hours, and the decision as to which "extras" require additional monetary compensation.

PAGES____ PAGE____

PROJECT REVISION

Project_____ Project Rev No. _____

Date_____ File No. _____

Description of revision:

Equipment affected:

Cause:

Action:

Extra work order   (Yes)   (No)   No. _____

Starting date_____ Completion date_____

Requested by _____

Originator_____ Project Engineer_____

Distribution

Div. Mgr.	Proj. Engr	Sales	Chief Dr.	Struct.	Elect.	Const. Mgr. (2)	Mech
Ch. Engr.	Process	Est.	Mat'l.	Piping	Inst.	Purch.	

Fig. 6 Typical project revision form.

PROFESSIONAL

The extent of the A/E's responsibilities is directly related to the role assigned to him by plant management. An A/E who is retained directly by management is considered a "prime professional." A prime professional has the responsibility of overall planning and coordination of the design and construction, administration of all professional services needed, cost estimating, budgeting, and cost control. The prime professional is directly responsible to management.

When the A/E serves management indirectly through another professional, the A/E is considered a "nonprime professional." As a nonprime professional, the architect/engineer must maintain control of work for which he has professional responsibility, whereas he may have no concern for the overall aspects of the job. The plant engineer, in conjunction with management, must decide on the role to be required of the A/E.

PAGE_____ OF__

DAILY ENGINEERING PROGRESS REPORT

Customer _____ Date _____
Location _____ Job No. _____

Project: _____

Number of personnel on project _____
Number of personnel absent _____

Classification	Personnel assigned	Additional requirements	Progress
Project staff Process Material control Piping Structral Architectural Civil Material handling Process equipment Instrument Electrical Clerical Service Miscellaneous			
			Delays:
			Remarks:
Total			

Project Engineer _____

Fig. 7 Typical daily engineering progress report form.

The plant engineer can expect the following basic services, regardless of the A/E's role. These, of course, should be mentioned in the contract. There are basic services in both preliminary phase and the design phase of every project.

In the preliminary phase these services include conferences with other architects, engineers, and others engaged in the project; conferences with management, building officials, and regulatory agencies to establish the scope of the project and the requirements of alternate designs; soil investigation; economic studies of alternate construction systems; preparation of preliminary designs; and counseling on building form materials and methods of construction.

Basic services in the design phase include conferences; calculations for structural, mechanical, and electrical design; preparation of contract drawings; preparation of a reasonable number of prints of work in progress; and participation in establishing the material testing, fabrication, and construction inspection programs.

If the A/E is retained as nonprime professional, the A/E's responsibility ends when the design drawings and specifications have been turned over to the owner. From this point on, all further work involved with construction is handled by the project engineer or prime professional. When the A/E's services extend into the construction phase, basic services can include assistance in procurement of bids; consultation and advice during construction; preparation of supplementary sketches and details needed to resolve field problems; review of shop and erection drawings; review of laboratory, shop, and mill tests; and observation of construction in progress. (Note: such observations assist in quality control and in achieving conformance with drawings and specifications but do not guarantee contractor's performance.)

Predictable special services are also arranged by explicit notation in the contract. They often require compensation far in excess of the original engineering fee. Services include land surveys, soils investigation, and technical inspection of construction by a full-time resident engineer or inspector and supporting staff, as required, who will review and approve requests for monthly and final payments to contractors. These personnel will also issue certificates of completion to management, provide "as built" drawings, make field measurements to verify existing construction, and prepare shop details regarding reinforcing steel, structural steel, and so on.

Unpredictable special services are usually not included in contracts. The services are outside the scope of a lump-sum contract and should be viewed as justifiable extras. Some services include excessive preliminary designs; preparation of alternate designs; design work abandoned before completion; design work completed for work not built; redesign for major changes after approval of preliminary plans; evaluation and recommendations on contractor's claims; assistance to management as an expert witness in litigation arising on a project; and observation of construction for a period prolonged beyond period of services.

The role the plant engineer assigns to the A/E must be given careful thought, since the role carries implicit professional responsibilities. But where do any of these responsibilities end? This question brings up a very sensitive subject: the extent of liability on the part of the A/E.

Many A/E firms carry "errors and omissions" insurance policies, but there is a broad range of interpretation of what is meant by "liability." An error by the A/E can be anything from a north arrow incorrectly indicated on a plan to an underdesigned bolted connection of a critical member in a structure. The cost of correction of either of these errors, once built, can be in the tens of thousands of dollars, far in excess of the professional fee paid to A/E. It is these types of errors that are generally covered by an insurance policy.

Other factors which affect the A/E's liability include the question of inspection or supervision services during construction. Another is changes made without the approval of the A/E. If management wishes to hold the A/E fully responsible for complete implementation of his services, he should be required to provide complete and continuous inspection. But the A/E must be paid for that service. In addition, all changes made should be submitted to the A/E for review and approval. If the A/E is to be held liable for the construction, he must be given authority to have the plans and specifications followed exactly. But proper, continuous inspection is very costly. Construction inspection has become a big business and, in some cases, inspection has cost more than the design of the project. Inspection can include testing of materials, compaction of soil, reinforcement, concrete, checking torsion on high-strength bolts, and so on through the scores of trades.

If the plant engineer does not specifically require the A/E to take full responsibility for construction, most firms will provide liaison with the job. They then feel that "adequate" inspection has been provided. There is a great difference between liaison intended to ensure adequate inspection and actually supplying inspection.

Many engineers feel that "adequate inspection" is provided by visiting the job a few hours each week. Serious problems can usually be spotted in this way, but complete, risk-free inspection is not necessarily being provided.

Because of the great time required to give detailed, continuous inspection, its cost should be carefully weighed by management. The entire question of inspection and supervision should be clarified in the negotiations or at least during the early phase of work. A practical solution to the dilemma can be found in assigning a project engineer from the plant engineering department to provide complete, continuous inspection. Such a supervisor would have the proper authority over the contractors. Any questions that arose would be referred to the A/E as part of the A/E's construction supervision, but responsibility for faithful reproduction of plans would lie with management and management's representative.

As a last note, in dealing with the A/E firm, the plant engineer should recognize the code of ethics which governs the activities of these professionals. A conscientious A/E would consider it unprofessional and inconsistent with honorable and dignified bearing to act in any of the following manners:

To accept any remuneration other than his stated charges for services rendered to his clients

Not to act as a faithful agent or trustee in professional matters to his client

To attempt to injure, falsely or maliciously, directly or indirectly, the professional reputation, prospects, or business of another engineer

To review the work of another engineer for the same client without the knowledge or consent of such engineer or if such engineer were still connected with the work

Both parties in any contractual agreement and business relationship must realize that they are dealing with professionals who perform their duties and services consistent with a code of ethics.

PROJECT PROBLEMS

Highly qualified plant engineers owe their ability to years of experience in which countless problems have arisen and were eventually solved. There is much to learn from their project problems. Some typical ones are listed below:

1. Change of scope of project due to changes in marketing, fund allocation, delivery of key equipment, etc.
2. Conflict of opinion on design between A/E. Contractor or plant engineer
3. Contractor-induced changes which are intended to save money for the contractor without changing the final product
4. Split responsibility of design and construction between plant engineering staff and A/E staff
5. A/E subcontracting most of his services to questionable firms
6. Gray areas of responsibility in interface of various facets of project
7. Overlapping responsibilities of two engineering firms
8. "Turn key" projects—when a contractor hires an A/E firm that is answerable only to the contractor
9. Extent of "engineering supervision" during construction.
10. Ownership of plans

Since there are no ready made answers to these problems, it is recommended that every plant engineer anticipate and prepare for them.

REFERENCES

1. *Professional Practice of Structural Engineering of Buildings,* ASCE Manual and Report on Engineering Practice, no. 45, American Society of Civil Engineers, April 1966.
2. *Consulting Engineering, A Guide for the Engagement of Engineering Services,* ASCE Manual and Reports on Engineering Practice, no. 45, American Society of Civil Engineers, April 1964.
3. Daniel W. Mead: *Standards of Professional Relations and Conduct,* ASCE Manuals of Engineering Practice, no. 21, American Society of Civil Engineers.
4. W.J. King: *The Unwritten Laws of Engineering,"* American Society of Mechanical Engineers.
5. *The Civil and Professional Engineers' Act—The Land Surveyors' Act Rules and Regulations,* State Board of Registration for Civil and Professional Engineers, State of California, 1967.

Chapter 3

Negotiation for Architect/Engineer Services

T. G. MEIKLE

Manager, Facilities and Plant Engineering Division, Jet Propulsion Laboratory
California Institute of Technology

INTRODUCTION

The architect/engineer negotiation process commences when the plant facilities engineer defines a certain goal to be accomplished requiring outside professional assistance to meet the objective. Upon defining the objective, it is then incumbent upon the plant facilities engineer to ascertain the type of professional architect/engineer services required.

Let us examine the definition of the goal to be accomplished, as it is most crucial to obtaining the proper professional services and the end result desired.

The most common way of defining work to be accomplished is for the plant facilities engineer to prepare a set of architect/engineer design criteria. Should the plant facilities engineer's staff be too small, this work can be performed by the selected architect/engineer and considered as studies.

The architect/engineer design criteria should include the following minimal information:

1. Project description and reference documents
2. Scope of work for architect/engineer services
3. Design instructions and codes
4. Site development design requirements
5. Architectural design requirements

6. Structural design requirements
7. Civil design requirements
8. Mechanical design requirements
9. Electrical design requirements
10. Landscape design requirements

Item 2 is the essential ingredient to a successful architect/engineer negotiation. A typical scope of work may be as follows:

SCOPE OF WORK FOR ARCHITECT/ENGINEER SERVICES

General   In general terms, the scope of work includes the engineering design effort, and drawing materials which are required to produce final design drawings, specifications, bidding documents, and cost estimate in order to accomplish the following building construction: addition to owner's plant B, a new production building wing.

1. In specific terms, the architect/engineer shall perform the services and furnish related materials as indicated in the following tabulation:

1.1 Attend a discussion with plant facilities engineer to accomplish the following:

1.1.1 Review project scope and design concepts

1.1.2 Review problems on selection and availability of materials

1.1.3 Examine design, construction, and installation problems peculiar to this project

1.2 Visit the project site to acquaint the responsible architect/engineer project team members with building conditions and operations which relate to the design and construction effort. Inspect the site and related mechanical and electrical systems to determine and locate required connection points. Make record of these findings by field notes and sketches. This effort should include all necessary field information required for civil, architectural, structural, mechanical, and electrical design.

1.3 Prepare and present a concept submittal for the project which will document the design concepts and scope of work discussed under paragraph 1 above. This submittal is to include schematic drawings or single-line drawings in each design discipline involved in the project along with studies as may be necessary to resolve design and cost trade-offs. This submittal shall also include a budget cost estimate based on cost allocations to each section of the technical specifications which will be required for the project.

1.4 Submit preliminary review documents for the project which will include the information listed below:

1.4.1 Architectural plans, elevations, and sections.

1.4.2 Civil drawing(s) to show relation of project work to other structures, access, contractor work area, construction vehicle traffic control, and geographic data.

1.4.3 Structural engineering calculations and drawings adequate for sizing major structural elements and estimating structural cost. Where applicable, indicate methods of connections to existing structures.

1.4.4 Single-line mechanical flow sheets and calculations adequate for describing and sizing each system and estimating its cost.

1.4.5 Electrical single-line drawings adequate for system description and preliminary cost estimates. Indicate type of lighting design and include related calculations. Circuits beyond or downstream from lighting panels are not to be shown on these single-line drawings.

1.4.6 Outline specifications in brief form to indicate materials and equipments proposed for the project.

1.4.7 Preliminary cost estimate adequate for monitoring cost of the project and adjusting design or scope, if required, in order to hold within budget funds. Include breakdown of mechanical and electrical accounts in this cost estimate to define the totals in these disciplines.

1.4.8 Attend a one-day review of this preliminary design material at site for the purpose of resolving comments and questions related to the work as early as possible during the design phase.

1.5 Provide separate final design documents, including technical specifications drawings and cost estimate suitable for soliciting advance bids on long delivery items.

1.6 Submit checked final design drawings, technical specifications (owner will prepare bid invitations along with general provisions), calculations, and cost estimates for owner's review. Following the owner's review, correct the final documents as required to reflect the review comments and submit the original vellums to owner for final approval and signature.

1.7 Attend a final review meeting at owner's site to resolve all comments.

1.8 Provide revised drawings and specifications addenda as may be necessary during the bidding period to clarify or correct the bidding documents originally prepared in the architect/engineer's office.

1.9 Provide the reproduction work as tabulated below:

1.9.1 *Items or submittal estimates*   *Number of copies or prints*

Based on concept	10 sets
Preliminary design	10 sets
Final design	10 sets
Estimate based on bid drawings	Furnish originals

1.9.2 *Drawings*

Concept	10 sets
Preliminary review	10 sets
Final review	10 sets
For bid	Furnish originals

1.9.3 *Specifications*

Outline—preliminary	10 sets
Final review	10 sets
For bid	Furnish originals

1.9.4 *Calculations*

Based on concept	10 sets
Preliminary review	10 sets
Final review	10 sets
Related to bid drawings	Transparencies

2. Cost estimate to be prepared on the basis of costs in effect year of construction.

DESIGN INSTRUCTIONS AND CODES

I. Basic criteria. This facility is being built for a privately owned corporation and is subject to all local, state, and national codes affecting its construction and occupancy.

II. Design requirements. Specific design requirements in architecture and engineering will appear in subsequent sections.

III. Design instructions. The design instructions listed below are to be observed in preparing the plans and specifications.

    A. Drawings

      1. Size. Owner will furnish all drawing vellums with owner's title blocks. Vellum size will be 28 × 40 inches. All design drafting is to be placed on this size sheet. The architect/engineer may use a space not exceeding 3½ × 6 inches for his title block, placed preferably to the left of the owner's title block.

      2. Identification. Use the project name as the job title along with such other information as is necessary to describe the information included on the drawing. The type of work shown on each drawing shall be identified by letter per the following table:

> A—Architectural
> C—Civil
> S—Structural
> P—Plumbing
> M—Mechanical
> E—Electrical

      3. Scales

        a. Architectural: ¼ inch required for floor plans.

        b. Civil: 1 inch = 20 feet, with further requirement that civil drawings be keyed to coordinate system in effect at location of work.

        c. Structural: ¼ inch or ⅛ inch per foot.

        d. Mechanical: ¼ inch = 1 foot or larger if required.

        e. Electrical: ¼ inch = 1 foot or larger if required.

4. Symbols.   Prefer ASA standard symbols for respective types of work. Symbols in current use in architect/engineer's office are acceptable.   All symbols shall be identified on symbol lists included on the drawings.

5. Revised drawings.   All drawings used for bidding purposes shall be considered initial use, i.e., no revisions.   Drawings bearing revision notations may be used for reference or information in a bid set, if needed, in order to show existing conditions.

6. Drafting standards (civil).   In order to attain uniformity of presentation and to facilitate making additions and alterations to existing civil record drawings, it is necessary that the following drafting practices be observed:

   a. All existing contours on the 1 inch = 20 feet scale drawings will be shown as dashed lines.   These lines will be drawn with a sharp pencil and will be neat and legible.

   b. All new contours for construction will be shown as solid lines.

   c. All contours will be drawn at 2-foot intervals.   In the case of steep banks, they may be drawn at 10-foot intervals.

7. Reflected ceiling plans

   a. Must be ¼-inch scale

   b. Must show all light fixtures including exit and emergency

   c. Must show public address speakers and smoke detectors

   d. Must show air supply and return registers

   e. Must show sprinklers

   f. Must show any cableway or duct affecting reflected ceiling

   B. Specifications

   1. The Construction Specifications Institute (CSI) format shall be used in preparing technical specifications.

   2. The architect/engineer is to type the technical specifications on white bond paper which does not have a watermark.   The size is to be 8½ by 11 inches. Scope of Work for architect/engineering services will indicate whether or not the architect/engineer is to reproduce the specifications.

   3. The use of manufacturers' names or brand names is to be avoided in the specifications and on the drawings unless authorized by owner.   All items should be biddable by three or more manufacturers or vendors who produce like items of comparable quality.

   4. The technical sections are to indicate those items on which shop drawings are to be submitted.   Also, the individual technical sections are to indicate the items which require data for the operating and maintenance manuals and have the subcontractors' purchase orders include these requirements.   In instances where the architect/engineer has responsibility for preparing these manuals, the manufacturers' data will be delivered to the architect/engineer's office; otherwise, these data will be delivered to the owner.

IV. Construction cost estimates

   A. These estimates are generally classified as follows:

   1. Budget estimate

   2. Preliminary estimate

   3. Final estimate

   4. Change order estimate

   B. The above classifications relate to the degree of detail available at a given time for a given project.   On this basis, the following definitions evolve:

   1. *Budget estimate* is an estimate which plans or allows for the costs of the major elements of a project.   Thus the budget estimate is to have the following cost breakdown:

   a. Site work

   b. Architectural, civil-structural

   c. Mechanical

   d. Electrical

   e. Collateral equipment (usually indicated by owner if applicable)

   2. *Preliminary estimate* is an estimate based on information available on preliminary drawings, specifications, and construction requirements.   In this usage, "preliminary" should be construed as meaning "subject to change."   Design docu-

ments cease to be "preliminary" when they are approved by both the architect/engineer and owner. A preliminary estimate must be adequate for monitoring the estimated construction cost of a project in order to assure that the total cost can be held within available funds. Therefore, the architect/engineer must review estimated construction costs continuously and notify the owner's project engineer when these costs exceed 90 percent of the available funds.

The preliminary estimate is to be an engineering estimate subdivided by division and related subject as arranged in the CSI format for construction specifications. The material related to each of these subject items is to be listed and determined by a drawing takeoff, and the unit price applied to each material item is to include profit and all costs to the general contractor for the item in place. The degree of detail in this estimate is to be commensurate with the degree of detail indicated on the preliminary drawings and specifications. Items located external to a 5-foot line from a building are to be listed under site work. Lump-sum estimates are to be avoided if possible.

3. The *final estimate* is to be an engineering estimate similar to the preliminary estimate, with the added requirement that material takeoff be based on the final design or bidding documents. For major items, the sources or basis for estimated cost should be indicated. The final estimate must not exceed the allotted budget for this project.

4. A *change-order estimate* is an estimate based on a material takeoff and estimated labor man-hours required to modify, install, or remove. This type of estimate is to be arranged and priced to permit comparison with an estimate as furnished by a construction contractor. Therefore, profit and all items of cost or credit are to be itemized and priced individually.

ARCHITECT/ENGINEER SERVICES

Let us now examine the architect/engineer services available to accomplish the work and the many options the plant facilities engineer has to choose from.

The following services, shown in Figs. 1 and 2, published by the American Institute of Architects,* are available to the plant facilities engineer.

Descriptions of Comprehensive Architectural Services

The following brief descriptions of architectural services listed in CCAIA Document 100–73-A are provided to facilitate analysis of architectural services; establish areas of responsibilities of the architect, the client, consultants and others who render services; and to establish a budget for both time and amount of compensation.

Phase I—Pre-design services

SERVICE 1. PROJECT DEVELOPMENT SCHEDULING. After reviewing the client's philosophy, objectives and function, the architect will establish with or for the client a schedule for the development of the overall project. This schedule may include a comprehensive definition of the architect's services; the client's responsibilities; the time sequence involved with providing and fulfilling both; and the length of time required for the construction process. When time is a major factor the scheduling can overlap the architect's services and the construction process through advanced construction of segregated portions of the project. Review of each phase of service is important and time should be provided to permit schedule adjustment.

SERVICE 2. PROJECT PROGRAMMING. Project Programming is the process by which a detailed set of requirements for a proposed building project is developed and written. Includes determination of the amount of each type of space to be included in the building and the functional inter-relationship between these spaces. The design concept is based on the adaptation of these requirements to the client's available resources; to technical requirements; to human, physical and economic forces; and to site limitations. Special program needs and analyses relative to future facilities, systems and equipment may be included.

SERVICE 3. INTERNAL FUNCTION, FLOW STUDIES AND SPACE PLANNING. Project studies of internal functions, flow patterns and space planning are customarily developed in collaboration with the client. These include the detailed analysis of all operating functions and of the internal flow of material, people and utilities, so the architect can develop adjacence and circulation requirements. Each study will relate to an established number of personnel, special

---

* Document #100–73, California Council, AIA, *Guidelines for Estimating Costs of Professional Services*, pp. 6–17.

COMPREHENSIVE ARCHITECTURAL SERVICES

FIRM: _____
CLIENT: _____
PROJECT: _____
LOCATION: _____

CONSULTANT SERVICES:

_____ Structural	_____ Mechanical	_____ Electrical	_____ Civil
_____ Acoustic	_____ Food Handling	_____ Traffic	_____ Landscape
_____ Hospital	_____ Educational	_____ Management	
_____ Other _____			

CLIENT RESPONSIBILITIES:

| _____ Site Survey | _____ Economic Feasibility | _____ Written Program |
| _____ Construction Manager | _____ Soils Investigation | _____ Budget |

COMPENSATION METHOD: Cost plus Professional Fee   Direct Personnel Expense   Other

| Phase | Responsibility of | | | Date | | SERVICES | Time Budget | Rate Charge | Compensation Based on: | | Accrued Comp: |
	Client	Arch't	Arch. to Coord.	Reviewed w/Client	Activity Begins				Budgeted Time	Actual Time: Current Month	
I – PREDESIGN SERV.						1. Project Development Scheduling					
						2. Project Programming					
						3. Internal Function, Flow Studies/Space Plan.					
						4. Existing Building Surveys					
						5. Governmental Agency Consultation					
						6. Initial Concept and Budget Review					
						7. Economic Feasibility Analysis and Reports					
						8. Promo. Mats. Fund Raising/Project Financing					
						9. Administrative Services and Conferences					
						10. Principal's Time					
						11.					
						SUB TOTALS:					
II – SITE DEVELOPMENT						1. Site Analysis and Selection					
						2. Site Master Planning					
						3. Detailed Site Utilization Studies					
						4. On-Site Utility Studies					
						5. Off-Site Utility Studies					
						6. Zoning Analysis and Processing					
						7. Administrative Services and Conferences					
						8. Principal's Time					
						9.					
						SUB TOTALS:					
III – DESIGN SERVICES						1. Architectural Schematic Design					
						2. Engineering Systems Analyses					
						3. Architectural Design Development					
						4. Statement of Probable Construction Cost					
						5. Special Design					
						6. Landscape Design					
						7. Interior Design					
						8. Graphics Design					
						9. Furniture and Special Fixture Design					
						10. Renderings, Models and Mock-ups					
						11. Governmental and Regulatory Agency Review					
						12. Administrative Services and Conferences					
						13. Principal's Time					
						14.					
						SUB TOTALS:					
						GRAND TOTALS:					

Fig. 1

facilities, equipment, programmed space usage, flexible space, material handling and provisions for future expansion. Includes presentations in graphic and written form.

SERVICE 4. EXISTING BUILDING SURVEYS. Includes photographic and measurement surveys of existing conditions to develop accurate data and drawings on existing facilities for use in alteration and/or addition projects. When working drawings are available from an original construction project, a building measurement survey to verify the drawing accuracy and to record any changes from the original may be necessary.

SERVICE 5. GOVERNMENTAL AGENCY CONSULTATION. Includes preparation of material for and consultation with local, county, regional, state and federal agencies having jurisdiction, regarding the applicable laws, statutes, building codes and regulations affecting the project, to insure that accurate information is available before the initial design concept is developed.

SERVICE 6. INITIAL CONCEPT AND BUDGET REVIEW. The initial concept is created following careful study and analysis of the project program and space planning requirements. Includes illustrating diagrammatically the size and relationship of the project components. A probable construction budget can then be prepared, using square foot cost figures as a basis for calculating the anticipated cost of the several elements involved, and presented for review.

SERVICE 7. ECONOMIC FEASIBILITY ANALYSIS AND REPORTS. Analysis of the economic feasibility of any building project includes establishing three things; total project cost,

Phase	Client	Arch't	Arch. to Coord.	Review w/Client	Activity Begins	SERVICES	Time Budget	Rate Charge	Budgeted Time	Actual Time: Current Month	Accrued Comp:
IV – CONSTR. DOCUMENT						1. Architectural Working Drawings					
						2. Structural Working Drawings					
						3. Civil Working Drawings					
						4. Mechanical Working Drawings					
						5. Electrical Working Drawings					
						6. Specifications and General Conditions					
						7. Governmental/Regulatory Agency Approvals					
						8. Special Bid Documents					
						9. Final Statement of Probable Construction Cost					
						10. Administrative Services and Conferences					
						11. Principal's Time					
						12.					
						SUB TOTALS:					
V – BID. & NEG.						1. General Bidding Documents					
						2. General Construction Bidding					
						3. Negotiated Construction Bidding					
						4. Segregated Construction Bidding					
						5. Addenda and Drawing Revisions					
						6. Construction Agreement					
						7. Administrative Services and Conferences					
						8. Principal's Time					
						9.					
						SUB TOTALS:					
VI – CONSTRUCTION						1. Construction Contract Admin./Conferences					
						2. Construction Job Cost Accounting					
						3. Quotation Requests, Review/Change Orders					
						4. Clarifications					
						5. Shop Drawings and Submittal Review					
						6. Construction Observation and Certification					
						7. Testing and Inspection Coordination					
						8. Full Time Project Representation					
						9. Final Acceptance					
						10. Administrative Services and Conferences					
						11. Principal's Time					
						12.					
						SUB TOTALS:					
VII – POST CONST.						1. Maintenance and Operational Programming					
						2. As-Built Drawings					
						3. Warranty Reviews					
						4. Client Conferences					
						5. Administrative Services and Conferences					
						6. Principal's Time					
						7.					
						SUB TOTALS:					
VIII – SPEC. SERV.						1. Special Studies					
						2. Computer Applications					
						3. Fine Arts and Crafts					
						4. Expert Witness					
						5. Architectural Competition Advisor					
						6. Administrative Services and Conferences					
						7. Principal's Time					
						8.					
						SUB TOTALS:					
						GRAND TOTALS:					

Fig. 2

possible financing needs and return on investment.   Total project cost includes land, construction cost, furnishings, architectural and engineering fees, interest during construction, taxes and insurance during construction, legal fees, miscellaneous and contingency items.   Financing needs include establishing the necessary equity and cash required and the amounts needed annually for interest and amortization.   The return on investment can be estimated by differencing the annual operating cost and amortization payments to the gross annual income.   Economic feasibility reports may indicate alternative design schemes and options for the client's project.

SERVICE 8.   PROMOTIONAL MATERIAL FOR FUND RAISING AND PROJECT FINANCING SERVICES.   Promotional material to assist the client in raising funds includes the preparation of written descriptions of the project and reproducing diagrammatic plans of the initial concept.   Perspective drawings, renderings and/or models may be included if the architectural design has been developed.   Project financing services include preparation, delivery and presentation of design drawings, specifications and reports to lending institutions in the client's behalf.

SERVICE 9.   ADMINISTRATIVE SERVICES AND CONFERENCES.   Includes all research, travel, correspondence, discussion and management performed by the architect in providing all pre-design services required for the client's building project.   Conferences with consultants, officials and the client in developing the project and in gaining the client's approval of each service are listed separately for scheduling purposes.

Phase II—Site development services

SERVICE 1.   SITE ANALYSIS AND SELECTION.   Includes assisting the client in evaluating a site for a proposed project or locating a site for the client to meet the needs of the proposed building project.   Includes comparative studies of the physical characteristics of alternate sites to test the adequacy of each with regard to the proposed project.   Site analysis includes a detailed study of the topographic and subsurface conditions, utilities, zoning and land use requirements, parking and traffic flow regulations and a determination of any deed restrictions and any existing or proposed easements.   Studies of labor potential, availability of special skills, labor relations and public relations values may also be included.

SERVICE 2.   SITE MASTER PLANNING.   Includes the delineation of a long-range master plan for the future overall development of the entire property, and phasing of the development, to assure the best utilization of the property and creation of a pre-planned total environment.

SERVICE 3.   DETAILED SITE UTILIZATION STUDIES.   A more detailed analysis of the particular site, to develop its full utilization capability and the optimum location of facilities. Includes review of the existing conditions, the topographic survey, the soils report and all code and planning requirements to establish all facility locations, grounds improvements and landscaping needed to prepare site development drawings.   Also includes consultation with structural, mechanical, electrical and civil engineers.

SERVICE 4.   ON-SITE UTILITY STUDIES.   Includes development studies of all on-site utility requirements to determine practical and economical solutions prior to preparing for design review, engineering and final working drawings.   May include electrical service and distribution, sewer and storm collection and drainage, water supply and distribution, fire control and alarm emergency lighting and protection, air conditioning and pollution control, site illumination and telephone service.

SERVICE 5.   OFF-SITE UTILITY STUDIES.   Includes establishing the size, capacity and location of all existing utilities adjacent to the building site and determining the cost and physical requirements for making connection thereto in preparation for engineering and final working drawings.   Includes design and engineering for additional off-site utilities and environmental impact studies.

SERVICE 6.   ZONING ANALYSIS AND PROCESSING.   Includes consultation with the client and planning director to determine whether the project conforms in use to the district in which the site is zoned.   Includes applying for adjustments, variances or use permits with supporting data and providing evidence that conditions designated thereby will be complied with.   Includes petition of amendment for rezoning when practical, attending all hearings and appealing as required.

SERVICE 7.   ADMINISTRATIVE SERVICES AND CONFERENCES.   Includes all research, travel, correspondence, discussion and management performed by the architect in providing all site development services required for the client's project.   Conferences with consultants and the client in developing the site and in gaining the client's approval of each service are listed separately for scheduling purposes.

Phase III—Design services

SERVICE 1.   ARCHITECTURAL SCHEMATIC DESIGN.   Schematic design studies may offer one or more possible solutions to the client for selection and approval.   Studies may include simple diagrammatic plans, vertical sections and perspective sketches illustrating the project program.   Client approval of one scheme is essential.   A statement of probable construction cost may then be made using the cost per square foot of floor area method with the scheme approved by the client.

SERVICE 2. ENGINEERING SYSTEMS ANALYSES.   Systems analyses are developed by the architect and his engineering consultants with plans, sections and calculations of the various engineering design options available for the project.   They may include structural, plumbing, air conditioning, electrical, sound, emergency, fire control and acoustical control systems.   Technical data is based on site conditions, exposure, weather, environmental and load requirements, local geophysical and aerodynamic conditions and economics.

SERVICE 3. ARCHITECTURAL DESIGN DEVELOPMENT.   With the approval of one schematic design study, the architectural design may then be developed and expanded in variable three dimensional design.   This includes more detailed development of the building's size, appearance and form with sketches, perspectives and drawings of plans, elevations, sections and certain critical construction details.   The various engineering systems analyzed are carefully considered in order that the final architectural design concept can be carried out efficiently and economically.   Client approval of the final architectural design is essential.   A statement of probable construction cost may then be made using the enclosure method with in-place units of cost based on the design approved by the client.

SERVICE 4. STATEMENTS OF PROBABLE CONSTRUCTION COST.   The probable construction cost of any project can only be estimated to a degree of accuracy commensurate with the level of design developed by the documents prepared for the project.   The size, quality and complexity of the project must be considered when the cost is to be predetermined.

Service includes preparing statements of probable construction cost using the cost per square foot of floor area method for the approved schematic design or the enclosure method with in-place units of cost for the approved design developed in three dimensions.   A reasonable contingency must be included before the contractor's overhead and profit percentage is added.   This service does not include a detailed estimate of construction cost with a quantity survey of material.

SERVICE 5. SPECIAL DESIGN.   When either existing conditions or a new project requires special design and research, studies may be performed by the architect with special consultants.   Service may include studies involving acoustics, chemistry, design, education, emergencies, fine arts and crafts, fire control, food service, health, heat control, insurance, industry, law, medical facilities, parking, pedestrian conveyance, safety, space, structures, traffic, vision and weather, etc., and reports to the client.

SERVICE 6. LANDSCAPE DESIGN.   Includes analysis of natural, physical and social determinants and studies of the locations of all planting and ground improvements after the building has been located on the site.

SERVICE 7. INTERIOR DESIGN.   Includes design studies of all interior space requiring special division, finishes, space use, furniture and equipment layouts, lighting, sound attenuation, texture and color control with sketches and material specifications for client approval.

SERVICE 8. GRAPHICS DESIGN.   Includes design studies, sketches, layouts and cost determinations for special signs, symbols, space enumeration and identification, operational and functional indicators, and directional signing.   May include graphics work in corporate symbolism, letterheads, office forms, special effects design such as "supergraphics," brochures, advertising and type, color and material selections.

SERVICE 9. FURNITURE AND SPECIAL FIXTURE DESIGN.   Includes design studies, sketches and layout drawings for the manufacture of custom furniture, custom fittings, special fixtures, hardware and building accessories with cost determinations and material specifications for client approval.

SERVICE 10. RENDERINGS, MODELS AND MOCK-UPS.   Building projects may require the use of varying types of finished renderings, models or mock-ups for design presentations.   Services include establishing the media to be used, framing, size and the reproduction characteristics of renderings; the scale, finish and material of models; and the location of development and the size of mock-ups.   Services also include the preparation of suitable drawings to be used by delineators, artists, model makers and contractors for cost quotations, for client approval and for the completion of the work.

SERVICE 11. GOVERNMENTAL AND REGULATORY AGENCY REVIEW.   Includes presentation of preliminary portions of construction documents to the necessary governmental and regulatory agencies for review and information.   Service may involve correspondence, applications, paying fees and making presentations to federal, state, regional, county or community agencies and utility companies depending on the project type and location.   Examples include review by planning commissions; building departments; fire officials; public works, public health, industrial safety, civil defense, flood control, street and highway departments; sanitary districts; fine arts commissions; subdivider committees; and telephone, water, power and gas companies.   Their authority is established by law, code, ordinance, deed restriction and service in the interest of public health, safety and welfare.

SERVICE 12. ADMINISTRATIVE SERVICES AND CONFERENCES.   Includes all research, travel, correspondence, discussions and management performed by the architect in providing all project design services required for the client's project.   Conferences with consultants, officials and the client in the design development and in gaining the client's approval of each service are listed separately for scheduling purposes.

Phase IV—Construction document services

SERVICE 1. ARCHITECTURAL WORKING DRAWINGS. The architectural working drawings are prepared from the approved Design Phase drawings with two dimensional graphic presentations such as plans, elevations, sections and details illustrating the design, location, size and dimensions of the project and of the parts thereof. Notes on the drawings support and explain the graphic representations. Schedules are tabulations of items of a similar nature used to limit repetitive drawing and notes. Standard symbols and material indications are used to simplify drawing explanations.

SERVICE 2. STRUCTURAL WORKING DRAWINGS. Includes preparing structural working drawings, in concert with the architectural working drawings, which present graphically the complete structural concept of the project and include all details, schedules, notes and information necessary to facilitate its construction. Includes the preparation of engineering calculations which establish the size, dimension and capacity of foundations, structural reinforcing, walls, columns, beams, floor and roof structure and confirm the ability of the structure to withstand various lateral forces. Includes careful coordination with mechanical, electrical, civil and architectural drawings and design.

SERVICE 3. CIVIL WORKING DRAWINGS. Includes preparing civil working drawings from the approved Site Development studies to represent graphically those features dealing with on- and off-site improvements such as utilities, roadways, bridges, culverts, drainage, grading, excavation, compaction, shoring, underpinning, retaining walls, parking lots and fire systems. Includes the preparation of engineering calculations which establish the size, shape, dimension and capacity of the work involved. Includes careful coordination with landscape design and mechanical, electrical, structural and architectural drawings.

SERVICE 4. MECHANICAL WORKING DRAWINGS. Includes preparing engineering calculations for all heating, ventilating, air conditioning, plumbing work and fire protection systems required by the approved architectural design and engineering analysis to establish the size, shape, dimension and capacity of the various elements involved. Includes preparing mechanical working drawings to represent graphically with plans, sections, details, schedules and notes, all information necessary to construct the mechanical work. Includes careful coordination with the structural, electrical and architectural drawings to insure proper clearances and location for all duct work, piping, support and equipment.

SERVICE 5. ELECTRICAL WORKING DRAWINGS. Includes all electrical engineering services, following the approved engineering systems analysis and architectural design, for power acquisition and generation (on- and off-site), major power distribution, interior and exterior lighting, telephone and communication systems, low voltage systems, direct current applications, emergency and special effects lighting. Includes preparing electrical working drawings to represent graphically with plans, sections, details, schedules, diagrams and notes all information necessary to install the electrical work in conformance with applicable codes, regulations and safety orders. Includes careful coordination with mechanical, structural, civil and architectural drawings to insure the correct location for all outlets, lighting fixtures, panels, switchgear, equipment and appurtenances.

SERVICE 6. SPECIFICATIONS AND GENERAL CONDITIONS. Includes the preparation of specifications which are written requirements that the Contractor shall provide all labor, material, tools, equipment and services necessary to fabricate, furnish and install all material, finishes, construction systems, equipment, furniture and fixtures called for by the drawings and described therein and to construct the complete building and everything incidental thereto in the best and most workmanlike manner.

General Conditions are standardized provisions of the construction contract describing the rights, responsibilities and relations of parties to the contract as well as the related duties and responsibilities of the architect.

Supplementary General Conditions may be written to modify or extend the general conditions as the special details or location of a building project may require.

SERVICE 7. GOVERNMENTAL AND REGULATORY AGENCY APPROVALS. Service includes making application to federal, state, regional, county or community agencies and utility companies; presentation of copies of the completed construction documents; paying fees and attending hearings to acquire the necessary governmental and regulatory agency approvals and permits for the construction of the building.

SERVICE 8. SPECIAL BID DOCUMENTS. Special drawings and specifications for alternate bid proposals may be required when the client needs to insure a bid within a limited appropriation. Alternate bid documents may cover better material quality, additional finishes or equipment and added stories, wings, rooms or areas for the project.

Special drawings and specifications for advanced bid proposals may be required when the client needs to occupy the new building at the earliest possible date. Advanced bid documents may cover subcontracts for site preparation, foundation or structural steel contracts to permit fast tracking or phased construction while the architect is completing the contract documents.

Special drawings and specifications for segregated bid proposals may be required when the client needs to order certain mechanical equipment, furniture, fixtures or technical services prior to the receipt of bids from the prime contractors.

SERVICE 9. FINAL STATEMENT OF PROBABLE CONSTRUCTION COST. When the working drawings and specifications are nearly complete a final statement of probable construction cost which includes alternative adjustments for the project can be made. At this stage the quantity and cost method of cost analysis can best be used to calculate the probable costs. Includes determining the quantity and cost of all materials, labor, tools, equipment and services needed for the work. To this total direct cost must be added the Contractor's overhead, the cost developed by the general conditions, a reasonable contingency and the Contractor's profit.

The Final Statement serves as a check on the budget, provides valuable information for bid review, approval of progress payments and evaluation of future contract modifications. In comparison, a detailed estimate of construction cost with a quantity survey may best be prepared by a professional construction cost estimator.

SERVICE 10. ADMINISTRATIVE SERVICES AND CONFERENCES. Includes all research, travel, correspondence, discussion and management performed by the architect in providing all construction document services required for the client's project. Conferences with consultants, officials and the client in the preparation of construction documents and in gaining the client's approval of each service are listed separately for scheduling purposes.

Phase V—Services during bidding and negotiation

SERVICE 1. GENERAL BIDDING DOCUMENTS. Services include the preparation, review, checking and reproduction of all of the General Bidding documents such as the Invitation to Bid, Instructions to Bidders, Proposal Forms, the Conditions of the Contract (General, Supplementary and other Conditions), the Working Drawings, the Specifications, all Addenda issued prior to the receipt of bids, and an example of the Agreement form. May include bid security requirements, performance bond and labor and material payment bonds.

SERVICE 2. GENERAL CONSTRUCTION BIDDING. Services include issuing copies of the Bidding Documents to either a selected list or an open list of bidders; answering any questions which the bidders may have about the design or the accuracy of the bidding documents; distributing of addenda to the bidders with notices of any changes in the bidding procedure; and presiding at the formal bid opening. May include pre-qualification of bidders and bidders conferences.

SERVICE 3. NEGOTIATED CONSTRUCTION BIDDING. Includes assisting the client in the direct selection of a Contractor with whom the cost and terms of the contract may be negotiated. Includes providing advanced bid documents when the completion schedule requires some portion of the work begin at an early stage in the preparation of the documents. Includes monitoring the proposal for the work and the contractor's performance.

SERVICE 4. SEGREGATED CONSTRUCTION BIDDING. When the electrical, mechanical, structural or any part of the general construction is to be performed separately there are many items of service which must be segregated such as separate special documents, accounting and additional administrative services to take bids, develop agreements and arrange for the work to be completed on schedule.

SERVICE 5. ADDENDA AND DRAWING REVISIONS. Addenda are written or graphic instruments issued prior to the execution of the Contract which modify or interpret the bidding documents, including drawings and specifications, by additions, deletions, clarifications or corrections. Addenda will become part of the Contract Documents when the Construction Contract is executed.

Drawing revisions may be necessary when the client makes a change in the program which requires additions to or deletions from the working drawings being prepared.

SERVICE 6. CONSTRUCTION AGREEMENT. Includes notifying the successful contractor of his award of the contract, and drafting an Owner-Contractor Agreement form for review and approval by the Owner's attorney; providing complete sets of the Contract Documents for signature and distribution to the Owner and the Contractor; receiving certificates of the required insurance and bonds and notifying the Contractor to proceed with the work.

SERVICE 7. ADMINISTRATIVE SERVICES AND CONFERENCES. Includes all research, travel, correspondence, discussion and management performed by the architect in providing all services during bidding and negotiation of the contract for the client's project. Conferences with consultants, contractors, attorneys and the client in the preparation of the Contract are listed separately for scheduling purposes.

Phase VI—Services during construction

SERVICE 1. CONSTRUCTION CONTRACT ADMINISTRATION AND CONFERENCES. Includes all research, travel, correspondence, discussion and management performed by the architect, established by the Client-Architect Agreement and the General Conditions of the

Contract, in providing all construction contract administration required for the client's project other than the services specifically listed in this phase. Conferences with consultants, contractors, building officials and the client during the construction period may be required as the work progresses.

SERVICE 2. CONSTRUCTION JOB COST ACCOUNTING. Includes maintenance of records on the Cost of the construction and all changes (additions and deductions) thereto; evaluation of the amount owed to the Contractor based on the progress of construction and payments certified theretofore; adjustments for unsatisfactory or uncorrected work. The complexities of job cost accounting increase as the construction contract arrangements vary from lump sum to unit price to cost plus. This service does not include anything more than the exercise of judgment relative to the value of work performed or verification that the Contractor has paid his Subcontractors, material suppliers or workmen.

SERVICE 3. QUOTATION REQUESTS, REVIEW AND CHANGE ORDERS. Includes preparation and issuance of the necessary drawings and specifications to describe the work to be added, deleted or modified; review for general accuracy the Contractor's quotation and detailed breakdowns of quantities of labor and materials and their costs; review for general validity of any changes in the contract completion time; recommendations to the Owner to accept, reject or question the quotation; secure the Owner's approval to act upon the modification; preparation of appropriate documents to modify the Owner-Contractor Agreement.

SERVICE 4. CLARIFICATIONS. Includes receipt of, and processing of, requests for clarifications of the Contract Documents received from the Contractor, including errors and/or omissions in the documents; consultation with and advice to the Owner on those matters which may effect the utilization of the project, extra cost or additional time; issuance of the appropriate instructions to the Contractor or modifications to the contract documents.

SERVICE 5. SHOP DRAWINGS AND SUBMITTAL REVIEW. Includes receipt, review, or comment on all Shop Drawings, samples, material submittals and other submittals required by the contract documents; review of those items with the Owner of particular interest to him; provision of copies to full time project representative; return of copies to the contractor, properly marked as to their disposition and status; and verification that changes required are actually complied with.

SERVICE 6. CONSTRUCTION OBSERVATION AND CERTIFICATIONS. The architect shall make periodic visits to the site to familiarize himself generally with the progress and quality of the Work and to determine in general if the Work is proceeding in accordance with the Contract Documents. Based on his observations at the site and on the Contractor's applications for payment, the architect shall determine the amount owing to the Contractor and shall issue Certificates for Payment in such amounts.

SERVICE 7. TESTING AND INSPECTION COORDINATION. Includes making arrangements, on behalf of the client, with the independent testing and inspection agencies to perform those services either specified or required which the client will pay for; determines and informs those agencies what materials or procedures are to be tested and/or inspected and the frequency thereof; establishes a procedure for notification of the agencies as to when their services are required; ascertains whether the required services are being performed; reviews the reports generated thereby for compliance of the materials or procedures with the requirements of the Contract Documents.

The architect does not conduct technical tests and inspections personally, nor does he make arrangements for having conducted those which are to be paid for by the Contractor, or to be made by governmental agencies having jurisdiction. He does review any reports generated by the same for compliance with the requirements of the Contract Documents.

SERVICE 8. FULL-TIME PROJECT REPRESENTATION. The architect may recommend to the client that the architect be represented at the project site on a full time basis. With the client's authorization, the architect's service includes the interview and review of the technical, physical and personal qualifications of a representative; includes responsibility for his technical performance, personal conduct and direction; and includes the commencement, maintenance and termination of his employment.

The duties, responsibilities and limitations of authority of the Full-Time Project Representative should be set forth in an exhibit appended to the Client-Architect Agreement and/or the General Conditions of the Construction Contract.

SERVICE 9. FINAL ACCEPTANCE. Includes a detailed inspection and comparison of the work with the Contract Documents; conveyance to the Contractor, by an appropriate means, of the nature of any discrepancies found; inspection of the work with the Owner if desired; reasonable reinspection to ascertain whether corrections have been made; certifications to the Owner as to the completeness of the Work and for final payment. Includes, filing of Notice of Completion, receipt and review of warranties, and receipt of lien release of or bond indemnifying the Owner against any lien.

Phase VII—Post construction services

SERVICE 1. MAINTENANCE AND OPERATIONAL PROGRAMMING. Includes setting up a proper program and staff, either in-house or by contract, for the operation and maintenance of the physical plant and its equipment. Provision can be made for instruction by equipment manufacturer's representatives and the preparation of an operations manual for staff use.

SERVICE 2. AS-BUILT DRAWINGS. Includes securing from the appropriate source all information, drawings, etc., which indicate those matters as they actually are constructed which the Owner is, or will be, interested in; checking them generally for accuracy periodically during the course of construction and at final submission at construction completion; transmission to the Owner with appropriate identification and indication of their importance. Reproducible record drawings may be prepared by the architect for the Owner showing all significant changes made during construction as a part of this service.

SERVICE 3. WARRANTY REVIEWS. Includes consultation and advice in the event a particular item, material or piece of equipment fails to perform its expected function during the warranty period. Includes either conducting, or participating in the conduct of, a detailed inspection prior to completion of the warranty period, specifically looking for failures of items, materials or equipment which may not have been previously detected. Includes report of findings of said inspection and instructions to the Contractor for the correction of defects noted.

SERVICE 4. CLIENT CONFERENCES. Includes all research, travel, correspondence, discussion, and conferences performed by the architect in the preparation of any post construction period information requested by the client.

Phase VIII—Special services

SERVICE 1. SPECIAL STUDIES. Before, during or after project development, the architect may be authorized to make special studies for particular problems which relate to a specific project. Services include research and reports for special equipment items such as pipe organs; for color control of material and methods of handling; for radiation shielding analysis; for value analysis; and for studies involving marketing, human resources, public relations or security, etc.

SERVICE 2. COMPUTER APPLICATIONS. Architectural design, engineering calculations, project development scheduling, construction scheduling and cost analysis can all be aided by utilizing computer applications. Service includes preparation of input data, arrangements for software and hardware use, interpretation of printouts and the distribution of prepared results to concerned parties.

SERVICE 3. FINE ARTS AND CRAFTS. Includes making architectural design provisions for the use of stained glass windows, tapestry, paintings, mosiacs, frescoes, sculpture, mobiles, statuary and other objects d'art within any building project or site development. Includes aid in the selection of and in developing an agreement with a competent artist, or artisan, to design and create any fine art, craft or art form allied with architecture; providing them with design criteria; and making arrangements for the support, installation, illumination and protection of their work.

SERVICE 4. EXPERT WITNESS. A witness in a court case or other legal proceeding, or in an arbitration proceeding, who, by virtue of his experience, training, skill and knowledge of a particular field or subject, is recognized as being especially qualified to render an informed opinion on matters relating to that field or subject. Preparation for this service may include deposition review, study and pretrial conferences with the attorney presenting the witness. Testimony should be concise, direct and delivered in lay language.

SERVICE 5. ARCHITECTURAL COMPETITION ADVISOR. Following agreement to serve as an architectural competition advisor the architect establishes the competition process and type with the client. Establishes time schedule, compensation for and the total number of designs to be premiated. Develops program criteria through discussion, research and study of similar projects. Prepares competition program and designs program presentation for the client's approval. Recommends names and number of jurors and obtains AIA approval of program. Mails competition description and sends program to entrants. Answers questions on the program, receives entries, obtains hall for judgment and display, and reports to the jury on program compliance by all entries received. Attends judgment, receives the jury report, notifies the client and the entrants of design premiated by the jurors and maintains all public relations for the competition.

Once the goal has been defined and the type of professional service necessary has been determined, the negotiation process can commence. The plant facilities engineer at this stage must know exactly what the total project cost budget is, including architect/engineer fees, as well as having a general conception of the complexity of the project in terms of architect/engineer time required and number of drawings required to be produced. The construction schedule and beneficial occupancy date must be considered in the plant facilities engineer's estimate of construction cost. It is imperative that the plant facilities engineer ascertain the construction budget prior to entering negotiations, as approximately 80 percent of all architect/engineer fee negotiations are based upon a percentage of the construction cost.

ARCHITECT/ENGINEER'S COMPENSATION

The normal basis for architect/engineer compensation is:
1. As a percentage of the construction cost of a project
2. As a professional fee plus reimbursement of expense
3. As a multiple of direct personnel expenses

The percentage method (1) is the most used and has equity for both parties. It is essential, however, that a clear definition of scope of work be made and agreement be reached as to the construction cost budget and time of construction. The architect/engineer is responsible for producing a complete set of engineering documents that will produce the defined end result at the agreed-upon construction cost for a specified fee. The architect/engineer contract is binding upon both parties and therefore the plant facilities engineer, at the time of negotiation, should be represented by corporate legal counsel or retain legal counsel for the specific contract. In adopting the percentage of construction cost, the plant facilities engineer must be acutely aware of the impact either upward or downward on construction cost of owner-furnished equipment to be installed at time of construction.

The architect/engineer's proposal should be delineated in schedule form, identifying such items as studies, program definition, administration, meetings required, site planning, decorative and cabinet work, landscape work, etc.

When the project construction cost cannot be defined it may be necessary to adopt either (2) architect/engineer's professional fee plus reimbursement or (3) a multiple of direct personnel expense. Both these options give the plant facilities engineer the opportunity to use outside professional services to determine the scope of work and a project construction cost. A request for an architect/engineer preliminary engineering report usually obtains the desired results and is effective in programming a total construction project, from architect/engineer services through completion of construction.

A letter of invitation to propose, mailed together with the project criteria to the architect/engineer, is the normal way for the negotiation process to commence. After allowance of a reasonable number of days for the architect/engineer to review the written proposal, a conference of all interested parties is held at the plant facilities engineer's office to review in detail the written criteria. It is at this time that both parties have an opportunity to reach a common understanding of the project and also, where possible, to visit the site where the construction work will take place. It is important that the architect/engineer bring all supporting consultant engineers to this meeting so that all technical elements of the project may be reviewed. All ambiguities, clarification, and/or changes to the written criteria should be duly noted and officially documented, to be followed immediately by official addenda to the original proposal request letter. The architect/engineer shall then forward the proposal in writing in accordance with the specified criteria. If the architect/engineer proposal is satisfactory to the plant facilities engineer, a contract can be authorized and the work initiated. In the event that the architect/engineer proposal is unsatisfactory, it will then be necessary to have another meeting to review the proposal in detail until mutual agreement is reached as to scope of work and fee.

The plant facilities engineer and architect/engineer negotiation is unlike any other plant negotiation or contract in that two professionals are negotiating on the nebulous basis of an engineering concept. The negotiation should result in a mutually agreeable professional fee that will obtain the necessary architect/engineering services and documents, resulting in a usable facility in which both architect/engineer and plant facilities engineer can take pride.

Chapter **4**

Project Management

R. D. SHAFFER

Department Head, Facilities Engineering Department
Nuclear Division
Union Carbide Corporation

INTRODUCTION

The success of capital enterprises today is dependent to a significant extent on the ability to implement actions and manage costs and schedules in an effective and expeditious manner. For purposes of this chapter, capital projects are defined as those which involve such construction activities as the erection of new buildings or building additions and the installation or modification of equipment and facilities. In this era of rising and somewhat unpredictable economic escalation, close management and frequent reassessment of resources—whether they be equipment, materials, or personnel—are essential.

Experience has shown that these objectives can best be accomplished by centering the responsibility for such leadership in a qualified member of management, preferably with an engineering background, who acts as project manager. Any individual chosen for such an assignment, regardless of stature or position, assumes a vital role that is vulnerable to fortuities and developments that cannot be fully controlled. Those with the skills and aptitudes necessary to bring their project to a successful, timely closure within the allotted funds generally find such a task rewarding. Contrariwise, those who, through a lack of planning and capability, encounter constant difficulties during the course of the work and never gain effective managerial control may understandably rue the day they were asked to accept such a responsibility. One of the primary objectives of an experienced, talented project manager is not to allow small daily problems to grow into troublesome long-term crises.

MANAGEMENT TEAM CONCEPT

The essential prerequisite of successful project management is the selection of a manager with demonstrated administrative attributes and technical ability and a group of specialists to act as assistants. With this "team concept," each individual is chosen on the basis of qualifications. After being assigned specific duties, each is expected to shoulder full responsibility for the implementation of a particular phase of the project. The specialist team should be divided into functional groups: managers, design complement, engineering support, and representatives from other involved plant organizations. The type and number of members in each group should be dependent on the scope of work and overall job complexity.

Million-Dollar Projects

In addition to the project manager, the team roster for projects costing in the range of several million dollars should be made up of a principal design engineer to coordinate the complete design effort; responsible engineering designers in each required discipline (such as electrical, mechanical and structural) to develop, with the aid of draftsmen, the necessary drawings and specifications and to assist in the resolution of technical problems; a facility or project engineer to maintain liaison with all groups outside of engineering and to handle the business and administrative details; a cost engineer to provide detailed cost breakdowns of all facets of the work by participant and/or predetermined work categories and to formulate and update the official cost estimates; a procurement coordinator to maintain contact with outside vendors and ensure, as much as possible, that they furnish the desired materials or facilities in accordance with the specifications and schedule; and a construction engineer to conduct on-site inspections and ascertain that the field and shop work is being performed in accordance with the approved engineering documents. Personnel from maintenance, production, safety, and other participating plant organizations represent their interests in the project design and construction phase. This complement of people is considered the minimum necessary and should not impose an unreasonable overhead burden for projects in this expenditure range.

Multimillion-Dollar Projects

When the work scope entails an expenditure of several tens of millions of dollars or more, it is considered prudent to appoint several principal design engineers, each with a group of responsible engineering designers, and to assign each task force the responsibility for a major segment of the project. Depending on the complexity of the work, it may also be desirable to utilize several project engineers, cost engineers, procurement coordinators, and construction engineers. However, the division of a major project into several large sectors requires special vigilance on the part of the project manager in areas of interface.

Hundred-Thousand-Dollar Projects

For small jobs, the team can be limited to the responsible engineering designers and associated draftsmen and a cost, construction, and project engineer. The latter, in addi-

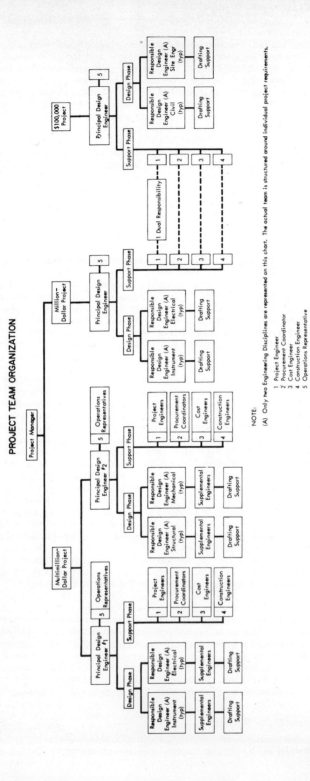

Fig. 1 Project team organization.

tion to assuming liaison and administrative duties, should also coordinate the design effort and the procurement phase.

A typical project organization and potential variations in team roster (depending on the magnitude of the work) are shown schematically in Fig. 1. Regardless of project size, it is suggested that a personnel index be published to list those assigned to the team and their primary responsibilities.

MANAGEMENT TEAM PROFILE

The specific duties of each member of the management team, as well as the prerequisite work experience and background judged essential for the selected individuals, are discussed below.

Project Manager

As head of the specialist team, the project manager is accountable for all phases of the work and directly supervises the activities of all team members whenever they are engaged in project-related functions. The project manager serves as the direct contact with higher management for the resolution of those problems requiring special dispensation. As company representative, the project manager coordinates that portion of the definitive design effort that may be performed by a commercially retained architect/engineer. Preferably, the project manager should be an experienced member of engineering supervision who is familiar with the overall plant operations, particularly in that area in which the special work is to be undertaken. Such a background provides insights into potential production and maintenance problems which might be encountered with the new facilities, a factor sometimes overlooked by those chiefly oriented toward engineering alone.

Principal Design Engineer

The person holding the next key role in the team, after the project manager, is the principal design engineer. In addition to coordinating the definitive design activities, it is recommended that the principal design engineer be designated as alternate to the project manager and assume responsibility for the entire effort in the manager's absence. During the course of the work, the principal design engineer should be continually aware of the design progress and make certain that all engineering tasks are being accomplished within the authorized funds and in compliance with the approved engineering and construction schedules. This individual should possess a technical background in the field of engineering which has the greatest impact potential on the overall design, i.e., that discipline which has the largest or key share of the work. An overall familiarity with plant operations would also prove beneficial, particularly when several design alternatives are available and one could afford a significant operational advantage. For exceptionally large projects where the work can be segregated into several parts, two or more principal design engineers may be utilized, each reporting to the project manager, as shown in Fig. 1.

Responsible Engineering Designers

Each responsible engineering designer is charged with producing an economical, reliable, safe design which meets the project criteria and conforms to applicable local, state, and national building codes and standards. This designer's activities are coordinated with those of the procurement coordinator to assure that all equipment specifications can be translated into real hardware at a reasonable cost. When a number of designers are required in a specific discipline to maintain the desired engineering schedule, one is selected as the responsible engineering designer.

Facility or Project Engineer

The duties of this team member include maintaining liaison with all personnel outside the engineering organization to inform them of the progress to date; reviewing all drawings and specifications with those plant officials who are in a client role to establish a common understanding of the basic design features; obtaining the necessary special approvals from such groups as the safety, medical, industrial hygiene, and mechanical test departments; and implementing the business and administrative details. The project engineer should issue all engineering documents for either comment or construction and make the financial arrangements necessary to ensure that the funding authorization is never exceeded. This individual should have a thorough knowledge of the operations in the area in which the special work is to be performed and be familiar with the applicable engineering, safety, and standard plant procedures.

Cost Engineer

This team member is held accountable for the formulation of all official cost estimates, working from bills of material and detailed drawings. The cost engineer's duties include predicting the labor required by crafts to perform a given task and considering the impact of the working environment on the manpower productivity. As the construction proceeds, the cost engineer adjusts the contingency to provide the minimum necessary to ensure that the remaining work can be performed within the authorized funding. The cost engineer's qualifications should include a background in engineering and construction estimating and a knowledge of material pricing, escalation, normal indirect burdens, acceptable profit margins, and other similar factors.

Procurement Coordinator

The primary responsibility for the timely purchase and delivery of materials and equipment should be assigned to the procurement coordinator. This individual has the responsibility for assessing the capability of commercial vendors to participate in the project. In order to minimize construction delays, the procurement coordinator must expedite the delivery of critical materials and equipment on a continuing basis. This person should possess an engineering background and be familiar with manufacturing practices. The procurement coordinator must, of course, be indoctrinated in the procurement procedures and have sufficient knowledge of cost estimating to judge the relative economical attractiveness of various sources of supply.

Construction Engineer

This member of the team is charged with ensuring that the field and shop work is performed safely and in accordance with the drawings and specifications. Whenever existing field conditions dictate a significant revision to the certified design, the construction engineer must in good time inform the principal design engineer. The required changes should not be initiated until a check has been made that sufficient funds are available to authorize the work. To perform these project activities effectively, the construction engineer should be familiar with safe construction methods and avoid proposed procedural shortcuts which could jeopardize job quality.

CONTROL TECHNIQUES

The team employs universally recognized techniques and methodology to pursue its mission. These include the development of an achievable plan for the engineering, procurement, shop fabrication, and construction phases; the establishment of a realistic schedule for each phase; a step-by-step implementation of the plan in accordance with the schedule; and a periodic review of the project status to reassess the anticipated total cost, to realign the remaining contingency, to reevaluate the viable uncertainties, and to rectify any serious scheduling problems. It is again emphasized that the successful management of a capital project cannot be accomplished by one person. There are too many details which require prompt attention. Such an undertaking must combine the talents of a number of individuals serving on a well-integrated team.

Developing the Plan and Schedule

Detailed planning and scheduling of each major phase of a project are essential before the definitive engineering is initiated. It is assumed that sufficient conceptual engineering has been completed to explore the practical alternatives and that the project as scoped represents the optimum installation.

Predesign meeting As a start, the project manager should call a predesign meeting for all team members. In addition to clarifying the definitive design criteria, the pertinent interfaces with other organizations should be discussed; the desired schedule for both the engineering and construction phases should be reviewed; and the funding picture should be assessed. The design-team members should then be familiar enough with the project scope to predict their participation and the resources they will require to perform their assigned tasks within the requested time. Similarly, the members of the engineering-support team should have a clear picture of their involvement and the funding limitations, which will serve as restraints in subsequent project planning and implementation.

Project Segmentation

In the initial planning, the project manager and the manager's associates decide on the best way to divide the overall work into the minimum number of manageable parts to facilitate a meaningful analysis of job progress. Some example formats for structuring scopes into proper segments are included in the text. While many different formats might be employed, those presented herein are of proved utility with regard to these examples. For large projects, many segments may be necessary; for smaller ones, two

ENGINEERING ANALYSIS SHEET

PROJECT SEGMENT	WORK DESCRIPTION	DWGS & SPECS SCHEDULED	DWGS & SPECS ISSUED	ESTIMATE OF ENGR COST	TOTAL ENGR EXPENDED TO DATE ($)	ENGR COMPLETED (%) BASED ON		ENGINEERING CONTINGENCY	
						DOCUM'TS ISSUED	DOLLARS SPENT	%	$

Approved: Project Manager _____ Principal Design Engineer _____ Date _____

Project Engineer _____ Cost Engineer _____

Note: Costs in thousands; update monthly

Fig. 2 Engineering analysis sheet.

or three may suffice. In segmentation, it is recommended that each new building, building addition, new process, or new facility be listed separately. An appropriate short descriptive title for each segment should be entered in the column headed "work description" on the engineering analysis, construction analysis, and project analysis summary sheets, Figs. 2, 3, and 4, respectively. The order in which the segments are tabulated is not important; however, each should be assigned a number in the column headed "project segment," and the same order and number should be utilized on each figure. It is suggested that the segments be listed in chronological order, i.e., those phases of the work that must be accomplished first should be listed first. The above three figures, in combination with the drawing and specification schedule, Fig. 5, and the procurement status sheet, Fig. 6, usefully serve as control documents during the course of the project.

Engineering plan To plan the definitive engineering, the responsible engineering designers should list the drawings and specifications they must prepare to depict their portion of the design. After approval by the principal design engineer, each document should be assigned a brief title and then listed on Fig. 5 in the expected order of completion. The drawings should be tabulated on a separate sheet from the specifications, but the same form should be utilized for each. Where possible, each document should be prenumbered to expedite cross-referencing between disciplines. It is recommended that whenever there are many project segments, separate drawing and specification schedules be prepared for each.

Engineering schedule For each entry on Fig. 5, the responsible engineering designers should indicate the anticipated start and issued-for-approval dates in the appropriate column. The principal design engineer must be sure that the last drawing or specification is planned for issuance in time to meet the associated procurement or construction schedule and that the interdependency of one discipline on another for critical engineering criteria has not been overlooked in the formulation of the overall schedule.

For those projects involving the purchase and installation of special equipment, the responsible engineering designers and the principal design engineer should confer with

CONSTRUCTION ANALYSIS SHEET

PROJECT SEGMENT	WORK DESCRIPTION	PROCUREMENT SUMMARY		OPER CONTR FIELD		CONSTRUCTION CONTRACTOR		PROCUREMENT CONTINGENCY	OPER CONTR CONTG'Y	CONST CONTG'Y	TOTAL CONST CONTG'Y
		EST COST	CTD*	EST COST	CTD*	EST COST	CTD*				

Note: Costs in thousands; update monthly
* Cost to Date

Fig. 3 Construction analysis sheet.

PROJECT ANALYSIS SUMMARY SHEET

PROJECT SEGMENT	WORK DESCRIPTION	OVERALL PROJECT SCHEDULE						ENGINEERING COSTS			CONSTRUCTION COSTS					TOTAL PROJECT COSTS		
		DEFINITIVE DESIGN		PROCUREMENT		CONSTRUCTION		OPER CONTR	OUTSIDE A-E	TOTAL ENGR	OPERATING CONTRACTOR				CONSTRUCT'N CONTRACTOR	TOTAL EXCLUD CONTING'Y	CONTINGENCY	TOTAL WITH CONTING'Y
		START	COMPLETE	START	COMPLETE	START	COMPLETE				PROC	FAB	FIELD	TOTAL				
		S*																
		A*																
		S																
		A																
		S																
		A																
		S																
		A																
		S																
		A																
		S																
		A																
		S																
		A																
		S																
		A																
		S																
		A																
		S																
		A																
		S																
		A																
		S																
		A																
		S																
		A																
		S																
		A																
		S																
		A																
		S																
		A																

Approved: Project Manager ______ Principal Design Engineer ______ Project Engineer ______ Cost Engineer ______ Date ______
Note: Project schedule should include month and year; costs should be in thousands
* S - Scheduled; A - Actual

Fig. 4 Project analysis summary sheet.

the procurement coordinator regarding the order in which the associated drawings and specifications should be issued. In this manner, the longest delivery items can be placed on order first. Similar consultations with the project and construction engineers can provide the planning insight needed to be certain that all documents required for a given construction package are issued at the same time. Sometimes such an effort can circumvent a lengthy delay for a few drawings or specifications.

To complete the engineering schedule, the issued-approved date should also be in-

DRAWING & SPECIFICATION SCHEDULE

DRAWING OR SPEC NUMBER	EQUIPMENT NUMBER	DRAWING OR SPECIFICATION TITLE		START	ISSUED FOR APPROVAL	ISSUED APPROVED	PERCENT COMPLETE
			S*				
			A*				
			S				
			A				
			S				
			A				
			S				
			A				
			S				
			A				
			S				
			A				
			S				
			A				
			S				
			A				
			S				
			A				
			S				
			A				

Principal Design Engineer	Responsible Engineering Designer	Project Segment
Project Engineer	Design Supervisor	Procurement Coordinator

* S – Scheduled; A – Actual

Fig. 5 Drawing and specification schedule.

PROCUREMENT STATUS SHEET

EQUIPMENT DESCRIPTION	SPECIFICATION		EST COST	VENDOR	DELIVERY SCHEDULES		
	NO.	ISSUED FOR PROC			REQUIRED BY	PROMISED BY	SHIPPING DATE

Principal Design Engineer _____   Cost Engineer _____

Procurement Coordinator _____   Project Segment _____

Fig. 6 Procurement status sheet.

serted by the responsible engineering designer; this is obtained by adding the number of calendar days needed to obtain all the necessary approvals plus that required to incorporate the comments to the issued-for-approval date. The total number of drawings and specifications for each project segment should also be entered in the third column of Fig. 2 and the earliest start and latest complete dates for the design of each project segment should be entered in the appropriate columns on Fig. 4.

The above engineering planning and scheduling concept recognizes the role that each member must play to assure successful attainment of the project goals.

Procurement plan   The decision concerning which materials or equipment should be purchased by the plant (i.e., the client) is made by the procurement coordinator. Normally, the client might purchase only those items that require such a long delivery time that orders should be placed even before a construction contractor is selected and those that are of great complexity, requiring a specialized knowledge that the construction contractor might not be reasonably expected to have. Similarly, the question of in-house fabrication in the plant maintenance shops versus purchase from outside sources also is the responsibility of the procurement coordinator; this judgment should be based on the relative economics, the impact on the in-house labor force, and the improvement in the construction schedule which might be attainable by fabricating key items in the plant shops. After approval by the project manager, the procurement coordinator should list the direct-purchase items in the left-hand column on Fig. 6. The specification number and the schedule date for issuance, obtained from the responsible engineering designers, should also be entered on Fig. 6, thus completing the procurement plan.

Procurement schedule   All direct-purchase items should be placed on firm order at an early date. The project manager and the project engineer should establish the required delivery dates for the special equipment based on the operational needs and the potential avoidance of construction delays. These critical dates should be entered on Fig. 6 by the procurement coordinator, who then should inform the principal design engineer of the date on which the related engineering document must be approved for purchase. Sufficient time must be allowed for the solicitation of firm quotations and subsequent manufacture. The earliest start or order date and the latest complete or delivery date entered on Fig. 4 by the procurement coordinator will complete the procurement scheduling.

Construction plan   Local shortages of many building materials and certain types of skilled craftsmen make it prudent to plan all construction work carefully. It is sometimes advantageous to employ several smaller construction contractors rather than a large firm. Such a circumstance arises when a significant portion of the construction is amenable to securing firm fixed prices for specific work segments. This approach can lessen the impact on the overall engineering completion date by allowing some construction to proceed while definitive design work not related to that construction package is still underway. The principal design and project engineers should assume the responsibility for this segmentation. One of the basic criteria for this planning step is to recognize the operational commitments and not propose a construction sequence which would result in frequent outages to production facilities. In a typical project involving the erection of a new building or building addition, the site work and installation of underground utilities could constitute the first package; the erection of the structure itself, including the interior services such as lighting, heating, ventilation, and the utility piping would make up the second; and the installation of the special equipment or systems would be the last. For extremely large projects, it may prove advantageous to subdivide the equipment installation by major areas within the building, thus allowing beneficial occupancy by the operating group in one sector while the construction is still in progress in another. Two factors are worthy of repetition: first, each package should be made up of a much similar work as possible to afford the most economical contract; second, each package should be large enough to interest several contractors, thereby promoting a competitive environment.

Construction schedule   With the construction properly segmented, the project and construction engineers should schedule each package consistent with the total work effort and the operational demands. The time allowed in each contract should be limited to that required to perform the specified work in a safe, orderly fashion. An excessively long construction period often leads to extra costs and undue managerial problems. The insertion of the start and complete dates for each project segment on Fig. 4 finishes the construction scheduling.

Developing the Cost Estimate

A crucial phase of project administration entails developing a meaningful cost estimate. This demands a careful appraisal of the engineering and construction work and the incorporation of that amount of contingency judged consistent with the degree and accuracy of the information available. The responsibility for this facet of project management belongs to the cost engineer. As stated previously, it is assumed that some prior arrangements had been made regarding project funding and that the anticipated project costs—previously developed from conceptual or preliminary plans and specifications—included the proper allowance for contingencies. With this as a start, the cost engineer should update the official estimate as the project planning, scheduling, and implementation proceed.

Engineering estimate   With the projected drawing and specification output as shown on Fig. 5, the principal design engineer in collaboration with the cost engineer should calculate the anticipated cost for the definitive design by project segment. The inclusion of a sufficient allowance for the support engineering personnel involved in cost estimating, procurement coordination, liaison, and construction inspection and for the administrative expenses will yield the projected total expenditure for engineering. These data should be entered in the appropriate column on Figs. 2 and 4. As a guide, the cost estimating should involve between 5 and 10 percent of the definitive design cost, depending on the job complexity; the field inspection should generally range between 3 and 10 percent of the construction expenditure, again varying directly with job complexity; and the administrative functions should add approximately 7 to 10 percent to all other engineering costs. If part of the definitive design is to be accomplished by a commercially retained architect/engineer, the estimated costs involved here should also be included on Fig. 4.

Total engineering costs vary widely depending upon the complexity and size of a project. A band which would cover 90 percent of the spectrum is 5 to 25 percent. The upper figure applies to small projects involving intricate process equipment and systems. The lower percentage limit is considered adequate for the erection of very conventional small buildings which have many repeatable elements.

When the services of a commercial architect/engineer are engaged, some effort is required on the part of client personnel to prepare the design criteria, which serve as the bases for the architect/engineer's effort. Also, the client's engineering staff must check the drawings and specifications generated by the architect/engineer prior to issuance for construction.

Construction estimate   As the definitive drawings and specifications are completed, the original estimate should be rated upward based on the approved design. This work should be supported by detailed bills of material taken directly from the drawings and material and equipment quotations obtained from reputable vendors. The labor rates should be those which will be in effect during the anticipated construction period. If the construction schedule extends beyond the term of the current union contracts, an appropriate escalation to the year of projected expenditure should be applied. It is suggested that this be a composite of three rates: one for labor, one for equipment, and one for construction materials as defined by such national publications as the *Engineering News-Record* and *Chemical Engineering Indices.*

Total project estimate   The total anticipated expenditure can be derived by adding an appropriate contingency allowance to the estimate for the engineering and construction phases. With the project scope defined in preliminary terms, a factor of from 15 to 25 percent of other costs would be prudent. Next, the total estimate should be subdivided into the project segments by the cost engineer with the aid of the principal design engineer, the project engineer, and other staff members.

When the cost engineer is satisfied that the current estimate is based on the real and total project scope, the engineering costs appear realistic, and sufficient contingency allowance has been included to cover the potential uncertainties, the cost engineer should obtain approval of the project manager and then enter the information in the appropriate columns on Figs. 2, 3, 4, and 6. The dissemination of these data to all team members will provide them with a complete picture of the anticipated expenditures and will indicate the cost boundaries within which all project segments must remain.

PROJECT IMPLEMENTATION

It is recommended that all concerned members of the client's staff be present at the predesign meeting to reconfirm that the project is properly scoped. After all last-minute changes have been incorporated, the project engineer should issue a copy of the entire package to all team members as well as to other interested plant personnel. Each month thereafter during the course of the work, these figures should be revised by the appropriate team member to show the progress to date by project segment.

Monitoring Engineering Progress

As the design proceeds, the principal design engineer should update the information on Fig. 2 regarding the number of drawings and specifications issued, the engineering costs for the current month, the total engineering cost expended to date, and the percentage engineering completed based on the documents issued and the total costs incurred. A comparison of the "scheduled" versus "actual" number of documents issued will indicate how well the engineering is proceeding. Similarly, a monthly analysis of the difference in the percentage engineering completed to date derived on the basis of documents issued versus expenditures incurred will provide a good clue of the overall engineering cost picture. The work in progress will cause the percentage computed by the first method to be lower than that given by the second, but whenever the incremental change is significant for several consecutive months, the current engineering authorization for this project segment may not be sufficient. In this event, the principal design and project engineers should increase the allocation as required; the additional funds must be obtained from the engineering contingency. Each month, the cost engineer should recompute the percentage of unused contingency based on the engineering work yet to be performed. If the remaining contingency percentage exceeds that originally provided by more than 10 percent and there are no foreseeable engineering overruns, the excess contingency should be allotted to the construction phase to fund project uncertainties.

As each drawing and specification is issued for approval, the respective responsible engineering designer should record the date in the appropriate column on Fig. 5. Similarly, after all comments have been incorporated and the document is issued "approved," this fact should also be noted. A comparison of the "scheduled" versus "actual" dates will reflect the engineering progress. If most drawings and specifications for one particular discipline are being issued "for approval" more than two weeks late, the principal design engineer should make arrangements to have additional manpower assigned to this task. The "percent complete" column on Fig. 4 should also be updated each month by the responsible engineering designer to show the current progress in terms of documents issued. A compilation of these data from all engineering disciplines will give the principal design engineer another "barometer" by which to evaluate design progress.

As the drawings and specifications are finished for each discipline's package of work, they should be checked by the engineering team before being issued "for approval." During this intensive review, efforts should be concentrated on eliminating design inconsistencies, dimensional errors, and construction interferences. Also, the proposed materials of construction should be scrutinized to ascertain that they are adequate for the intended service yet are the most economical available. After all comments of plant personnel have been satisfactorily resolved, the definitive design documents are ready for issuance as "certified for construction."

Updating Cost Estimate

As the drawings and specifications are released for construction, the cost engineer should refine the estimate on that portion of the project. These refined estimates should be inserted in the appropriate columns on Figs. 3, 4, and 6, after which the associated contingency should be adjusted to yield the same percentage as before. Implementation of this procedure until completion of design will result in an official project cost estimate based on the "certified for construction" drawings and specifications and a realignment of the contingency commensurate with the overall cost breakdown. It is hoped that ample project funding has been provided; if not, the contingency for all project segments should be lowered consistently to remain within the funding authorization.

The cost engineer should also insert in the appropriate columns on Figs. 3, 4, and 6 the firm quotations for the special equipment and construction packages as they are received in place of the official cost estimates. The contingency should then be adjusted to 5 percent of the fixed price for equipment and to 10 to 15 percent of the construction contracts, depending on the complexity of work. The former allowance is to cover such incidentals as shipping costs and sales tax, whereas the latter is to fund the field changes which always arise during any construction program. These values should also be entered on Fig. 3. When firm commitments are received for the in-house fabrication and fieldwork, these projections should also supersede the prior engineering cost estimates. A 10 to 15 percent allowance for contingency should be utilized here also. The procurement coordinator should enter the name of the successful vendor and his promised delivery schedule in the appropriate columns on Fig. 6. When this type of information has been received for all equipment to be purchased and for all construction contracts to be let, a complete synopsis of the anticipated construction funding is available.

Monitoring Project Progress

The status of each project phase should be kept current by a periodic update of the information on the management documents. Routine meetings of the project team will afford an opportunity to review the current status and discuss the potential uncertainties. As several of the project segments near completion, the cost engineer should adjust the associated contingency downward to leave an allowance for only that authorized work which remains. The money thus released should then be made available to fund either the field change notices brought to the attention of the team by the construction engineer or those uncertainty items which, if incorporated, would enhance the programmatic effectiveness of the facility. The latter category generally encompasses those refinements not absolutely mandatory to provide a satisfactory installation but considered highly desirable to improve such characteristics as flexibility. Items in this category are sometimes labeled "client preferences." Any such scope revisions should require the approval of the project manager.

Project Closure

Upon completion of each work package, the project engineer should make arrangements to have all affiliated accounts closed. Any uncosted authorizations and the remaining contingency should be assigned to other project segments on the basis of need. In this manner, the funding available at any given time is utilized to the maximum extent feasible.

When all phases of construction have been accepted from the contractors and the preoperational testing has successfully debugged all new equipment and facilities, a completion report should be issued, as discussed in more detail in Section 3, Chapter 5.

Experience has indicated that the features of project management described herein can be applied successfully to most capital projects.

Chapter 5

Completion and Acceptance

JOHN A. CARRARO
President, International Consultants

INTRODUCTION

The primary objective of any construction project is, naturally, completion of the project in a manner satisfactory to the owner, the architect, the prime contractor, and the members of the community in which the project is located. To assure realization of such a happy state of affairs, it should be recognized from the beginning that each of these people or groups of people involved have certain specific responsibilities to accept and act upon. Satisfactory completion of a project is seldom achieved without this candid realization that each party has certain definite duties and functions to perform.[1]

The preceding statements are part of a paper entitled "What the Owner Should Consider to Assure Contract Performance," by William E. Prather, which was delivered at the Industrial, Institutional and Commercial Building Design Conference held in Cleveland in March 1966. The balance of this paper is well worth reading and serves to complement the present writer's statements on the subject.

We also recommend review of "Merits of Incentive or Penalty Provisions in the Contract," a paper by George E. Stone, Jr., which was presented at the same conference. Mr. Stone outlines other methods that may help to bring a construction project to completion in the most efficient and economical manner possible. These are covered in the portion of the paper involving the "incentive" or "penalty" provisions of the contract.

COMPLETION AND ACCEPTANCE

Completion of construction of the facility by the general contractor and subsequent formal written acceptance by the owner are always the two long-awaited and last phases of the construction processes. But these two phases are by no means ever to be considered synonomous. The owner or his duly authorized representative on the project, in evaluating the general contractor's proverbially optimistic proposed construction completion schedule or CPM chart, may be so naïve as to consider these two elements of the project as one and the same, thus assuming that acceptance and completion necessarily occur on the very same date! Nothing is further from the fact and, in our actual operating experience, it has been proved time and again that there can be considerable lapse of time between the date of submission of the general contractor's final invoice for the "completed" facility and the actual date of formal acceptance by the owner and payment of the final invoice. In some cases, depending upon the effectiveness and capability of the project members of the team directly concerned with the welfare of the owner, this specified time period could be as little as one month; but a period of three to six months is not uncommon. There are cases on record where the owner and his project representative have unwittingly become involved in long and bitter negotiation or arbitration. This unfortunate situation occurs because of controversy with the architect and general contractor in situations where substantial claims for extra charges were made and their validity was challenged.

Definitions

To understand more clearly why this situation occurs so often, it is necessary to consider the definitions of the terms "completion" and "acceptance." The definition in Webster's *New World Dictionary* for "completion" or "complete" is as follows: "1. lacking none of the parts, entire, finished, concluded, 2. ended, finished, concluded, 3. thorough, perfect. Syn.: 1. inclusion of all that is needed for integrity, perfection or fulfillment, 2. not a single part has been omitted or demeaned."* Webster's definition for "acceptance" is "1. receive with favor or willingness, 2. any form or act by which one positively or constructively acknowledges the validity or sufficiency of an act done another, 3. agrees to the terms of a contract, 4. to take it as it comes, to accept the inevitable."*

No real problem should be encountered in bridging the ever-widening gap between these two categories of the construction project if (1) the scope of the project is well defined; (2) there exists good communication and close cooperation between the architectural/engineering firm involved in the design and the other project team members; (3) the full extent of the architect/engineer's contract has been well defined during the period of initial architect/engineer contract and general construction contract negotiations; (4) the project manager or construction management consultant is well qualified, has a good grasp and understanding of the project, and performs *all* his duties in a highly capable and ethical manner. The problem, however, *does* exist simply because few projects, as they are constructed, ever come close to approaching the ideal working environment (as outlined above in items 1 through 4) for various reasons. Part of the blame falls in the area of "practical operating considerations" confronting many of today's management personnel; many such people cannot operate effectively because they have, no doubt, reached "the level of their incompetence."[2]

Too often the owner is not knowledgeable in today's highly complicated field of building design and construction. Consequently he falls prey to and is almost entirely dependent upon the advice of professionals and specialists. These individuals may or may not be qualified or perhaps are not too concerned with ethical considerations or the owner's welfare. We are, therefore, proceeding on the assumption that very few, if any, ideal situations exist. Hence we must address our remarks to those situations where problems have been created and which require some time and effort on the part of the contractor to correct. All this difficulty, of course, is time-consuming and occurs between the "alleged" construction completion and the owner's formal acceptance.

Final payment is usually made 30 to 60 days after the work is completed. This payment, when accepted by the general contractor, is considered a waiver of all claims by

* *Webster's New World Dictionary,* College Edition, World Publishing Company., Cleveland, 1972.

the owner except for faulty workmanship which may show up within a year's time or for any other unsettled claim or lien. At this point we deem it necessary to call attention to the normal provisions that are generally included in the construction contract documents to protect the owner and encourage early acceptance. Included among these provisions is the normal one-year guarantee against defective workmanship, inferior materials, and substandard building equipment.

In over 40 years of experience in the field of building design and construction, the writer has made innumerable construction completion inspections for projects both large and small located in almost every section of the United States and in Europe. Over these many years, we have developed a most helpful, if not indispensable, tool as a stock in trade: namely, a guideline checklist of problem areas which are most often overlooked during inspections. This type of checklist simplifies paper work and the laborious handwriting of each item to be considered. The list requires, in most cases, only an entry or a check mark in the proper box or category and includes carbon copies for instant distribution to the qualified parties involved when the inspection has been completed. Following is a copy of a typical checklist.[3]

Checklist Guide for Building Inspectors

"Quality control" is a term commonly applied to the area of industry involved in production of automobiles and household appliances. It applies also to the construction industry and can be maintained at a high standard only by capable, competent inspectors. This checklist expedites the job of identifying those defects or omissions which could interfere with profitable and efficient use of the facility. It makes possible the most comprehensive coverage in the time available and serves to help the inspector and owner review the data, prepare his report and is also useful for future reference.

A. Requirements of the Owner. Obviously, the inspector must be knowledgeable about the use to which the building will be put. It is surprising how many otherwise well-informed executives expect a building inspector to evaluate a building without prior knowledge of the proposed occupancy. (Building requirements and environmental features for a warehouse, obviously, are far different than those for a laboratory.)

B. Outline of Typical Building Inspector's Report
    1. Letter of transmittal
    2. Cover
    3. Contents
    4. Summary
    5. Proposed occupancy
    6. Description of facility
    7. Evaluation of construction
    8. Summary of defects, major and minor
    9. Conclusions and recommendations
    Appendixes
    a. Building survey
    b. Plot plan
    c. Floor plan
    d. Building cross sections
    e. Photographs

C. Drawings—"As Built." In this area, responsibility for producing the "as-built drawings" (plans which are brought up to date to include all changes authorized and made in the field), rests with the architect. Most competent architects will make the corrections during the course of construction, so that little time is required to produce the as-built drawing at the time of building completion. There are cases, however, where weeks and months have elapsed before the architect has caught up with and made the necessary revisions.

D. Describing Defects and Omissions. Deficiencies should be listed specifically and in sufficient detail to permit the owner to determine whether they would interfere with the use of the facility. A minute cataloging of every crack is not necessary. There usually are some minor items which will not affect the facility operation or maintenance and these the owner will waive. Photos are a useful adjunct to the inspection report, particularly for illustrating defects not easily described. They need not be taken by professionals as long as they are clear enough to show the important features. Polaroid photos have the advantage of immediate availability and permit making notations upon them. A disadvantage is the problem of making duplicate copies.

Obviously the most serious defects merit the greatest amount of attention in the report. A reasonably correct estimate of the cost involved in making the necessary corrections would be helpful to the owner.

The inspector's findings and analysis must be condensed in the report, and the word "condensed" is used advisedly. Only those details need listing which are of direct interest to the owner, who must make the final decision on acceptance. Other details can be relegated to an appendix or retained in the inspector's file. The usefulness of the report is greatly enhanced by a few carefully chosen drawings such as the following:

1. Site plan very much reduced in size, showing relation of building to plot, roadways, parking, etc.

2. Reduced scale floor plans, partial elevations, schematic drawings of utility piping and electrical systems

3. Photographs

This proposed guideline may appear somewhat lengthy and detailed; however, its value to the owner in making his evaluation of completion and subsequent acceptance makes the added time spent worthwhile. Too often the inspection process is taken too lightly. The inspector should approach his responsibility as though *he* were the owner.

    E. Facility Inspection Report

      1. Inspection survey data

        1.1 Date of survey

        1.2 Members of inspection team

        1.3 Other persons contacted

        1.4 Drawings and specifications reference

        1.5 Any other reference materials or data

      2. Tenants' Requirements

        2.1 Tenant

        2.2 Proposed occupancy

        2.3 Basic physical date of facility, i.e., floor area by buildings and total area, column spacing, ceiling height, etc.

        2.4 Building utility requirements

          (a) Heating

          (b) Ventilation

          (c) Air *conditioning*

          (d) Lighting

      3. General Data

        3.1 Building name and address

        3.2 Governmental agency having jurisdiction over building codes

        3.3 Owner's name and address

        3.4 Architect

        3.5 Consulting engineers

        3.6 General contractor

        3.7 Electrical contractor

        3.8 Mechanical contractor

      4. Site and Site Development

        4.1 Drainage

        4.2 Landscaping and plantings

        4.3 Paved walks

        4.4 Roadways

          (a) Surfacing

          (b) Drainage, snow removal, etc.

          (c) Condition

      5. Utilities

        5.1 Water supply and distribution

        5.2 Storm sewer

        5.3 Sanitary sewer

        5.4 Electric power supply and distribution

        5.5 Gas supply and distribution

        5.6 Telephone service

        5.7 Other

      6. Architectural and Structural

        6.1 Structural

          (a) Foundations, retaining walls (evidence of cracking, settlement)

          (b) Substructure drainage

          (c) Structural system expansion joints, connections, rusting, fireproofing

        6.2 Building exterior

          (a) Exterior wall joints and connections, condition of surface, cracks, leaks, flashings, evidence of wall settlement

      7. Plumbing and Drainage

        7.1 Condition of fixtures and toilet partitions

        7.2 Floor drains

        7.3 Condition of all piping and insulation (hot water, cold water, sanitary drains, waste)

       7.4 Septic tanks, leaching fields
       7.5 Sanitary disposal plant
   8. Heating
       8.1 Condition of heating equipment
       8.2 Fuel lines, oil, gas, etc.
       8.3 Capacity of heating equipment
       8.4 Fuel storage
   9. Ventilation and Air Conditioning
       9.1 Condition of equipment
       9.2 Capacity of equipment
       9.3 Ductwork and discharge grills
  10. Sprinkler and Fire Protection
       10.1 Condition of piping, hangers, valves, etc.
       10.2 Water source
       10.3 Fire department connection
       10.4 Central supervisor service
       10.5 Standpipes and hose stations
       10.6 Fire or smoke detection equipment, fire walls
  11. Electrical
       11.1 Incoming service (current and voltage ratings)
       11.2 Disconnects, fused switches, circuit breakers
       11.3 Power panels, capacity—spares, overcurrent devices, feeder sizes
       11.4 Motor control centers, feeder sizes, and overcurrent device ratings
       11.5 Distribution system
       11.6 Lighting fixtures and method of suspension
       11.7 Light meter readings
       11.8 Intercommunication systems, public address, telephone, signal and alarm, security, etc.
  12. Other equipment
       12.1 Elevators and dumbwaiters
       12.2 Conveyors, dock levellers
       12.3 Incinerator, compactor
       12.4 Clean rooms, cold rooms
       12.5 Lightning protection
       12.6 Other

GUIDELINES FOR ARCHITECTURAL/ENGINEERING CONSTRUCTION CONTRACTS

The following is taken from a report which the author prepared in 1972 to be used as a guideline for plant engineers involved in contracting for architectural/engineering services and construction contracts.

"There have been in the past disagreements and misunderstandings which in some cases involved requests by the architect and engineers for substantial payments to cover services not included in the Basic Contract. (AIA Document B-131, 1970 Edition.)

"In most cases, the problem results from failure of the owner to understand and accept the fact that a considerable portion of the required engineering services falls in the category of 'Article #2, Additional Services.' In this area, it is most important, in order to avoid further misunderstandings, to include in the initial agreement all of the additional services which may be required. It may be that over the years in which some firms have been dealing with their own company-operated architectural/engineering group, no formal agreement was required and therefore there was no need for a clear definition of the engineering services to be performed as in the case when dealing with outside engineers or consultants."

See also Consulting Engineers' Council, Owner-Engineer Agreement OE-1, 1969 Edition. In particular with reference to this subject, we recommend review of the following sections of A.I.A. Document B-131: ARTICLE 1: 1.1.10, 1.1.11, 1.1.12, 1.1.14, 1.2, 1.2.3, 1.2.4, 1.3, 1.3.10, 1.3.11, 1.3.15, 1.3.17, 1.3.18, and 1.3.19; ARTICLE 2: 2.2 and 2.8; ARTICLE 11: 11.1, 11.2, and 11.3. Also Consulting Engineers' Council, Owner-Engineer Agreement OE-1, 1969: 1.6.9, 2.1.7, 2.1.13, 2.1.14, 2.1.15, 2.1.17, and 2.2.

According to J. Edward Genheimer:[4]

    The industrial company that builds infrequently is probably a small to medium size company which, due to its size and infrequent activity, does not maintain a staff of architects, engineers and construction specialists as do many of the country's largest corporations. In this situation, it is of utmost importance that the Owner who contemplates a new facility be cognizant of and avail himself of the experience and up-to-date knowledge of the construction industry.

One of the first and very important things that executives of an industrial company must recognize it that designing and constructing a new facility is not a simple matter to be handled casually. The design and construction of today's quality industrial building which is a complex structure requires technical knowledge and attention to detail for the mechanical, electrical, structural and architectural systems and materials. A serious and continuing effort in coordinating the details of such buildings is necessary and the final effectiveness of this coordination and technical effort is directly dependent upon total teamwork throughout the design and construction activities. The building construction industry combines the Architect, the Engineer and the General Contractor as principal elements supported by a myriad of other participants, i.e., material suppliers, equipment manufacturers, testing laboratories, sub-contractors, and others. The Owner, in addition to his financial obligation, has an inherent responsibility related to organization that must be discharged as part of the total team effort.

If any team is to be successful, all members must recognize and appreciate the functions and responsibilities of others involved. Many troubles and delays on a project can be related to a lack of understanding, creating poor attitudes toward cooperation.

Interpreting Payment Provisions of Construction Contracts[5]

The Plant Engineer's problems with construction contracts and documents are not limited to interpretation of the scope of work outlined in them (PE 5/4/72, p. 89); payment to contractors for work done and services rendered also can prove troublesome, if the payment schedules covering that work or service are not properly written.

Many construction contracts provide for payment *after* acceptance of work by the owner. A single date of acceptance is often difficult to establish, because as portions of the project are completed, they are usually occupied or put into use by the owner. Then, if there are delays in acceptance or a refusal to accept, the contractor holds that the owner's actions have implied acceptance of the work. To avoid this dispute, the contract documents should indicate that the use of a portion of the project *does not constitute acceptance* or in any way waive any of the owner's rights under the contract.

The contractor's right to the full contract amount *at the completion of the work* is generally not abrogated by his failure to follow contract requirements that do not directly affect that which was constructed. In one case, for example, it was determined that the contractor's failure to furnish a list of subcontractors (as required by the contract) would not affect his right to full payment after the work was completed.

If there is a mistake in plans furnished by the owner and, as a result of this error, the contractor is required to do less work than was originally specified, he is nevertheless entitled to the contract amount. However, when plans or specifications are changed—and the change is accompanied by a proper work order—the original contract price will be modified.

If the price is fixed in the contract, the contractor is entitled to receive only the fixed amount —even though it is below the reasonable value of the labor and materials furnished.

Extras or changes in the work   Extras and changes made as work progresses are responsible for much of the litigation arising from construction projects. An appreciable amount of the blame for these misunderstandings can be traced to the allegation that contractors bid a job low, planning to make their profit by charging disproportionately high prices for extras and changes.

Several general rules apply in the legal interpretation of the effect of extras on a construction contract. On a project where the work and the price for that work are defined, if—at the request of the owner—the contractor does work not covered by the contract, he is entitled to compensation for that work. Also, if materials more expensive than those originally specified are provided at the request of the owner, the contractor is entitled to be reimbursed for his extra cost. Even though the contract makes no provision for extras or changes, no supplemental contract is required to enable the contractor to recover for his extra costs in these instances.

This same logic would prevail if the cost of the work were increased by errors in the plans or specifications which prove to be the fault of the owner.

The construction contract usually provides that extras or changes must be ordered by the owner in writing. If they are not in writing, it is generally held that the owner does not have to pay for them.

For example, consider the situation where extras or changes result from a verbal instruction or suggestion given the contractor. Both parties understand that the work is not included in the plans and specifications, but it is associated with the work covered by the contract. The contract says a written order is required. In these circumstances the contractor would not be entitled to recover for his extra costs when the work was completed.

Controversy resulting from nonpayment for extras is so acrimonious in many cases that legal solutions must be sought. Two of these—waiver and new contract—are applicable.

A court might find that, by their conduct, the parties to the contract have waived the requirement for a written order. One court said: "Contractor was not barred from recovering for extras performed under building construction contract because of failure to comply with paragraph of contract requiring writing for extra work performed under the contract, where extras were done upon request with full knowledge of the owners and neither party suggested compliance with the paragraph . . . their conduct waived compliance. . . ."

For example, if a contract required a written order for extras or changes, but, during construction, extras and changes were regularly ordered verbally and the owner regularly paid for them, the parties have clearly waived the requirement of a written order.

The second interpretation courts have given to contract provisions which deny payment to the contractor is to consider any extras as work being done under a new contract. That is, the work was outside the scope of the existing contract which required a written order. Under this interpretation, no writing would be required to enable the contractor to recover, since, in effect, a new contract was entered into for the additional work.

In another case where extras were verbally ordered and the contractor provided them, the contract said that a written order was required for changes or alterations. The court said that this requirement applied to changes or alterations only—not extras—and the contractor was entitled to collect for extras, even if verbally ordered.

What kind of writing is required to comply with the provision of the contract that requires a written order for changes or extras? Legally, a standard work order complies. It has also been held that a letter written by the contractor to the owner requesting approval for an extra is satisfactory compliance, if the letter is returned to the contractor marked "approved." There is a disagreement among the authorities, however, as to whether a plan or drawing furnished to the contractor by the owner can satisfactorily replace a written order.

The message to the plant engineer on how to avoid difficulties with changes or extras is clear: the contract should require a written order; he should furnish that written order promptly; and he should not allow the contractor to undertake any changes or extras without a written order.

Retainage can become a problem when extras or changes have increased the contract price. The usual rule is that where the amount retained by the owner depends on the contract price, the price must include the cost of extras or changes.

Payment to the contractor—cost plus. Under a cost-plus contract, the contractor is entitled to recover his costs plus an agreed percentage—or a fixed fee. If the contract is silent as to what items are to be included in determining the contractor's cost for the work, the contractor is entitled to charge for the supplies and materials which went into the job, the wages of his workers, and certain other costs directly associated with the job. However, the courts have generally held that the contractor, in determining his costs, may not include general or overhead expenses such as telephone service, office supplies, or the time spent by executives of his firm visiting the jobsite.

One of the plant engineer's primary responsibilities in working with a cost-plus contract is to completely and clearly itemize all allowable contractor's costs. A specific example of charges involved in these contracts is that of a cost-plus contract which expressly provided that the cost and time for moving equipment to the job from the contractor's yard and the cost and time of moving it back would be charged at a designated rate. In performing the work, the contractor actually moved his equipment from a job in the vicinity, and when completed, moved it to another local job. When the charges were contested, the court held that charges based on movement of equipment from and to the contractor's yard—as provided in the contract—were proper.

Under a cost-plus contract, the contractor must perform the work in a skillful, workmanlike manner. Normally, then, the expense of correcting any errors or defects in the work which are the fault of the contractor is not a legitimate charge in a cost-plus contract. This is the rule applying to major defects or errors. One court reached a contrary conclusion, which would seem to apply only to minor defects and damage. It said: "Unquestionably we think on a cost-plus basis some mistake will be made on a job and certain work will have to be altered or changed so as to meet standard requirements. In the absence of a standard agreement, providing such repair work shall not be included in the basic cost of a cost-plus undertaking, we think the item complained of has a proper place in the cost of the job."

It is obvious that the plant engineer, acting as the owner's representative in dealing with construction contractors, *can become involved* in argument, compromise—or even litigation. It is equally apparent that most of this disagreement *can be avoided* by the simple expedient of preparing, then enforcing, a tightly written set of contract documents that leave no doubt as to their intent.

Timing in Contract Change Orders

Werner E. Ellmann[6] has written:

Another hazard involved in the "custom-built" character of the construction industry is the uncertainty of the date of "final completion." By its very nature, the construction of a building does not permit any of the many specialty contractors involved to work continuously on the site. An electrical contractor will install conduit during the early stages of the project and then leave, to return later to pull wire through the previously installed piping. He will then be off the job again, pending the installation of ceiling panels, after which he will reappear to mount the lighting fixtures.

Similarly, the air handling and the refrigeration contractors will install the large mechanical items such as fans and compressors, before walls and partitions are constructed. Later will come the installation of ductwork, followed by another period of inactivity after which grilles and diffusers are set in place. The painter must wait for the plastering contractor. The glazier must work intermittently with the bricklayer. The plumber does the initial "roughing-in" rather early in the schedule, but must wait until the final stage to install plumbing fixtures.

Last, but by no means least, there are installation errors that must be corrected. There is a door that the carpenter must shorten to clear the carpet in the first vice-president's office. There is a short in one electrical circuit that must be corrected and an undersized fuse in another circuit which must be replaced. There is a faulty damper motor in one of the air handling systems and an entire wall that was painted the wrong color.

All of these, and many similar items, are common to every building project and they appear on what has come to be known as the "punch list." The shorter the punch list, the less the frustrations of the owner who is anxious to move into his new building and who would like to do so without having meetings interrupted by tradesmen making final adjustments and repairs.

The completion of mechanical punch lists at the earliest possible moment, like the elimination of mechanical change orders, depends to a great extent on the competence of the mechanical specialty contractors and on the professional zeal of the consulting engineer. Needless to say, these qualities are not necessarily synonymous with the cheapest price or the lowest fee.

PROJECT INSPECTION

Care must be taken to differentiate between the terms "supervision" and "inspection" of construction. In the last few years the term "supervision" has been replaced by "inspection" when the project manager or design engineer is retained to make his inspection. The term "supervision" covers the responsibility of the contractor, i.e., to supervise the contractor's workmen and their construction methods. The difference in these two terms can result in legal responsibility for the engineer if the term "supervision" is used.

At this point we find our constant companions cropping up—*who, why, where,* and *when?* The answers to why, where, and when are quite obvious. We need to be more concerned with who should make the inspection. Preferably the inspector would be on the owner's staff and be fully competent and qualified to pass judgment and to make the necessary unbiased appraisals. Essential is familiarity with the project scope, plans, and specifications. In the case where the owner does not have an "in-house" design staff, he must depend upon the services of the architect and include this responsibility in the "additional services" of the AIA architectural design contract documents. Usually, in this case, the services of a construction inspector are included in the architectural contract documents and the inspection is made by this same individual. In cases where a construction consultant has been retained by the owner, this individual will, of course, make the inspection. Every possible incentive must be provided to ensure that the construction inspector puts the owner's interests above all other considerations. Too often the construction completion inspection is taken too lightly. The acceptance too frequently is based on verbal agreements. Entirely too much dependence is placed upon a so-called friendly relationship established between the architect/engineer, the contractor, and the project manager. It may be well to consider that the innumerable lunches, dinners, and entertainments paid for by the contractor and the architect are only a means of paying the piper when the chips are down with regard to which standard of construction is acceptable to the owner's representative. In any case, the owner should be aware of the heavy responsibility resting upon the shoulders of the construction inspector and consider carefully the selection of this individual.

In the final analysis, we should not overlook the benefit and value of retaining a qualified, trained professional in the field—the construction consultant project inspector. As a trained specialist, this individual has acquired valuable experience and background in the course of making almost daily inspections and is in a position to ably protect the owner's interest. The inspector should bring to the project an open mind—unbiased by daily contact with the contractor—and accordingly should operate as a free agent. Above all, this inspector has a professional reputation to uphold and of course is legally responsible to the client.

We have known of instances where the contractor has led the owner to believe he has completed all work only as a subterfuge to get the inspector out early and make a "punch list" for him.

In summary, we find there should be no difficulty in making a physical inspection of a construction project when comparing the finished results with clearly defined drawings and specifications. The difficulty lies in the process of attempting to make an expert appraisal and properly evaluating the degree of perfection attained by the contractor and architect in executing the project.

The next logical step is to determine if the degree of perfection attained is acceptable to the owner. To the best of our knowledge and experience, we have never seen, nor do we expect to see, a perfectly executed project. However, it may be that evaluating a completed building is like evaluating whiskies—"some are of better quality than others."

ACCEPTANCE

As the final act, acceptance of the completed facility by the owner can and should be an exciting, pleasant experience providing the same thrill as that experienced in the groundbreaking ceremonies. At this time, the owner hopefully looked forward to an early completion and envisioned impressive and beautiful results, very much like those depicted in the architect's rendering—down to the last silver oak tree, the wide expanse of lawn, and the clean white roof, free even of the first process exhaust stack and ventilation system intake, vents, and ductwork.

Not even the most naïve inspector or owner expects to find the completed project to be as perfect as that depicted in the artist's rendering. "Architectural license" is accepted universally as a sales tool, not only for the architect but also for selling the project to the client's board of directors.

For the owner, formal acceptance usually follows serious and lengthy discussions with the construction inspector in (1) evaluation of contractor's progress in correcting faulty workmanship; recognition and provision for inclusion of any and all omissions, replacement of items not approved as acceptable substitutes, etc., all as required and clearly covered by the drawings and specifications; (2) records of contractor's and subcontractors' affidavits and liens; (3) receipt of copy of as-built drawings incorporating all changes in design; (4) receipt of adequate number of copies of all building equipment operating instructions and maintenance manuals; (5) evidence that the contractor has obtained proper certificate of compliance with state and/or local inspectors of electrical, heating, ventilation, air conditioning, and plumbing work as well as necessary building occupancy permit. All this must be turned over to the owner prior to acceptance.

Following the owner's final review with the building inspector and the architect and assuming all conditions are reasonably satisfied, the owner should be in a position to send to the contractor a formal letter of unconditional acceptance of the project. One would hope that this letter would be one of commendation, expressing satisfaction with the manner in which the project was executed. For the contractor meriting it, such a letter provides satisfaction which cannot be expressed in the monetary consideration of the final payment. Where justified, a final gesture by the owner is in order, wherein the letter of acceptance is formally presented to the contractor at a luncheon in his honor arranged by the owner and attended by appropriate personnel involved in the project as well as members of the local press.

REFERENCES

1. W. E. Prather: "What the Owner Should Consider to Assure Contract Performance," paper delivered at the Industrial, Institutional, and Commercial Building Design Conference, Cleveland, March 21–24, 1966.
2. Lawrence J. Peter, and Raymond Hull: *The Peter Principle: Why Things Always Go Wrong,* Morrow, New York, 1969.
3. Joseph Horowitz: "Checklist Guides Building Survey," *Plant Engineering,* February 1970, pp. 76–79.
4. J. Edward Genheimer: "Obtaining Best Teamwork among the Architect, Consulting Engineer and General Contractor," paper delivered at the Industrial, Institutional, and Commercial Building Design Conference, Cleveland, March 1966.
5. Gordon M. Betz: "Interpreting Payment Provisions of Construction Contracts," *Plant Engineering,* June 29, 1972, pp. 67–68.
6. Werner E. Ellmann: "The Importance of Timing in Contract Change Orders," *Environment,* vol. 3, no. 2.

Use of In-House Design Group

ROBERT H. O'NEILL
Executive Director of Engineering, McNeil Laboratories, Inc.

INTRODUCTION

The planning and design of plant facilities is extremely important, for construction programs require large financial commitments and new facilities have a significant long-term effect on the profitability of an operation. A properly administered program minimizes the risk of under- or overdesign and generally results in an efficient operating unit.

Certain plant operations are highly specialized and require large in-house design engineering groups to respond to the design and construction needs of their sophisticated operations. These groups perform their own design, develop working drawings, and manage the entire construction program. Most companies, however, cannot justify a sizable in-house design staff due to their infrequent construction requirements and the standard nature of their operations. A small, versatile design staff is sometimes practical when it provides regular assistance to the plant operating departments on equipment selection and designs and coordinates minor building renovations in addition to participating in the building programs.

The various facets in planning, designing, and constructing plant facilities in which the design staffs can participate are as follows:

1. *Planning phase*
   - *a.* Analysis of present facilities
   - *b.* Definition of intent and magnitude of the new facility
   - *c.* Develop and evaluate alternate methods of accomplishment
   - *d.* Preliminary program and operational requirements
   - *e.* Facility location
   - *f.* Project schedule
   - *g.* Budgets and approvals
2. *Design phase*
   - *a.* Selecting the design team
   - *b.* Schematic design
   - *c.* Design development
   - *d.* Cost analysis of preliminary design
   - *e.* Working drawings and specifications
3. *Construction phase*
   - *a.* Evaluation of bids and the construction contract
   - *b.* Shop drawings
   - *c.* On-site inspection and field coordination
   - *d.* Final testing and acceptance
4. *Occupancy phase*
   - *a.* Final project documentation
   - *b.* Evaluation of new materials and updating standards

Further explanation of each activity will be given in detail on the following pages; however, no attempt has been made to define the extent of the design group's role. We will assume for this chapter that the majority of company design staffs are small and as such require outside professional assistance with the design, documentation, and construction management of the building programs. To effectively contribute to a building program, the small design staffs should concentrate their efforts in areas such as establishing design criteria, evaluating design concepts, reviewing design documents, etc., where familiarity with the plant operations is necessary in understanding the full extent of the project requirements. The small design group, however, should never assume too ambitious a role because this will inevitably result in a delay of the project. The use of outside professionals provides the necessary talent and manpower to expeditiously complete the project.

ANALYSIS OF PRESENT FACILITIES

When an addition to an existing plant is being planned, the initial step for the design staff consists of determining the current status of the existing facilities. These include land, structures, utilities, and the processing operations. The purpose is not to determine if the facilities are adequate to accommodate the contemplated expansion, since these requirements have not yet been developed, but to define the present status to determine availability. Sometimes, during the analysis, operating inefficiencies are uncovered and afford an excellent opportunity for the design group to improve existing operations.

A current site plan should be developed showing all the property lines, special zoning restrictions, roadways, existing structures, and the complete topography. All available soil data including test borings and/or seismic surveys should be compiled to facilitate the foundation analysis for the new facility.

For those structures directly affected by the proposed facility, the plans should be updated to reflect any renovations and additions since the initial construction. All field changes during the initial construction affecting the substructure, sewer inverts, etc., should be included in the updated documents.

Perhaps the most difficult determination is the current status of the building services. These include the steam plant, chilled-water plant, electric power, domestic water, hot

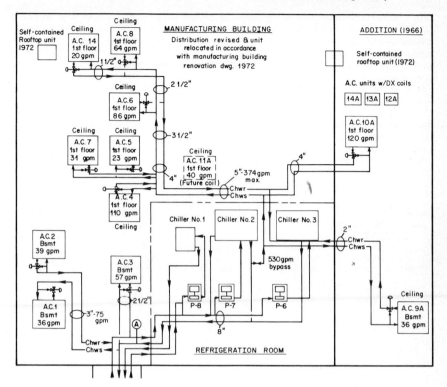

AC No.	Serving	Location	cfm Total	tons Design 45°	gpm Design 45°
	Manufacturing				
AC-1	Cafeteria	Room M-19	3600	24	36
AC-2	Control lab	Room M-19	6500	25	39
AC-3	Pilot plant	Room M-13	7200	38	57
AC-4	Tablet compression	Room 143	12100	73	110
AC-5	Tablet coating	Room 150	4500	15	23
AC-6	Packaging dept.	Room 157	17000	58	86
AC-7	Pharmacal dept.	Room 136	5900	20	31
AC-8	Shipping dept.	Room 168	12400	42	64
AC-9A	Office area	Room A-1	10000	24	36
AC-10A	Mixing dept.	Room A-112	13200	80	120
AC-11A	Drying (future)	Room M-145	3000	(30)	(40)
AC-14	Order dept.	Room 168	3000	7	20
	Totals chilled water system load —	Current		406	622
		Future		436	662

Fig. 1 Typical distribution plan and equipment consumption tabulation for determining current status of chilled-water plant.

water, compressed air, gas, etc. An up-to-date building distribution plan for each service is recommended, together with a complete tabulation of the individual equipment requirements. A chilled-water distribution plan and equipment tabulation is shown in Fig. 1. Always adjust the processing equipment requirements with a diversity factor and allow for increased usage to accommodate production increases. Installation of permanent submetering for each operation certainly provides accurate consumption data; however, this practice is expensive and, in most cases, portable meters can be installed temporarily to determine the actual consumption.

Accurate determination of the processing equipment status is extremely important since quite often management's request to initiate the planning of the new facility is based on the belief that the processing equipment is inadequate to meet anticipated requirements. In most organizations the industrial engineering group will routinely analyze the operating load, determine maximum capacity, and forecast new equipment requirements. If an industrial engineering group is not available to furnish these data, the in-house design group should develop the required information or use the services of an outside consultant. A production capacity analysis to determine current departmental capability is shown in Fig. 2.

The design group should thoroughly review all available data to familiarize themselves with the operations and evaluate the possibility of revamping the existing process to achieve the required capacity without necessarily constructing an additional facility. In rare instances, locating and eliminating a process bottleneck or revising the operating procedures will provide the required production capacity.

OUTPUT ANALYSIS

Department _____ A _____   Operating hours per day—eight (8)

Date _____ 15 May 1973 _____   Operating days per week—five (5)

Year	Product size	Forecasted batches per year		Standard hours per batch	Total hours per year	Total days per year	Days per week required
1974	1 oz	17	X	8.0			
	2 oz	160	X	4.0			
	5 oz	120	X	4.0	1,256	157	3.0
1975	1 oz	19	X	8.0			
	2 oz	180	X	4.0			
	5 oz	150	X	4.0	1,472	184	3.5
1976	1 oz	21	X	8.0			
	2 oz	200	X	4.0			
	5 oz	190	X	4.0	1,728	216	4.2
1977	1 oz	23	X	8.0			
	2 oz	230	X	4.0			
	5 oz	240	X	4.0	2,064	258	5.0
1978	1 oz	25	X	8.0			
	2 oz	260	X	4.0			
	5 oz	300	X	4.0	2,440	305	5.9

NOTE: The above analysis indicates that product demand forecasts through 1977 can be met if employees perform at a work pace of 100% of standard.

Fig. 2   Production capacity analysis to determine current departmental production capability.

DEFINING INTENT AND MAGNITUDE OF NEW FACILITY

Management's decision for the design group to proceed with planning only indicates a need for the facility but does not specify the best method of accomplishment. To attempt to define the complete project scope at this time only tends to inhibit the consideration of alternate operating schemes to determine the most economical and functional system. The design group should define management's intent for the proposed facility and compile sufficient information on the operating objectives to determine the magnitude of the operations. Once the intent and magnitude have been determined, they become the so-called project goal.

For example, the project goal of a new warehouse facility might be defined as follows: The facility is to service departments A, B, and F and provide efficient warehousing for all raw materials, in-process goods, and finished products. The systems shall be compatible with the current materials control procedures. A total of 5,000 random storage locations are to be provided for a maximum unit load size $42 \times 52 \times 60$ inches high. Minimum load weight is 280 pounds and the maximum load is 2,500 pounds. The facility should permit future orderly enlargement to 10,000 unit loads. Ultimate material flow is approximately 175 placements and 175 retrievals per 8-hour shift, with a maximum hourly activity level of 25 placements and 25 retrievals. The complete facility should be operational by July 1976.

Quite often engineers spend considerable time in developing operational schemes that are inconsistent with the true intent of the facility. Every consideration during the planning phase should be examined to determine if it is fully responsive to the project goal.

DEVELOPING AND EVALUATING ALTERNATE METHODS OF ACCOMPLISHMENT

Once the project goal has been defined, the next task for the design staff is to develop different operating schemes for the proposed facility. Each scheme should be thoroughly evaluated to finally determine the optimum operating arrangement. The building requirements—i.e., area, clear height, etc.—will vary with each scheme; therefore it is necessary to finalize the operating methods before documenting the building program.

Warehouse handling equipment	*Unit load handling method*
1. Conventional lift truck	1. Palletless
2. Narrow-aisle truck	2. Two-way pallet
3. Side-loading truck	3. Four-way pallet
4. Reach truck	4. Wing pallet
5. Straddle truck	5. Skid
6. Stock picking truck	
7. Stacker crane	
Storage arrangement	*Plant distribution systems*
1. Bulk storage	1. Fork truck
2. Conventional rack	2. Towline conveyor
3. Mobile rack	3. Roller conveyor
4. Drive-through rack	4. Tow tractor
5. Live storage	5. Manual truck

Fig. 3 Partial list of alternate considerations for warehousing schemes.

These schematic studies should be initiated quite early in the planning phase to allow the design group ample time to develop many different and innovative schemes. Before proceeding with the actual studies, the design group should familiarize themselves with the criteria on which management based their decision to proceed with the facility and visit other like facilities to become familiar with the current state of the art. Always utilize the latest systems and methods in the schematic development and include, as part of each consideration, the building requirements. Failure to recognize the impact of certain bay sizes, clear height, floor loading, etc., sometimes results in construction cost penalties that might have been avoided had they been considered during the planning phase. In practice, however, all efforts are concentrated on the operating schemes, and the building requirements are determined later, during design. This sometimes results in compromising the optimum equipment and processing layouts by attempting to redesign the operations to fit a certain structural system. In some cases this is expedient; however, in a great many instances the process efficiency is reduced.

The design group should always consider every conceivable combination to ensure selection of the best system. Figure 3 lists various material handling equipment and systems that should be considered when developing alternate warehouse schemes. As alternate operating schemes are developed, all the related activities should be considered and a totally integrated operation planned.

Finally, each of the operating schemes must be thoroughly evaluated. This includes an analysis of the capital outlay, projected operating costs, physical life, etc. If the structure and process operations are complex and square-foot costs cannot logically be applied, there are outside professional estimators who will prepare the capital estimates. Operating costs are developed internally by the design group in cooperation with the plant departments. After the cost analysis is complete, the return on investment is calculated for each scheme. When two schemes have approximately the same return, then factors such as operating flexibility, future expansion, etc., will help highlight the optimum scheme.

DEVELOPING THE SPACE PROGRAM AND SPECIAL EQUIPMENT LAYOUTS

Once the operational scheme has been selected, the next step for the design group is to make a comprehensive breakdown of all operations in the new facility that require space. Ultimately, several related operations may share common space; however, at this stage, to ensure complete consideration, it is best to define each space requirement.   Many companies have adopted standard floor areas for their offices, laboratories, warehouses, production centers, etc., and these values are assigned to each operation to determine the total net floor area required for the new facility.   For those operations where standard areas do not exist, it is best for the design group to perform an operation analysis.   This consists of developing flow diagrams, physical requirements of the equipment, and operating procedures and from these to construct a block layout in order to determine the floor space requirements.

Another important consideration in documenting the program is to provide for future growth.   This provision can normally be determined from production and personnel forecasts.   This growth area is always subject to some adjustment when the building frame size is finalized.

Once the total net area is approximated, the figure must be adjusted to compensate for building services such as corridors, mechanical and electrical spaces, etc.   This adjustment varies with each type of facility and normally ranges between 25 and 30 percent of the gross building area.   This adjustment is made by adding 33 to 43 percent to the net floor space.   Figure 4 illustrates a space program defined by using area standards and determining other areas by analysis.

Once the space requirements of the facility are documented, the design group should define all the operational requirements.   These consist of detailed equipment layouts, special room finishes, service requirements, and any other special structural, mechanical, and electrical systems.   Figure 5 illustrates an equipment schedule.   Adequate prepara-

PRELIMINARY CAFETERIA BUILDING PROGRAM				
Area/operation	No. people and/or units	Unit area sq ft	Total net area, sq ft	Remarks
CAFETERIA				
General seating	300/feeding	15	4,500	
Kitchen, serving, etc.	350/feeding	15	5,250	
Dining room A	10	22	220	
Dining room B	40	20	800	
CONFERENCE/TRAINING FACILITIES				
General meeting room	160	12	1,920	
Audio-visual room	—	—	400	See Layout A-1
Conference room A	20	10	200	
OCCUPATIONAL HEALTH				
Doctor's office	1	120	120	
Examination room	1	—	110	See Layout A-2
Reception area	3	—	200	See Layout A-3
Rest room	1	50	50	
Reclining room	1	60	60	Code requirement
Storage area	1	—	120	See Layout A-4
PERSONNEL DEPARTMENT				
Manager's office	1	160	160	
Secretarial space	1	80	80	
Assistant manager's office	1	120	120	
General office clerks	2	70	140	

Total net area = 14,450 sq ft
TOTAL GROSS AREA = 20,230 sq ft
(14,450 × 1.4 service factor)

Fig. 4   Example of building space program.

EQUIPMENT REQUIREMENT SCHEDULE

Room No.	Equipment	C.W.	H.W.	D.W.	C.A.	Gas	Drain	Dust coll.	Exh.	Stm.	Volts	Amps	Remarks
		Mechanical									Electrical		
127	Cleaning station				X		X	X			480	4.5	Existing unit relocated
130	Pkg. line no. 1				X		X	X			480	26	
	Pkg. line no. 2				X		X	X			480	39	
	Floor scale						X				110	—	Elec. reqd. for printer
134	Refrigerator	X					X				480	2.5	Walk-in unit
	Weighing table							X			110	—	
143	200-gal. mixer	X	X				X	X			480	63	
	Oscillator		X	X				X			480	4.5	
	Blender	X						X			480	14	
147	Oven no. 1						X		X		480	4.5	Existing unit relocated
	Oven no. 2						X		X	X	480	85	Existing unit relocated
	Oven no. 3						X		X	X	480	7.5	Existing unit relocated
148	Conveyor no. 1				X				X		480	3.3	
	Heat sealer				X				X		480	38	
154	2,000-gal. tank	X	X	X			X		X		480	7.5	
	1,000-gal. tank	X	X	X			X		X		480	4.5	
	200 gal. tank										110	—	
	Pump no. 1	X					X				110	—	
	Pump no. 2	X					X				480	2.5	Existing unit relocated

Fig. 5 Machinery and equipment schedule.

tion in documenting these requirements helps to expedite the design phase and minimizes costly additions to the construction contract.

LOCATING THE FACILITY

Although most construction involves additions to existing sites, the exact location of the building cannot logically be determined until this matter is studied by either the design group or outside professionals. The exact configuration of the new building has not been finalized at this stage; however, we should assume a multistory or single-level structure based on the existing operations and develop several alternate site locations in relation to the existing facilities. After evaluating each location for its effect on departmental relationships, communications, material and people flow, future growth, etc., the most feasible location will become evident.

In cases where a new site is required for the facility, the design group should coordinate the site selection program. There are many competent professionals who specialize in plant location, and engaging such an organization is highly recommended. Specific location standards must be supplied to the outside professionals. In addition to marketing, distribution, raw material, and labor requirements, information must be compiled by the design group regarding fuel, electric power, water and waste disposal requirements, the environmental impact, approximate site size and topography, and other pertinent matters concerning the new facility. After the recommendation of one or more sites by the outside consultants, the design group should inspect each site under consideration and alert management to any potential problems regarding geology, topography, utility supply, etc. A joint effort on the part of the design group and the outside consultant will produce a satisfactory site that will prove, over the years, to be a worthy selection.

PROJECT SCHEDULE

Developing a realistic project timetable is the responsibility of the design group. It is usually at this stage in the project that the type of design and construction contract is determined. When time is of the essence and is insufficient to permit completion of the working drawings to solicit lump-sum bids, either a design and construct contract or a building team concept is then called for. Based on the arrangement selected, an accurate project schedule is developed from time estimates to design, construct, equip, and debug the new facility. A realistic schedule is required by the plant operating departments to forecast their material and labor requirements, and such a schedule also assists the plant controller to establish preliminary cash flows. Figure 6 illustrates a simple project schedule. The particular scheduling method is totally dependent upon the design group and ranges from a simple bar chart to very sophisticated techniques.

BUDGETS AND APPROVALS

Most operations require that some form of appropriation request be prepared and submitted to management for project approval. Figure 7 shows a typical appropriation request format. The design group, in cooperation with the plant accountants, are generally responsible for compiling the request. The project description, reasons for undertaking project, funds required, economic life, cash recovery, return on investment, spending schedule, and project timetable data must be assembled and presented in a clear, concise manner. Although the capital estimate is preliminary, it should be adequate to cover any contingencies that may arise during the design and construction phases. If the design group is not proficient in developing an accurate cost estimate, they should enlist outside assistance. A preliminary site plan and building layout for the facility are helpful in clarifying the project scope and should be included with the appropriation request. The request should be completed within the project time frame to permit adequate consideration by management.

SELECTING THE DESIGN TEAM

The design staff plays an important role in selecting the outside design professionals. Regardless of the type of design and construction contract, a competent firm must be selected to document the new facility. Every firm under consideration should review the design group's planning documents and, based on this, submit a proposal containing the following:

1. Qualifications of principals
2. Completed projects
3. Current projects
4. Estimated time to design and document the project
5. Fee schedule

Once this information is received, the in-house engineers should inspect several of the facilities designed by each firm and discuss the following questions regarding design

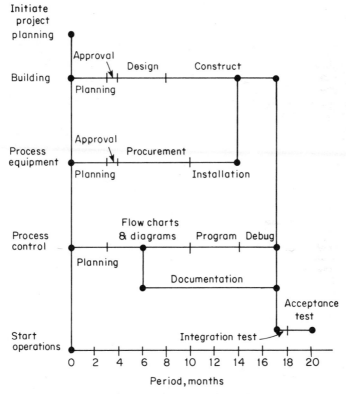

Fig. 6   Project schedule for building addition.

economy, scheduling, operating performances, etc., with the building owner or the owner's representative in order to determine the design professional's past performance:

1. Has the firm successfully done work of a like character?
2. Are they able to understand the project requirements?
3. Do they have the administrative ability to expedite the entire project?
4. Are they capable of producing a design within the authorized budget that meets the owner's requirements?
5. Are they schedule-conscious and capable of developing a realistic schedule and progress reporting system?
6. Is their internal cost control and invoicing format acceptable?
7. Do they have the required in-house expertise or a satisfactory working relationship with a specialty firm?
8. Have they had adequate experience to evaluate the competency of the construction bidders?

9. Are they adequately staffed to handle the project within the required time frame? These inspections should include some of the design professional's older projects to verify if the materials and construction systems selected are providing adequate physical life.

REQUEST AND AUTHORITY FOR CAPITAL EXPENDITURE

_____ DIVISION/PLANT

Request Number	Budget Reference No.	Date submitted
Project Title		
Amount to be Capitalized $	Maximum Funds Required $	19
Amount Provided in the Capital Budget $	in 19 and $	in 19
Expense Portion included in most recent Financial Forecast $	in 19 & $	in 19
Proposed Source of Funds		
Economic Life Years	Project Classification	
Year in which all Cash Outlays will be recovered		
Average Return on Investment		
Description of Project:		
Reason for Undertaking Project:		
Date to Start		
Completion Date		

SIGNATURES	APPROVALS	
Proposed by		Date
Checked for Controller		Date
Recommended		Date

Fig. 7   Appropriation request format for capital budget.

When your initial evaluation is complete, discuss any questionable findings with the design professional involved.

In many instances a negative performance can be attributed to a situation forced upon the designer by the client. After completing your evaluation, including estimated fees, you should present your recommendation to management.

SCHEMATIC DESIGN

The outside design professionals should be fully apprised of all preliminary data developed by the in-house group before proceeding with their schematic design. If some owners are reluctant to disclose such information in order to protect the confidential nature of their operations, a nondisclosure agreement should be executed with the outside professionals to protect against disclosure of any confidential information concerning existing or contemplated machines, products, processes, techniques, know-how, etc. To intentionally withhold pertinent data from the outside professionals only results in the costly and time-consuming development of schemes already judged unacceptable by the in-house group. Schematic design affords the opportunity to have outside professionals critique the in-house design group's conclusions and also to develop any possible alternate schemes that, in their opinion, may be more fully responsive to the project intent. Alternatives developed by the outside professionals are, on occasion, viewed pessimistically by the in-house engineers; however, the in-house engineers should always enthusiastically consider any constructive suggestions that may result in a program improvement.

The scope of schematic design usually varies with each type of facility but consists essentially of determining the building footprint, parking areas, ingress and egress roadways, specific building features (i.e., structure type, configuration, exits, stairs, etc.), layouts of only the functioning spaces, and a narrative that describes the basic building systems and the overall job scope. The development and definition of a specific building system during schematic design is generally required when that particular system or component constitutes a major project cost item. For example, the exterior walls of a high-rise office building have a major impact on the project cost, therefore the exact wall system should be developed during the schematic phase. In contrast, the exterior walls of a large single-story factory building have little cost impact and in most cases need not be defined during schematics. As you may recall, we recommended earlier that documentation of any structural peculiarities be included as part of the preliminary planning by the in-house group. If these data were developed because the process requires a special enclosure or building, the outside professionals should review the criteria established for the building (i.e., special high-bay clearance, overhead crane operations, etc.) and fully define this special structure during schematics.

The main role of the in-house group during schematic design is first to acquaint the outside professionals with all the data developed to date and then to encourage the further development and refinement of the various schemes. Finally, the in-house group should constructively evaluate all recommendations and proposals by the outside consultants. Under no circumstances should the outside group be discouraged from performing their own schematic design.

DESIGN DEVELOPMENT

Once the schematic design studies have been completed and approved by the in-house group, the outside professionals should proceed to prepare the design development documents, which consist essentially of plans, elevations, and outline specifications documenting and illustrating the exact size and character of the facility in terms of materials, systems, etc. At this time, the in-house design group should convey to the outside professionals their so-called *preference list*. This information usually consists of certain design standards, preferred materials, systems, etc., that should be incorporated into the design. Most companies have standardized to some degree on particular materials and systems that they feel are preferable for their application. Common inventory of spare parts and familiarity with existing systems are but a few of the reasons why most companies develop a preference list. It is extremely important that this information be promptly conveyed to the outside design professionals before they actually proceed with the design development. Figure 8 illustrates an in-house standard for connecting steam unit heaters. You will note the elimination of the usual valved bypass at the steam trap, since the owner's plant maintenance personnel prefer this arrangement so operators cannot open the bypass valves in the event of a trap malfunction and neglect repairing the trap. The extent of the preference list depends entirely on the particular company and its operations. The outside professionals should always be given an opportunity to challenge those preferences that, in their opinion, do not represent the optimum selection. Technological improvements in construction materials and systems are constantly occurring, and the in-house design group should make comparative evaluations of their preferred systems with the outside professionals' recommendations to assist in the selection of a method or system that best suits the project requirements. As the design development progresses, the in-house group should meet regularly with the outside designers in order to review their calculations and documentation and to ensure that they fully understand the operational requirements.

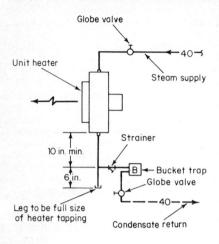

Unit Heater Piping Arrangement

Fig. 8 Design standard for connecting steam unit heaters.

In addition, every major systems or construction method selected by the consultant should be reviewed by the in-house design group to determine if the scope is within the project budget. Too often, when the design development is not monitored properly, the final design encompasses systems that far exceed the actual requirements and result in expensive and time-consuming redesign to bring the project within budget. Since the in-house group have already established the project budget, they are fully responsible for controlling the design within the approved budget. The in-house group should also review all the various aspects of routine building maintenance (i.e., window cleaning, equipment servicing, housekeeping, etc.) as it relates to the new design to determine if any particular operational problems are evident and, if so, to rectify the design accordingly.

COST ANALYSIS OF PRELIMINARY DESIGN

Before proceeding to incur the expense involved in making actual working drawings, it is very important that the in-house group satisfy themselves that the project design is within budget. If the outside design firm does not have an estimating group, the in-house group should engage an independent construction estimator or a general contractor to perform a quantitative takeoff and produce an accurate estimate of the construction costs. Many owners are reluctant to incur the additional cost of an estimate; however, on most occasions a well-developed estimate highlights the high-cost areas and affords the in-house group the opportunity to revamp the design and save more than the cost of the estimate. This cost analysis will also enable the in-house group to adjust the project budget if such an adjustment is called for by major scope changes, requirements, etc.

WORKING DRAWINGS AND SPECIFICATIONS

These documents detail the actual work to be done and define the materials, workmanship, and equipment required for the site work and for the architectural, structural, mechanical, electrical, and general conditions of the construction contract. The in-house group's role is primarily that of coordination. It begins with the selection of a drawing size, scale, and identification system to be used by the outside professionals—a system that is compatible with the owner's existing files. Although the actual working drawings are developed by the outside professionals, the in-house group should periodically review their work to uncover any possible errors and unacceptable standards, check that the required facilities and systems have been included, that the documentation is in sufficient detail and, in general, observe if the work is proceeding according to schedule.

Another very important aspect of the in-house group's participation is the incorporation of any special project conditions required by the owner's operations. Any special work sequencing, property protection, temporary structures, connections to existing services, safety regulations, etc., that are required for this particular project should be determined and defined as a part of the contract documents. Adequate preparation in this area will prevent any serious disruptions to the owner's operations during the construction period. Figure 9 illustrates, for a new warehouse and renovation project, work sequencing and demolition requirements that enabled existing production operations to continue during construction.

The in-house design group should also coordinate the internal drawing review with the various plant operating departments within their own organization. Security, safety, maintenance, housekeeping, etc., should all review and comment on those items or areas directly affecting their operations. Working closely with the plant operating departments and soliciting their recommendations definitely results in an improvement to the project.

WORK PHASING AND COOPERATION WITH OWNER
(A) The work shall be phased so that the addition to the Manufacturing/Warehouse Building is completed before demolition work involving the existing building walls commences.
(B) The nature of the Owner's manufacturing operation requires extreme care to maintain the cleanliness of the environment. All work by Contractor requires conformance to this requirement at all times.
(C) Before beginning demolition work, arrange with Owner the limit of work by areas, timing schedule, and provisions for dustproof partitioning, completely sealed, as herein scheduled for work requiring demolition. Such partitioning shall not be removed until completion of the work and with Owner's consent.
(D) The following items indicate the necessary work phasing in order not to interfere with Owner's operations. Unless otherwise noted or directed, the items are to be completed in the order listed:
   (1) Complete entire new Warehouse Building Addition, encompassing Column Lines K–Q and 5–15, including all mechanical and electrical services. Such services extending into existing Manufacturing Building shall be completed to Column Line K. Access through doors into existing Warehouse Building will not be permitted during construction of the addition. Existing doors shall remain locked.

Fig. 9   Example of work sequencing to accommodate owner's operations.

EVALUATION OF BIDS AND THE CONSTRUCTION CONTRACT

Regardless of the type of construction contract (i.e., competitive bid, direct selection and negotiation, separate contracts, etc.), the in-house group should satisfy themselves as to the competence of the constructors under consideration. Parameters similar to those used for evaluating the outside design professionals—such as past performance, capability of handling the project within the required time frame, current financial status, internal cost control, etc.—should be used to evaluate each contractor. In fairness to both contractor and owner, any contractor not fully qualified to construct the facility should be excluded from further consideration. The in-house group should rely on the outside design professionals' assistance in developing a list of acceptable contractors.

The design group should assume full responsibility for soliciting the bids. If a competitive bid contract is being used, they should develop the general instructions to the bidders and a proposal format on which the contractors are to submit their proposals. Always allow an adequate bidding period in order to secure well-developed proposals and—in fairness to all parties—try not to extend the original due date. During the bid period several questions usually arise regarding the drawings and specifications. Immediate clarification should be documented by the in-house group and promptly issued to all bidders. Once the in-house group receives the bids, they should be tabulated with any exceptions noted. It is true that certain extenuating factors such as proposed working days to complete the project, unit costs, fees, etc., may influence awarding the contract to a specific bidder. However, if adequate screening of the prospective bidders was done by the in-house group prior to soliciting the bids, then generally the lowest bona fide bidder should receive the contract. This bidder should first be called in to review the drawings and specifications with the in-house group to ensure that no significant items have been omitted. Then, if the review is satisfactory, the contract is awarded.

The basic construction contract consists of the project drawings, specifications, general conditions, and an agreement between the contractor and the owner. Bidders always receive the drawings, specifications, and general conditions, but on many occasions the agreement form is not part of the bidding documents. Problems generally arise when the successful bidder is requested to sign an agreement that contains certain conditions (i.e., additional insurance coverage, time of completion, guarantees, etc.) which were not included in the bid. For this reason, a blank copy of the planned owner-contractor agreement should be part of the bid documents so that all bidders will know the owner's requirements before submitting their proposals. The in-house group should always clear the construction agreement with their legal and financial departments and also with the outside design professionals for their concurrence.

SHOP DRAWINGS

Although these documents are usually submitted to the outside design professionals for approval of general conformance to the contract documents, the in-house design group should also review the shop drawings to further assist in detecting any possible discrepancies. It is certainly more expedient to rectify errors before fabrication rather than in the field, with subsequent job delays. While reviewing the shop drawings for general conformance, the in-house engineers should also consider all the important operating aspects such as general access, convenience of replacement, etc. In addition, shop drawings are a valuable tool to the in-house group, since their submission timing is an indication of the contractor's general progress. They also contain valuable information for ordering future replacement parts and assist the in-house design group in documenting any future changes to the area. Needless to say, these important documents should be properly cataloged and included as a permanent part of the engineering file.

ON-SITE INSPECTION AND FIELD COORDINATION

The purpose of field inspection during construction is to ensure adherence to job standards, assist in the interpretation of the contract documents, and protect the mutual interests of both the contractor and owner. The in-house design group usually assumes the full responsibility for field inspection. Those in-house design engineers who have actively participated in the project development and are thoroughly familiar with the plans and specifications are excellent inspectors.

The most important inspection activity involves those portions of the work that are ultimately concealed. Foundations, backfill, flashings, reinforcing, etc., are all items that should receive considerable attention by the in-house inspector, since they are eventually built into the work. Too often, minor building leaks and cracked walls could easily have been avoided had the flashing and reinforcing been properly inspected.

Although the in-house engineers can usually coordinate all field activities and assist the contractor in the interpretation of the documents, they should also call in the design professionals in cases requiring specific expertise. It is always a good practice to have the design professionals attend job meetings and tour the facilities under construction for their general concurrence that the work quality is satisfactory.

FINAL TESTING AND ACCEPTANCE

During the course of any construction contract, numerous field tests are required; accordingly, the in-house design engineers should thoroughly review the proposed test procedures and witness the actual tests. Compaction of backfill, watertightness, hydrostatic and pneumatic pressure tests, short circuit, insulation resistance, etc., are but a few of the various on-site tests that the design engineer should witness. The results should be documented and kept permanently as part of the project records. In addition, adequate documentation of all air- and water-balancing data, equipment performance, etc., is extremely important, since it provides permanent data for future reference. The design group should review each section of the specifications and general conditions to determine if the construction contract has been satisfied. Since final acceptance is based on all work being completed in a first-class manner, areas cleaned and in an unmarred condition, safety devices provided and operational, previously condemned work corrected, and all systems balanced for proper operation, the in-house group should have the authority to withhold final payment until all items are satisfactorily completed.

FINAL PROJECT DOCUMENTATION

Once the construction project is completed and the facilities are occupied, the in-house design group should review the as-built drawings submitted by the contractor to ensure that all known field changes have been incorporated. If as-built drawings are not part of the construction contract and the in-house design group assumes the responsibility for preparation of these documents, then all marked up field drawings should be secured from each major trade and these changes documented on the original project tracings. Although most outside design professionals hold that the original project tracings are their property, the owner should insist on an agreement whereby the outside professionals are furnished with a complete set of sepias or transparencies for their files and the original tracings are turned over to the owner. These original tracings, together with copies of all the design calculations, are invaluable to the in-house design group for use on future renovations and additions. Also included as part of the final project documentation should be a complete summary of all major problems encountered during the entire project for use as a future reference. Thus, problems that have once been solved can be avoided in the future.

EVALUATION OF NEW MATERIALS AND UPDATING STANDARDS

Very often we change materials and/or systems and, once they are in operation, rarely evaluate the results of these changes. Several months after startup, the in-house design group should inspect the new facility to determine if any of the construction requires corrective work and if the new materials and/or systems appear satisfactory. In addition and just before the expiration of the construction contract guarantees, a comprehensive inspection should be conducted to determine if the construction materials and systems have met the guarantee conditions and also to conclude if those new materials and systems should be incorporated into the company design standards.

Chapter **7**

Work Input and Output Controls for In-House Design Staff

JOHN C. GORTON, P.E.
Manager, Review & Estimates, Xerox Corporation

INTRODUCTION

The preceding chapter discusses the use of an in-house design staff. The justification for maintaining this staff may be based on economics, quality control, the time factor, or a combination of all of these. Having made the decision to employ an in-house design staff, the problem of direction, regulation, and coordination of the activities must be solved.

The design group is one of six sections of a corporate facilities department. The other sections, which should be employed whether or not design is performed in-house, are:
    Planning and scheduling
    Construction management
    Review
    Estimating
    Accounting
For the purpose of this chapter only, the design section and the functions of the planners–schedulers will be discussed in depth.

ORGANIZATION

Overall direction of the design group is supplied by the head (director) of the corporate facilities department, to whom all the above section managers report. The director, having a broad background in design, construction, and operation of facilities, is the spokesman for the department and must be able to communicate effectively with the heads of the other departments of the company in order to provide answers to their space problems. The director should have a position on the company's managing committee so as to be able to advise on proposed capital expenditures.

To aid the director in the control of the design section, the planners, schedulers, and accounting sections furnish the necessary data. The planners do the actual work of interviewing the managers of the marketing, production, administration, and research departments to obtain specific data for the long-range plans. They help to assemble preliminary feasibility studies in the preparation of business proposals which are submitted for approval to the managing committee. The planners develop the alternative schemes and recommend the "best" solution. These long-range plans affect the expansion and modification of the physical plant and cause the formulation of a master plan. From this type of planning, the major construction projects can be studied and scheduled. A yearly updating of the long-range plans will reflect the changes in sales, production, and research, which, in turn, affect the construction program. Added to these planned projects are the numerous requests for renovations of existing facilities brought about by new methods, machinery, and systems; revised governmental regulations (i.e., ecology, OSHA); and local or national crises (i.e., water, fuel, and power shortages). To estimate the total magnitude of these miscellaneous projects, one must rely on past experiences. If a source for these data is lacking, a large contingency fund must be established to cover the expenses.

Thus, the director and his staff can prepare a list of projects based on planning and experience. With these data, the regulation of the work can begin. The actual work input is a function of the quantity of the work, the size of the staff, and the time factor. Assuming that the staff members are to be long-term employees, the quantity of work should be regulated to fit the optimum-size design staff. With the master plan at hand, the average annual capital expenditure can be forecast. From this an estimated design fee amount can be calculated. To determine the size of the design staff, the following general guideline can be used: The annual staff payroll, including all benefits and taxes, should not exceed 50 percent of the fees prescribed by the American Institute of Architects for the various types of projects involved.

The basis for the reduction of the fee is that the company provides the auxiliary services, such as rent, telephone, computer time, and construction management. In most cases, in-house design results in a reduction of costs for traveling, entertainment, printing, and blueprinting.

The basic design team might consist of two qualified professionals in each of the following disciplines: architecture and civil, electrical, industrial, and mechanical engineering. A chemical engineer should be included to cope with processing and pollution problems. Two designers in each discipline are required to provide the necessary checking process and coverage during vacations, seminars, and sick leaves. Add to this a chief draftsman and a staff of one draftsman for each designer.

If the quantity of work, translated into design fees, cannot justify this payroll, then the in-house design approach should be forsaken.

Assuming that the design staff is justified, the size of the staff is determined by the average annual quantity and the "flavor" of the work involved. For instance, if most projects are interior renovations, the size of the civil engineering section may be small; but if there are many additions, separate buildings, and site developments, then a larger section will be required. The director and the schedulers must determine which projects to perform in-house. This depends on the magnitude of the project, the expertise of the staff, and quality and time control considerations. In some cases, the in-house personnel may possess the only available knowledge of certain research or manufacturing processes. Other projects—such as office buildings, boiler houses, or bridge designs—should be given to outside consultants who have demonstrated their abilities in these types of projects. In this way, the best results will be obtained.

MINOR PROJECTS

To this point we have discussed those projects which have been carefully studied and planned. Many projects originate from the requests of section managers who want to increase efficiency and production. Their work usually falls into the classification of minor projects which cost less than $50,000. Due to their proprietary nature, these are designed in-house. These requests are submitted at random throughout the year, but most of them must be addressed at once and be fitted into the schedule.

To organize these requests, a standard form must be utilized. This form will state the location of the project, a description of the work to be accomplished, completion date

```
1. REQUESTER'S REF. NO. _____      8. DATE _____

2. PROJECT NO. _____        9. REVISED _____

3. CLASSIFICATION _____        10. PROJECT COST DATA:
                                                a. Budget Center_____
4. TIME REPORTING DATA:                         b. Account No. (Expense)_____
   a. Requesting Dept. _____          c. Program No. (Capital)_____
   b. Transfer Status _____          d. Budget  $_____
                                                e. Cost of Requested Service to
5. PROJECT TITLE _____              be Charged to _____
   _____

6. LOCATION_____
   _____

7. ORGANIZATION PROJECT COORDINATOR
   _____    11. PHONE _____
12. SCOPE OF PROJECT:                     13. COMPLETION DATES:
    a. Study Estimate _____          _____
    b. Design Construct _____          _____
    c. Technical Support _____          _____
    d. (            ) _____           _____

14. PROJECT ASSIGNMENTS:
        A. PROJECT MANAGEMENT _____
        B. INTERIOR DESIGN _____
        C. OFFICE SERVICES _____
        D. REAL ESTATE _____
        E. SPACE UTILIZATION _____
        F. TELE-COMMUNICATIONS

15. CORPORATE STAFF:
        A. DISTRIBUTION _____
        B. EH & S _____
        C. INSURANCE _____
        D. MEDICAL _____
        E. SYSTEMS _____

16. ADDITIONAL ASSIGNMENTS:
```

Fig. 1a Request for corporate facilities services.

desired, and the project's purpose and expected benefits for the company. The form entitled "Request for Corporate Facilities Services" might be similar to Fig. 1. In order to regulate incoming requests, each department must recognize that it will be charged for engineering time. This will ensure that only bona fide projects will be submitted, and only after careful study by the originators and their superiors. Therefore the scheduler must require the signatures of the section manager and head of the department on every request. The scheduler must determine the priority and assign the work to the section which performs the feasibility studies and cost estimates. This group will interview the requestor, make studies, set forth preliminary plans and specifications, and formulate cost estimates. This package is presented to the requesting department and becomes part of the report submitted to the company's managing committee for its approval. Upon approval, the project is returned to the scheduler for assignment to the design section.

The scheduler gives a number to each project and assigns it to a job captain. A widely used means of numbering is a five-digit system in which the first two numbers designate

4. DATE _____

1. REQUESTOR _____
5. PHONE _____
2. ORGANIZATION _____
6. BUDGET CENTER _____
3. LOCATION _____
7. REQUESTOR'S REF. NO. _____

8. SERVICES REQUESTED:

A. ☐ INVESTIGATION AND ESTIMATE ONLY   B. TO BE COMPLETED BY _____

C. ☐ AUTHORIZED TO PROCEED WITH WORK   D. TO BE COMPLETED BY _____

E. COST OF WORK TO BE CHARGED TO:

   1. BUDGET CENTER _____   3. CAPITAL PROGRAM NO. _____

   2. ACCOUNT NO. _____   4. AMOUNT AUTHORIZED _____

F. REQUESTOR _____   H. COST OF REQUESTED
                                          SERVICES TO BE
G. APPROVAL _____   TRANSFERED TO _____

9. PROJECT DESCRIPTION:

A. PROJECT TITLE _____
B. LOCATION _____
C. DESCRIPTION OF WORK: _____
_____
_____
_____
D. OTHER DATA: _____
_____
_____
E. ☐ ADDITIONAL DATA (SKETCHES, PLANS, SCHEDULES, LETTERS, ETC.) ATTACHED

10. PERSON TO BE CONTACTED FOR FURTHER DETAILS: (If other than Requestor)

A. NAME _____
B. ORGANIZATION _____
C. LOCATION _____   D. PHONE _____

Fig. 1b   Request for corporate facilities services.

the year and the last three denote the project number. For instance, #75021 denotes the twenty-first project assigned in the year 1975. Upon the assignment of the number and the job captain, an interoffice memorandum containing these facts are sent to all sections of the corporate facilities, the requesting department, and the corporate legal and finance departments.

WORK CONTROL

To maintain control over the work input (and output), it is necessary to compile a chart of all the projects. A wall chart will provide a quick visual means of appraising the status of each project. The chart should show both the proposed and actual time taken in each stage of design, review, and approvals. Target dates needed for coordination must be shown. With all the projects charted, the scheduler can determine when the in-house capacity will be exceeded. Then, with the director's advice, the projects will be selected for in-house design. Those projects given to outside consultants should be transferred to a separate chart.

The scheduling chart must be updated daily to give the current situation of the work

TIME SHEET

WEEK ENDING _____

DRAFTSMAN/DESIGNER _____

HOURS WORKED/PHASE OF WORK (SEE LEGEND)

JOB NO. PROJECT	MON.	TUES.	WED.	THURS.	FRI.	SAT.	TOTAL

Legend: C-conference; JC-determination of job conditions; P-preliminary drawings; RP-revisions to preliminary drawings; W-working drawings; RW-revisions to working drawings; S-specifications; A-analysis of bids; SD-checking shop drawings; CR-checking requisitions; SC-supervision of construction; PE-preliminary cost estimate; E-detail cost estimate; F-foundation design; X-checking architectural, structural, mechanical designs.

Fig. 2 Time sheet.

load. The scheduler must appraise the load and the production of the staff, being ready to shift assignments or recommend the use of additional personnel. For example, in a large organization, one of the design teams may reach a stage of extended delay on a project. This team can be utilized to expedite the completion of another design or to take on an emergency project. The scheduler must coordinate the vacation schedule with the work load.

Along with the chart, an important tool is the compilation of time-card data. A typical

time card is shown in Fig. 2. Time is assigned to preliminary design, preliminary drawings, final design, final drawings, checking, reviewing shop drawings, specifications, etc.
Each category can be given a number or abbreviation to be entered on the time card.
From the time cards, a clerk can make summations of the various categories. From this
data, future schedules can be produced. This data can also serve as a check against
current jobs of the same scope.

DESIGN TEAM

In the design stage, the job captain and the chief draftsman will set the schedules to meet
the target dates. Together they will assemble the team to fit the particular job. A weekly
(informal) meeting of the team will help to focus on problems so that immediate solutions
can be attempted. Responsibilities should be explicitly designated so as to avoid overlapping or omissions.

The design team must initiate the preliminary design by obtaining the pertinent criteria from the client (requesting department). To guide these important interviews, a
master checklist for construction projects should be employed. The major sections of
this checklist are as follows:

1. *Site*
   a. Geographic location
   b. Political jurisdiction, including environmental agencies
   c. Available utilities and capacities
   d. Transportation facilities—traffic studies
   e. Topography

Figure 3 shows an example of the civil engineering topics. Similar lists are made for
mechanical, electrical, and environmental health and safety topics.

2. *Details of design*
   a. Principal function—auxiliary
   b. Live loads, vibration, seismic
   c. Architectural style—exterior materials
   d. Interior design—materials
   e. Environmental criteria—HVAC, pollution
   f. Health and safety requirements
   g. Existing conditions, if renovation or addition
   h. Vertical transportation
   i. Site design

Figure 4 is an example of plumbing design data.

3. *Assignment of responsibility.* In order to obtain all the necessary data, the project managers will assign specific tasks to key personnel such as corporate real estate, a
chief chemist, an outside architect, or a production manager.

Figure 5 shows a chart to be used to achieve this goal.

4. *Space requirements.* This is the detailed listing of the needs for each space, giving
the required dimensions, occupancy, equipment sizes and locations, utility requirements
including diversity factors, temperature and humidity criteria, illumination levels,
security, and telecommunications.

Figure 6 is a typical list of subjects to be covered.

5. *Traffic flow and interface of groups.* This section supplies the information needed
to produce an efficient interior layout. Flexibility must be provided for the inevitable
future changes.

Upon completion of the master checklist, the project manager must submit this document to the requesting department for review and approval. In this manner, errors
and/or omissions in communications will be avoided.

From this approved checklist and the detailed space requirements, the preliminary
design is formulated. A minimum period of four weeks must be allotted for completion
of the preliminary design and cost estimate. These data are submitted to the requesting
department for approval. It is important that all parties agree at this stage, for there
should not be any major changes in the scope of the work once working drawings have
been started.

STANDARDS

The preparation of working drawings and contract documents should be guided by the implementation of "standards." These are contract documents, specifications, construction details, and drawing formats which have been formulated by past experience to give the desired results and/or performance. The contract documents—such as the instruc-

---

1. U.S. Coast & Geodetic Survey Maps
2. Survey of property
3. Topographical survey
4. Data on soil conditions, test borings, test pits, soil tests (including permeability) etc.
5. Existing easements on property
6. Location and elevations of adjoining roads or streets
7. Storm sewers

     a. Location
     b. Size—material
     c. Inverts
     d. Who pays for extension, if necessary?
     e. Manhole locations & inverts
     f. Permissible effluent
     g. Flood history
     h. Representative's name and address

8. Will easements on other properties be required for service or road access?
9. Existing buildings or structures
10. Woods, rocks, brook, swamps, or other notable features
11. Rainfall data and snow accumulation
12. Water table data/mean high tide elevation
13. Frost depth
14. Prevailing winds
15. Sanitary sewers

     a. Location
     b. Size—material
     c. Manhole locations and inverts gradient
     d. Who pays for extension, if required?
     e. Permissible effluent
     f. Representative's name and address
     g. Process waste pretreatment?
     h. Connection cost

16. Water main

     a. Location
     b. Size
     c. Inverts
     d. Type of system
     e. Pressure
     f. Residual flow
     g. Is meter required for water and/or fire service? What type or manufacture of meter?
     h. Who pays for required water meters?
     i. Who pays for extension, if required?
     j. Rate schedule
     k. Water analysis
     l. Representative's name and address

17. Gas main

     a. Location
     b. Size
     c. Pressure
     d. Heating value
     e. Who pays for meter and run to buildings?
     f. Rate schedule
     g. Representative's name and address

18. Is well water available?

     a. Quantity
     b. Temperature
     c. Quality
         1. Approval of Health Department
         2. Minerals, hardness, pH

19. Fire protection

     a. Name
     b. Requirements

Fig. 3 Site survey—civil engineering.

tion to bidders, general and special requirements, and the agreement—should be composed by the project management and legal section. The specifications and drawings are under the jurisdiction of the design section.

Drawing format includes dimension of sheet, title box, title page, and numbering of sheets. An important control instrument is the drawing number system. Prefix and

1. Floor drains other than for equipment
   a. Number
   b. Locations
   c. Use
   d. Size
   e. Bleeder fed
2. Industrial waste
   a. Type
   b. Quantity
3. Water filtering, softening, or other treatment required
   a. Type
   b. Quantity
4. Process water requirements
   a. Pressure
   b. Temperature
   c. Maximum demand
   d. Usage factor
   e. Quantity
   f. Special treatment
5. Drinking fountains—location
   a. Type
   b. Number
6. Stainless steel or other special sinks
   a. Type
   b. Size
   c. Location
7. Fire protection
   a. List of materials used
   b. Type of hazard
   c. Nonheated areas or canopies
   d. Extra hazardous areas
   e. Hose racks
   f. CO_2 or other special fire protection systems
8. Gas
   a. Quantity
   b. Pressure
   c. Heating value
   d. Usage factor
9. Vacuum
   a. Quantity
   b. Pressure
   c. Usage factor
10. Oil or grease interceptors
11. Other services required
    a. Nitrogen
    b. Distilled water
    c. Compressed air
    d. Other

Fig. 4 Design data—plumbing.

suffix letters can be employed to denote preliminary design, work drawings, conformed contract drawings, and as-builts.

Thus, as each set is issued, it is entered into the drawing log for a permanent record. The director or any of the staff can ascertain the status of the design from the drawing number. By checking the log, the latest issue can be determined. The following illustrates a number system. These numbers can be repeated on any job, since the project number appears in the title box.

2	10/3	Changed location of toilets
1	9/10	Added balconies
No.	Date	Revisions

BUILDING 201—FIRST FLOOR PLAN

Drawn J. Jones	Approved	Project no.
Checked A. Brown	Scale	Drawing no. A-1, W-2

A-1 denotes architectural plan no. 1
W-2 denotes a working drawing, second revision.

The drawing log must be updated each time prints are issued. A drawing log is kept for each project, along with a separate journal in which the printings are listed chronologically.

A project drawing log may be set up as follows:

Project no. _____			Job captain _____	
Date	Drawing no.	No. of prints	Received by	Firm
9/13/73	A-1, W-2	6	J. Jones	A. B. Contracting

This tells the reader that on September 13, 1973, J. Jones of the A. B. Contracting Company received six prints of drawing A-1, W-2. From the entries in the log, one can tell if and when the latest prints were issued. With the help of a well-kept transmittal file, the manager can keep control over this function.

The size of the sheets should be controlled by physical limitations of the drafting tables and file cabinets, but their usage in the field is of prime importance.

The title sheet should be plain but informative. The company name should be prominent, with the name and location of the project the main feature. A list of drawings and the name, address, and telephone number of each design captain should be shown. The site plan (if any) should contain a chart indicating the size of the structure, ground coverage as a percent of the total site, number of parking spaces provided, and the zone district (i.e., office, light manufacturing, heavy manufacturing).

Standard drawings should be on file, such as those showing door schedules, partition details, finish schedules, typical curbs, manholes, pavement sections, railing and fencing details, and built-up roof and flashing details. These details and schedules should be organized on standard sheets in order to save design and drafting time.

Standard symbols should be employed. However, distinctive symbols for door open-

Plans & Layouts	Responsibility	Due date	By	Not required
1. Site plan and topo map				
2. Overall building plan				
3. Office area				
4. Laboratory				
5. Medical and personnel				
6. Kitchen and cafeteria				
7. Factory				
8. Warehouse				
9. New plant equip. layout				
10. Exist. plant equip. layout				
11. Exist. building drawings				
12. Organization chart				

Fig. 5   Design data—general.

FORM I   FORM II

1. Area or room number
2. Area or room name
3. Use
4. Population
   a. Maximum shift
   b. Total
5. Location
6. Size
7. Clear height
8. Finishes
   a. Floor
   b. Wainscot
   c. Walls
   d. Ceiling
9. Doors
   a. Vision panel
   b. Soundproof
   c. Door closer
   d. Label
10. Fire loading
11. Floor loading
12. Private toilet
13. Closet

14. Carpet
15. Soundproofing
16. Air conditioning
    a. Temperature
    b. Humidity
    c. Day/night operation
17. General Ventilation
    a. Number of air changes/hour
18. Heating
    a. Temperature
19. Other services
20. Drinking fountains
21. Lighting intensity
22. Convenience outlets
23. Telephone
24. Clock
25. Equipment
26. Supplementary lighting
27. Explosionproof, dustproof, vapor-
    proof required
    a. Type
28. Lighting control
29. Remarks

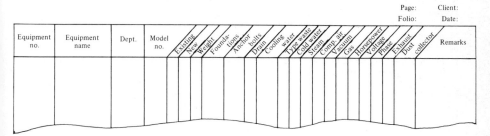

Fig. 6 Design data—general area and room data.

ings which give the door number, frame type, and hardware set number can be utilized. Methods for numbering cross sections to other sheets can be utilized. Standards should be set forth for required information on foundation drawings, such as top-of-wall elevations, top-of-footing elevations, type of footing, and bottom-of-footing elevation. Maintain a standardized list of notes on such matters as allowable soil pressure, strength of concrete, codes governing design, and live loads.

A master specification from which appropriate sections can be copied for a specific project should be on file in the office. Each project should have its own technical specification. Do not print the entire master specification with a massive addendum deleting unwanted sections. This saves neither time or money and it can lead to trouble in the field. Compose each specification from the master. To make it distinctive, each division (e.g., concrete work) must have a section detailing a list of the scope of work to be performed under other divisions or separate contracts. These detailed lists must be prepared in concert with the drawings. In this way, a more complete comprehension of the work is achieved.

Unless the project is of a monumental nature (e.g., a corporate headquarters), details should be simple or common in the trade and materials should be readily available at a competitive price. Otherwise, the estimated cost of the project will surely differ widely from the bid prices. If constant growth and change are a hallmark of the company, then it behooves the designer to stress flexibility, mobility, and availability.

Interior finishes should be selected to fit the life expectancy of the space as well as the function. It is a mistake to select an expensive carpet for an office space which will experience many partition changes each year.

CHECKING PROCESS

One of the most important quality controls of an in-house design is the checking process. It is often neglected due to the crush of the work load and the lack of sufficient time. However, errors and omissions in the plans and specifications will lead to loss of time and money during construction; in severe cases, they can lead to property damage and loss of life.

Therefore, it is most important that a formal review be made. The criteria must be reviewed for their practicality and flexibility. Calculations must be thoroughly checked and results formally verified. Drawings and details must be reviewed to ensure compliance with building codes and government regulations. All this checking should be done within the design group. A separate checking process is performed at the different stages of completion by the review section of the corporate facilities department. This review section provides the "outsider's" critical reaction to the proposed design. The responsibility for checking and review must be specific. It is important that errors be corrected in-house. A constant source of poor-quality design must be removed from the team. Therefore, the countersigning of calculation sheets, selection of equipment, and the working drawings should be a requirement of the section.

CONSTRUCTION MANAGEMENT

It is important that the construction management section obtain and turn over to the design group all as-built drawings, shop drawings, and operating manuals. The drawings to be retained in the drawing morgue must be the latest updated set. All others should be discarded. At the end of the job, construction management should submit a master list which states—for each division of the work—the contractor and his address, the materials used, and the manufacturer's name and address. This information is invaluable in future years as a reference for design and evaluation.

Construction management should give constant feedback to the design staff. A formal critique should be held at the completion of a project of the in-house design staff.

There are several methods that can be used to evaluate the performance of the in-house staff:

1. *Design cost to produce the documents.* Compare these with AIA fee schedule.

2. *Construction cost.* Compare with similar projects designed by outside design firms. Caution must be used in comparing quantities and quality. Employ factors for geographic location, site complications, and inflation.

3. *Number of change orders issued.* A well-designed project will have less than 3 percent extra cost due to change orders involving errors and omissions in the design as shown on the drawings and specifications. Changes in the scope of the work required by the clients should be kept separate. Extra costs due to latent soil conditions and acts of God shall be excluded.

4. *Performance and maintenance costs.* The design can be evaluated on its durability, both structural and aesthetic, and by the cost of operation and maintenance. The maintenance department should keep records to indicate the types of problems encountered with the equipment, materials, and types of construction. The formal transmission of these data back to the design group will help reduce future problems.

5. *Feedback from project management.* Information regarding the practicality of the design, the cost and availability of materials and skilled labor, and the actual field conditions must be fed back to the design group. This constant updating on the state of the art will prevent stagnation.

The above methods cannot be used individually but must be studied as a group to ascertain how one affects the other. A low first cost may result in high operating costs. A low design cost may result in high construction and change order costs. By this evaluation process, the in-house design staff as well as its methods and standards can be improved.

Chapter 8

Specifications

H. RICHARD MATHISON
Manager, Technical Services, Xerox Corporation

INTRODUCTION

A dictionary definition of the word "specification" will be exhaustive enough to explain the nature of architectural and construction specifications. It is true that these specifications include the detail particulars governing the scope and magnitude of work to be performed; but starting from that understanding, architectural and construction practice has evolved definitions and meanings of its own. Usually, for the average construction project, the specifications are ponderous volumes of typewritten sheets and, except for one or two individual divisions, offer as much reading interest as the dictionary.

The purpose of this chapter will be to attempt to describe the organization, intent, and use of specifications as applicable to the construction industry.

Up to now, no standard format for the composition and organization of specifications has been developed. There are, however, recommendations by both the American Institute of Architects and the Construction Standards Institute as to best practice. These recommendations are based upon years of work and experience, and they offer what the author would consider to be the only authoritative information available.

It is well that architects, engineers, and contractors have the greatest impact in writing and compiling specifications, for truly this is what a project is all about. But it must at all times be remembered that specifications are a legal document, written and organized in such a way as to withstand trial by jury. Perhaps the most valuable source of specification dos and don'ts would be an analysis of arbitrated disputes involving specifications that have been tested. In most cases, specifications are written by architects and engineers, interpreted by contractors, and then—if differences occur—defined by lawyers. The importance of proper language clearly understood by all involved is primary, and some rules to meet this goal have been included herein.

The persons who will have recourse to the specifications will range from workmen to professionals, and the specifications will be the tool used in establishing the cost of the work.

BOUND SPECIFICATIONS

The specifications are usually typewritten pages, inexpensively bound together, with punched holes and metal fasteners. The cover is usually heavyweight paper, with the job identified by name of the architect, engineer, or other publisher of the specifications. The identification also usually includes the name of the client and the date. The practice has usually been to utilize standard 8½ X 11 inch paper. Reproduction of the specifications varies in accordance with the equipment and sophistication of the firm producing the job, but copy machines are becoming almost standard. The specifications are composed in various ways that range from laborious typing by hand to complex computer printout systems with suitable programs to fit a wide variety of work.

Title Page

The first page of the bound set of specifications is a title page. Exhibit 1 shows an example of a title page.

The title page usually denotes the name of the project; the project number; identification of the owner, architect, and engineer; and the date.

EXHIBIT 1   Sample of Title Page

```
        SPECIFICATION
             FOR
   ALTERATIONS & ADDITIONS

        XYZ PLANT #1

   DOESVILLE, NEW YORK

      XYZ CORPORATION

   DOESVILLE, NEW YORK

    NOVEMBER 1, 1973




              Best Engineers, Inc.
              16 Lee Street
              New York, N.Y.
```

Index

Immediately following the title page is an index page or pages, a typical example of which is shown in Exhibit 2.

The index offers several clues to the overall organization of a set of specifications. The major separations are called divisions. In our illustration, the first division has been identified by the capital letter "A." The use of capital letters for divisions is not a standard. They may also be numbered, with either Arabic or Roman numerals, but the use of capital letters is convenient and provides for the logical sequence needed. The divisions set forth the major contractual portions of the work to be performed in the approximate sequece of consideration. Minor subdivisions are called sections, and the sections have been identified by the capital letter of the division followed by a numeral. Page numbers are also given. On each page, the job number appears in the lower left-hand corner. Some specification writers utilize different color paper for rapid identification of divisions. Although this is not consistent practice, it is an excellent idea for separation and identification.

REFERENCE DOCUMENTS

As stated in the introduction to this chapter, there is no standard way of organizing specifications. There are, however, accepted methods of assembling them that have

EXHIBIT 2 Sample of Index Page

TABLE OF CONTENTS

Section No.	*Title*	*Page Nos. Inclusive*
	Reference Documents:	
	Form of Proposal	1–2
	Agreement	1–5
	General Requirements of the Contract Documents	1–17
1	Instructions to Bidders	1–2
2	Requirements of the Contract	
	Supplementary General Requirements	1–8
	Special Requirements	1–13
3	General Scope of Work	1
4	List of Drawings	1–2
	Division A—General Construction	
A-1	Demolition	1
A-2	Excavation	1–2
A-3	Concrete Work	1–10
A-4	Structural Steel	1–4
A-5	Miscellaneous Iron Work	1–5
A-6	Masonry	1–5
A-7	Membrane Waterproofing and Damp-proofing	1–2
A-8	Hollow Metal Doors & Trim	1–4
A-9	Unassigned	
A-10	Finishing Hardware	1–8
A-11	Metal Furring, Lathing & Plastering	1–4
A-12	Floor Coverings	1–3
A-13	Painting	1–5
A-14	Glass & Glazing, Caulking	1–4
A-15	Acoustical Ceilings	1–2
A-16	Laboratory Furniture	1–4
	Division B—Mechanical Work	
B-1	Plumbing	1–8
B-2	Fire Protection	1–4
B-3	Heating, Ventilating & Air Conditioning	1–11
B-4	Valves, Pipe & Fittings	1–36
B-5	Air Handling & Treatment	1–7
B-6	Air Outlets	1
B-7	Ductwork & Casings	1–14
B-8	Pumping Equipment	1–3
B-9	Plumbing Fixtures	1–4
B-10	Equipment Bases & Supports	1–3
B-11	Insulation	1–14
B-12	Controls & Instruments	1–8
B-13	Painting	1–2
B-14	Refrigeration	1–3
B-15	Motors & Electrical Work	1–2
B-16	Accessories & Specialties	1–5
	Division C—Electrical Work	
C	Electrical Work	1–29

grown from practice and use within the construction industry, and it is basically these that are discussed here.

Usually there is a section in the very first portion of the bound specifications entitled "Reference Documents." These are what is referred to in legal jargon as "boiler plate." They represent legal and general overall requirements for the contract. They provide the ground rules for the "game to be played" or tell how the project will be conducted.

Instructions to Bidders

Included in the reference documents is one entitled "Instructions to Bidders" (Exhibit 3), which set some very primary rules to contractors who are bidding as to identification of the owner, the architect, and the engineer and the location of the work. There may be identification of governing codes or insurance underwriter requirements that will affect the contract. There are usually some requirements set by the contract for affirmations as to full knowledge of site and conditions based on field inspection.

The instructions to bidders will identify the time, place, and method for submitting

---

EXHIBIT 3   Instructions to Bidders

---

1. *Procedure*

   1.01 Bidders shall obtain the Bid Documents from the Project Manager.
   1.02 The Proposal which forms a part of the Bid Documents shall be completed in full in ink or by typewriter.
   1.03 Proposals shall state prices both in writing and in figures. In the event of discrepancy between the writing and the figures, the writing shall govern.
   1.04 Proposals shall be signed by the bidder; if the bidder is a partnership, by a general partner, or if a Corporation, by a duly authorized officer thereof. Copies of resolutions or powers of attorney authorizing the execution of proposals shall be submitted with the proposal if so requested by the OWNER.
   1.05 Proposals shall be prepared in duplicate sealed in an opaque envelope which shall state the following on the face thereof:
   - In the lower left-hand corner the project number as given in the proposal and "DO NOT OPEN—CONFIDENTIAL INFORMATION."
   - In the upper right-hand corner the return address.
   - In the center the address as provided in the proposal for the submission of the bid.
   1.06 The bid shall be hand-delivered or sent by registered mail.

2. *Rejection of Bids*

   2.01 Bids and any modifications thereto shall be accepted by OWNER only if they conform with the requirements as set forth above in Paragraph 1 (captioned "Procedure").
   2.02 Any interlineation, alteration or erasure may cause rejection of the bid.
   2.03 OWNER shall be required to accept only those proposals which shall in all respects comply with the Bid Documents, including by way of specification, but without limiting the generality of the foregoing, materials, construction equipment and methods specified in or required by the Bid Documents.
   2.04 The OWNER hereby reserves the right to reject any or all bids with or without cause and to award any contract to other than the lowest bidder.

3. *Withdrawals of the Bid*

   3.01 A bidder may withdraw his proposal without prejudice by communicating such withdrawal together with a short statement setting forth the reason therefor in writing or by telegram directed to the OWNER, at any time prior to the close of bidding. In such event, the proposal will be returned to the bidder unopened.
   3.02 By the submission of a proposal the bidder hereby agrees that such proposal may not be withdrawn for at least 45 days after the close of bidding.

4. *Inspection of the Site*

   4.01 Prior to submitting a bid, and for the purpose of determining the conditions of the site, each bidder shall inspect the Project site and shall satisfy himself as to such conditions including existing obstructions, elevations and other

bids. There will be an identified source to answer questions and perhaps information as to how charges will be handled.

Proposal Form

The proposal form (Exhibit 4) is the bid. The primary purpose of this form is to establish uniformity in submissions by the contractors to be used as a basis of value judgment in awarding the contract. The proposal form includes acknowledgments or affirmations concerning the bidder's knowledge of the specification, drawings, and conditions necessary. It includes the prices, allowances, and schedule the contractor wants considered.

General Requirements or Conditions

The general requirements for the project that apply to all contractors and subcontractors alike, together with a set of ground rules governing the interrelationship of the various parties (such as the architect, owner, and contractor), are set forth in the body of a document generally entitled "General Conditions." The American Institute of Architects has produced a standard form document entitled "A201—General Conditions."

---

matters which might in any way affect his bid. The OWNER's Project Manager shall log or record such visits.

5. *Addenda Prior to the Close of Bidding*

    5.01 OWNER may modify any or all documents or parts thereof included in the Bid Documents at OWNER's sole discretion, provided, however, the OWNER shall immediately notify each bidder in writing the exact nature and extent of such modification. All such modifications shall be captioned "Addenda No.: _____" and shall be numbered consecutively in seriatim.

    5.02 To obtain OWNER's approvals to substitute materials, construction equipment or methods prior to the close of bidding, bidders shall submit written request to the Project Manager at least one week prior to the close of bidding. Requests shall clearly describe the substitute for which approval is sought. If the substitute is accepted, the Project Manager shall approve it by an addendum which shall immediately be issued to all bidders of record.

6. *Discrepancies*

    6.01 Bidders shall notify the OWNER in writing immediately if any omission or discrepancy is discovered in the plans, drawings or specifications portion of the Bid Documents.

7. *Return of Bid Documents*

    7.01 Unsuccessful bidders shall return all Bid Documents to OWNER free of marks and in usable condition.

8. *Taxes*

    8.01 All Federal, State and local taxes, including sales, use and excise taxes that may be imposed as a result of the work or otherwise in the construction of the Project, shall be included in the aggregate amount bid or any other costs agreed on between the OWNER and the successful bidder.

SLIP SHEET TO BE USED WHEN BID SECURITY IS REQUIRED

    3.02 Paragraph 3.02 is hereby deleted and the following is substituted in lieu thereof:

Bidder shall submit a certified check to the order of OWNER in the amount of $_____(_____) or a bond naming OWNER as the insured party having a penal sum in the same amount. Such bond shall be issued by a surety company satisfactory to OWNER. No proposal shall be deemed effective unless accompanied by either such check or bond. If a bidder is determined by OWNER to be the successful bidder, then the proposal submitted by such successful bidder may not be withdrawn, revoked or otherwise rescinded within 45 days after the close of the bidding, except upon forfeiture to the OWNER of such check or the penal sum of such bond.

EXHIBIT 4   Sample Proposal Form

PROPOSAL FOR XYZ PROJECT NO.: _____

OFFICIAL NAME OF THE PROJECT: _____

TO: XYZ CORPORATION

FROM: _____

                                           Bidder

                                         Address

                                     City State

1. *Acknowledgment*

   The Bidder having examined the Bid Documents and having complied in all respects with the Instructions to Bidders forming a part hereof does hereby offer to complete the Projects as defined in the Bid Documents for whichever base bid set forth below Owner shall accept.

   In conjunction with the submission of this proposal Bidder represents to Owner that (i) no finder's fee or other compensation of a similar nature will be paid to any person, firm or corporation in conjunction with the submission of the proposal or if Bidder is successful in conjunction with the performance of the work or completion of the Project; and (ii) no disclosure of any documents, drawings, specifications or other information of any kind whatsoever has been made directly or indirectly to any other bidder.

2. *Base Bid*

   The Bidder proposes and agrees to provide all labor, materials, plant, equipment, transportation and other facilities as necessary and/or required to execute all of the work necessary to complete the Project for the total consideration of: _____Dollars ($_____), such amount being hereinafter referred to as the Base Bid or Base Bid Proposal.

3. *Alternates*

   When alternate proposals are required by Bid Documents, the Bidder proposes to perform alternates for stated resulting additions to or deductions from the Base Bid. Additions and deductions shall include any modifications of work or additional work that Bidder may be required to perform by reason of the acceptance of any alternate. (Note: Include all alternates as required by Bid Documents.) Number of lines below do not necessarily denote number of alternate proposals required. If necessary, add additional sheets in proposal to accommodate proposals for all required alternates. Under column headed "Alternate Number" insert identifying number taken from Bid Documents.

Alternate Number	Add	Deduct
_____	$_____	$_____
_____	$_____	$_____
_____	$_____	$_____
_____	$_____	$_____

4. *Addenda Acknowledgment*

   The Bidder acknowledges receipt of the following addenda: (List by number appearing on addenda.)

Addendum No.	Date	Addendum No.	Date
_____	_____	_____	_____
_____	_____	_____	_____
_____	_____	_____	_____

5. *List of Drawings Acknowledgment*

   The Bidder acknowledges receipt of all drawings as stated on the following list, as part of the Bid Documents. (The Bidder may state below numbers inclusive of identification of a complete list of drawings below or provide as an attachment to this Proposal, a complete list of drawings as received.)

_____

_____

_____

6. *Time of Completion*

The Bidder proposes to perform the work in accordance with the following schedule:
A. Substantially complete all work under the Agreement within _____ calendar days after execution of the Agreement.
B. Final completion within _____ calendar days after execution of the Agreement.
C. Start work within _____ calendar days after the execution of the Agreement.
D. Furnish complete shop drawings _____ within _____ calendar days after execution of the Agreement.

(Additional shop drawings requirements)_____

_____

_____

7. *Changes in the Work*

The Bidder agrees that when changes in work are ordered which involve extra cost over and above contract sum, and when such work, due to an emergency, is ordered to proceed on basis of cost-plus-fee, such fee shall be as determined in accordance with the Bid Documents.

8. *Unit Prices*

Unit prices are complete for labor, equipment and material; overhead and profit for additions will be based on stated percentages below:

    Description (Unit Cost)
    _____ $_____   per_____
    _____ $_____   per_____
    _____ $_____   per_____
    _____ $_____   per_____
    _____ $_____   per_____

Percentages
a. For extra work performed to contract by Contractor's own forces, *direct cost plus 15%*.
b. For extra work performed to contract by Subcontractors, *direct cost plus 15%*.
c. Allowance to General Contractor or Subcontractors for work performed by their subcontractors, at the rate of 7%.

9. *Execution Date*

The Bidder agrees that within 10 days after the receipt of the Notice of Award and Award Agreement, he shall execute and deliver to Owner the Award Agreement and if so required, he shall cause to be issued a surety bond which shall in all respects comply with this proposal. Failure to execute the Award Agreement and deliver the Surety Bond if so required shall be considered a withdrawal as defined in Paragraph 3.02 of the Instructions to Bidders and shall result in a forfeiture of the Bid Security.

9a. *Bid Security Slip Sheet*

Bid Security in the amount of $_____ in conformance with Instructions to Bidders without endorsement is attached which shall become the property of Owner, in the event this proposal is withdrawn, revoked or otherwise rescinded within 45 days after the close of bidding. Any forfeiture of bid security because of such withdrawal, revocation or rescission, shall be considered as liquidated damages to Owner and not a penalty. If the Bidder becomes the successful Bidder, then Bidder agrees that Owner, in Owner's sole discretion, may retain fully executed bid security slip sheet and will deliver to Owner a Surety Bond naming Owner as insured and carrying a penal sum not less than the sum of the bid security and written by a Surety company satisfactory to Owner.

EXHIBIT 4   Sample Proposal Form (*Continued*)

10. *Assignment*

No assignment or transfer of all or any part of the Bidder's interest in this Proposal has been made or will be made without the prior written consent of the Owner.

11. *General Statement*

The Bidder has complied and/or will comply with all requirements of local, state and national laws, and avers that no legal requirement has been or will be violated in making or accepting this Proposal, in awarding the Contract to him and/or in the prosecution of the work required.

12. *Subcontractors*

The Bidder shall list all principal Subcontractors which the Bidder shall utilize on the Project; should the Bidder become the successful Bidder he shall utilize no other Subcontractors than those furnished with this Proposal.

Classification of Work	*Name of Sub-bidder*	*License No.*
Electrical		
Plumbing		
Heating, Ventilation and Air Conditioning		
Other		

13. *Funding and Accounting Breakdown*

The Bidder represents that, shall he become the successful bidder, he shall itemize the Contract amounts in subsequent agreed-upon prices into categories required by the Owner when requested. Such itemizations in no way shall be construed or used for establishing prices or additions to or deletions from the work.

Respectfully submitted, this ____day of_____, 19____

(Firm Name):_____

(Address): _____

_____

(Signature): _____ L.S.

(Name Typed): _____

(Title): _____

(SEAL IF BIDDER IS A CORPORATION)

Almost all architects and contractors are familiar with this document, and it can be used for almost any construction project. Many companies involved in a large amount of construction choose to create their own document for this purpose. An example of such a document entitled "General Requirements of the Construction Documents" is shown in Exhibit 5.

Supplemental General Requirements or Conditions

The purpose of supplemental general requirements or conditions is to modify the articles in the general document for deletions, changes, additions, or substitutions to particularly fit the project. The document is usually indexed, providing a complete summary of the articles thus amended.

EXHIBIT 5   General Requirements of the Construction Documents Form

ARTICLE 1   DEFINITIONS

1.1   *The Bid Documents.* The Bid Documents shall include the Instructions to Bidders, the Contractor's Proposal Form, the Notice of Award, the Award Agreement, the General and Special Requirements to the Contract, all Drawings, Specifications and other documents described in the Award Agreement and any and all Addenda issued by the Owner prior to the Close of Bidding as hereinafter described.

1.2   *Contract Documents.* The Contract Documents shall consist of the Bid Documents, Contractor's Release and Affidavit, Subcontractors' Partial Release and Affidavit, and all other agreements between Owner and Contractor related to the Project entered into after the Award Agreement.

1.3   *Close of Bidding.* The Close of Bidding shall mean the last day and the latest hours thereof specified in the Instruction to Bidders.

1.4   *Project Manager.* The Project Manager shall mean the employee designated by the Owner to supervise and coordinate the Work and to otherwise represent the Owner with respect to all matters relating to the Project.

1.5   *The Project.* The Project shall mean all improvements required to be performed under the Bid Documents and all subsequent modifications thereto, if any.

1.6   *The Work.* The Work shall mean all labor, materials, services and equipment required to complete the Project.

1.7   *Contractor.* The Contractor shall mean a person or organization who has a Contract with the Owner to perform all or any part of the Work. As used herein the term Contractor shall also include the authorized representative or Contractor assigned to the Project.

1.8   *Subcontractor.* The Subcontractor shall mean a person or organization who has a contract with a Contractor to perform part of the Work.

1.9   *The Specifications.* The term Specifications shall mean the technical particulars set forth under Divisions 1 through 16 as listed in the Table of Contents and revisions to the Specifications included in Addenda (if any) and Change Orders (if any).

1.10   *Drawings.* The term Drawings shall mean those drawings listed under Special Requirements as List of Drawings, and revisions to the Drawings included with Addenda (if any) and Change Orders (if any).

1.11   *Shop Drawings.* The term Shop Drawings shall mean those drawings, diagrams, illustrations, schedules, performance charts, brochures, and other data which are prepared by the Contractor or any Subcontractor, manufacturer, supplier or materialman, and which illustrate some portion of the Work or constitute a graphic relating to some portion of the Work.

1.12   *Samples.* The term Samples shall mean physical examples presented to Owner or Architect by the Contractor to illustrate materials, equipment or workmanship, and to establish standards by which the Work will be judged by the Architect.

1.13   *Separate Contract.* The term Separate Contract shall mean a contract between the Owner and another contractor, other than the Contractor under this Contract, for the construction or furnishing a portion of the Work.

1.14   *Field Order.* The term Field Order shall mean an order issued by the Project Manager to the Contractor to carry out minor revisions in the Work. The Contractor's field superintendent shall be authorized to supply quotations for such revisions directly to the Project Manager, Such Field Orders shall be numbered consecutively in chronological order.

1.15   *Change Order.* The term Change Order shall mean a document prepared by the Project Manager or Architect as a change to the Contract, incorporating approved Contractor's proposals for changes in the Work. Change Orders shall be numbered consecutively in chronological order, and shall refer to the Bulletin(s) or Field Order(s) covered.

1.16   *Final Completion.* The term Final Completion shall mean the performance of all of the Work required to complete the Project, including by way of specification but without limiting the generality thereof, the satisfactory operation of all equipment, the correction of all unacceptable or incomplete portions of the Project to the satisfaction of the Owner and the Architect, the settlement of all claims and the securing the release of record of all mechanics and materialmen liens or liens of a like nature, and if the Architect is other than the Owner, the delivery to the Owner of an Architect's Certificate of Completion, the issuance by an appropriate government authority of a Certificate of

EXHIBIT 5   General Requirements of the Construction Documents Form
(*Continued*)

Occupancy or similar certificate permitting the Owner to occupy and utilize the project and the removal of all rubbish, surplus materials, scaffolding and equipment from the site of the Project whether or not the same be left by or belongs to the Contractor.

1.17   *Substantial Completion.* Substantial Completion shall mean that stage of completion of the Work when all major items of work have been satisfactorily performed, all equipment has been operated and tested, the Work has been inspected by the Architect and governmental agencies, and the premises can be safely and legally (Certificate of Occupancy) occupied by the Owner.

1.18   *Beneficial Occupancy.* Beneficial Occupancy shall mean that occupancy by the Owner of any part of the premises before the final acceptance of the work (see Article 13).

1.19   *Bulletin.* A Bulletin shall mean a written document issued by the Architect to instruct the Contractor and Owner of changes to the drawings and/or specifications including instructions to the Contractor to submit proposals for the changes in work and make any claims for delays and/or damages.

ARTICLE 2   SAFETY AND INSURANCE

2.1   Contractor shall (1) conduct the Work in a safe manner and shall initiate and maintain safety precautions and programs; (2) comply with all Federal, State and Local laws, ordinances, codes and regulations in the performance of the Work relating to safety; (3) and otherwise conform to generally accepted safety standards in the construction industry.

2.2   Contractor shall designate a safety director for the Work who shall be responsible for policing and enforcing all the obligations of Contractor under 2.1 above.

2.3   The Safety Director shall modify any program submitted hereunder as may be reasonably required by Owner's Manager of Environmental Health and Safety for the purpose of complying with any law, ordinance, code or regulation, and accepted safety standard.   Thereafter and at such times as Owner may direct whether verbally or in writing, the Safety Director shall report to such Manager of Environmental Health and Safety the status of program compliance and any other matters relating to the safe condition of the Work.   Contractor shall direct its Safety Director to cooperate fully with the Owner, insurance carriers writing insurance in connection with the Work and appropriate governmental agencies.   The Safety Director shall maintain all records necessary for Owner to determine that Contractor is complying with the requirements hereof and shall make a full and complete record of all accidents and injuries connected with the performance of or any way related to the Work.

2.4   Owner shall notify Contractor in the event of any non-compliance with the provisions hereof.   Thereupon Contractor shall take such steps as may be required to immediately correct such non-compliance.   And if Contractor fails to promptly make such correction, Owner may stop all or any part of the Work in progress until such correction is effected.   Owner shall not be liable for any costs, expenses or loss incurred by Contractor as a result of such stoppage.

2.5   The Contractor shall provide and maintain the following insurance coverage in the limits specified until Final Completion or if a longer period of time is required, for such longer period: (a) Workmen's Compensation and Employer's Liability Insurance affording (i) statutory protection under the Workmen's Compensation Laws of the States in which the work is to be performed and, if applicable, the United States Longshormen's and Harbor Workers' Compensation Act, and (ii) Employer's Liability protection subject to a limit of $100,000.; (b) General Liability (All Hazards) and Automobile Liability (All Hazards) Insurance.

   Bodily Injury: $1,000,000 each person
                     $1,000,000 each accident/occurrence
                     $1,000,000 annual aggregate
   Property Damage $1,000,000 each accident/occurrence
                     $1,000,000 annual aggregate

2.6   The general liability insurance shall include coverage for (i) the liability assumed by the Contractor under Paragraph 2.9 hereof and (ii) the explosion, collapse and underground property damage hazards (commonly referred to as the "x," "c," and "u" hazards) and the Certificates of Insurance furnished by the Contractor shall show by specific reference that each of these items has been provided for.

2.7   The Contractor shall maintain Completed Operations Insurance for at least two years following completion of the contracts with a limit of liability of not less than those set forth in Paragraph 2.6.

2.8   Valid certificates of the Contractor's insurance required under Paragraphs 2.5 and 2.7 be filed with the Owner prior to the commencement of the Work. Such certificates shall include a provision obligating the insurers to give at least fifteen (15) days prior written notice of any material change in or cancellation of any such insurance.

2.9   The Contractor shall indemnify and save Owner harmless from all liability and loss because of injury (including death) to any person, or damage to any property that may occur or may be alleged to have occurred during the performance of the Work, as a result, directly or indirectly, of Contractor's or any subcontractor's fault or negligence, or of their 'agents and employees, and whether or not such injury or damage is also attributable to Owner's fault or negligence. The Contractor shall defend all suits or claims alleging such injury or damages and shall pay all charges of attorneys, court costs and other costs and expenses in connection therewith. The provisions hereof shall survive completion and acceptance of the Work.

2.10   Owner shall purchase and maintain property insurance upon the Project to the full insurable value thereof. This insurance shall include the interests of Owner, the Contractor and subcontractors and shall insure against the perils of fire, extended coverage, vandalism and malicious mischief.

ARTICLE 3   INTENT OF CONTRACT DOCUMENTS

3.1   In the event any design drawing (other than a shop or working drawing), specification or other document not identified and signed by the Owner and Contractor or not clearly referred to in a document signed by the Owner and Contractor is disputed as not forming a part of the Contract Documents, such disputes shall be referred to the Architect and Architect's determination whether such disputed document is a part of the Contract Documents shall be final and binding on Owner and contractor.

3.2   Meanings of technical or trade language used herein shall be determined in accordance with common definitions consistently recognized in the construction industry.

3.3   The Work shall be performed in accordance with sound construction practices. The sequence, division of labor or other performance of the work shall not be governed by the form or manner in which the specifications are organized or divided nor shall the organization and divisions used in the specifications be construed as criteria for the subcontracting of Work.

3.4   Prior to the commencement of the Work, the Contractor shall verify all of the details of that portion of the Work to be performed with the Architect including the accuracy of all working drawings, and specifications. Where the Owner has agreed to substitute any material with material of a different kind than that provided in the specifications the Contractor shall obtain a verification from the Architect that such substitution complies with Owner's authorization.

3.5   Written interpretations necessary for the proper execution or progress of the Work, requested by Contractor shall be submitted to Architect. Owner shall instruct Architect to render such interpretation with reasonable promptness and in accordance with any previously agreed schedule. Such interpretations shall be consistent with or reasonably inferable from the Contract Documents. Except as provided in Article 15 (Arbitration), all interpretations shall be binding on Owner and Contractor.

3.6   Unless otherwise provided in the Contract Documents, the Contractor will be furnished, free of charge, all copies of Drawings and Specifications reasonably necessary for the execution of the Work.

ARTICLE 4   ARCHITECT

4.1   The Contract Documents shall constitute the authority for the Architect to act on behalf of the Owner where such authority is required under the Contract Documents. The Architect will act as the Owner's representative providing general administration of the construction contract during construction and through the date of final payment.

4.2   The Contractor acknowledges that Architect's obligation to Owner with respect to the Project are as follows:
   (a) To make such visits to the site as necessary so that the Architect may become generally familiar with the progress and quality of the Work for the purpose of determining if the Work is in conformance with the Contract Documents.
   (b) To protect the Owner against defects and deficiencies in the Work on the basis of knowledge obtained from his own outside observations and to keep the Owner informed progressively of his findings; provided, however, that nothing herein contained will make the Architect responsible for the construction means, methods,

EXHIBIT 5   General Requirements of the Construction Documents Form
(*Continued*)

techniques, sequence or procedure or any other obligations of the Contractor specified with the Contract Documents.

(c) To determine amount of and concur with payments to the Contractor and issue Architect's Concurrence therefor in accordance with the Contract Documents, and the Contractor's Application of Payments.

(d) To judge the performance of the Work and render interpretations where necessary for the proper execution of the Work. Such judgments and interpretations shall be performed within a reasonable time so as not to delay the progress of the Work.

(e) To render impartial decisions on claims and disagreements or questions arising between the Owner and the Contractor relating to the execution or progress of the Work. All such judgments shall be made in writing and become part of the Contract Documents; provided, however, that any such decisions in matters relating to artistic effect will be final only if consistent with the intent of the Contract Documents.

(f) To review shop drawings and samples submitted to him by the Contractor and return them to the Contractor in conformance with the Construction Schedule so as not to delay the progress of the Work. Such review and approval of shop drawings and samples will be for the purpose of conformance of the defined concept of the project and with information stated in the Contract Documents.

(g) To prepare Change Orders and order minor changes in the Work.

4.3   Any claim, dispute or other matter that has been referred to the Architect, except those relating to artistic effect and except any which have been waived by the making or acceptance of final payment as provided in Article 12 hereof be subject to arbitration upon the written demand of either party to the other. However, no demand for arbitration of any such claim, dispute or other matter may be made until the earlier of:

    a. The date on which the Architect has rendered his decision, or

    b. The tenth day after the parties have presented their evidence to the Architect or have been given a reasonable opportunity to do so, if the Architect has not rendered his written decision by that date.

4.4   If a decision of the Architect is made in writing and states that it is final, but subject to appeal, no demand for arbitration of a claim, dispute or other matter covered by such decision may be made later than thirty (30) days after the date on which the party making the demand received the decision. The failure to demand arbitration within such thirty (30) days' period will render the Architect's decision binding upon the Owner and the Contractor. If the Architect renders a decision after arbitration proceedings have been initiated, such decision may be introduced as evidence.

ARTICLE 5   CONTRACTOR

5.1   The Contractor shall have the responsibility for workmanlike supervision and coordination of means, methods and techniques involved in the performance of the Work.

5.2   Except for the building permit, for which the Owner shall pay, the Contractor shall pay all ancillary costs incurred in performance of the Work including but not limited to, temporary structures, utilities, transportation, sales, taxes, consumer taxes and similar taxes, permits, governmental fees and licenses for the proper execution of the Work.

5.3   The Contractor shall comply with all legal requirements in the performance of the Work both on and off site.

5.4   The Contractor shall employ such personnel including a Superintendent and assistants as may be required to insure the orderly and diligent performance of the Work. The Superintendent shall be approved by the Architect and the Owner and shall act as the representative of the Contractor on the Project site.

5.5   The Contractor shall at the commencement of the Work submit a complete schedule of Work for approval by the Architect and the Owner. Such schedule shall be comprehensive in nature and shall encompass all aspects of labor, material and equipment to be utilized within the scope of the Work. Thereafter the Contractor shall each month submit an up-date of the Schedule of Work for approval.

5.6   The Contractor shall maintain on the site for the Owner, a complete set of Contract Documents and all copies of approved shop drawings progressively filed and updated to reflect the latest changes.

5.7   Prior to submission for Architect's approval, the Contractor shall review and approve in writing all shop drawings and samples to be utilized in the Work. Such drawings or samples to be submitted shall be at least two in number, properly identified in such manner as Architect may direct and shall be submitted in accordance with the Work schedule. In the event the Architect withholds his approval because of non-conformance of such drawings or samples, Contractor shall at Contractor's own expense cause such drawings to conform to the Contract Documents. No work involving the use of such drawings or material represented by such samples shall commence until Architect's approval thereto is obtained in writing.

5.8   The Contractor's approval of Shop drawings and samples is acknowledgment of review and selection as required by the Contract Documents. It shall be the Contractor's responsibility to satisfy the Architect with the submission of shop drawings and samples, any corrections thereto and resubmission of such until approval is obtained.

5.9   Upon completion of the Work the Contractor shall remove all equipment, tools, surplus material and machinery from the site. Contractor shall clean all glass and leave the Work and the site "broom clean." Should Contractor fail to perform as required hereunder, the Owner may do so and all costs incurred as a result thereof be paid for by the Contractor.

ARTICLE 6   SUBCONTRACTORS

6.1   All work performed for the Contractor by a Subcontractor shall be pursuant to an appropriate agreement between the Contractor and the Subcontractor (and where appropriate between Subcontractors and Sub-subcontractors) which shall contain provisions that:

(a) Preserve and protect the rights of the Owner and the Architect under the Contract with respect to the Work to be performed under the subcontract so that the subcontracting thereof will not prejudice such rights;

(b) require that such Work be performed in accordance with the requirements of the Contract Documents;

(c) require submission to the Contractor of applications for payment under each subcontract to which the Contractor is a party, in reasonable time to enable the Contractor to apply for payment in accordance with Article 12;

(d) require that all claims for additional costs, extensions of time, damages for delays or otherwise with respect to subcontracted portions of the Work shall be submitted to the Contractor (via any Subcontractor or Sub-subcontractor where appropriate) in sufficient time so that the Contractor may comply in the manner provided in the Contract Documents for like claims by the Contractor upon the Owner;

(e) waive all rights the contracting parties may have against one another for damages caused by fire or other perils covered by the property insurance described in Article 2 except such rights as they may have to the proceeds of such insurance held by the Owner as trustee under Article 2; and

(f) obligate each Subcontractor specifically to consent to the provisions of this Article 6.

6.2   Where Contractor subdivides portions of the Work the entire responsiblity for the subdividing of the Work rests with the Contractor. The Owner and the Architect are not responsible for the manner of the subdivision of the Work and neither will enter into nor settle disagreements or disputes between Contractor and Subcontractors. The arrangement of Specifications and the manner of graphic illustration of drawings are for convenience of reference and do not comprise any exacting method of subdividing work for purposes of subcontracting, except where the Contract Documents require an undivided responsibility for certain work.

6.3   Contractor shall require each Subcontractor to (1) inspect surfaces and job conditions before beginning Work at site, (2) accept or cite necessary corrections in surfaces or job conditions before beginning Work at site, and (3) protect his own materials and equipment and Work from damage, injury or loss due to weather or due to Work of the Contractor, other Subcontractors or other Contractors, if any. The best means of protection shall be supplied and removed when no longer required.

6.4 (a)   The Contractor shall pay each Subcontractor upon receipt of payment from the Owner, an amount equal to the percentage of completion allowed to the Contractor on account of such subcontractor's Work, less the percentage retained from payments to the Contractor. The Contractor shall also require each Subcontractor to make similar payments to his Subcontractors.

(b)   If the Architect fails to issue a Certificate for Payment for any cause which is the fault of the Contractor and not the fault of a particular Subcontractor, the Contractor shall pay that Subcontractor on demand, made at any time after the Certificate for Payment should otherwise have been issued, for his Work to the extent completed, less the retained percentage.

(c)   The Contractor shall pay each Subcontractor a just share of any insurance moneys

EXHIBIT 5   General Requirements of the Construction Documents Form (*Continued*)

---

received by the Contractor under Article 2, and he shall require each Subcontractor to make similar payments to his Subcontractors.

(d) The Architect may, on request and at his discretion, furnish to any Subcontractor, if practicable, information regarding percentages of completion certified to the Contractor on account of Work done by such Subcontractors.

(e) Neither the Owner nor the Architect shall have any obligation to pay or to see to the payment of any moneys to any Subcontractor except as may otherwise be required by law.

ARTICLE 7   SEPARATE CONTRACTS

7.1 The Project may be separated into such parts as the Owner in Owner's sole judgment shall determine and separate contracts entered into covering the Work to be performed with respect to each such part.

7.2 Should the Project be separated as above provided, the Contractor shall coordinate Contractor's activities in the performance of the Work in such a manner so as not to hinder other contractors on the Project. In the event such portion of the work to be performed by Contractor depends on or relates directly to portions of the Work to be performed by others, Contractor shall inspect such portion performed by others and, in the event of any deficiency or defect therein, Contractor shall immediately inform Owner. Failure to inform Owner of any such deficiency or defect shall be construed as an acceptance of such portion of the Work performed by others.

7.3 If Contractor shall damage any portion of the Work whether performed by Contractor or by others, the Contractor shall, at Contractors's sole expense, immediately repair such damage.

7.4 In the event the Contractor is required to cut, fit or otherwise change the Work for the sole purpose of adding to such portion of the Work done by Contractor, then Contractor shall first obtain the written permission of Architect to the cutting, fitting or patching as the case may be.

7.5 Any costs incurred by Owner as a result of poorly timed or defective work shall be borne by Contractor and shall be immediately reimbursed to Owner upon receipt of Architect's written statment to that effect.

ARTICLE 8   CHANGES IN THE WORK

8.1 The Owner may order extra work or make changes by altering, adding to, or deleting from, the Work. All such Work shall be executed as provided hereunder, except that any claim for extension of time caused thereby shall be adjusted at the time of directing such change.

8.2 All changes must be authorized in writing and if by the Architect in accordance with Article 1, or if Owner's authorized representatives, then as set forth below. Authorized representatives for the purpose of this Article include only those persons to whom authority to direct changes has been delegated by Owner in a written authorization signed by the Owner and approved by the Contractor.

8.3 In giving instructions, the Architect shall have authority to make minor changes in the work not inconsistent with the purposes of the Project. Except in an emergency endangering life or property, no extra work or change shall be made unless in pursuance of a written direction from the Architect signed or countersigned by Project Manager of Owner or his authorized representative and no claim for additional costs or increases in schedule shall be valid unless so directed. If requested by Owner, Contractor will correct or remove, at its own expense, changes or extras not properly authorized under this Article.

8.4 Contractor will not be entitled to increases in cost or schedule where claims, requests or directions are not presented as specified in Articles 8.2 and 12 or where the Project Manager of Owner has not been kept informed as required by the Contract Documents. In any event Owner shall be liable to Contractor for only those amounts which Contractor shall set forth in a change memorandum from which Owner authorizes Architect a Formal Change Order.

ARTICLE 9   PROGRESSION OF THE WORK

9.1 The times as stated in the Contract Documents are of the essence.

9.2 If the Contractor encounters delays which in the sole judgment of the Owner are caused by circumstances beyond the control of the Contractor, the contract times shall be changed by Change Order to such new times as may be determined by the Owner to reflect the delay. Contractor shall make written claims within ten (10) days of date of delay.

9.3 Nothing herein contained shall relieve the Contractor from his duty to oversee and direct the performance of the Work in accordance with the Contract Documents.

9.4 Interference with Owner's business operations caused by the performance of any portion of the Work shall be coordinated with Owner in such a manner to insure that such interference will be kept at a minimum during Owner's normal working hours.

ARTICLE 10 INSPECTION OF THE WORK

10.1 The Work including any part thereof is subject to the inspection of the Architect. Where a request by the Architect for inspection requires the damaging or destruction of a completed portion of the Work and such portion is found to be in conformance with the Contract Documents the cost of repairing such damage or destruction shall be borne by the Owner.

10.2 The Contractor shall promptly correct any portion of the Work found to be in non-conformance with the Contract Documents during the period of one (1) year following the completion of the Work. The cost of correcting that portion of the Work that is not in conformance with the Contract Documents shall be borne by the Contractor including removal of Work deemed to be defective and the restoration of any other portion of the Work damaged or destroyed in course of such correction.

10.3 If within a reasonable time after Owner requests Contractor to correct any non-conforming portion of the Work and Contractor shall fail or neglect to make such correction, Owner may, but is not required to, correct such non-conforming portion and all expenses incurred as a result thereof shall be borne by the Contractor. If Owner shall determine that it would be inexpedient to correct such non-conforming portion equitable deductions from the Contract Sum shall be made therefor.

10.4 All guarantees and warranties relating to any material or equipment installed in pursuance of the Contract Documents shall be assigned to the Owner by the Contractor or subcontractor as the case may be as and when received.

ARTICLE 11 TERMINATION OF THE CONTRACT

11.1 If the Work is stopped for a period of thirty (30) days under an order of any court or other public authority having jurisdiction, or as a result of an act of government, such as a declaration of a national emergency making materials unavailable, through no act or fault of the Contractor or a Subcontractor or their agents or employees or any other persons performing any of the Work under a contract with the Contractor, or if the Work should be stopped for a period of thirty (30) days by the Contractor for the Owner's failure to make payment thereon as provided in Article 12, then the Contractor may, upon seven (7) days' written notice to the Owner and the Architect, terminate the Contract and recover from the Owner payment for all sums due to date of termination for that portion of the Work completed less any sums previously paid to Contractor.

11.2 The Contractor acknowledges the right of the Owner to stop the Work whenever Owner shall (1) reasonably deem it necessary for proper performance of the Contract, or (2) in Owner's sole judgment determine that the Project is no longer required. In such event Owner shall pay Contractor any amount which may be due to Contractor as of termination date as computed in the same manner for termination under 11.1 above.

11.3 The Owner without waiver of such other rights as it may have, may terminate the performance of the Work under this Contract whenever the Contractor shall be adjudged a bankrupt, make a general assignment for creditors, become involved in a receivership of its assets, default in performance of its obligations under this Contract, or shall so fail to make progress in the prosecution of the work hereunder as to endanger the performance of this Contract at the times stated herein or otherwise, in accordance with the terms of the Contract; provided however, that if Owner desires to terminate because of Contractor's failure to make progress, Contractor shall have ten (10) days to cure the failure to make progress prior to terminating such performance. Termination of the work hereunder shall be effected by delivery to the Contractor of a Notice of Termination for Default specifying that termination is for default or failure to make progress in the prosecution of the Work and the date upon which such termination shall become effective.

11.4 After receipt of a Notice of Termination for Default, the Contractor, except as otherwise required by the Owner, shall terminate the Work on the date specified in the Notice of Termination for Default, assign to such party or parties as the Owner may require, in the manner and to the extent required by the Owner, all the right, title and

EXHIBIT 5   General Requirements of the Construction Documents Form (*Continued*)

interest of the Contractor in the Work and all right, title and interest of the Contractor in the subcontracts for the performance of any work terminated by the Notice of Termination for Default, and take such action as the Owner may require for protection and preservation of property which is in the possession of the Contractor and in which the Owner has or may acquire an interest.

11.5   In the event this Contract is terminated as provided in this Article, the Owner may (1) enter upon the Site and for the purpose of completing the Work take possession of all materials, tools and equipment on the Site, and (2) employ any other person or persons necessary to complete the Work. The Owner shall either purchase or pay the Contractor reasonable rental for such tools and equipment owned by the Contractor which Owner shall use in the completion of the Work.

11.6   Upon termination of this Contract as provided in this Article, the Owner shall (1) to the extent that the Owner so advised the Contractor in writing, assume and become liable for any or all obligations and commitments which the Contractor may have theretofore in good faith undertaken or incurred in the performance of the Work in accordance with the provisions of these Contract Documents including all liabilities incurred on account of termination of subcontracts as provided in subparagraph 11.7 of this Article, (2) reimburse the Contractor for all costs reasonably incurred, not previously reimbursed, in the performance of the Work in accordance with the terms of the Award Agreement, and (3) make no additional payments of fees as provided by the Award Agreement after the date of the termination notice to the Contractor. Provisions of this Article shall not limit or affect the rights or remedies of Owner stated in other provisions of the Contract Documents or provided by law.

11.7   The obligation of the Owner to make any payment under this Article shall without limitation thereto be subject to (a) deductions in respect of all payments made to the Contractor prior to the date of the termination notice, (b) any claim or set-off which the Owner may have against the Contractor in connection with the performance of the Work under this Contract, and (c) any claim of any materialman or subcontractor whose subcontract is related to the performance of the Work under this Contract.

ARTICLE 12   PAYMENTS AND COMPLETION

12.1   Each month the Contractor shall deliver to the Project Manager of Owner and the Architect, a statement in accordance with the provisions of subparagraph 12.2 immediately following. The Owner, upon approval of the Project Manager and concurrence by Architect, shall pay to the Contractor such portion or all of such statement which may be approved by the Project Manager within fourteen (14) days of delivery of the statement to both of the above. Any acceptance of such money by the Contractor after expiration of the fourteen (14) day period will not excuse the Owner from making all future payments within the required time.

12.2   As soon as practicable after the tenth (10th) day of each calendar month the Contractor shall present to the Project Manager of Owner and the Architect a copy of an accurate, detailed and complete statement of all accounts charged to the work which have then been paid, other than those for which a like statement has previously been made, together with a current accounting statement for the funds previously paid, and also a written detailed estimate of all payments to be made through the fifteenth (15th) day of the month next succeeding such calendar month (hereinafter referred to as "The Application for Payment") and an estimated cost to complete the Project with estimated variance from stated budget if requested by Owner during the previous month. A completed schedule of values which shall include the following listed categories shall be submitted to the Architect with each Application for Payment:

Project Overhead

Site Work	*Sealants—Waterproofing*
General Site Excavation	*Doors, Windows and Glass*
Rock Excavation	Metal Doors
Curbs and Paving	Aluminum Entrance Work
Exterior Drainage System	Aluminum Windows
Exterior Concrete Work	Special Doors
Miscellaneous	Glass and Glazing
Building Excavation	
Fine Grading	

Concrete
Structural, Slabs or Grade
Floors
Precast

Masonry
Exterior—Face Brick—Block
Interior—Tile—Block

Steel
Structural and Joists
Roofs and Floor Deck
Miscellaneous

Carpentry and Millwork

Roofing, Insulation and Flashing

Finishes
Painting
Accoustical Ceilings
Resilient Flooring
Ceramic Tile
Lath and Plaster
Stone Flooring
Metal Pan Ceilings
Quarry Tiles
Vinyl Wall Coverings
Epoxy Coating

Specialties
Toilet Enclosures and Doors
Toilet Accessories
Roof Scuttle
Skylights
Loading Dock-Bumpers
Lockers
Kitchen Equipment

Plumbing
Site and Building

Fire Protection
Site and Building

Mechanical
Site and Building

Electrical
Site and Building

The Contractor shall break down each division into systems with piping, conduit, equipment, specialties, fixtures for each system.

No deletion to this Schedule shall be made unless authorized in writing by the Architect.

12.3   If payments are to be made on account of materials or equipment not incorporated in the Work but delivered and suitably stored at the Site, or at some other location agreed upon in writing, such payments shall be conditioned upon submission by the Contractor of bills of sale or such other document satisfactory to the Owner to establish the Owner's title to such materials or equipment or otherwise protect the Owner's interest including applicable insurance and transportation to the Site.

12.4   The Contractor warrants and guarantees that title to all Work, materials and equipment covered by an Application for Payment, whether incorporated in the Project or not, will pass to the Owner upon the receipt of such payment by the Contractor, free and clear of all liens, claims, security interests or encumbrances, hereinafter referred to in this Article 12 as "liens"; and that no Work, materials or equipment covered by an Application for Payment will have been acquired by the Contractor or by any other person performing the Work at the Site or furnishing materials and equipment for the Project, subject to an agreement under which an interest therein or an encumbrance thereon is retained by the seller or otherwise imposed by the Contractor or such other person.

12.5   The issuance of an Architect Concurrence will constitute a representation by the Architect to the Owner, based on his observations at the Site and the data comprising the Application for Payment, that the Work has progressed to the point indicated; that, to the best of his knowledge, information and belief, the quality of the Work is in accordance with the Contract Documents (subject to an evaluation of the Work for conformance with the Contract Documents upon Substantial Completion, to the results of any subsequent tests required by the Contract Documents, to minor deviations from the Contract Documents correctable prior to completion, and to any specific qualifications stated in his Concurrence); and that the Contractor is entitled to payment in the amount certified.   In addition, the Architect's final Concurrence will constitute a further representation that the conditions precedent to the Contractor's being entitled to final payment as set forth in subparagraph 12.11 of this Article 12 have been fulfilled. However, by issuing an Architect's Concurrence the Architect shall not thereby be deemed to represent that he has made exhaustive or continuous on-site inspections to check the quality or quantity of the Work or that he has reviewed the construction means, methods, techniques, sequences or procedures, or that he has made any examination to ascertain how or for what purpose the Contractor has used the moneys previously paid on account of the Contract Sum.

EXHIBIT 5   General Requirements of the Construction Documents Form
(*Continued*)

12.6   No certificate for a progress payment, nor any progress payment, nor any partial or entire use or occupancy of the Project by the Owner, shall constitute an acceptance of any Work not in accordance with the Contract Documents.

12.7   The Architect may decline to approve an Application for Payment and may withhold his Concurrence in whole or in part, to the extent necessary reasonably to protect the Owner, if in his opinion he is unable to make representations to the Owner as provided in subparagraph 12.5 of this Article 12.   The Architect may also decline his Concurrence because of subsequently discovered evidence or subsequent inspections, he may nullify the whole or any part of his Concurrence previously issued to such extent as may be necessary in his opinion to protect the Owner from loss because of:

1. Defective work not remedied;
2. Third party claims filed or reasonable evidence indicating probable filing of such claims;
3. Failure of the Contractor to make payments properly to Subcontractors or for labor, materials or equipment;
4. Reasonable doubt that the Work can be completed for the unpaid balance of the Contract Sum;
5. Damage to another contractor;
6. Reasonable indication that the Work will not be completed within the Contract Time; or
7. Unsatisfactory prosecution of the Work by the Contractor.

12.8   When the above grounds in subparagraph 12.7 are removed, payment shall be made for amounts withheld because of them.

12.9   If the Owner should fail to pay the Contractor within seven (7) days after the date of payment established in the Agreement any approved amount awarded by arbitration, then the Contractor may, upon seven (7) additional days' written notice to the Owner and the Architect, stop the Work until payment of the amount owing has been received.

12.10 When the Contractor determines that the Work or a designated portion thereof acceptable to the Owner is substantially complete, the Contractor shall prepare for submission to the Architect a list of items to be completed or corrected.   The failure to include any items on such list does not alter the responsibility of the Contractor to complete all Work in accordance with the Contract Documents.   When the Architect on the basis of an inspection determines that the Work is substantially complete, he will then prepare a Certificate of Substantial Completion which shall establish the Date of Substantial Completion, shall state the responsibilities of the Owner and the Contractor for maintenance, heat, utilities, and insurance, and shall fix the time within which the Contractor shall complete the items listed therein.   The Certificate of Substantial Completion shall be submitted to the Owner and the Contractor for their written acceptance of the responsibilities assigned to them in such Certificate.

12.11 Upon receipt of written notice that the Work is ready for final inspection and acceptance and upon receipt of a final Application for Payment, the Architect will promptly make such inspection and, when he finds the Work acceptable under the Contract Documents and the Contract fully performed, he will promptly issue a final Architect's Concurrence for payment stating that to the best of his knowledge, information and belief, and on the basis of his observations and inspections, the Work has been completed in accordance with the terms and conditions of the Contract Documents and that the entire balance found to be due the Contractor, and noted in said final Concurrence, is due and payable.

12.12 Neither the final payment nor the remaining retained percentage shall become due until the Contractor submits to the Architect (1) an Affidavit that all payrolls, bills for materials and equipment and other indebtedness connected with the Work for which the Owner or his property might in any way be responsible, have been paid or otherwise satisfied, (2) consent of surety, if any, to final payment, and (3) if required by the Owner, other data establishing payment or satisfaction of all such obligations, such as receipts, releases and waivers of liens arising out of the Contract, to the extent and in such form as may be designated by the Owner.   If any subcontractor refuses to furnish a release or waiver required by the Owner, the Contractor may furnish a bond satisfactory to the Owner to indemnify him against any such lien.   If any such lien remains unsatisfied after all payments are made, the Contractor shall refund to the Owner all moneys that the latter may be compelled to pay in discharging such lien, including all costs and reasonable attorneys' fees.

12.13 If after Substantial Completion, Final Completion is materially delayed through no fault of the Contractor, and the Architect so confirms, the Owner shall, upon certification by the Architect, and without terminating the Contract, make payment of the balance due for that portion of the Work fully completed and accepted. If the remaining balance for Work not fully completed or corrected is less than the retainage stipulated in the Agreement, and if any labor and material or performance bonds have been furnished, the written consent of the surety to the payment of the balance due for that portion of the Work fully completed and accepted shall be submitted by the Contractor to the Architect prior to certification of such payment. Such payment shall be made under the terms and conditions governing final payment, except that it shall not constitute a waiver of claims.

12.14 The acceptance of final payment shall constitute a waiver of all claims by the Contractor except those previously made in writing and still unsettled.

ARTICLE 13 BENEFICIAL OCCUPANCY

13.1 Unless otherwise specified in the Award Agreement, prior to Substantial Completion, the Owner may occupy or use portions of the Project, upon prior notice to Contractor, provided however, that the Contractor shall be entitled to an adjustment of time or compensation in addition to the Contract Sum to the extent such occupancy results in delay in or hindrance of the normal accomplishment of the Work.

13.2 In the event a Project has not been completed at the time provided for in the Award Agreement, the Owner may occupy such portions of the Project as may be completed or substantially completed without additional obligation to Contractor.

ARTICLE 14 OTHER PROVISIONS

14.1 The law of the jurisdiction where the Project is located will govern the Contract.

14.2 The Contract Documents and each part of them shall be binding upon the Owner and Contractor and their respective successors legal representatives and assignees as the case may be.

14.3 Contractor shall not assign the Contract or any part thereof or any Work to be performed thereunder without the prior written consent of the Owner, nor shall the Contractor assign any moneys due or to become due under the Contract without prior written consent of the Owner.

14.4 If written notices are delivered in person to the individual or member of the firm or to an officer of the corporation for whom it was intended or if delivered at or sent by registered or certified mail to the last business address known, it shall be deemed to be duly served.

14.5 The Owner shall have the right to require Bid, Labor and Material and/or Performance Bonds in connection with the Work.

14.6 The Contractor shall pay all royalties and license fees and provide for the defense against infringement or patent right claims. Contractor shall save the Owner harmless from loss because of such claims except where such claim is the result of particular product or design carried in the Specifications. The Contractor shall promptly notify the Architect when Contractor or any agent of the Contractor has any reason to believe that any portion of the Specifications may infringe upon any existing patent.

14.7 If any portion of the Work requires a test for any reason whatsoever, the Contractor shall notify the Architect in sufficient time prior to the test so that Architect may be present. The costs of such tests shall be borne by the Contractor.

14.8 All applications for payment, change orders and other documents involving monetary statements shall have totals rounded off to the nearest whole dollar amount. All items below fifty cents ($.50) shall revert to the previous whole dollar amount and above fifty cents ($.50) to the next dollar amount.

14.9 Contractor shall comply with all provisions of Executive Order No. 11246 and all rules, regulations and relevant orders of the Secretary of Labor relating to equality of employment opportunity.

14.10 All working drawings and other documents relating to the Project shall be returned to or supplied to the Owner within ten (10) days after final acceptance.

ARTICLE 15 ARBITRATION

15.1 All claims, disputes and other matters in question arising out of, or relating to, the Contract Documents or the breach thereof except for claims which have been waived by the making or acceptance of final payment as provided in Article 12 shall be decided by arbitration in accordance with the Construction Industry Arbitration Rules of the

EXHIBIT 5   General Requirements of the Construction Documents Form (*Continued*)

American Arbitration Association then obtaining. The award rendered by the arbitrators shall be final and judgment may be entered upon it in any court having jurisdiction thereof.

15.2   Notice of the demand for arbitration shall be filed in writing with the other party to the Contract Documents and with the American Arbitration Association, and a copy shall be filed with the Architect. If the dispute is one arising under Article 4, the demand for arbitration shall be made within the thirty (30) day period. In all other cases the demand shall be made within a resonable time after the claim, dispute or other matter in question has arisen but in no event may a demand be made after institution of legal or equitable proceedings based on such claim, dispute or other matter in question would be barred by the applicable statute of limitations.

15.3   The Contractor will carry on the Work and maintain the progress schedule during any arbitration proceedings.

The supplemental general conditions or requirements are usually preambled by a statement, such as this:

The Supplementary General Requirements contain changes and additions to the General Requirements. The Contract Documents are modified or voided by the Supplemental General Requirements. The unaltered provisions shall remain in effect.

Special Conditions

Where additional legal provisions are required for the contract, such as liquidated damages, completion of work, insurance, and similar protection, it is usual to provide such clauses in the special condition or requirement section. It has been usual to include in this section some items to be furnished by the contractor, such as trailers, temporary lighting, barricades, and traffic control. The Construction Standard Institute has recommended, as standard practice, not to mix legal requirements or provisions with items to be furnished by the contractor. Such items should be included in Division A of the specifications.

General Scope of the Work

This (Exhibit 6) consists of a brief summary of the work in an all-encompassing statement.

EXHIBIT 6   General Scope of Work Sample

SECTION 3—GENERAL SCOPE OF WORK

The work covered in the Specifications includes the furnishing of all labor, materials, equipment, and the performance of all work required for the alterations and additions for the expansion of the facilities in the existing XYZ #1 plant of the XYZ Corporation in Doesville, N.Y.

The work includes the following:
1. General construction work
2. Plumbing and process piping
3. Heating, ventilation and air conditioning
4. Fire protection
5. Electric light and power

List of Drawings

An example is given in Exhibit 7.

The list of drawings represents a set of contract documents separately identified and referenced in by the inserted frame of reference called "The List of Drawings."

The age-old expression that "a picture is worth a thousand words" does not always apply to architectural and engineering specifications and drawings. It can almost be said that drawings will identify the plot and the specifications the story. This can be modified to the extent that if a construction feature can be more explicitly and exactly described in words than in drawings, it should be described in the specifications. Cost is another feature, as drafting is expensive. As a general rule, details and overall dimensions, size of prefabricated items, location of water outlets and fixtures, location of finishes and openings, interrelationship of materials and equipment, and the swing of doors are examples of items generally better shown on the drawings.

Items that can be better described in the specifications are the finishes of materials, qualities, types of workmanship, methods of fabrication, and gauges of materials. In general, the drawings show "what" and the specifications show "what kind."

Trends in costs are rapidly changing. Where once notes on drawings required hand-lettering, today's pasteup drafting techniques, with templates and typewritten notes,

---

EXHIBIT 7   List of Drawings Sample

SECTION 4—LIST OF DRAWINGS

A set of drawings, numbered and listed below, dated 11/1/73, has been prepared to show the work to be done.

All drawings are a part of the contract, and the drawings and this specification shall be considered as cooperative so that anything or matter shown upon the one, or described by the other, or fairly implied by either or both, shall be done and performed the same as if shown upon and described by both.

Drawing No.   *Title*
Architectural

A-1	First Floor Plan & Exit Plans
A-2	Mezzanine Floor Plan & Sections
A-3	Finish & Door Schedules, Details & Reflected Ceiling Plans
A-4	First Floor Plan, Reflected Ceiling Plan & Details
A-5	Miscellaneous Details

Structrual

C-1	Mezzanine Framing Plans & Details

Mechanical

M-1	Plumbing—Plans & Details
M-2	Plumbing—Plans & Details
M-3	Plumbing—Service Riser Diagrams
M-4	HVAC—Plans & Sections
M-5	HVAC—Plans & Sections
M-6	HVAC—Schedules & Details
M-7	Sprinkler—Plans & Details

Electrical

E-1	First Floor Power & Mezzanine Power & Lighting Plans
E-2	First Floor Lighting Plan
E-3	First Floor & Mezzanine Power & Lighting Plans
E-4	Demolition & Miscellaneous Plans & Details
E-5	Symbol List, Lighting Fixture & Panel Schedules

---

reduce the cost of creating drawings and allow for a better separation of graphic and written specifications.

In some cases, drawings are being eliminated by models built to exacting scales—models that are necessary for use as project specifications. The models used for such purposes then form part of the contract. It is usual to make the model available to all bidders for estimating purposes.

Schedule Drawings

It has become a practice, where many similar items are included in a project, to utilize a tabulated form referred to as a schedule. The schedule more or less comprehensively lists the pertinent data needed to individually identify and total the quantities and locations of the item. Schedules for finishes; door hardware; doors; heating, ventilating, and air conditioning units; pumps, and other items applicable to the project may be shown. An example of a typical schedule is shown in Exhibit 8.

EXHIBIT 8   Example of Typical Schedule

SERVICE	MARK	LOC	TYPE	DRIVE	FLUID TYPE	FLUID °F	FLOW GPH	FLOW HD.FT	SIZE PUMP	SIZE IMPEL	MTG	DISCH	MOTOR RPM	MOTOR HP	REMARKS
CHILLED WATER	CHA-1	9-3	CENT	FC	WATER	40	122	475	4X6	17"	BASE	VERT	—	1750	25	AURORA
	CHA-2	9-8		FC		40	122	475	4X6	17"	BASE	VERT	—	1750	25	
CONDENSOR WATER	CNR-1	9-3		FC		30	76	705	5X6	10"	BASE	VERT	—	1750	20	
	CNR-2	9-8		FC		30	76	705	5X6	10"	BASE	VERT	—	1750	25	
	CNR-3	9-3		FC		30	88	130	22X3	11/2"	BASE	VERT	—	1750	20	
PRIM.HEAT HOT WATER	PHW-1			FC		200	77	240	22X2	31/2"	BASE	ENDSUCT	—	1750	25	
SEC. HEAT HOT WATER	SHW-2	9-3		CC		200	50	56	24	7"	IN-LINE	—	—	1750	71/2	B&G

(a)

									STAT PRES	STAT PRES	WHEEL	WHEEL	WHEEL			
MARK	LOC	SERVICE	MTG	TYPE	ARGT	CAP CFM	OUTLET VEL		TOT	EXT	NO	DIA	TYPE	DRIVE	MOTOR HP	REMARKS
RAF-1	7-8	RETURN AIR	IN-LINE	AXIAL	9	26820	2175		—	2.0	1	44	920	BELT	20	TRANE Q44
RAF-2	8-8				9	2520	2045		—	2.0	1	44	910		20	TRANE Q44
RAF-3	7-8				9	25320	2090		—	2.0	1	44	912		20	TRANE Q44
RAF-4	7-8				9	25245	2090		—	2.0	1	44	912		20	TRANE Q44
HEF-1	7-8	HOOD EXH. AIR			9				—	1.5	1	30			10	TRANE Q30
HEF-2	7-9				9				—	1.5	1	30			10	TRANE Q30
HEF-3	8-8				9				—	1.5	1	32			10	TRANE Q34
HEF-4	9-8				9				—	1.5	1	33			10	TRANE Q33
HEF-5	9-8				9				—	1.5	1	30			10	TRANE Q30
HEF-6	9-8				9				—	1.5	1	30			10	TRANE Q30
HEF-7	9-8				9				—	1.5	1	30	1140		10	TRANE Q30
TEF-1	7-3	TOILET EXH. AIR			—	2255			3/8	—	1	—	1140	DIRECT	1/2	JENN-AIR 141
TEF-2	7-8				—	1935			3/8	—	1	—	320		1/2	JENN-AIR 141

RETURN & EXHAUST AIR FANS — GENERAL / FAN DATA / REMARKS

(b)

THE WRITING OF SPECIFICATIONS

The creation and writing of specifications starts almost immediately upon a construction project being thought of. Whether it be a housewife assembling the thoughts of her dream house or a major company starting to think of a needed facility, certain requirements are envisioned that qualitatively and quantitatively must eventually be defined in the language of specifications. Notes should be kept and thoughts jotted down to provide a program for the project. Eventually, a concept will be established and developed into a design for which the notes and program will be used to create the specifications. The architect and engineers will continually make other notes and records during their concept thinking. These, too, will eventually be translated into specifications. Ultimately, it will be the specifications that will provide the narrative description enabling the construction team to generate a finished project in exactness as envisioned by the user, the architect, and the engineer. The specification writer must, therefore, have the ability to describe what is wanted.

The past experience of the specification writer is an important factor in how well the writing job is done. If the writer has had experience with similar work, certain portions of the tried and proved previous specification can be included if they are known to be in exactness what the architect and engineer had wanted. Manufacturers of materials in almost every instance have specifications that can be utilized. Care must be taken to reduce the possibility of using manufacturers' specification that include minor, unique features which are not really desired and which will prevent competition among potential suppliers. Information for specifications can be obtained from printed codes and ordinances of jurisdictional governmental bodies, recognized standards of testing institutions and professional societies, and recognized master specifications published for the construction industry.

Good knowledge of standards is essential for proper specification writing because of the time-saving feature and accuracy of being able to reference the standard rather than attempting to have to rewrite detailed descriptions. It is regarded as good practice to use references to codes, standards, or accepted published data in writing specifications, but this should not be done unless a copy of the reference source is available so that it may be read in detail to make sure that it is actually what is wanted or required.

Each section of the specification usually constitutes a portion of the work that could involve a separate contract or trade. The sections are assembled in a sequence as close as possible to the actual sequencing of the construction itself. It is customary to preamble each section with a sentence that will tie the work in the section to all the provisions of the contract documents. Exhibit 9 is a typical example for demolition.

There have been some differences of opinion whether or not it is necessary to preamble this section with a "scope or tie-in statement," since the general condition and reference documents have already stated that such is the case. It is the author's experience that most sets of specifications are prepared with "scope paragraph introductions." This is not necessary, but if such a paragraph is worded properly, it will not harm the specification. Perhaps its chief value would be to the subcontractor, further alerting him to read carefully all of the reference documents that could affect his portion of the work.

EXHIBIT 9   Contract Documents Sample—Demolition

The work under this Section of the Specifications is subject to the provisions of the Contract and of all Contract Documents which in any way affect the work herein specified.

The Contractor shall furnish all labor, materials, equipment, fuel and supplies and shall perform all demolition work as shown on the drawings or as specified herein.

The Contractor shall be governed and bound by Sections 1, 2, 3 and 4 of these Specifications in doing the work covered by this Section.

Demolition

Contractor shall demolish all parts, equipment and appendages of the present structure as is necessary to permit the installation of the new work.

Remove all debris from the Owner's property.

Disconnect and turn over to the Owner all equipment such as fans, motors, starters, controls and laboratory tables that are required to be removed. Lighting fixtures that are removed and not reused are to be turned over to the Owner.

Sprinkle all rubbish as necessary to lay the dust.

Sections   Each section of the specification is meant to separate and assemble the work that might be included in an individual separate contract. It is organized in such a way as to logically sequence the performance of the contract. As an example, Exhibit 10 shows a specification for acoustical ceilings.

Notice in the above:

1. Scope
2. Shop drawings
3. Existing conditions
4. Materials
5. Installation
6. Alterations to existing ceilings
7. Guarantee

The sequence in the above is very close to the order in which the contractor might have to perform the work. Other sections might set forth testing requirements or inspection requirements immediately after installation, but in all cases a logical order should be followed.

Organization

The specifications are put together gradually from the earliest conception of the project, and the information will be gathered in the form of notes, clippings, former specifications, manufacturers' information, catalogs (such as Sweet's), codes, ordinances, and master specifications. From all these, it is anticipated that a draft of the text will be prepared, revised for optimum organization, and finally prepared in its finished form. Two of the sets will be prepared in such a manner that they can be identified as the contract documents or at least the official set referred to in the agreement signed for the contract. It is wise to have each page of these sets and each drawing included in the list of drawings individually initialed by both parties concerned. Most often, all that is done is that the job or project number appear on each page of the specification.

EXHIBIT 10   Example of "Acoustical Ceilings" Specification

Acoustical Ceilings

Scope

The Work under this Section of the Specifications is subject to the provisions of the Contract and of all Contract Documents which in any way affect the work herein specified.

The Contractor shall furnish all labor, materials, equipment and supplies and shall perform all work required for the Acoustical Ceilings as shown on the Drawings and as specified herein unless otherwise definitely excluded.

The Contractor shall be governed and bound by Sections 1, 2, 3 and 4 of these Specifications in doing the work covered by this Section.

Shop Drawings

Furnish complete shop drawings for all parts of the work in accordance with the procedure given in Section 2 showing suspension systems, method of installation and all necessary details. These shop drawings are to indicate lights, sprinkler heads, diffusers, air outlets, and all other features which must be coordinated for the ceiling installation.

Existing Conditions

Before commencing work, verify all governing conditions at the site and report to the Engineers, in writing, any conditions which prevent the proper performance of the work herein specified.

Materials

Aluminum perforated or unperforated acoustical ceiling panels in areas indicated on the "Finish Schedule," shall be manufactured by Simplex Ceiling Corp., and shall be similar in size and surface finish to existing metal ceilings in present adjacent areas. Ceilings manufactured by Acoustics Manufacturing Corp., Baldwin-Ehret-Hill, Inc., or Steel Ceilings Division of the E. F. Hauserman Co. will be acceptable if they meet the requirements of this Section of the Specifications.

Acoustical Pads—For perforated panels only—shall be incombustible polyvinyl chloride film wrapped around a glass fiber pad. Pads shall be placed on top of the panel flanges.

Suspension System—Size and weight of suspension members including main runners, cross runners, channels, tees, mouldings, clips, wire, etc., shall be the manufacturer's recommendation for the room dimensions and patterns shown to suit ceiling materials and limit deflection of members to 1/360th of span.

Use supplementary channels or angles fastened to the building structure as required to provide adequate support for the suspension system hangers. Where required, furnish and install beam clamps on the structural steel or hanger inserts or wires in the formwork before concrete slabs are poured, to receive the ceiling hangers.

Installation

Hangers shall be space 4'–0" along the snap bars. Suspend hangers from the structure above by means of clips or fasteners approved by the Engineers. Panels shall be inserted in the snap bars. Provide molding around all perimeter areas.

Alterations to Existing Ceilings

Where noted on the Drawings, revise the present metal pan ceiling. Materials used shall match carefully the existing adjacent materials.

Guarantee

Manufacturer shall guarantee the completed installation for a period of five years against defects in materials and workmanship and deterioration due to moisture conditions. Any work becoming defective during this period shall be replaced at no expense to the Owner.

Writing

The specification writer has the goal of presenting, narratively, all the information that the engineer, contractor, and workman need to clearly understand the drawings. It is, therefore, essential that the wording selected be such that it is precise and technically exact without eloquent or legal terminology and without allowing flexibility in interpretation. The measure of the specifications' worth will be how well these goals are met—not its length. It is good practice to utilize complete sentences, as these contribute to better understanding of the specifications throughout the range of materials and methods that may be included. Abbreviations that are correct and well known for dimensions, units, and materials can be used. If metric dimensions are used, it is wise to spell them out until such time as prevalent usage creates uniform understanding. Some words are sometimes deliberately improperly spelled to shorten them. For example, "gage" instead of "gauge." It is the author's feeling that this is poor practice, although some consider it acceptable. Correct spelling is a sign of exactness and should be adhered to. The use of proper punctuation is essential for clear understanding, but complex sentence structure should be avoided to limit the necessity of punctuation.

Tense

There is no need to be completely consistent in verb tenses as long as inconsistent tense does not destroy the clearness of the specification. Emphatic future tenses are usually used to denote responsibilities and requirements. Any substitution of either present infinitives or simple imperatives is acceptable to reduce verbiage and complexity. For example, "The Contractor shall remove, relocate, or adjust all ductwork, all piping, or equipment" can be said more simply thus: "Remove, relocate, or adjust ductwork, piping, or equipment."

Section Subdivisions and Capitals

Important words, particularly those that have been defined in the general conditions, are usually capitalized throughout the specifications. These are words such as "work," "owner," "contractor," and "architect." Proper nouns and the first word of all sentences are capitalized. Other words, where easy reference is preferred, can be identified in all capitals. This is commonly true of individual materials to be supplied, since specifications are not cross-referenced. Underlining items is a further method of achieving emphasis. Most sectional subdivisions are identified by using all capitals, capitalizing the first letter, and underlining. The acoustical ceiling specification (Exhibit 10) is illustrative of the above. Section subdivision outline numbering and lettering is not recommended except for large work, since it is more time-consuming. Margin indentations or block forms are both acceptable. Block forms are generally reserved for small jobs and indentation numbering and lettering are used in large projects.

Grammar

The use of pronouns can sometimes cause confusion in specifications, particularly if compound subjects are included. A better practice is to avoid pronouns and use the noun which the pronoun was meant to replace.

The use of "shall" and "will" in specifications denotes the emphatic future tense, but with some difference in the degree of emphasis. In order not to allow differences or degrees of obligation, it is customary to use "shall" for obligations of the contractor and material suppliers. "Will" is generally used in connection with acts of the owner or architect. This rule should be consistently applied throughout the specifications and reference documents.

Other phrases denoting obligation, such as "must" or "is to," are similarly subject to interpretation as a degree of obligation when compared to "shall" or "will." It is better writing practice to maintain consistency by substituting "shall" for the above terminology.

There are certain catch phrases that are commonly used to denote a desired result or material supplied. The use of general statements such as "to the architect's satisfaction," "workmanlike job," "or equal," should, as a matter of good practice, not be used. It is much more precise to describe in detail the results wanted. If the specification writer is aware, and he should be, of the result desired, he should state it as such. The use of "etc." should be discouraged, since it can be almost open ended and leave room for interpretation. The word "any" can be construed as denoting a choice and should be avoided. The aim of specification is to be short, exact, and to the point. Certain words can be easily eliminated, shortening but not changing the requirements of the specification. Articles such as "the" are sometimes unnecessary. The preposition "of" similarly can be avoided. For example, instead of "floor of the manufacturing area," say "to manufacturing area floor." Redundancy should be eliminated as much as possible. If a statement in connection with the work—i.e., "The Contractor shall provide" or "Contractor shall furnish and install"—is contained in the proposal or other reference documents, it need not be repeated in the sections.

ADDENDA

Prior to a set of specifications being finalized as a bid document, certain changes may arise. These modifications can occur up to the time of bid closing. The modification to the original set of specifications are called addenda. All addenda are numbered in sequence.

The format for addenda is shown in Exhibit 11.

EXHIBIT 11   Format for Addenda

Best Engineers, Inc.
16 Lee Street
New York, New York
November 2, 1973

ADDENDUM NO. 1
SPECIFICATION
FOR
ALTERATIONS & ADDITIONS
AT XYZ PLANT #1
DOESVILLE, NEW YORK
XYZ CORPORATION, NOVEMBER 1, 1973

This Addendum shall become a part of the original Specification Sections and all Addenda thereto prepared by Best Engineers, Inc. All clauses in the original Specifications not mentioned or modified shall remain in force.
   1. Mezzanine floor slab indicated in Section B-B on Drawing A-2 is revised from 6″ to 4″ to agree with slab thickness shown on Drawing C-1.
   2. *Electrical Work*
      Page C-2—Add the following item:
   3. *Demolition*
      Removal of certain electrical systems, equipment, material, etc., shall be performed as shown on the drawings. Before proceeding with such work, the Contractor shall take all steps necessary to prevent disruption of other circuits, systems and the Owner's operations. Removals shall be done with due care for safety of individuals and existing facilities.

CHANGE ORDERS

After an award agreement is signed establishing the contract, some changes are almost certain. These changes may occur because the work in the field has uncovered conditions not envisioned in the original specifications for the project. Such changes are implemented by a change proposal setting forth the contractor's findings and asking the architect and engineer to issue or approve a change order, along with specifications and design, to meet the need. The changes modifying the specifications and/or design are issued by the architect and engineer. They are issued in the form of bulletins and are identified as were the addenda and numbered in sequence. They become official portions of the specifications and contract.

REFERENCES

1. H. Griffith Edwards: *Specifications,* D. Van Nostrand Co., Inc., Princeton, N.J.
2. *Manual of Practice,* Construction Specifications Institute, January 1967, documents 001 and 003.

Chapter 9

As-Built Drawings

P. S. RIDLEY, P.E.
Director, Plant Engineering, RCA Corporation

DEFINITION OF AS-BUILT DRAWINGS

Working drawings are prepared for the purpose of accurately portraying the design architect/engineer's intent for the construction or installation of nearly every structure, machine, device, or technical system that is in use. However well thought out the original concept may be, changes are often required during construction or installation, and these changes cause the original drawings to be inaccurate as a representation of what was actually built or installed. These inaccuracies, preserved in a historical record, create problems that may range from minor annoyance to a potentially serious hazard where, for example, a structural system is installed with a much lower load-bearing capability than originally designed due to a postdesign reduction in requirements. It is important, therefore, that all original working drawings be modified during or at the conclusion of construction or installation to portray accurately what was finally completed. Such modified drawings are called as-built drawings, or, "as-builts." As used in this chapter, this term will be applied to buildings and building utilities.

References herein to "architect/engineer" mean the architect or engineer of record who originally designed the building, equipment, or system and who is legally and contractually responsible for its adequacy. This individual may be an independent consultant or an employee of the owner or contractor, depending on the circumstances of the project. With few exceptions, no design changes should be made by anyone other than the architect/engineer of record, as a successor may not be fully aware of the original intent and could unwittingly introduce an inadequate or hazardous design element.

REASONS FOR DESIGN CHANGES

The reasons for changes between completion of original working drawings and the completion of construction are many. Some of the more common are these:
1. Increase or decrease in building size
2. Relocation of walls or partitions
3. Relocation of on-site facilities such as substations, storage tanks, or underground utilities
4. Changes in size, capacity, or location of piping or electrical systems in buildings
5. Substitution of alternate materials
6. Reduction in construction cost

Such changes occur on nearly every construction project, as the necessity for modifications of these kinds cannot be anticipated during the design development phase.

CATEGORIES OF CHANGES

Design changes, materials substitutions, and the equipment data acquired during the construction phase that will be used in the preparation of as-built drawings fall into three broad categories, as follows:
1. Postbidding but preconstruction design changes or materials substitutions
2. Design changes or materials substitutions during construction
3. Equipment data and test results acquired during the construction phase that will be incorporated into as-built drawings

PRECONSTRUCTION CHANGES

During the postbidding, preconstruction period, changes in project details, materials, or scope often take place as a consequence of last-minute design modifications that were too late to be included in the bid documents or as a consequence of negotiations with the contractor. These changes should be reflected in fully corrected sets of drawings issued at the actual start of construction, and these drawings become the first phase of as-builts. All required revisions must be made by the architect/engineer and all of the now incorrect original drawing issues recalled and destroyed to eliminate confusion or error during the execution of the work. Since the revised drawings at this stage of the project are reissues of originals, they must carry any required professional registration seal. Any of the original drawings that previously required submission to state or local code enforcing agencies or to insurance companies for approval may require another submission in the revised form for reapproval. In all such cases, the architect/engineer must determine the need for resubmission. Structural modifications, alterations in personnel egress patterns, and changes in the fire rating of buildings are examples of design modifications that could require resubmission. When all preconstruction drawing corrections have been made and required approvals have been obtained, the drawings become final construction documents and should be issued to the contractor, each drawing carrying a large rubber stamp identifying the drawing as a final construction document with revision date, issue date, and the architect/engineer's signature.

CHANGES DURING CONSTRUCTION

Changes during construction may originate from the owner, the architect/engineer, or the contractor, depending upon the nature of the change. Regardless of the origin of the change, the contractor, or, in some instances, the architect/engineer, accumulates the data on field changes and maintains at the jobsite from one to several sets of drawings for the purpose of collecting the data on changes. The number of drawing sets depends on the complexity or organization of the work.

As changes are made during the construction phase, they must be marked, at once, on the drawings maintained for this purpose. The marking is often done with a colored pencil for better visibility. In the course of such changes, it is essential to maintain a record of signed approvals either on the drawing itself or by other documentation. In all cases, the architect/engineer must approve the changes, and in many cases the owner as well, depending on the contractual agreement with the architect/engineer or contractor. The nature and extent of the change must be clear and complete. To identify a substitute material by its generic designation only provides no information as to its grade or strength nor, in many cases, does it affirm that it is even of the same dimension. It is not uncommon during the construction phase to have a need develop for modifications that are of such nature as to require approval by code enforcing authorities or insurance companies. Should this occur, a resubmission will be required, as described under "Preconstruction Changes."

In certain cases changes will develop that are of such magnitude as to be beyond the practical scope of a marked-up print. When this occurs, a new sketch or drawing must be made by the architect/engineer for release to the contractor. These additional sketches or drawings must be clearly identified as being beyond the scope of the original construction drawings and must not duplicate an original drawing number unless they are replacements of original drawings.

Since the marked-up set of field drawings contains valuable data that could easily be damaged or lost, it is essential that a duplicate set be maintained at another location and that the duplicate set be continually updated to match the status of the field set. Good practice would have the duplicate set in the possession of the architect/engineer, not only for ultimate use in preparing the as-builts but as a day-by-day record of the project. The architect/engineer's set of marked-up drawings should be updated weekly or more frequently if conditions so require.

SPECIFICATIONS

The written specifications that are always prepared to accompany and complement the drawings contain much detailed information on materials, methods of assembly, testing, etc., and these specifications should be kept up to date as changes are made during the execution of the work. Specifications can be modified more easily than drawings, and these modifications can take the form of deleting paragraphs or sections that no longer apply, followed by the preparation of addenda that describe the new material or method using the same format as the original. As with the drawings, all such changes should be made by the architect/engineer.

EQUIPMENT AND TEST DATA

The original bid documents rarely indicate the specific make or model number of major pieces of equipment such as steam boilers, air compressors, or power transformers unless such equipments were advance-ordered well before the bidding procedure. Good practice dictates that all pertinent nameplate data from the more important pieces of equipment be put on the as-built drawings as a quick and accurate reference source. It is often easier to locate equipment data on the drawing beside the representation of such equipment than to locate it in the files, particularly if many similar items are installed. The owner's appraisal or property identification number should also be shown where such numbers are used.

It is standard practice on original drawings to show door and window schedules, finishes, and the schedules for both electrical and mechanical equipments. Among other things, these schedules list important data on building components or equipments in tabular form. The schedules should be maintained up to date as additional components or equipments are added and should follow the same form as the original. Since items with quite different characteristics from any shown on the original drawings may be added at a later date, it is necessary, in such cases, to utilize the blank spaces remaining in the original tabular schedule or to extend the table if additional space is needed.

Common practice portrays process or system flow diagrams on drawings in schematic form for clarity and ease of interpretation. Process and environmental control systems are so treated, along with electrical systems. As field changes are made during or following construction, it is essential that all such schematic diagrams be included in the program leading to as-builts, since schematic diagrams are an invaluable reference source in the future when system changes are contemplated or operating problems develop.

Good practice requires that all mechanical and electrical systems be tested upon project completion to ensure that performance equals or exceeds the design conditions. A wealth of data is thus accumulated and these data reflect the system operating conditions when the systems are new and in perfect working order. Subsequent system modifications, repairs, or deterioration from age or neglect can radically alter performance, often in a relatively short time; it is, therefore, essential that all original performance data be recorded on a set of as-builts. For convenience, this could be a separate set of drawings, and all recorded data should be identified as to date. As new test or performance data become available later on, they can be added to the original as-builts, using an overlay. This will permit performance comparison at any time thereafter.

CONTRACTUAL AGREEMENTS FOR AS-BUILT DRAWINGS

The preparation of as-built drawings involves a cost to both the architect/engineer and the contractor, and there must be recognition of this cost in design contract agreements with architect/engineers and in construction contracts with contractors.

During the negotiation of terms and conditions for a design contract with an architect/engineer, there should be included in the contract a clause calling for the architect-/engineer to deliver as-built drawings to the owner within a reasonable period of time following completion of construction. If the owner wishes to have the architect accumulate the field data for subsequent incorporation into as-built drawings, this additional scope of work should be included in the contract. The design contract should also state the form that the as-builts will take, i.e., corrected original tracings or reproducibles. The correction of original tracings involves erasure followed by redrawing, while the reproducible takes the form of a sepia-toned reproduction of the original drawing that is corrected by eradicating the unwanted portion, followed by redrawing. Correction of original tracings may be the preferred method if the changes are relatively minor, while substantial correction is perhaps better handled by the reproducible method.

Regardless of the method used, the preparation of as-built drawings should be performed only by the architect/engineer so as to retain undivided responsibility for design.

In the majority of cases, the contractor will accumulate the field data from which as-builts will be prepared, and this condition must be included in the bid solicitation to the contractor. During negotiations with the selected contractor prior to the start of construction, the subject of as-built drawings must be reviewed by owner, architect/engineer, and contractor so that a clear understanding is reached as to how the work will be done, what approval procedure will be followed, and what degree of accuracy will be required by the architect/engineer in the recording of field data.

DIMENSIONAL ACCURACY

Caution must be exercised in the correction of drawings to avoid introducing errors that could have serious consequences later on. To change a dimension on an otherwise fully scaled drawing without clearly noting that the new dimension is not to scale could lead to a costly mistake in the future. This may happen if the altered portion of the drawing is scaled on the assumption that it is correct.

MAINTENANCE OF AS-BUILT DRAWINGS

The all too common practice of preparing as-built drawings upon project completion and then failing to keep the drawings up to date thereafter should not be condoned. A formal procedure should be in effect that will provide for regular updating of all drawings on a continuing basis throughout the life of the facility. This procedure may involve several people, depending upon the size and complexity of the operation, but the method of implementation should come from the chief engineer or the plant engineer. The technique to be used generally follows that which was used during original construction and requires that a marked-up set of drawings be maintained during all plant expansions or rearrangement programs and that the field data thus collected be transferred to the master set of drawings at regular intervals. These changes may be quite different from those encountered during original construction, since they are dictated by the ever-changing requirements of plant operations; but they are no less important, and apparently minor items should never be ignored since they may turn out to be of considerable significance later on.   Two types of changes which are of the greatest importance involve electrical and piping systems.   Electrical requirements in plants change constantly, and this requires that new loads be added to lighting and power distribution panels; concomitantly, loads may be removed.   Under these circumstances, an accurate record of all changes must be maintained, as failure to do so can result in a set of drawings that are hopelessly out of date in a short time.   This absence of accurate data soon results in an inability to plan for future changes and usually leads to a costly survey to bring the drawings up to date.   A parallel problem exists with piping systems, and for the same reasons.

PRESERVATION OF DRAWINGS

Since as-built drawings, kept current, are an invaluable record, it is important that they be treated with above-average care.   At least one set, in the form of positive prints, should be readily available for frequent reference, and this set should not be taken from the office.   In all cases, the master set of original corrected tracings or reproducibles should be kept in protective tubes and stored in a remote vault fully protected against loss from fire or water.   The masters will be periodically removed from the vault for updating, but in such instances they must be returned to the vault at the end of each workday. Microreproduction techniques where available, can be used to advantage.

Section 4

Maintenance Management

Chapter 1

Managing Maintenance with Planning and Scheduling

RAYMOND P. McFARLAND
The Emerson Consultants, Inc.

INTRODUCTION

The two terms "planning" and "scheduling," though closely related, serve two separate functions. *Planning* is the process of analyzing each job to:

1. Determine the nature of the job and the results desired
2. Specify the logical sequence of the job and apply manpower estimates for each sequencial step
3. List predeterminable material, tools, and special equipment
4. Estimate the total cost to meet the required results

Scheduling is the efficient daily allocation of manpower and special equipment to jobs based on operational requirements as indicated by the priority system. It also includes the delivery of materials, tools, and equipment to the jobsite. Planning, therefore, answers the questions "who," "what," "where," and "how" to establish the best approach to meet the desired results at the least overall cost. Scheduling, on the other hand, establishes when the job will be done to meet the requirements for *all* customers of maintenance services.

The purpose of planning and scheduling is to make the maintenance department efficient and effective. "Efficiency" is defined as the optimum utilization of all resources (men, material, tools, and equipment) to keep delays and nonproductive activities to a minimum. Effectiveness is the utilization of resources at their levels of proficiency to anticipate and correct problems before they call for major repairs. An efficient and effective maintenance organization can take on additional workload in a period of expansion without increasing manpower. Likewise, a constant workload can be accomplished with fewer craftsmen.

Proper planning and scheduling allows craftsmen and foremen to concentrate on their prime responsibilities. For craftsmen, this means longer sustained time at the jobsite without interruption, because all predeterminable work requirements are supplied before the job is scheduled for execution. For foremen, this means more time at the jobsite for supervision and on-the-job training of the maintenance craftsmen. Planning and scheduling, when properly done, will assure that equipment receives required attention at the prescribed intervals. Increased maintenance service is reflected in greater equipment reliability, which in turn reduces overall equipment costs.

During the late 1950s, new planning and scheduling techniques were developed to monitor and control large construction jobs and massive military armament projects. These techniques proved to be successful, and they are now standard practice in most large corporations. The Gantt Chart (bar graph) schedule gave way to the program evaluation and review technique (PERT) and the critical path method (CPM) of planning and control. PERT and CPM help the project controller meet scheduled target dates, and they pinpoint possible delays so corrective action can be taken before the target date is past. PERT and CPM are useful to the maintenance manager who is constructing a building or rearranging a major manufacturing process. These conditions are generally short term and represent a minor portion of the total maintenance department workload.

While there is considerable top management interest in these major projects, the good maintenance manager is the one who can efficiently and effectively accomplish all maintenance work. This chapter, therefore, addresses itself to the nonpublicized jobs that represent the bulk of the maintenance effort. The planning and scheduling techniques discussed in this chapter can easily encompass the more sophisticated approach of PERT and CPM.

BASIC REQUIREMENTS FOR PLANNING AND SCHEDULING

There are five basic requirements for planning and scheduling to assure management control of the maintenance function. The first is a formal procedure for defining, approving, and authorizing maintenance work to be done. This is documented in a manual of maintenance operation. The manual gives a common set of ground rules so both the maintenance department and its customers will know how the other is to operate regarding maintenance work. It is absolutely necessary to have a common set of guidelines, because the maintenance manager controls no more than 50 percent of those factors which adversely influence overall maintenance costs.

The second requirement is a job order system that permits the effective communication of job needs and work requirements so jobs are completed as desired. This includes a job order form with sufficient space to identify the job requirements and plan the work details. Space is needed for control categories such as job order number, cost accounting number, and capital expenditure number.

Along with the job order system, there needs to be a priority system which classifies the job as to urgency and need date. These data then provide the necessary information for the fourth requirement, which is a scheduling system.

The final requirement for an effective planning and scheduling program is control and follow-up. Unfortunately, the control phase of the planning and scheduling procedure receives far too little attention. Feedback is the key element to determine whether or not the planning and scheduling process is reducing maintenance costs. Management by definition implies control, and planning and scheduling in maintenance is the maintenance manager's tool for control of his operation. Without this final phase, a planning and scheduling section is little more than window dressing in an attempt to follow the current trends in the maintenance function. Part of the ground rules in the manual of maintenance operations will specify the procedures for planning and scheduling in the maintenance department operation. The remaining parts of this chapter constitute a basic outline for the planning and scheduling of operations as they might appear in that manual.

The job order   The written job order is the principal document to plan, estimate, and schedule the job and to accumulate charges for management information reporting. To properly fulfill its role in controlling maintenance through the planning and scheduling system, the job order (see Figs. 1 and 2) provides space to record basic data about the job. Blocks are provided for the specific data needed, and the information falls into these major categories:

Financial Data: Includes numbers for cost center, account classification, capital classification and equipment number.

Requirements data: Includes who requested the job and when, priority and need date, and a description of what is wrong or what is needed.

Approval and authorization: Includes blocks for approval and authorization of the work and acceptance of the completed job.

Maintenance Job Order

Requested	Date	Date Required Dono	Pri	Just	Job Number		
Unit	Review After Est. ☐ Yes ☐ No	Permit Required ☐ Yes ☐ No	Eng. Required ☐ Yes ☐ No	Date Equip. Avail.	Cost Center	Account Number	
First Approval	Second Approval	Authorized	Zone	Area	AFE Number	Equip. Number	
Job Title And Description							

Job Description — Materials — Equipment	Seq.	Craft	Code	Field M	Field Hours	Shop M	Shop Hours
Total							

Refinery Equipment ☐ Scaffold ☐ Cherry Picker ☐ Bucket Truck ☐ Crane ☐ Back Hoe ☐	Other (Specify)		Estimated Costs
			$ Labor
Job Est. By	Date	Blinds Required	$ Materials
			$ Equipment
Engineering Drawings		Material Delivery Number	
Date Complete	Job Complete	Job O.K.	$ Total

Fig. 1 Maintenance job order.

Maintenance Job Order Addendum

Sheet	Of	Job Est. By	Job Number

Job Description — Materials — Equipment	Seq.	Craft	Code	Field M	Field Hours	Shop M	Shop Hours
Total							

Fig. 2 Maintenance job order addendum.

Planning and scheduling control: Includes an individual, unique number for each job; estimates for personnel, material, and equipment costs; and a shortened description of the job if the job order system is computerized.

Job requirements: Includes space to list the specific requirements to complete the job, which are broken down by sequential steps with manpower and material estimates. Special equipment, tools, and material requirements are also listed on the job order.

The number of job order copies and their distribution depends on the organizational structure of the maintenance department and whether or not the job order system is computerized. The minimum number of copies would be three, distributed as follows:

One copy is returned to the requester with the estimate and job order number.

One copy is given to the maintenance foreman when the job is scheduled for execution.

The final copy is retained in the planning office until the job is completed.

The work execution copy of the job order becomes the permanent record copy because it contains not only the maintenance foreman's notes but also the acceptance signature of the requester.

Job order approval and authorization One of the principles of maintenance cost reduction is to fix the responsibility for the level of maintenance on the equipment owner. Therefore only the equipment owner can approve and authorize maintenance work on the equipment. The equipment owner budgets for the maintenance work received and is held accountable for the maintenance costs incurred. But the equipment owner does not have free license to request all services provided by the maintenance department. A distinction is made between the authority to approve and authorize "repair in kind"-type jobs and those that involve "manufacture, modification, or installation." The equipment owner has fairly wide-ranging authority for "repair in kind"-type jobs within the approved maintenance budget. The latitude for authorizing "manufacture, modification, and installation" work, on the other hand, is very narrow. This latter point is particularly true for process or assembly-line operations, where each function is engineered for maximum efficiency.

The philosophy of reducing maintenance costs through planning and scheduling rests on the assumption that jobs are requested far enough in advance to assure that proper planning and scheduling attention is applied to each job. Therefore any person who perceives the need for a maintenance job can prepare a written job order. But only the equipment owner can approve and authorize the work to be done.

There is a very distinct but greatly misunderstood difference between approving and authorizing a job order. *Approval* means that the condition requiring maintenance work has been physically verified and that the job specified will correct the deficiency. *Authorization* means that the equipment owner can afford (through a maintenance budget) the job requested and will be held accountable for the application of the maintenance dollars.

The authority to proceed with a job may require higher-level authorization, particularly on "manufacture, modification, and installation"-type jobs and high-cost repair work. Specific authority limits are required for each level of supervision to properly control the expenditure of maintenance dollars. For example, the equipment owner or first-line supervisor may have the authority to authorize "repair in kind"-type jobs up to $1,000 for each job but may only be able to authorize "manufacture, modification, or installation"-type jobs up to $100 each.

The proper authorization signature on the job order (for "repair in kind" only) means the maintenance department can make all necessary arrangements to complete the job within the approved estimate. All sundry operations—such as material ordering, purchase order requisitions, shop work, outside services, etc.—can be handled by the maintenance department without further authorization from the equipment owner. Therefore one authorizing signature covers the entire job.

Job order numbering system Each job requested from the maintenance department requires a separate, written job order for proper control and follow-up. Therefore each job order requires a separate job order number, which distinguishes the job from all other jobs for accounting, budgeting, planning, scheduling, and control purposes. Job order numbers are controlled by the maintenance department by using a job order register. The job order register (see Fig. 3) contains the date the job was received, the cost center where the work will be done, the next highest number in the series for the type of work requested, a brief description of the job, and a completion date. The job order register

JOB ORDER REGISTER

Job order No	Unit	Zone	Area	Description	Coordinator	Shop	Insp.	Open	Close	Date comp.

Fig. 3 Job order register.

is maintained in the planning office and job order numbers are assigned as job orders are received.

Besides giving each job order a separate number, there is a great advantage to grouping jobs for summarization and management information reporting purposes. Most companies would find a five-digit job order number sufficient for categorizing jobs they receive within a year. A representative classification of work by job order number follows, and a small company may find a four-digit number more than adequate for its needs.

	Job Order Classification Numbers
00001–39,999	Routine "repair in kind" jobs of $1,000 or less
40,000–49,999	Routine "repair in kind" jobs greater than $1,000
50,000–59,999	Manufacture, modification or rearrangements less than $5,000
60,000–69,999	Major overhaul projects
70,000–79,999	Preventive maintenance
80,000–89,999	Standing job order numbers for repetitive work or minor repair jobs of one man-hour or less and $50 of material or less
90,000–91,999	Capital projects
92,000–94,999	Expensed projects over $5,000
95,000–98,999	Safety jobs and OSHA work
99,000–99,989	Jobs that need special handling for legal or insurance reasons
99,990–99,999	Nonproductive time

The job order number is the basic number for the entire job. All labor, material, outside services, purchase orders, rentals, etc., are charged to the job order number for the job. All shop work is charged to the basic job order number for which the work is done. This gives the maintenance management and the equipment owner a total cost figure for the entire job. The job order number is the communication link for work control and job follow-up during all phases of the job order life.

Signing off completed job orders   Since the equipment owner is held accountable for the money spent for maintenance work, the owner is also responsible for accepting a job when completed. The owner does this by going to the jobsite with the maintenance supervisor to inspect the completed job. If the job is done to the owner's satisfaction according to the work intent specified on the job order, the owner signs the work execution copy of the Job Order to signify acceptance of the job. This closes out the job order and prevents the maintenance department from doing any more on the job until another properly approved and authorized job order is received from the equipment owner. It also prevents the maintenance department from making any further labor charges to the job order number.

Changes in job order nature   Many times, the nature of a job changes as the work progresses. If the change is significant, then a new job order is needed from the equipment owner to change the scope of work. The maintenance department reestimates the job and the equipment owner is given the opportunity to evaluate the desirability of the requested service. The newly planned and estimated job order provides the necessary information to properly schedule the job to completion. A couple of examples will highlight this point. When a repair is being done and undetected wear or damage indicates a need for complete overhaul, then the overhaul is requested on a separate job order. During an emergency, a job order is issued to correct the emergency condition; but a separate job order is necessary to make any repairs caused by the emergency. In the case of a fire, an emergency job order is prepared to record the costs for fighting the fire; but separate job orders are issued to repair the equipment and put it back in original condition.

Emergency job order   Prior to the start of any planning and scheduling system in maintenance, a considerable part of the work effort is expended on emergencies. Maintenance craftsmen dash from one emergency to another without completing the previous task. Little time is left for the preventive maintenance that might have eliminated the emergency condition in the first place. A constant exposure to emergency conditions is demoralizing to the conscientious craftsman and the maintenance customers are irritated by half-completed jobs. Therefore emergencies are handled as special cases under the job order system.

Emergencies represent the most inefficient use of maintenance resources, because there is little chance for proper planning and scheduling and the tendency is to over-man the job as an insurance precaution. The concerted effort of every employee is needed to keep emergency conditions within acceptable limits. Closer attention to equipment condition by the equipment owner and requesting maintenance service at the first hint of impending failure will greatly reduce emergency occurrences.

The first step for controlling emergencies is a clear statement of what constitutes an emergency condition. The following definitions would apply in most industries. An emergency exists:

1. When the situation poses grave danger for life, limb, or property

2. Where there is immediate threat of catastrophe or the rapid deterioration of the situation would preclude proper planning and scheduling of the job

3. When reduced production causes unacceptable financial losses or jeopardizes delivery commitments

4. When the company will violate legal statutes if the condition is allowed to continue

5. When the company will lose community goodwill if the situations are not corrected immediately

The basic definitions for emergency maintenance must be strictly adhered to if the maintenance department is to be efficient and effective through the planning and scheduling system.

Emergencies do not require a written job order for the maintenance department to start work. When properly authorized, the equipment owner notifies the maintenance department that an emergency exists. The maintenance supervisor will take the necessary steps to pull people from scheduled jobs to correct the emergency condition with the least interruption to the daily work schedule as possible. Once an emergency is declared, it represents an automatic authorization for overtime (when needed) to counter the emergency situation. Craftsmen should work around the clock (if necessary) to overcome the condition which caused the emergency. In no case should a job be declared an emergency if it does not meet the definition criteria. Close records are maintained on emergencies for review by management to prevent the abuse of the emergency classification of work.

Shortly after declaring the emergency and before the work is completed, the equipment owner must supply a written job order to cover the emergency work. In the case of call-out work after normal working hours, the written job order is presented to the maintenance department the following morning. All cleanup and ensuing repairs are requested on separate job orders.

THE PLANNING PROCESS

A job order—once it has been prepared, approved, and authorized—is handed over to the maintenance planner for processing. The planner quickly reviews the job order to be sure the requester has supplied all the required data and verifies that the authorizer can in fact sign for the size and scope of the job desired. The priority designation and need date are discussed with the equipment owner to assure job completion in the time required with the available maintenance department manpower. The final preliminary step is to give the job order a unique number by entering the job in the job order register within the job's specific work category.

The planner is then ready to assess the actual maintenance department requirements to accomplish the job as effectively and inexpensively as possible. A considerable part of the planner's time is spent in the field, seeing the job in three dimensions. The planner particularly looks for constraints to effective work progress, making a determination of what is needed to correct the problem and estimating the resource requirements to complete the work. Some of the planner's field time is spent in conversation with maintenance foremen, equipment owners, and engineers to arrive at the best approach to the requested job. The planner does as much planning and estimating at the jobsite as possible to assure that nothing about the job is forgotten.

The planner breaks the job done into sequential steps and applies manpower and material estimates for each step. This is a critical part of the planning process because it is essential for proper work scheduling. Most jobs fall into logical steps, and the planning and scheduling of the job by these sequential steps saves many wasted man-hours while craftsmen wait for other craftsmen to finish their portions of the job. Space is provided on the job order to write the specific work steps and to apply estimates by individual craft codes. An addendum (Fig. 2) is used to continue the sequencing of the job if the planner runs out of space on the basic job order form.

In addition to planning the manpower requirements for the job, the planner also lists the specific material requirements. Any tools and special equipment needed by the craftsmen for the job are also listed. The planner will indicate if operating action is needed, such as equipment shutdown, before the job can be started.

The job requirements are translated into a total estimate for personnel, material, and equipment in terms of man-hours and dollars. The planner signs and dates the job order when the estimate is complete. The planner may find it necessary to return the entire job order to the requester for additional authorization signatures if the job is larger than

Stores Material Transfer	Tran Type	AFE Number	Cost Center	Job Order Number	Account Number

Deliver to	Delivery Station	Date	Delivery Type □Normal □Hot Shot	□Next Round	Counter □Issue

Quantity	Stock Number	Cond *	U/M	Item Description	Bin Number	Est. Code
Requested By		Filled By			Total	

*Cond Code: 1 = New, 2 = Recond., 3 = Used, 4 = Junk

Fig. 4   Stores material transfer.

expected. In all cases, the requester receives a numbered and estimated copy of the job order.

In most cases, the maintenance planner can complete the job planning and estimating phase on the day the job order is received. It is not always necessary for the experienced planner to visit the jobsite to determine the requirements for the job. This enables the planner to plan and schedule work for more maintenance craftsmen.

The planner may also have to get safety department or fire marshall approval if the job has safety implications. Hot or cold cutting permits or welding permits for the job will be obtained on the days these activities are scheduled. Now that OSHA requirements are a large factor in all industries, the safety and environmental implications of a job must be taken into consideration by the planner.

The next phase of the job planning process is for the planner to determine the availability of the necessary resources to complete the job. In most cases, material is the item which is lacking, and it is the responsibility of the planner to contact the stores department to determine the availability of the required material for the job. The planner prepares stores material transfers (Fig. 4) to withdraw the necessary items from stock and charges them to the job order number. The planner also prepares purchase order requisitions if outside services or materials are required. The planner determines the availability of tools and special equipment and makes all necessary arrangements to have them available when the job is scheduled for accomplishment.

One of the key premises for the effective control of the maintenance operation with planning and scheduling states that no job will be scheduled until all resources necessary to start the job are on hand. Therefore it is the responsibility of the maintenance planner to make all predeterminable job arrangements before the job is started. When all the resources are available, the planner puts the job order in the active file and schedules the job according to the regular scheduling procedures.

Two of the key items used by the planner in scheduling a job is the priority code and the need date. The priority designation, along with the availability of manpower and jobs in progress, will determine which jobs are scheduled on the daily work schedule.

Job order priority system   The job order priority system establishes understanding between the maintenance department and its customers regarding the urgency and importance of requested work. The equipment owner is responsible for the assignment of priorities on the job order. This is best handled in a direct negotiation with the maintenance planner. The equipment owner is held accountable for the priority distribution put on jobs, and records are kept to assure that the priority classification is not being abused. Least urgent priority classifications should be used as much as possible, since they allow the maintenance department the greatest opportunity to fully plan and schedule the job.

The priority system should be as simple as possible; the following gradations would function in most applications:

Priority Code	Description
E—Emergency	The job must meet one of the definitions for emergency described earlier in the chapter.
1—Urgent	The job must be started the next day or within 24 hours or there is considerable risk of emergency condition.
2—Essential	The job must be started within 5 days or there is substantial risk of equipment break down.
3—Needed	The job is essential but can be deferred, and it should start within 3 weeks. This category operates as fill-in work on the daily work schedule.
4—Deferrable	These jobs are best done at the time of a major overhaul or when the equipment is down for other reasons.

In addition to the priority definitions, these points are essential for the proper operation of the priority system:

1. Once a job is scheduled, it will be worked to completion regardless of the original priority of the job order.

2. The maintenance planner will not change the priority classification without first consulting the equipment owner.

3. The priority distribution is part of the management control reports prepared to measure the effectiveness of the maintenance department and those persons who influence its operations.

MAINTENANCE SCHEDULING

The scheduling function is best handled by the person who planned the job, although the two functions can be carried out by separate individuals. The planner prepares a daily work schedule based on priority designation, need date, and operational requirements. The purpose of scheduling is to outline a distribution of jobs based on man-hour estimates. This assures that every maintenance craftsman if fully occupied each work day.

Job orders are only scheduled when all the resources (personnel, material, and equipment) needed to start the job are on hand. The objective of scheduling is to assure that necessary materials, tools, and special equipment are delivered to the jobsite when needed and to eliminate any chance of them being lost or mislaid. Scheduling assures that all necessary craft skills are provided in the proper sequence and at the correct time to prevent time delays while one craftsman waits for another craftsman to complete his work. Job orders are scheduled so travel time between jobs is kept to the bare minimum. Proper scheduling and execution of jobs through a coordinated effort between operations and maintenance will keep out-of-service time within controlled limits.

Each day the planner prepares a daily work schedule (Fig. 5), to be executed the following day, for each maintenance foreman. The planner, in order to schedule jobs for execution, must know the number of craftsmen available for work the next day. As the schedule is prepared, the planner will deduct the scheduled man-hours from the available man-hours until all the man-hours have been scheduled. The planner will balance this schedule with the other planners, adding and deleting jobs where craftsmen are needed on critical jobs in other areas.

The preparation and entry of jobs on the daily work schedule follows a set pattern. Carryover jobs are the first to be entered on the schedule as the result of communication between the foreman and the planner regarding jobs not completed that day. Next, priority 1 and 2 jobs are added to the schedule. Finally, priority 3 jobs are added to the schedule until all the available man-hours have been scheduled.

Once a tentative set of schedules is ready for the following day, the planner(s) has a brief meeting with the maintenance manager and a representative from operations to approve the daily work schedule. This fixes the schedule as the plan of action the maintenance manager is expecting to be executed the following day. The planner then makes all necessary arrangements to have the materials, tools, and special equipment delivered to the jobsite. The following day's schedule, job order copies, stores material transfer copies, prints, and drawings are then delivered to the maintenance foreman. The foreman reviews the work package and makes any necessary arrangements prior to starting the job the following day.

The daily work schedule shown in Fig. 5 is designed for several purposes. In addition to being a list of jobs the forman is expected to work and complete, it also shows the relative importance of the job by indicating priority classification. The schedule indicates the sequence steps of the job order to be worked. This is important, since not all parts of some jobs can be worked on at the same time or on the same day. The daily work schedule operates as a guide to the maintenance foreman for allocation of manpower to specific job orders based on scheduled job estimates. In addition, the daily work schedule is used to report job status and actual man-hours expended on jobs and nonproductive time distribution for cost accounting purposes. Copies of the schedule are used to coordinate material deliveries and production equipment shutdown. Finally, the daily work schedule is one of the primary sources of management information data for maintenance control reports. Therefore it must be signed as correct by the maintenance foreman when returned to the planner at the end of the day.

In addition to the daily meeting with the maintenance manager, the planner(s) has a weekly workload meeting. Here, all major jobs in hand are discussed and a tentative plan for daily scheduling is approved. As in the daily meeting, operational personnel are key contributors to the success of the scheduling effort and are included in the weekly meeting. The backlog charts are prepared and discussed at the weekly meeting to determine if manpower adjustments are required to meet current needs.

Communication between the maintenance department and its customers is vital to an efficient and effective maintenance operation. The daily and weekly meetings are tailored to meet this communication void and to foster a spirit of cooperation and understanding between all parties.

Scheduling assures a full day's workload for each maintenance craftsman based on job order estimates. The schedule lists the jobs needed to meet operational requirements with the available manpower on hand. However, the prerogative of assigning workers to individual jobs and the order in which jobs are worked remains with the maintenance foreman. Except for emergency interruptions, the foreman is expected to complete the daily work schedule, and to determine how this is to be done.

The planning and scheduling process sounds easy on paper, but it takes a lot of technical knowledge and years of actual on-the-job maintenance work. Experience is probably the major criterion when selecting people for the function of maintenance planner. The author has found that maintenance foremen with clerical aptitudes make the best planners. The planner should be equal to or slightly higher than the maintenance foreman in the organizational structure.

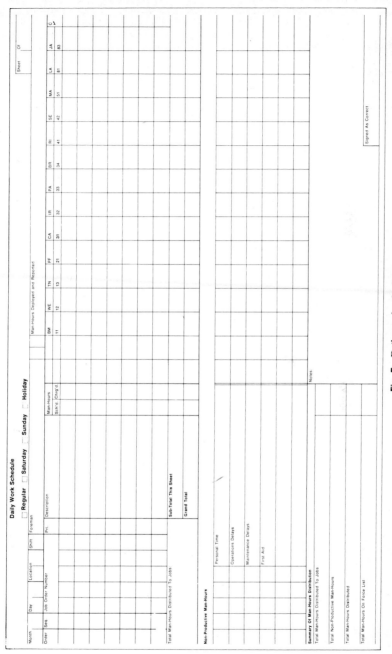

Fig. 5 Daily work schedule.

Minor maintenance jobs   All maintenance jobs are documented to assure proper communication and control for accomplishment, but some jobs are too small to justify the use of a written job order. An arbitrary lower limit should specify which jobs require a job order for execution. The remainder of the work falls in the category of minor maintenance jobs and requires a separate method for handling. Jobs of one man-hour or less which requires less than $50 worth of material may be a convenient place to draw the line on minor maintenance jobs.

The unit log book (Fig. 6) is used to record these minor maintenance jobs. The log book is maintained by the operating foreman in a centralized location in the area. The operating foreman enters the date, standing job order number, description of the work, and location of the job on one line of the unit logbook. The maintenance foreman

UNIT LOG BOOK

DATE	J/O #	DESCRIPTION OF JOB WANTED	LOCATION	DATE COMPLETED	AREA FOREMAN	JOB O.K.

Fig. 6   Unit log book.

reviews the log book several times each day to see if there are any minor jobs that can be handled *within* the daily work schedule. These minor jobs act as fill-in work when scheduled jobs are completed ahead of time or unexpected delays cause scheduled jobs to be set back. Therefore these minor jobs are noncritical in nature and could tolerate a couple of days' delay if not executed right away. The maintenance foreman signs and dates the log book when the work is completed and the operating foreman initials an OK of the completed job. The maintenance foreman enters the standing job order number on the daily work schedule and charges the actual time spent on the job against the standing job order number.

If an excessive number of minor maintenance jobs appears on the unit log book, they can be requested for accomplishment on a single job order. This provides the necessary manpower to clear the log book of the unaccomplished entries. Under *no* circumstance is the maintenance foreman to break the daily work schedule to do unit maintenance log book jobs. All emergency jobs regardless of size are requested on a job order form and are not part of the unit log book procedure. The maintenance planner will check the log book daily to be sure its provisions are not being abused.

MANAGEMENT CONTROLS FOR MAINTENANCE

A lot of emphasis is placed on planning and scheduling within the maintenance function, and much of the available literature describes varying planning and scheduling techniques. What is generally missing are the controls which allow the maintenance manager to monitor the effectiveness of the operation through the planning and scheduling section. Without this vital feedback information, the maintenance manager cannot determine if the highly expensive planning and scheduling function is carrying its weight toward operating efficiencies in the maintenance department. In the following paragraphs, we will describe the periodic reports and charts prepared by the maintenance planner for the maintenance manager to effect quick control over the maintenance operation.

Unreported man-hours   As indicated earlier in this chapter, the maintenance foreman records on the daily work schedule the actual hours expended by the maintenance crew each day. The first control indicator is, therefore, the relationship between the actual hours reported by the maintenance foreman and the direct worked hours paid to the craftsmen. This is vital information because all other control reports are based on reported hours by the foremen, and a wide variance between paid hours and reported hours will discount the reliability of other reports. The foreman must account for every hour worked by the crew, including all overtime. Unreported man-hours represent the difference between reported man-hours and paid man-hours. The control indicator is unreported hours as a percent of total hours paid, and the target figure is zero percent (see Fig. 7).

Scheduled man-hours   The next important indicator is the percentage of available man-hours scheduled. The maintenance work force is normally available for work a fixed number of hours per week; on a day-to-day basis, there should be a full day's work planned and scheduled for each maintenance craftsman. This indicator tries to determine if this goal is being met within reasonable limits. The difference between regular hours available and man-hours scheduled is reported as a percent of regular hours available (see Fig. 8). The target figure is zero plus or minus 5 percent.

Zero percent cannot be consistently maintained, because the difference between available man-hours and scheduled man-hours is affected by unexpected absences or workers returning from absences. The planner must know the number of people available for work and which people are absent. The planner anticipates the return of men from planned absences, such as vacations, and schedules jobs for them on the day they return to work. Any reading which exceeds the control limits must be investigated by the maintenance manager. The benefits of planning and scheduling can only be realized when each maintenance craftsman is scheduled for a full day's work every workday.

Scheduling compliance   In addition to scheduling a full day for each maintenance craftsman, the maintenance manager must make sure that jobs are being completed as planned and scheduled. This is illustrated by the chart shown in Fig. 9. The chart shows the percentage of man-hours worked as scheduled and the percentage of jobs completed as scheduled. The target figure is 90 percent or better.

When jobs are not worked or completed as scheduled, the maintenance work force is not being utilized to its most efficient level. The maintenance manager has delegated the responsibility for daily work scheduling to the maintenance planner. The planner prepares a recommended plan of action for the following day in the form of a daily work schedule for each maintenance foreman. The daily work schedule is reviewed and modified, if necessary, and approved by the maintenance manager. Therefore, the maintenance manager is expecting the work execution forces to complete the daily work schedule as it was approved except for emergency interruptions. The maintenance manager monitors the compliance to schedule by reviewing the percentage of man-hours and jobs completed within the target range.

Performance on completed jobs   The next important indicator is performance of the maintenance work force against the job estimates. Estimates serve three prime functions. First, they help the equipment owner decide if the job is worth the cost. Second, and most important, they aid the planner in scheduling the job to properly align jobs and manpower availability. Finally, estimates are used to measure performance. This last use can act like a double-edged sword, because there are many variables which adversely affect the ultimate outcome of a job.

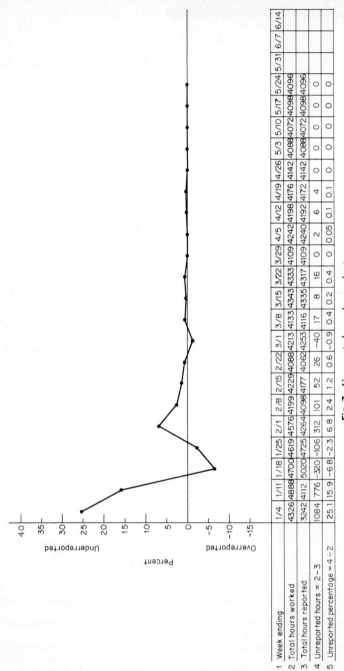

1 Week ending	1/4	1/11	1/18	1/25	2/1	2/8	2/15	2/22	3/1	3/8	3/15	3/22	3/29	4/5	4/12	4/19	4/26	5/3	5/10	5/17	5/24	5/31	6/7	6/14
2 Total hours worked	4326	4988	4700	4619	4576	4199	4229	4088	4213	4133	4343	4333	4109	4242	4198	4176	4142	4088	4072	4098	4096			
3 Total hours reported	3242	4112	5020	4725	4264	4098	4177	4062	4253	4116	4335	4317	4109	4240	4192	4172	4142	4088	4072	4098	4096			
4 Unreported hours = 2−3	1084	776	−320	−106	312	101	52	26	−40	17	8	16	0	2	6	4	0	0	0	0	0			
5 Unreported percentage = 4÷2	25.1	15.9	−6.8	−2.3	6.8	2.4	1.2	0.6	−0.9	0.4	0.2	0.4	0	0.05	0.1	0.1	0	0	0	0	0			

Fig. 7 Unreported man hours chart.

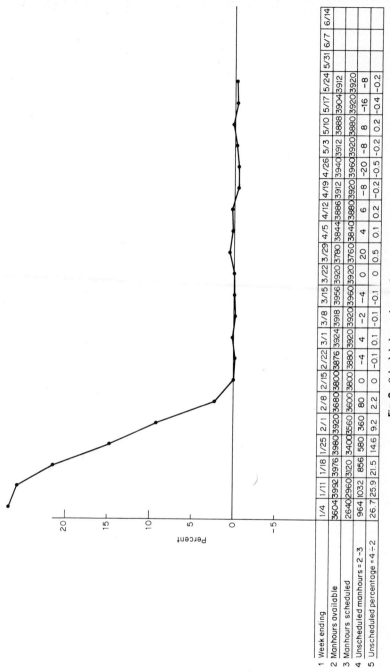

1 Week ending	1/4	1/11	1/18	1/25	2/1	2/8	2/15	2/22	3/1	3/8	3/15	3/22	3/29	4/5	4/12	4/19	4/26	5/3	5/10	5/17	5/24	5/31	6/7	6/14
2 Manhours available	3604	3992	3976	3980	3920	3680	3800	3876	3924	3918	3956	3920	3780	3844	3886	3912	3940	3912	3888	3904	3912			
3 Manhours scheduled	2640	2960	3120	3400	3560	3600	3600	3880	3920	3920	3960	3920	3760	3840	3880	3920	3960	3920	3880	3920	3920			
4 Unscheduled manhours = 2-3	964	1032	856	580	360	80	0	-4	4	-2	-4	0	20	4	6	-8	-20	-8	8	-16	-8			
5 Unscheduled percentage = 4÷2	26.7	25.9	21.5	14.6	9.2	2.2	0	-0.1	0.1	-0.1	-0.1	0	0.5	0.1	0.2	-0.2	-0.5	-0.2	0.2	-0.4	-0.2			

Fig. 8 Scheduled man hours chart.

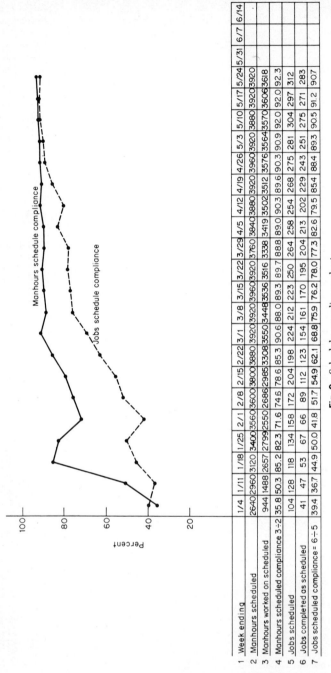

1 Week ending	1/4	1/11	1/18	1/25	2/1	2/8	2/15	2/22	3/1	3/8	3/15	3/22	3/29	4/5	4/12	4/19	4/26	5/3	5/10	5/17	5/24	5/31	6/7	6/14
2 Manhours scheduled	2640	2960	3120	3400	3560	3600	3800	3880	3920	3920	3920	3920	3760	3840	3880	3920	3960	3920	3880	3920	3920	3920		
3 Manhours worked on scheduled	944	1488	2657	2799	2550	2686	2985	3308	3550	3448	3516	3338	3419	3502	3512	3576	3564	3570	3606	3618				
4 Manhours scheduled compliance 3÷2	35.8	50.3	85.2	82.3	71.6	74.6	78.6	85.3	90.6	88.0	89.3	89.7	88.8	89.0	90.3	89.6	90.3	90.9	92.0	92.0	92.3			
5 Jobs scheduled	104	128	118	134	158	172	204	198	224	212	223	250	264	258	254	268	275	281	304	297	312			
6 Jobs completed as scheduled	41	47	53	66	89	112	123	154	161	170	195	204	213	202	229	243	251	275	271	283				
7 Jobs scheduled compliance = 6÷5	39.4	36.7	44.9	50.0	41.8	51.7	62.1	68.8	75.9	76.2	78.0	77.3	82.6	79.5	85.4	88.4	89.3	90.5	91.2	90.7				

Fig. 9 Schedule compliance chart.

4-18

Failure to meet estimates by the maintenance work force is just an indication that further analysis is required to uncover the actual cause of the problem. Extenuating circumstances can greatly affect many maintenance jobs because the extent of repairs cannot be determined until the work force is well into the job. Internal wear and damage is a prime example of this particular case. Other reasons for not meeting estimates include the inability of the planner to anticipate the job requirements. The scope of the job can change as the work progresses. The work force may not be working efficiently, and the job then takes longer to complete than originally estimated. Small jobs of 4 man-hours or less can play havoc with the performance against estimates, because small time differences make large percentage changes on the chart. This is particularly true if the predominance of the work falls in this small-job category.

The trend pattern of the indicators is what the maintenance manager monitors on all control charts, and this is particularly true for performance against estimate. Figure 10 illustrates the type of chart useful for reporting performance on completed jobs. Initially the maintenance manager should seek a percentage level where all jobs are completed at 100 percent plus or minus 15 percent. This means that performance is judged on a total-jobs basis and not on just one or two key jobs which have management's attention.

Backlog Backlog is one of the key factors which indicate how well the maintenance organization stays abreast of the workload level. Backlog is a desirable state of affairs because it provides the planner the opportunity to properly balance and distribute the work force to meet all operational requirements. A backlog that is too high means that the work force cannot do the work within a reasonable period and that some important jobs, such as preventive maintenance, are not done. On the other hand, a backlog that is too low means that the work force cannot be effectively utilized and the probability of excessive people is fairly high. A backlog of 2 to 4 crew weeks of work that is ready to be executed is a reasonable level to keep the work force occupied and still meet most demands.

Backlog is derived by dividing the total outstanding estimated man-hours on jobs ready for execution by the normal available man-hours per week. The backlog trend is the key factor, and a chart such as Fig. 11 will help the maintenance manager make personnel adjustments as necessary. If backlog has a tendency to peak during short intervals, outside contracting is the best method to stabilize the backlog trend. Backlog trends also indicate where to schedule annual or semiannual preventive maintenance jobs to best take advantage of dips in the workload level. While Fig. 11 only shows total backlog, the maintenance manager would find it advantageous to show backlog by individual crafts.

A long-term rise in backlog indicates the need for additional craftsmen; conversely, a long-term drop in backlog indicates the possible need to reduce staff. Decisions of this magnitude must take into consideration future expansion or alteration plans of the company.

A second helpful backlog figure is the total crew weeks of work waiting to be executed, including those jobs for which all the resources are not yet available. This backlog should average between 5 to 6 crew weeks of work.

Emergencies and overtime The percentage of emergencies (as defined earlier) and percentage of overtime are key factors in judging the performance of the maintenance function. See Fig. 12 for the chart which shows these indicators. Overtime should be kept within a range of less than 5 percent of all regular hours worked. Emergencies represent an interruption of the daily work schedule and work efficiency is decreased. Therefore jobs classed as emergencies should be kept to less than 10 percent of all work, otherwise the benefits of planning and scheduling cannot be achieved. (It is decidedly unlikely that real emergencies will routinely amount to more than 10 percent of all work.)

Every effort possible is required by each company employee to anticipate maintenance requirements as far in advance as possible if the maintenance department is to be efficient and effective. Fewer emergencies means that maintenance can do more jobs with the same work force, and everybody reaps the benefits.

Nonproductive time The classification of jobs listed earlier indicated a group called *nonproductive time*. A review of the trend patterns for nonproductive time will indicate whether there are opportunities for increasing efficiency by analyzing the factors which contribute to the nonproductive time. Some of these nonproductive times are unavoidable, but a percentage indicating higher than normal levels should be investigated to

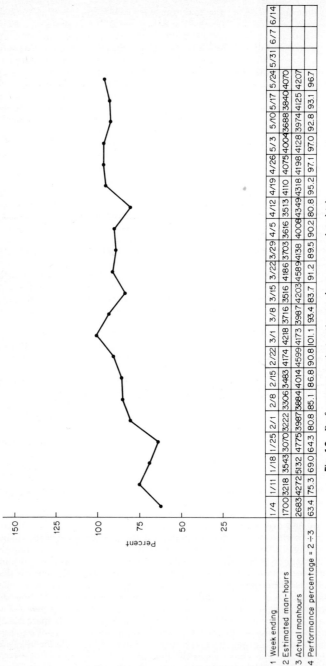

1 Week ending	1/4	1/11	1/18	1/25	2/1	2/8	2/15	2/22	3/1	3/8	3/15	3/22	3/29	4/5	4/12	4/19	4/26	5/3	5/10	5/17	5/24	5/31	6/7	6/14
2 Estimated man-hours	1700	3543	3070	3222	3306	3483	4174	4218	3716	3516	4186	3703	3616	3513	4110	4075	4004	3688	3840	4070				
3 Actual manhours	2683	4272	5132	3987	3884	4014	4599	4173	3987	4203	4589	4138	4008	4349	4318	4198	4128	3974	4125	4207				
4 Performance percentage = 2÷3	63.4	75.3	69.0	80.8	85.1	86.8	90.8	101.1	93.4	83.7	91.2	89.5	90.2	80.8	95.2	97.1	97.0	92.8	93.1	96.7				

Fig. 10 Performance against estimate chart on completed job.

4-20

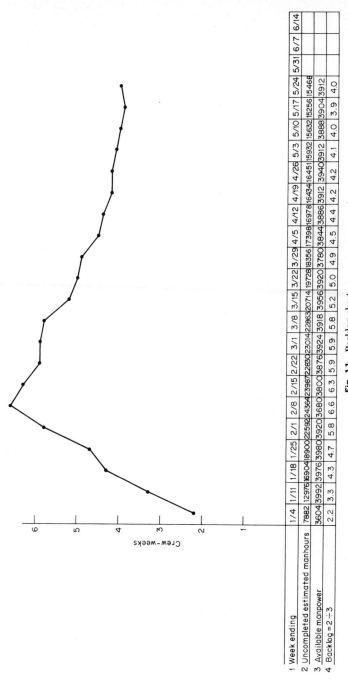

1 Week ending	1/4	1/11	1/18	1/25	2/1	2/8	2/15	2/22	3/1	3/8	3/15	3/22	3/29	4/5	4/12	4/19	4/26	5/3	5/10	5/17	5/24	5/31	6/7	6/14
2 Uncompleted estimated manhours	7882	12976	16904	18900	22592	24364	23987	22830	23014	22863	20714	19728	18356	17398	16978	16434	16451	15932	15632	15256	15468			
3 Available manpower	3604	3992	3976	3980	3920	3680	3800	3876	3924	3918	3956	3920	3780	3844	3886	3912	3940	3912	3888	3904	3912			
4 Backlog = 2÷3	2.2	3.3	4.3	4.7	5.8	6.6	6.3	5.9	5.9	5.8	5.2	5.0	4.9	4.5	4.4	4.2	4.2	4.1	4.0	3.9	4.0			

Fig. 11 Backlog chart.

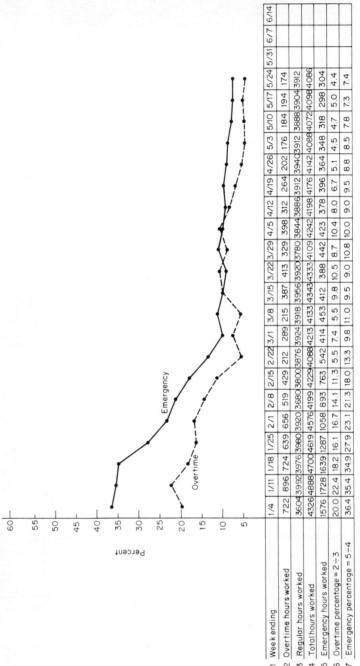

	1/4	1/11	1/18	1/25	2/1	2/8	2/15	2/22	3/1	3/8	3/15	3/22	3/29	4/5	4/12	4/19	4/26	5/3	5/10	5/17	5/24	5/31	6/7	6/14
1 Week ending																								
2 Overtime hours worked	722	896	724	639	656	519	429	212	289	215	387	413	329	398	312	264	202	176	184	194	174			
3 Regular hours worked	3604	3992	3976	3980	3920	3680	3800	3876	3924	3918	3956	3920	3780	3844	3886	3912	3940	3912	3888	3904	3912			
4 Total hours worked	4326	4888	4700	4619	4576	4199	4229	4088	4213	4133	4343	4333	4109	4242	4198	4176	4142	4088	4072	4098	4086			
5 Emergency hours worked	1576	1728	1639	1287	1058	893	763	542	414	453	412	388	442	423	378	396	364	348	318	298	304			
6 Overtime percentage = 2÷3	20.0	22.4	18.2	16.1	16.7	14.1	11.3	5.5	7.4	5.5	9.8	10.5	8.7	10.4	8.0	6.7	5.1	4.5	4.7	5.0	4.4			
7 Emergency percentage = 5÷4	36.4	35.4	34.9	27.9	23.1	21.3	18.0	13.3	9.8	11.0	9.5	9.0	10.8	10.0	9.0	9.5	8.8	8.5	7.8	7.3	7.4			

Fig. 12 Overtime and emergency chart.

resolve bottlenecks to effective operations. Nonproductive time is expressed as a percentage of regular hours worked and includes such factors as:

    Waiting for tools and material
    Waiting for transport
    Transportation to the jobsite
    Waiting for equipment to be shut down
    Coffee breaks
    Training
    Union business
    Medical attention
    Idle or no work available

Work classification   An analysis of the man-hours expended by work classification is a good guide toward decision making in maintenance. Preventive maintenance, for example, should represent approximately 15 to 25 percent of the work effort. The percentage of man-hours expended on rearrangements, modifications, and capital work can help guide the maintenance manager in manpower forecasts for the following year based on anticipated expansion and modification plans. A rise in safety or accident work can indicate an opportunity for changes in plant practices to reduce costs.

EDP reports   Where electronic data processing (EDP) capability is available, total job costs can be reported through the job order system. The equipment owner receives a cost summary for the completed job. The report shows the original estimate and the actual costs for the job. The report is used by the equipment owner to assess the value of the job received for the cost incurred. This can guide the owner in requesting similar jobs in the future. The equipment owner can also use the report to ask the maintenance department for an explanation for cost overruns. A copy of the same report is also prepared for the maintenance manager.

With a computerized job order system, many of the reports and summaries mentioned earlier can be calculated and printed using the computer. The job order system forms the data base for other maintenance reports such as cost accounting, equipment cost reporting, and equipment reliability studies. Preventive maintenance reporting and the comparison of breakdown costs to preventive maintenance costs can be extracted from the job order system. The completed job order cost report and the work execution copy of the job order are filed in an equipment history file for future reference. The equipment history file is the source of analytical data for resolving recurring maintenance problems. In all these reports and records, the job order and job order system supply the basic data for management decision making in the maintenance department.

Work sampling   The work sampling technique is an inexpensive way of measuring the effectiveness of the supervision, planning, and scheduling process. It is used to determine how the maintenance work force spends its time during the work day. Obviously, the maintenance craftsmen are not expected to work every minute of the day, but 50 to 60 percent of the workday should be spent at the jobsite working with the tools in hand. The national average runs from 35 to 45 percent.

The purpose of work sampling is to show the magnitude of the nonwork time by recording activity observations on a random basis. When these factors are known, methods can be devised which decrease the time spent on nonproductive activities. Work sampling operates on the laws of probability. If the sample is large enough, the characteristics of the sample will be similar to the characteristics of the total group. The key factor is that activity observations must be taken randomly to assure unbiased results.

Most maintenance managers would find the following sampling categories sufficient to measure their maintenance operations:

    Late starts/early quits
    Waiting for tools, material, and equipment
    Traveling to the jobsite
    Carrying or searching for tools and material
    Coffee breaks and smoking
    Normal personal time
    Job-related supervisory contact
    Idle unexplained
    Direct work

Many of the activities other than direct work can either be eliminated or minimized by proper planning and scheduling. To show progress of the planning and scheduling system, it is best to make a work sampling study prior to implementing the planning and scheduling procedures. The work sampling study is then repeated every 6 to 9 months to show improvement in the direct work activity.

SUMMARY

This chapter outlines the purpose of planning and scheduling and has outlined some of the benefits to be gained by using planning and scheduling techniques in the maintenance department. The fundamental requirements for the planning and scheduling systems have been presented and examples of the necessary forms have been shown. The basic techniques for the planning and scheduling process have also been described. The reports and charts necessary to control the maintenance operation are also included. What is not present are the detailed procedures the maintenance manager will have to tailor for the particular organization concerned.

The controls section of this chapter needs closer attention by the maintenance manager. The indicators can show deviations from past practices or trends in undesirable directions; and here corrective attention may prove beneficial. The important point is to set goals for each indicator and then measure progress toward meeting those goals. Close attention toward meeting the goals means the associated costs that go along with the indicators will take care of themselves and show an overall reduction. The important point about indicators is to put them in terms that are easily understood and controlled by the person being measured. The planning and scheduling techniques and performance measurement indicators described in this chapter give the maintenance manager the tools that are needed to manage his maintenance operation.

Chapter **2**

Preventive Maintenance Scheduling

LLOYD R. CALAWAY
Bonner & Moore Associates, Inc.

SCOPE AND PURPOSE

This chapter has been prepared to aid plant engineering management in establishing and carrying out an effective preventive maintenance program.

General preventive maintenance concepts and activities which are requisite to a preventive maintenance system installation are discussed in this introductory section.

Specific components of a system are detailed in the last half of this chapter.

GENERAL CONCEPTS

The purpose of preventive maintenance is to minimize breakdowns and excessively rapid deterioration of equipment. In order to achieve maximum effectiveness at minimum cost, however, the need for preventive maintenance must be analyzed and a systematic approach to it must be adopted. The function of a preventive maintenance system, then, is to control preventive maintenance activities.

A preventive maintenance system should provide for routine inspections and periodic servicing and overhaul on equipment selected for preventive maintenance coverage. All capital assets, including building, manufacturing, rotating, instruments, safety, electrical, tools, mobile, and other types of equipment should be considered for inclusion within a preventive maintenance program.

A preventive maintenance program can be effective only if the facilities and equipment are in fairly good condition. Equipment that must constantly be repaired is not ready for preventive maintenance. Such equipment must be reconditioned to an acceptable level of stability before preventive maintenance can be applied. If this is not done and the equipment fails at random intervals, the preventive maintenance program will most likely be ineffective.

DEFINITIONS

Plant engineering terminology varies from one locale to another. So that the terms used in this chapter will be understood, the following definitions are given:

Preventive maintenance: The periodic servicing, inspection, and overhaul of existing facilities to either prevent or discover and correct conditions which will lead to equipment breakdown, production interruptions, or accelerated deterioration of equipment.

Inspection: The investigation of equipment at its service location to determine if application and operation is according to design. Inspection procedures may include many kinds of testing—from routine visual examination to use of modern diagnostic tools.

Servicing: Tuning, adjusting, lubricating, cleaning, and the like, as well as minor repairs of not more than 1 or 2 hours' duration.

Overhaul: The restoration of operating equipment to a "like new" condition.

The results of preventive maintenance servicing, inspection, or overhaul may reveal additional work which is beyond the scope of the work defined in the preventive maintenance job tasks. When this is so, then a separate work order should be initiated for the additional work.

SYSTEM OBJECTIVES

The objectives of a preventive maintenance system are as follows:
- To aid in minimizing the unanticipated failure of equipment in order to avoid the resulting downtime and loss of production
- To minimize the cost of emergency repair
- To minimize hazards to personnel and equipment
- To maximize the efficiency and safety of production equipment operation
- To prolong the useful life of equipment covered by the program

ESSENTIAL PREVENTIVE MAINTENANCE PROGRAM ELEMENTS

The five essential elements of any preventive maintenance program are these:
1. An itemized listing of equipment to be included in the preventive maintenance program
2. A schedule file
3. A job tasks file
4. An equipment history file
5. An organization capable of using the preventive maintenance system

Itemized Equipment Listing

Individual pieces of equipment to be covered by a program should be identified according to the following guidelines:
- Where possible, preventive maintenance should be focused on the top 20 percent of equipment items that account for 80 percent of the cost of downtime or loss of production. Attention should also be given to the instrumentation and electrical equipment that controls and services these high-priority equipment items.

• Items are to be included if, after a reasonably predictable period of equivalent operating time, wear-out has been established as the cause of failure.

• Preventive maintenance inspections are to be set by safety codes or laws.

• Preventive maintenance should include all service-type activities, such as changing oil, changing filters, lubricating, and greasing, as well as periodic inspections, using either visual examination or nondestructive testing equipment and modern diagnostic tools.

• It is up to preventive maintenance to determine whether breakdown could cause serious damage to equipment.

• Care is to be exercised to assure that easily deferrable, long-term maintenance needs (such as structural steel and vessel corrosion, roofing, flashing, painting, electrical insulation, instrument recalibration, and other such items) will not be overlooked.

Certain pieces of equipment should specifically be excluded from a preventive maintenance program. No preventive maintenance program should include all equipment. Neither should all breakdowns be eliminated, even if this were possible. Items not included in a preventive maintenance program would be:

• Noncritical fractional horsepower motors

• Equipment expected to become obsolete within its normal life span

• Equipment that requires inspection which would cost more than a breakdown repair project

Schedule File

This element within a preventive maintenance system includes descriptions of all equipment selected for inclusion in the preventive maintenance program, information on the frequency of preventive maintenance work for each piece of equipment, a specially designed plan for preventive maintenance work orders, a historical record of interval reviews and adjustments, and a calendar schedule for the performance of preventive maintenance work. The details on this file are covered in the latter part of this chapter.

Job Tasks File

While the schedule file provides information on what is to be done to each piece of equipment included in the preventive maintenance program and when it is to be done, the job tasks file provides information on how specific tasks should be done and/or a record of tasks performed. Tasks for performing preventive maintenance work are detailed and made accessible or integral with the preventive maintenance work orders for use in connection with the scheduling function. Details on what is to be included in the job tasks file are covered later in this chapter.

Equipment History File

The equipment history file provides a means for recording and accessing histories on equipment of interest. Information from this file is used in modifying a preventive maintenance program for improved effectiveness and lower costs. The history records are dependent on a feedback procedure for reporting conditions, failures, and repairs. This feedback procedure and the equipment history records are explained in detail further along.

Organization

Upon instituting a preventive maintenance program, a staff position should be established for constantly monitoring the entire maintenance program and seeking ways to improve its effectiveness and to reduce its cost. This person may be called the methods improvement engineer or given a similar title.

It should be among the methods improvement engineer's duties to:

• Be responsible for the preparation of all maintenance inspection and repair procedures

• Prepare improved job plans on repetitive maintenance for the use of a planner

• Analyze the failure history, seeking out the items causing trouble and finding ways to improve their performance

• Be responsible for the keeping and analysis of all maintenance records

• Keep abreast of the field, seeking new materials, equipment, tools, procedures, etc., and recommending those with potential benefits

• Plan, prepare, and present maintenance and safety training when necessary

The following principles apply to all preventive maintenance work:

• Workers from the regular maintenance force will perform the preventive maintenance activities

• Preventive maintenance work must not be interrupted by other maintenance work except that of higher priority

• Routine work generated by a preventive maintenance system should follow the same organization procedures as regular maintenance for authorization, accumulation of costs, and reports

• Preventive maintenance work execution should be directed by the same foremen who supervise all other maintenance work

The following pages include descriptions of the design, layout, and organization of each component within a preventive maintenance system

SCHEDULE FILE

Part of a preventive maintenance program should consist of a master file in which all preventive maintenance scheduling records are kept. Within the schedule file, a record is established for each piece of equipment, by equipment number, that is maintained under the preventive maintenance program. Each record is filed by equipment number in sequential order.

Each file record should consist of one or more of the following:

Equipment description
Work order schedule
Work order for preventive maintenance service
Record of interval reviews and adjustments
Work order for preventive maintenance inspection
Record of interval reviews and adjustments
Work order for preventive maintenance overhaul
Record of interval reviews and adjustments

Equipment Description Record

The equipment description record should include the permanent physical data concerning the equipment and its installation. The record should contain spaces for the equipment number, manufacturer name, manufacturer order number, serial number, size, type or model number, drawing number, purchase order number, vendor, appropriation number, shop order number, equipment cost, installation cost, total cost, date installed, location, and space for any other pertinent data or description about the equipment. Additional space should be provided for a listing of the spare parts. Electric motor, control valve, instrument, or other description records may be substituted for the equipment description.

Work Order Schedule

With each equipment record in the file there should be a preventive maintenance work order schedule. The schedule should list the equipment number, the year of the schedule, the preventive maintenance work order number, and a schedule of the interval of preventive maintenance work for each work order.

Each piece of equipment should have several scheduled intervals, with that for servicing (tuning, oil change, filter cleaning, greasing, oiling, etc.) being the most frequent. At intermediate intervals, inspections should be made for vibration frequency and amplitude, operation of controls, governors, overspeed trips, looseness, play, seal leakage, etc. At longer intervals, there should be overhauls or complete dismantling for clearance checks, bearing and other internal conditions, ultrasonic and magnaflux flaw and crack checks, tooth wear, etc. Normally, the levels of frequency on servicing, inspections, and overhauls are made to be even multiples so they will coincide with each other for convenience in scheduling. Tables of inspection intervals should be compiled for each piece of equipment in the program based on equivalent operating and/or calendar times, depending on which is most suitable in each instance. If elapsed time or running time meters are used, the periodic reading of the meters should be scheduled on preventive maintenance.

Similarly, the procedure will assure that the elapsed time of the appropriate intervals is reset to zero and that the remaining intervals are temporarily adjusted not only to avoid repeating work that has just been performed but also to reestablish the calendar coincidence of the various intervals. The actual intervals are recorded.

Scheduling is a method for determining when preventive maintenance work will be performed. Preventive maintenance work is usually distributed evenly over the year to level the total maintenance workload.

Types of schedules   The type of schedule to be used must be determined. One thing that must be kept in mind is that regardless of the type of schedule chosen, it must remain flexible to take care of any changes in the preventive maintenance intervals and the deletion and addition of preventive maintenance work orders to the system. Schedules involving intervals of less than a week are normally made a function of operations or routine maintenance and are not included in the preventive maintenance scheduling system.

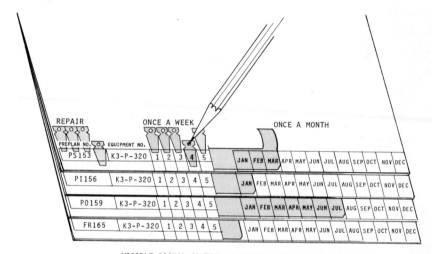

VISIBLE SIGNAL CONTROL SPOTLIGHTS MAINTENANCE SCHEDULES

Fig. 1   Visible signal control.

Visual schedules may consist of wall or desk calendars or visual file cards. The use of commercial wall or desk calendars is the most limiting kind of scheduling system because there is so little space for each date. The wall calendar can be hand drawn on chart paper, or it may consist of magnetic or slotted chart boards for listing of multiple equipment items. Such calendars usually show weeks or months of the year. The preventive maintenance work to be performed is listed on the calendar at scheduled intervals. Lists of preventive maintenance work to be performed must be copied from the wall schedules and transmitted to the field. All changes must be manually updated. Such a system has physical limitations as to the number of items handled.

Visible file cards consist of files of preventive maintenance work kept in loose-leaf binders, file drawers, tub files, rotary files, etc., with a visible tab designating the calendar time the preventive maintenance work is due. The preventive maintenance work order may be moved to fit the calendar date or the date can be changed by hand. Figure 1 shows one sort of visible tab system in which a change to next calendar due date is made by hand. With this arrangement, a much larger preventive maintenance system can be handled than with a calendar system. Furthermore, additional records of equipment descriptions, preventive maintenance work orders, and history records can be included in the same file.

Mechanized schedules involve some mechanical or electronic method of sorting preventive maintenance work orders when they are due for scheduling. Two commercial varieties of slotted cards are available.

One variety employs a card with one or two rows of holes punched on its four sides. Each hole or group of holes is slotted to the edge of the card so as to designate certain alphanumeric information. A sort is made by taking the cards involved and inserting a wire needle through the holes that designate the required information. When the cards are lifted with the needle, those containing the required information will fall since their holes are slotted to the edges. Figure 2 shows one variety of slotted card.

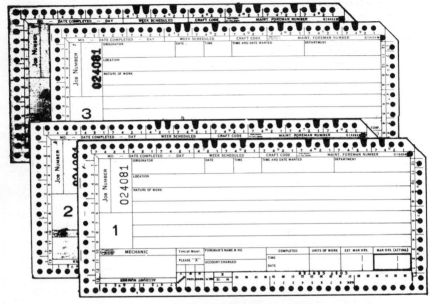

Fig. 2   Slotted card.

Fig. 3   Metal tab.

The other method of sorting uses a keyboard arrangement which picks slotted cards from a specially manufactured file drawer.

Mechanical keypunch cards may be used for tabulating the due dates, work order numbers, job tasks, and numbers of the equipment required for preventive maintenance. These cards are regularly sorted on an electronic sorter for scheduling. They can be duplicated or listed for transmittal to the field.

Metal tabs attached to metal plates (which have the required preventive maintenance information embossed on them) are also available. The tabs can be selected either visually or mechanically. The information on the plates can then be reproduced onto practically any designated form for transmittal to the field. Figure 3 shows a typical metal tab used for scheduling.

Each of the mechanized schedules offers certain advantages and/or disadvantages for any specific system. Regardless of the system chosen, one person should be designated to be responsible for its implementation.

Computerized schedules are the most expensive to install and operate, but they offer advantages in scheduling, feedback information, and exception reports which cannot be approached by the other means of scheduling. All the files, equipment listings, work orders, schedules, job tasks, and equipment history described herein can be incorporated into the computer system. The advantages are obvious.

Preventive Maintenance Work Orders

Work orders can be filled out for service, inspection, and overhaul preventive maintenance class work. The work order should contain all the data necessary for initiating a job.

Record of Interval Reviews and Adjustments

Intervals between the routine inspection, servicing, and overhaul of equipment are to be established. Initially these should be based on past experience, judgment, and manufacturers' recommendations. Intervals should be systematically increased on individual pieces of equipment—where criticality or unexpired warranties permit—until failures begin to occur, significant signs of wear appear, or signals from inspection or monitoring equipment indicate that significant changes in the equipment's behavior are taking place.

The review and adjustment record is designed to keep track of the basis upon which the frequency for a particular preventive maintenance work order is established. Listed on the record are equipment number, date of review, job task numbers, description of basis, and frequency for the type of preventive maintenance to be performed. Every preventive maintenance work order and related tasks should be reviewed at least annually, and the review and any adjustment to the schedules should be recorded.

The preventive maintenance job task description must not be confused with the work order. The preventive maintenance job task description tells the workman how to do the work and is a step-by-step outline of the work to be done. Preventive maintenance job task descriptions may range in size from a single sentence on the work order to volume and page reference in a manufacturer's service manual. Normally, the job task description will consist of a separate document kept in a separate file.

A work order consists of one or more job tasks which are listed on the work order. A particular job task can be performed on more than one item of equipment, but work orders are written for only one item of equipment or only one group of equipment items on which particular tasks are to be performed.

PREVENTIVE MAINTENANCE JOB TASKS

Formal written tasks should be established for each type of equipment in the preventive maintenance program. The tasks are written so as to ensure that each particular job task can be performed on more than one equipment item. Figure 4 shows a typical task description.

Each item or step of the job to be performed is listed with a description of the work. The number of workers, skills, and duration (in tenths of hours) are estimated for each step of the job.

The description of the job is laid out in a stepwise manner and written in terms that the person doing the work can understand. The tasks description should make full use of drawings, diagrams, and pictures from the vendor's repair, operating, and training manuals. Exploded views and assembly drawings are particularly valuable and should, where possible, show the stock catalog number of each component.

The complete task is packaged, given a suitable reference number, and filed and indexed in such a way as to be easily retrievable. Alternatively, the tasks can be placed in manuals that are readily accessible to the field mechanics.

Page ___ of ___ Date _____ Initials _____	PM JOB TASK FOR 415 VOLT GENERATORS	J. P. No. __11-101__		
Equipment Class __26__		Type of PM __Insp.__		
Item	Description	No. Men	Skill	Dur.
1	Trip associated breaker and rack out.			
2	Apply padlock to bus bar shutters. Apply danger tag.			
3	Remove terminal box cover on generator or at switchboard, and check by means of voltmeter that apparatus is dead.			
4	Short circuit rectifiers where necessary.			
5	Megger main windings; record insulation resistance and temp.			
6	Megger field winding - record insulation resistance and temp.			
7	Inspect commutator and slip rings for cleanliness, wear, indication of arcing.			
8	Check brushes for wear, replace if necessary.			
9	Check brush tension; adjust if necessary.			
10	Check all connections for tightness, signs of overheating.			
11	Replace terminal box cover.			
12	Unlock bus bar shutters.			
13	Replace breaker, rack into position.			
14	Remove danger tag.			

Fig. 4 Preventive maintenance job task description.

Preventive maintenance job tasks are step-by-step outlines of the important elements in an inspection, service, or overhaul job. They bridge the gap between theory and practice.

A job task description offers the following advantages:

● It reminds the worker performing the preventive maintenance work to include all the steps necessary to complete the job.

● It provides the worker with the technical information needed to perform the work.

● It ensures that preventive maintenance work being performed by different workmen will be uniform and complete.

The preventive maintenance job task description may be used as a checklist for the worker to show whether or not each step was performed as described. This checklist would then indicate if additional scheduling of manpower were necessary to complete the preventive maintenance task.

Such checklists are not used for equipment history records. These are handled by feedback cards that indicate faulty conditions, the action taken to correct them, the cause of the faulty conditions, and the conditions found.

EQUIPMENT HISTORY FILE

Feedback is a procedure designed to assure that both the occurrence and the results of all maintenance inspection, servicing, overhauls, repairs, and other work performed on a piece of equipment—either because of preventive maintenance or the repair of a failure—are recorded for review and analysis by those who may initiate corrective action.

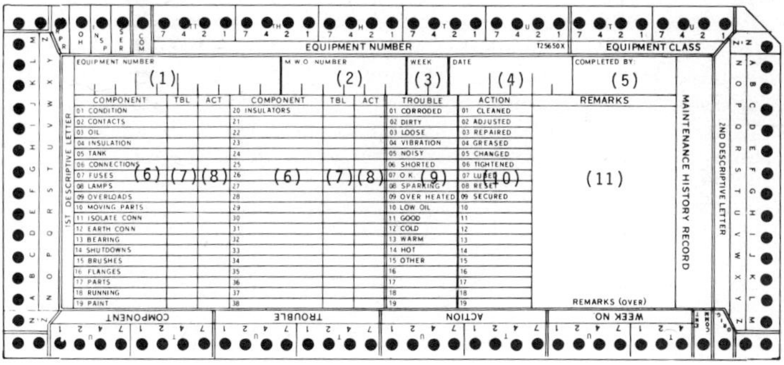

Fig. 5 Feedback card.

Figure 5 shows a copy of a typical maintenance history record card used for feedback. Feedback cards are designed for each major equipment class on which equipment history is desired. The card shown is for electrical work. The field indentification numbers in parentheses do not appear on the actual form but are used for each of the field explanations as follows:

(1) Equipment number: The number identifying the individual equipment on which a record is to be kept.

(2) Work order number: The number of the work order written to initiate the work being done.

(3) Week: The week of the preventive maintenance schedule in which the work is performed.

(4) Date: The date by day, month, and year on which the work order was completed.

(5) Completed by: Initials of the foreman or person who completed the maintenance history record card.

(6) Component: A list of nouns describing the names of the parts on which one wishes to keep history. The card that is shown lists the electrical components on which history will be kept.

(7) Trouble: A description of the trouble found on the component. It is usually reported on an exception basis; i.e., if nothing is wrong with the component, then nothing

is reported. The trouble is listed by number from field 9. A record of what was wrong with the component is recorded for future analysis.

(8) Act: The action taken to correct the trouble found and listed by number from field 10.

(9) Trouble: A list of adjectives describing what may be the cause of the faulty component's failure.

(10) Action: A list of verbs describing the action taken.

(11) Remarks: Any additional data that may be kept on the equipment or its components; also observations made that may contribute to the correction of any problem that may be apparent.

Once all the feedback cards are flagged for each of the components, the trouble is found, and the action is taken, these cards form the records for the equipment history file.

The file is used for the analysis of equipment failure by frequency, duration, cause, etc. Such analyses will allow engineering techniques to be applied for prolonging equipment life and to permit improved determination on preventive maintenance frequencies.

On certain pieces of critical equipment, trends in measured variables such as bearing, lubricant, and process stream operating temperatures and pressures; shaft position; vibration frequency and amplitude; and noise will be plotted in an attempt to identify the signal or combination of signals which precedes failure. Such "signatures"—which can indicate impending failure, rapidly increasing wear, or damage to equipment—are very useful in scheduling preventive maintenance work for greater effectiveness and at reduced costs. Where feasible and economically justified, certain measurements should be provided continuously by sensors installed on the equipment and monitored by the scan, log, and alarm features of a computer.

Through use of history data, procedures can be established to monitor the effectiveness of the preventive maintenance program. Routine review, analysis, and comparison of the ratio between failure-initiated work and actual work performed should be conducted. This analysis will be performed at successively higher levels of summary—ranging from individual items and groups and classes of equipment to geographical locations and ultimately the entire production facility. Charts should be maintained to detect trends and possible relationships to downtime, throughput, and costs.

Chapter **3**

Planning and Estimating Techniques

RONALD W. CHAMBERS

Manager, Maintenance Engineering, The Firestone Tire & Rubber Company

INTRODUCTION

This chapter will deal with planning and estimating techniques that can be used by maintenance planners in industry today. The basic techniques covered are:
1. Planning and estimating simple maintenance jobs
2. Planning and estimating 2- to 8-hour jobs
3. Planning using bar charts
4. Job estimating through the use of time standards
5. Planned major equipment breakdown program

QUALIFICATIONS OF A MAINTENANCE PLANNER

One of the first items that should be handled when planning group is being established is to decide on the qualifications an individual should have to become a planner. The basic qualifications are (1) some practical background and (2) ability to analyze problems so that this person can, in turn, prepare the plan of attack to be taken.

Minimum experience and educational qualifications should be those of a qualified craftsman with one year of supervisory experience or an individual with a 2-year associate degree from a technical school and one year of plant maintenance experience.

The use of an individual with a 2-year associate degree can be an excellent means of bringing new life into an older maintenance department. This type of individual will not take for granted the established bad practices and low level of efficiency that tend to appear acceptable to those who come up through the ranks.

DEFINITION OF PLANNED WORK

Before proceeding too far, we should define "planning." Almost every job performed by a maintenance man is accomplished through some planning, and therefore it is necessary to establish what is meant by a "planned job" in this discussion. A job is planned when:

1. The job has been investigated and a clear, concise description of the job has been written
2. The material required has been purchased and has been set aside for the planned job
3. Special equipment such as a boom truck, if required, is available
4. Special tools that may be required to perform the job are available
5. Sketches or drawings are provided with description of job when required
6. Estimated manpower and time required to perform the job, using some type of systematic estimating approach, is provided

When a job meets the above criteria, it can be classified as a planned job. Keep in mind that not all planned jobs will meet every condition as listed above, as the condition may not be necessary.

The actual planning of maintenance work can be accomplished in many ways; however, there is a basic format that will generally be followed. The intent of each of the following basic descriptions covering the various techniques is to provide general guidelines. Exact, step-by-step, detailed formats for planning, covering the specific degree of planning and estimating required for every type of maintenance job, would not be practical because of the varying nature of maintenance work from plant to plant as well as within any one plant.

If accurate estimates and adequate plans are made, the benefits of planning can be realized. The planner should keep in mind that planned jobs that are underestimated, have insufficient material available, or are overmanned will not result in good performance. Please note that the expected job performance has a bearing on the actual performance. For example, if a job is overestimated to take 8 hours for two men, the actual time taken will generally be that long. The same applies to a job that is poorly planned: that is, it will tend to be performed poorly.

PLANNING AND ESTIMATING SIMPLE MAINTENANCE JOBS

How do you plan the small, simple job, or, for that matter, *do* you plan it? Since it was stated earlier that all jobs are performed using planning to a certain degree, what needs to be answered is the question, "Is formal planning required for simple jobs?"

One parameter to follow is that if the job does not require material, it will no doubt not require formal planning. Examples of work of this nature are straightening bent brackets and refastening items that have fallen off. However, the same simple jobs that do require material will require planning to some degree.

Examples of jobs that fall under this category are replacement of sprockets, couplings, chains, V belts, pipe fittings, etc.

For the simple jobs that should be planned so that maintenance craftsmen will work at optimum efficiency, these guidelines can be followed:

1. A first-hand observation of the job must be made by the planner and a decision rendered on the corrective action required.
2. The determination of material requirements is made and listed on the work order.
3. Arrangements must be made by the planner to procure the required material.
4. Need for special tools or equipment must be determined (since job is minor in nature, this is usually found to be negative; however, it should not be overlooked).
5. Time required for performance of actual work must be estimated.

One aid that can be used for simplifying the planning of this type of job is a Polaroid camera. A snapshot or two of the problem area might save a lot of time that would otherwise have to be spent in preparing or giving instructions. An example of this might be the repairing of a switch on a column. The switch in question could be readily found if the photo included background equipment.

The requirement of planning small jobs must not be taken lightly. For example, if the planner provides a simple instruction, such as "Repair the guard as required," the craftsman may decide to make a complete new side for the guard when all that was really required was a patch to cover one end.

Planned work order

The objective of planning small jobs is to accomplish these tasks efficiently and without generating extra paper work. To minimize on the paper work aspect, it is recommended that small planned jobs be performed using the same work order that is used for emergency work. The work order can have a place for circling that it is a planned job as shown by Fig. 1.

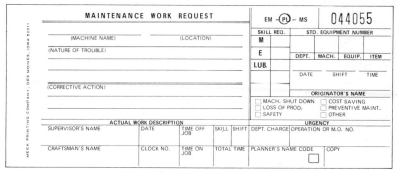

Fig. 1   Maintenance work request.

PLANNING AND ESTIMATING 2- TO 8-HOUR MAINTENANCE JOBS

The planning of a maintenance job that will take from 2 to 8 hours is basically not much different from planning a simple job. The major difference is that the degree of planning must be higher to obtain increased worker efficiency, since more time will be spent on this planned job by the craftsman.

In order to obtain a higher degree of planning for jobs that fall between 2 and 8 hours, these steps are recommended:

Step 1: Review the job on site and determine action required if possible. It may not be possible to determine exactly what is wrong at this point if the problem is of an internal nature. In this case, step 2 is taken.

Step 2: For internal equipment problems, a review of information (such as drawings and maintenance manuals) furnished by manufacturer is recommended before determination of action required is made.

Step 3: The plan of action that is required to correct the problem can now be formulated. It is this step that usually requires experience on the part of the planner. When replacement of a part that is part of a subassembly is required the planner must know how to disassemble the part and what is required for reassembly. This can be of special importance if items such as seals are involved. In most cases the planner should have all seals and gaskets available, for the probability that they will have to be replaced is high. In fact, due to their usually low cost in relation to the overall job, they should be replaced regardless of condition.

Step 4: A list of material required for the job is then made. Since this could include a number of material requirements, the planner may choose to use a planned work sheet. This sheet is especially beneficial if the work order used by the plant does not have ample space available. A typical example of a planned work sheet is shown in Fig. 2.

Step 5: Any required special instructions pertaining to the performance of the job or precautions that must be taken are listed on the planned work sheet.

Step 6: The time required to perform the job and the number of craftsmen that will be needed are estimated.

Step 7: Determine what sketches, drawings, or manual information should be attached to the work sheet as an aid for the maintenance supervisor or craftsman.

The job is now planned and ready for scheduling with the exception of the procurement of material. Material required should be purchased and placed in a special location, with the location noted on the planned work request.

PLANNED WORK REQUEST

Planner _____   Work order no._____

Date _____

Job description:_____
_____
_____

Equipment to be down: Date: _____ Time:_____

Material required:_____ Location of:_____
_____
_____

Special instructions:_____
_____

Estimated time & craft requirements:

Craftsmen X hr	By shift				

List of reference material attached:
_____
_____
_____

Maintenance supervisor's comments:
_____
_____
_____

Fig. 2   Planned work request.

PLANNING USING BAR CHARTS

This technique of planning should be followed for jobs that will be of a duration of more than two shifts, including ones that will last for 3 or 4 days.

The same basic steps are followed when using this technique as is explained by the previous planning method for 2- to 8-hour jobs.

To handle work of this nature, the planner provides a written procedure for the job in addition to the information provided for a 2- to 8-hour job. This written procedure is in simple, abbreviated steps, and a breakdown of time required to perform each step is shown. This written information is prepared using a bar chart format as shown by Fig. 3.

This type of chart provides the planner with a means of determining the following:

1. The overall time required, through the use of a logical method rather than an "educated guess"

2. A means to review each phase of the job in detail to see that items such as material and special equipment requirements are covered

3. Coordination requirements between crafts

4. Comparing alternative methods for performing the job

Jobs of this duration require the use of a good sound planning technique to get the jobs done efficiently and on schedule. When planning a job that will require a lengthy period of downtime to complete, the overall shutdown time usually is critical. There is nothing more damaging to a planning program than missed startup times.

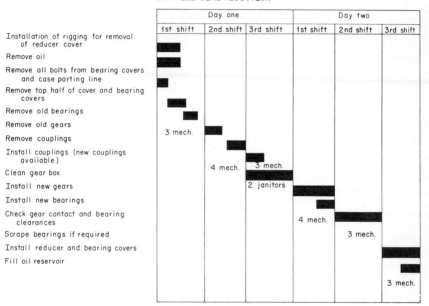

INSTALLATION OF NEW BEARINGS & GEARS
No. 1 MILL LINE REDUCTION

Fig. 3 Planning using bar charts.

The development of the bar chart starts with the listing, in column 1, of the steps that will be taken to perform the job (see Fig. 2). These steps should be listed for each element that will be removed and replaced on the machine. Each step should also be listed in sequence.

Next, time required to perform each step should be indicated in the next columns. Note that each column represents a shift of a particular day.

Then the overall job is reviewed for the purpose of determining if any steps can be handled simultaneously, thus saving time. After this review, the entire job should be reviewed with the maintenance supervisors who will perform the job.

This technique can be altered to use a PERT or critical path chart. The use of these two charts is not covered because their use in the average maintenance department cannot usually be justified. The development of these charts can be very time-consuming for someone who is not proficient in their use. After the overall basic planning techniques have been developed and full benefit is being realized from them, then these more sophisticated systems can be tried.

JOB ESTIMATING THROUGH THE USE OF TIME STANDARDS

The previous discussion suggested that estimating of times required to do a job should be established by using judgment based on experience. Realizing that this type of judgment estimating can only be based on an experience and that the experience may have been obtained under adverse conditions, some type of base should be used to evaluate the estimating experience. Different methods can be used for developing time standards. Two such methods are (1) time study specific jobs and (2) use of standard data that are available from consulting firms or various publications.

It is the author's opinion that time standards should only be used in maintenance work on a random basis and not for every planned job unless the intent is to go into piecework for the craftsmen. Maintenance jobs can be preplanned as well as postplanned using these data, so that a good cross reference can be obtained.

The use of a methods engineer for the development of in-plant time standards is an expensive means to accomplish this task. This is especially true if there is a wide variety of maintenance work. The approach could, however, perhaps be used for jobs that are repetitive in nature. Using data that have already been developed is far easier than developing them from scratch. Although these data may not be totally accurate, they will certainly provide the base that is required.

To use data that have been previously developed means that someone will have to be assigned this task. A maintenance planner can be trained to handle it effectively. The training can be given by an in-plant methods expert, a consulting firm, or perhaps a technical school.

PLANNED MAJOR EQUIPMENT BREAKDOWN PROGRAM

This technique deals with the planning of potential maintenance work that usually will be performed under emergency repair work conditions. It should be recognized that it is not practical to perform preventive maintenance to the point that component parts could be replaced before failure in every case, for in some cases this is strictly uneconomical. Besides the economical evaluation, the probability of failure is always present to some degree even with new equipment. Knowing that certain failures are probable and that if the failure did occur production would be lost, some type of a planned program should be developed. This technique deals with the development of such a program.

Since the planning covers *possible* work, it should be kept separate from the regular planned maintenance work. Therefore, the term "planned major equipment breakdown program" will be used to encompass all jobs planned by this technique.

Equipment name: _____

Possible failure	Special course of action if applicable	Repair action	Material required & location	Expected downtime	

Fig. 4   Planned major equipment breakdown program.

Each planned job that falls under this program can be filed by the name of the producing department or by the equipment name in a notebook available to each shift foreman so that each can refer to it when the need arises.

The steps taken for the development of this program are as follows:

1. To start the initial phase of development, a general meeting should be held with key maintenance personnel and engineering representatives in attendance. The agenda will include a statement of the program's purpose, an outline of the format that will be followed for its development, and the designation of the person who will coordinate these efforts.

2. A list of major equipment is then prepared, major equipment being that equipment whose unexpected failure would greatly cripple production.

3. This list is then reviewed and possible types of failure for each piece of equipment are added. This review should be made by the same individuals who attended the original meeting.

4. The list is then turned over to a planner for the development of course of action. To start the formal plan, the planner prepares a separate sheet for each piece of equipment shown in the master list, as shown by Fig. 4. The next thing the planner should do is review with production what action they would take in the case of a failure. This is important, for knowing what alternatives they have may lead to the first action that is to be taken by maintenance, which is not directly related to the repair of the breakdown. An example of this is in the case where five mills are being used to warm up material that is being fed to a major piece of equipment, and the mills are driven off a common line shaft. A failure occurs on one mill, causing the entire line to be down. Production therefore advises the addition of a short conveyor to bypass the mill, so that the mill could be removed from the line on a temporary basis. Accordingly, the first step of action to be taken by maintenance would be to install a short conveyor and remove the drive gear of this mill from the line shaft. This information is then shown in column 2 of the outline form (Fig. 4).

5. The repair action is then described briefly in column 3. The details for this work can be further planned by using one of the previously covered detailed techniques. The detailed breakdown can be filed right after the particular equipment sheet or can be kept in a separate file. If it is filed separately, its location should be noted on the master list.

6. A description of the material availability and location is provided. This may not be important in a small plant; however, having this information available without the need for further searching will certainly save time, especially if material is stored in a special location because of size or infrequent movement. In the case of multiplant operations, material may be shared between plants, with only one plant storing the material.

7. Next, the amount of anticipated downtime is recorded. This estimate should be made considering all the factors previously mentioned, such as the extra work that may be required by production management for temporary operation.

As the program is developed for various pieces of equipment, it should be reviewed by the group, too, for the purpose of making sure that it is both as factual and as realistic as possible. It should also be reviewed by the production management so that they are fully aware of what effects production could realize if the outlined type of failures did occur.

Chapter 4

Maintenance Cost Analysis

E. H. KITTNER, P.E.
Engineering and Maintenance Superintendent, Georgia-Pacific Corporation

INTRODUCTION

Many managers of plant engineering functions become so specialized that they often suffer from tunnel vision in viewing their maintenance costs. Such managers think that low maintenance costs are highly to be sought after and that high maintenance costs are similar to the black plague—something to be avoided in all situations. They treat the variations in costs from a fixed budget as a problem rather than a diagnostic tool. Budgetary variations should always be viewed as the effect of a problem—not a cause of that problem—if the proper approach to maintenance cost analysis is to be maintained. There is an optimum level of maintenance costs for any given plant, and exceeding this cost will only result in a wasteful expenditure of company profits. On the other side of the coin, an underexpenditure of maintenance funds can appear when some maintenance projects are deferred until a later date, eventually resulting in an excessive overall total expenditure of funds. Many a plant engineer has allowed the maintenance budget to be reduced in order that it might look good to management, only to find that a crisis situation develops when the deferred maintenance jobs accumulate into a dangerous backlog.

To effectively use your maintenance costs as a diagnostic tool, you must be concerned with variations from a realistic budgetary standard. When you analyze the variations from this standard, you will possess an early warning system for many maintenance problems.

SOME MAINTENANCE PROBLEMS

Maintenance costs need to be objectively analyzed to uncover either of the following possible maintenance problems: *Undermaintenance,* which can cause excessive production downtime, and overmaintenance, which can also reduce labor efficiency due to a restriction of output. This may be practiced by employees when the work demand is low.

Undermaintenance of production departments may result from long travel distances, a supervisor who does not complain, a personality clash between a production supervisor and maintenance supervisor, underestimation of the needs of a production department, a department with excessive employee damage, and other management defects.

In addition, individual production departments can be overmaintained because of friendship between maintenance and production supervisors, a production supervisor who complains continually to the plant engineer's superior, continuing a given level of maintenance after a reduction of machinery in a particular department, short travel distances, and many other maintenance management oversights.

Without an objective analysis of maintenance costs, a plant engineer can overlook maintenance department imbalances in crafts, such as too many or too few electricians, machinists, pipefitters, and other categories.

Many impending maintenance problems can be found with an objective analysis of maintenance costs. For example, in one Georgia-Pacific Corp. operation, it was observed that there was a large increase in the purchase of antifriction bearings over a 2-year period. A systematic analysis of the overexpenditure in ball bearings uncovered a failure in the lubrication department. The plant oiler was neglecting the difficult-to-reach bearings and overoiling those which were easy to reach. This problem was corrected before a crisis situation developed.

Your costs are analyzed along with other factors by your superiors to evaluate your performance. Therefore it would appear advisable for you to do the same in greater detail.

THREE PHASES OF MAINTENANCE COST ANALYSIS

The initial phase of an objective maintenance cost analysis is to establish a properly subdivided standard budget. The number of subdivisions in this budget can be enlarged or decreased, depending upon the size of the plant using this technique. The initial subdivision of the total maintenance funds is based on past history of the department. The subdivisions are then adjusted to their proper levels to avoid the previously mentioned maintenance problems. The items which are used to make the proper adjustment will be elaborated upon in detail later in this chapter. Once this adjusted standard budget is established, then any marked deviation will serve as an early-warning indicator.

The intermediate or weekly maintenance cost analysis is accomplished by an indirect method. Several parameters are chosen which are directly proportional to the total maintenance cost for the period. This method of weekly cost analysis was chosen in order that the detail clerical work required would be minimized. The primary item watched during this phase of cost analysis is the maintenance labor hours. Again, as previously mentioned, this phase of maintenance cost analysis is easily adaptable for any size plant by either increasing or decreasing the number of subdivisions.

The third and final phase of maintenance cost analysis takes place on a monthly basis. The actual maintenance costs are compiled and the variation from the budget standard is reported. When this deviates from the budget figure either plus or minus a predetermined percentage, then this deviation is analyzed in detail. A preset deviation is allowed to prevent overwork in analyzing short-term anomalies. This analysis of a variation becomes a valuable early-warning diagnostic tool for the plant engineer.

The following is a detailed description of each of the three phases of maintenance cost analysis. It should be reiterated that this is merely a systematic method of cost analysis that can be adjusted by increasing or decreasing the subdivisions within the system to meet any plant's requirements. The size of the plant, the available clerical help, and the accuracy desired are items which will determine the complexity of this system of cost analysis.

INITIAL PHASE OF MAINTENANCE COST ANALYSIS

Upper corporate management determines the level of expenditure at which a maintenance department is required to operate. This level is either arbitrarily set by upper management or is arrived at by modifying a budget that the plant engineer has submitted to management. The level of expenditures for a maintenance department depends upon upper corporate maintenance philosophy. Some managements prefer to replace machinery more frequently and thus keep maintenance costs at a minimum, while other managements expend more on maintenance and retain their machinery longer. *The choice of maintenance philosophy is upper management's, but it is imperative that the plant engineer recognize this choice so that management's desires can be translated into reality.* Once the total maintenance budget is obtained, most upper managements rely

Example of Basic Funds Distribution—Wallboard Manufacturing Department

Column 1 Year	Column 2 Actual wallboard maintenance labor costs	Column 3 Total plant maintenance labor costs	Column 4 Department percentage (column 2 ÷ column 3)
1974	$ 92,700	$272,100	
1975	97,200	291,000	
1976	81,000	372,000	
Totals	$270,900	$935,100	29.0%

1977 RAW WALLBOARD MANUFACTURING DEPARTMENT—
MAINTENANCE LABOR BUDGET

1977 allotted budget total plant maintenance cost X
percent department cost (column 4) = raw maintenance
labor distribution

Column 3 (proposed) X column 4 (percent) = column 2 (proposed)
$453,000   X   0.29   = $131,370

Fig. 1   Basic funds distribution example.

on the expertise of the plant engineer to subdivide this budget among the various departments within the plant. It is the objective distribution of the total funds available that is the key to good maintenance cost analysis. When the proper distribution of maintenance funds is made to the various manufacturing departments, then any wide variation from these standard budget figures becomes an early-warning indicator.

It is relatively simple to adapt this method of maintenance cost analysis to a small or large plant by varying the number of subdivisions. For example, a small plant might subdivide each department into maintenance labor, maintenance materials, and maintenance overtime. A large plant might subdivide its operation into 21 departments, and in each department maintenance functional subdivisions would be made, such as electrical labor, electrical overtime, electrical materials, mechanical labor, mechanical overtime, mechanical materials, etc. One note of caution: A sufficient number of breakdowns should be made so that the technique is usable, but there should not be so many subdivisions that the system is a clerical nightmare. This is a trial-and-error procedure to achieve the optimum number of subdivisions for each maintenance unit.

The unadjusted distribution of maintenance funds is first made on a historical basis, using either a two- or three-year experience to reduce the effect of any unusual one-time maintenance experiences. Then this raw distribution of funds is adjusted to eliminate any past bad practices that may have been inadvertently built into the maintenance department. This procedure is illustrated in Figure 1.

$131,370 becomes the raw maintenance labor distribution for the wallboard manufacturing department in 1977. The above procedure is repeated for each department and each subdivision within that department, with some adjustments being made where obvious maintenance emergencies have caused a drastic deviation from expected results. The above analysis need not be repeated every year where sufficient clerical help is not available. The adjusted column 4 percentages can be used for 2 or 3 years if judicious care is applied in eliminating past maintenance defects.

Some of these maintenance defects which one must be alert to detect are as follows:

Excessive maintenance efforts may be used in an individual manufacturing department because that department's supervision has failed. Some of the examples of supervision failure where the maintenance department has been asked to step in to maintain production are excessive absenteeism resulting in the maintenance department being asked to fill in on production functions; excessive equipment abuse by the production personnel; failure of operators to do the equipment servicing as assigned (check oil, water, etc., in mobile equipment); and poor housekeeping in a production department, which can cause the maintenance department to spend excessive time on repairs and also reduce the machinery life.

Excessive maintenance efforts have been given the production departments because of personality situations. For example, close friendships between maintenance and production department supervision has resulted in the production department getting preferential treatment. This is a serious problem in small plants because of the short lines of communication. There are also supervisors who get excessive maintenance because they are always complaining to their superiors. The old saying "the squeaky wheel gets the grease" applies in this instance. There is also the situation where a department gets excessive maintenance due to the intervention of a superior who favors this department for personal reasons.

Excessive maintenance efforts can be given to a department for other reasons. Short travel distances from central shops to a production department can sometimes result in excessive maintenance due to their proximity. In some instances a department will continue to be given excessive maintenance long after it had suffered a crisis situation which required additional maintenance time over a prolonged period. Production departments have received extra maintenance during modifications to the production system, above the additional effort actually needed, because they were in the center of upper management's eye. At times a manufacturing department may have the number of its machines reduced, yet out of habit the level of maintenance will not be lowered correspondingly. The other reasons for overmaintenance are too numerous to mention.

Insufficient maintenance efforts can also be a problem due to personality situations. For example, a personality conflict between maintenance and production department supervisors may result in a shortage of maintenance hours in the production department. Also, there is the opposite of the "squeaky wheel" problem, where the production department head does not request maintenance when it is needed. In some instances a department may suffer from a lack of maintenance effort because upper management has diverted the maintenance efforts to other departments.

Insufficient maintenance efforts can result from problems due to facilities. For example, insufficient and improper storage of spare parts can cause excessive delays. Departments which have had machinery added without the level of maintenance being increased can suffer a shortage of maintenance funds. Whenever higher levels of production are not accompanied by an increase in maintenance funds, an undermaintenance situation can develop. Undermaintenance is a major problem when an increased business level forces the maintenance department into overtime maintenance or a breakdown maintenance situation.

Insufficient maintenance efforts can result from many other problems such as an overall decrease in maintenance funds due to a business slump, when machinery is run after the end of its economic life is reached and is not given the maintenance it requires, or a failure in the maintenance management may result in inefficient application of maintenance funds.

Figure 2 shows a maintenance budget analysis form. Columns A,B,C,D, and E represent comparison items to establish an objective distribution of funds. These items can be varied in number and type depending upon the particular industry involved. The following five items have been found to give a good view of one industry's proper distribution: column A is the percent of breakdown maintenance; column B, future plans for equipment replacement; column C, ratio or past maintenance costs to the value of equipment in the department; column D, a use factor ratio that would show the capacity level versus maintenance costs; and column E, the percentage of connected or metered horsepower in each department.

Maintenance labor						date		

Code	Department	3-year distribution percentage	Adjustment indexes					Adjusted percentage
			A	B	C	D	E	

Fig. 2 Sample maintenance budget analysis form. The heading "Maintenance labor" would be changed for a large or small plant. For a large plant the heading would be changed to a department, for instance, "Press room department." Then the column for departments would be changed to "Crafts." The small plant analysis sheet would remain as shown except that additional sheets would be used for Maintenance materials and Maintenance overtime.

MAINTENANCE BUDGET ANALYSIS FORM DESCRIPTION

The following breakdown is a description of each column:

Column A: Breakdown of emergency maintenance This can be the ratio of emergency jobs to total maintenance jobs which have been completed in that department, or this column can be the percentage of the emergency jobs which were completed in a department versus the total number of emergency jobs at the plant. For a small plant with a 24-hour production operation but an 8-hour maintenance operation, "call-backs" can also serve as an excellent indicator of breakdown maintenance. A call-back or call-out is a situation where a maintenance man returns to the plant to fix a production machine in order that the operation can continue. These call-outs are directly proportional to the overall breakdown maintenance for a plant. In some operations, downtime percentages could be substituted for emergency maintenance. Keeping track of breakdown maintenance and/or downtime hours is one of the best ways that a maintenance department has for getting feedback to check its effectiveness. Any of the above items or a composite can be used in column A.

Column B: Future plans for equipment addition or replacement When you expect to replace some machinery in the near future or machinery has recently been replaced, the level of maintenance should be reduced for these units. When equipment is to be removed from a department and will not be replaced, the maintenance budget should also be adjusted downward.

Column C: Ratio of maintenance cost to total equipment value The normal expectation is that the higher the total equipment value in a department, the greater the amount of maintenance dollars that will be required by this department. This ratio is an excellent method of uncovering past imbalances in maintenance expenditures.

Column D: Ratio of maintenance dollars to a use factor A use factor is any item which is directly proportional to the amount of use of the machinery within the department. The greater the number of hours the machinery is used, the more maintenance is normally required. Some use factors are direct production man-hours, sales dollars of product produced, kWh of electricity used if each department if metered, total machine hours for each department if similar machinery is used throughout the plant, and any other item that is proportional to the productive capacity used.

Column E: Percentage of connected horsepower in each department This is usually a good indicator of the percentage of funds that a department should require. This comparison is valid only if there is a similarity between all machinery in a plant. The comparison is not valid if the plant has one department, such as a quarry, which is composed of radically different machinery. There is some interrelationship between column C and column E, with this difference: column C is the actual performance and column E is the theoretical distribution.

When the maintenance analysis form is completely filled in except for the adjusted percentages column, you are then ready for the final distribution of maintenance funds. To arrive at the adjusted percentages, one must compare the past three years' figures with the distribution as shown in columns A through E and judiciously adjust the budget to correct past mistakes. The primary purpose of all the preceding analyses is to arrive at an objective budgetary target so that variations from this target will serve as an early-warning indicator.

At this point we are ready for an intermediate phase of maintenance cost analysis which consists of weekly feedback of maintenance indicators. Since in most manufacturing plants final costing is done on a monthly basis, there is a need for intermediate indicators to serve as a guide during the interim.

INTERMEDIATE-PHASE MAINTENANCE COST ANALYSIS

As the value of objective cost analysis is realized, there will be a desire to maintain a feedback of information during the interim periods when costing figures are not available. Figure 3 shows a weekly maintenance work sheet, the medium through which continuity of maintenance analysis can be maintained. This analysis is valuable, as most companies do their costing on a montly basis, making it advisable to maintain continuity in the interim. This form is divided into three sections, the maintenance labor section, the emergency breakdown section, and the ratio section. Man-hours figures are used for this form as they are readily available and are historically comparable, and there is no delay while waiting for invoices or billings. When man-hour figures are used, the influence of wage rates changes, etc., does not affect the comparison with past results. To utilize this form for a small company, one sheet is used for the entire plant and the department column is added in front of the reasons column in the emergency breakdown section. If the plant which is using this form is a larger one, then an individual sheet is filled out for each department and the department column previously mentioned is omitted.

MAINTENANCE WEEKLY WORK SHEET
Georgia-Pacific, Blue Rapids

Date month	Plant man-hours (A)	Maintenance man-hours (M)	Construction man-hours (C)	Emergency man-hours (E)	Overtime man-hours (O)
Mon					
Tues					
Wed					
Thurs					
Fri					
Sat					
Sun					
Total					

EMERGENCY BREAKDOWN INFORMATION

Skill	Date	Hours	Dept.	Reason

Man-hour ratios

Maintenance man-hours vs. plant man-hours $\frac{M}{A}$ = _____ %

Construction man-hours vs. maintenance man-hours $\frac{C}{M}$ = _____ %

Emergency man-hours vs. maintenance man-hours $\frac{E}{M}$ = _____ %

Overtime man-hours vs. maintenance man-hours $\frac{O}{M}$ = _____ %

Fig. 3 Sample maintenance weekly work sheet.

MAINTENANCE WEEKLY WORK SHEET

The following is a detailed description of the maintenance weekly work sheet. Column A is the total direct production man-hours of the plant or an individual production department. The figures in this column will be directly proportional to the use of the production machinery. Indirect man-hours such as supervision, office functions, and quality control hours are omitted since they would be a constant factor which would dampen percentage variations.

Column B, the next column, is the total maintenance man-hours expended less the

---

LARGE PLANT MAINTENANCE COST STATEMENT

Department _____ Date _____

Subdivision	Actual cost	Budgeted cost	Variation + or −	Yearly Variation + or −
Electrical labor				
Electrical material				
Electrical overtime				
Total				
Mechanical labor				
Mechanical materials				
Mechanical overtime				
Total				
Pipe fitters labor				
Pipe fitters materials				
Pipe fitters overtime				
Total				

Fig. 4 Sample large plant maintenance cost statement.

construction man-hours.   Preventive, corrective, and productive man-hours are all included in this column.

The third column, C, contains the man-hours which the maintenance department utilizes on new construction.   The distribution of available maintenance department labor between maintenance and construction jobs is a very important area to watch. In particular, when a maintenance department has a large backlog of new equipment installation and total departmental personnel has not been increased, then either maintenance is neglected or construction is delayed.   The opposite situation can occur with a low construction backlog and no overall reduction of personnel in the department.   You will suffer with high maintenance costs and a low labor efficiency.

The fourth column is the total man-hours that are utilized in breakdown or emergency maintenance.   A note should be made that this column is the total hours of emergencies whereas the second section, emergency breakdown information, is only those emergencies that meet certain criteria.   This column is an accelerated feedback on the effectiveness of maintenance planning and scheduling.   In addition, when one compares this column with the overtime column, an excellent indicator is available to determine if the maintenance department has the proper number of personnel.   In some plants or industries, machinery downtime can be substituted for emergency man-hours to obtain the same results.

The fifth column is the overtime maintenance column.   Some engineers have the false notion that overtime in the maintenance department should be avoided at all costs. Many times it is far less costly to work the maintenance department on overtime than to operate a production department on overtime.   The overtime maintenance column will vary with both the business level and the number of personnel in the maintenance department.   This overtime column can be reduced to a minimum by overstaffing the maintenance department, which will also result in a decreased labor efficiency and excessive maintenance department costs.   There is an optimum level for overtime for every situation which can be found by the trial-and-error method.

The middle section of the maintenance weekly work sheet is the emergency breakdown information.   Items recorded in this section should be emergency or breakdown in nature and should meet certain criteria.   Some of the criteria that may be used are breakdowns that require three hours of maintenance time, breakdowns that result in one hour of downtime, or breakdowns that cost $100 in maintenance materials.   Guidelines for the items to be recorded in this section should be established to give sufficient entries to be useful, yet they should be limiting enough to prevent excessive time-consuming detail.   The skills entry in this section merely designates the craft used to repair the breakdown.   Initials such as "E" for electrician, etc., can be used.   The department column is only used for small plants (see Fig. 5) because the entire form will represent one department when the form is used in a large plant.   When the plant engineer considers the information in this section as the effect of a problem, he will have an excellent diagnostic tool; however, many maintenance people wrongly consider breakdowns as problems in themselves, and the maintenance management will jump from one breakdown to another without ever finding the basic cause.

The final section of the weekly maintenance worksheet is the ratio section.   After some historical data has been established and the acceptable ratios set up, the plant engineer can use this section to get a quick picture of the maintenance department.   An analogy that is applicable is that this section is to the maintenance personnel what the Dow-Jones averages are to the investor.   These ratios can be plotted on semilogrithmic graph paper for a quick visual picture of maintenance activity.

THIRD PHASE OF MAINTENANCE COST ANALYSIS

This phase of cost analysis uses two basic forms: the maintenance unusual material expense form (Fig. 6) and the maintenance department cost statement.   The unusual material expense form will list all the major purchases above a set value.   Again, the value should be set to give usable information but not excessive detail.   The basic idea behind this form is that the major material costs are where the large maintenance jobs are, and these areas should be given extra attention.   This form will give the plant engineer a quick overview of major expenditures, since there is usually a definite ratio between materials and labor in most plants.

The final stage of maintenance cost analysis is the comparison of the actual cost with the budget costs. When the budget costs are set up objectively, they become a target to aim at. Nevertheless, the plant engineer should bear in mind that variations from this

---

SMALL PLANT MAINTENANCE COST STATEMENT

Department _____ Date _____

Subdepartment	Actual cost	Budgeted cost	Monthly variation + or −	Yearly variation + or −
Maintenance labor				
Maintenance materials				
Maintenance overtime				
Total				

Department _____ Date _____

Subdepartment	Actual cost	Budgeted cost	Monthly variation + or −	Yearly variation + or −
Maintenance labor				
Maintenance materials				
Maintenance overtime				
Total				

Department _____ Date _____

Subdepartment	Actual cost	Budgeted cost	Monthly variation + or −	Yearly variation + or −
Maintenance labor				
Maintenance materials				
Maintenance overtime				
Total				

Fig. 5 Sample small plant maintenance cost statement.

target are an indicator, not something to adjust by work manipulation. A predetermined allowance of a plus or minus variation should be made to prevent excessive effort in tracking down temporary situations. When this variation exceeds the predetermined value, then the cause of the variation should be investigated in depth. When the cause of the variation is found, then the problem can be solved.

MAINTENANCE UNUSUAL MATERIAL EXPENSES
Georgia-Pacific, Blue Rapids

*Department_____   Date _____

†Department or subdepartment	Maintenance code	Amount	Explanation

*For a large plant "department" is used here; for a small plant "plant" is used here.

†For a large plant "subdepartment" such as electrical, mechanical, etc., is used in this column; for a small plant "department" is used in this column.

Fig. 6   Sample maintenance unusual material expense form.

CONCLUSION

Objective maintenance cost analysis can be as valuable a tool as a voltmeter, micrometer, transit, or level, depending upon how it is used. Excessive detail in any analysis system will destroy the effectiveness of the system, and insufficient detail will make the system worthless. The plant engineer should also keep in mind that the preceding maintenance analysis system can be enlarged or reduced to fit the size of the plant. If the budgetary variation is used as an indicator of a potential problem, then the plant engineer will be alerted and will eventually find a solution. On the other hand, if the variations are not noted or if the variation is treated as the problem, then the plant engineer can have a problem hanging over his head like the sword of Damocles.

Chapter **5**

Shop Scheduling Procedures

J. P. BEATTY
President, Plant & Maintenance Consultants, Inc.

INTRODUCTION

Maintenance scheduling is, in reality, the major part of maintenance management. Nothing that is a part of maintenance management is omitted from maintenance scheduling, from inception of a maintenance job to its completion. The essential parts of maintenance scheduling are:

1. Communicating need for and nature of the job to be done
2. Approval for the job to be done
3. Planning the job
4. Implementing the job

The only maintenance management facets that are not, truly, a part of "maintenance scheduling," are postjob activities, such as maintenance cost accounting and maintenance cost and performance analysis. But even postjob activities are vitally affected by methods and techniques used in maintenance scheduling.

However, many essential maintenance scheduling components are complete subjects in themselves, i.e., job standards, work estimating, etc. This discussion, therefore, will be concerned with only operational rather than technical aspects—aspects that are concerned with maintenance practices and procedures rather than those concerned with maintenance evaluation.

ELEMENTS OF MAINTENANCE SCHEDULING

The principal elements of operational maintenance scheduling are:
1. A work order procedure
2. A job priority procedure
3. A job planning procedure

WORK ORDERS

A work order procedure is the foundation of any maintenance scheduling program. Without a systematized method for requesting maintenance work and approving job implementation, maintenance activities will become chaotic.

Priority			MAINTENANCE & WORK ORDER			COMPANY
Date requested:	Charge:	Location:	Requested by:	Approved:	Number:	

Work to be done

_____ Date needed _____

Labor									Material		
Name								Quan.	Description		Cost
Date completed		Signed									

Total labor hrs. _____ Rate _____ Total labor cost _____ Total mat. cost _____

Fig. 1 Work order form.

To be most effective, the work order should be designed to accomplish eight purposes:
1. Describe the requested work
2. Show job location
3. Identify job requestor
4. Provide for approval action
5. Show job completion
6. Provide job identification (numbering)
7. Provide job priority assignment
8. Provide cost accounting for labor and material

Figure 1 illustrates a work order form that fulfills all the above requirements. Many variations are possible, depending on the nature and complexity of the maintenance operation and of the various other maintenance management and control procedures.

A most important facet of maintenance management is assurance that all expended labor is covered by a work order. When work is performed without a work order, control of maintenance activity becomes difficult, at best; and realistic maintenance cost accounting and evaluation is impossible.

Assuring that the person requesting a maintenance job signs the work order frequently eliminates unnecessary or frivolous work requests. When the work request originator becomes identified with that request by affixing his or her signature, it tends to cause more careful consideration to job consequences than is the case when the request can be made orally.

Requiring work order approval by the manager with fiscal responsibility is also necessary. Not only does this action assure that the manager paying for the work agrees with the work being requested, but it frequently eliminates conflicting or offsetting work requests.

The work description, job location, and requested completion date portions of the work order form provide the maintenance manager with sufficient information to plan and schedule work, at least on routine jobs, and to avoid spending job investigation time for each work request. Of course, if the originator merely states, "Case sealer doesn't work," without saying which case sealer and explaining how the machine does not work, then these descriptions are useless. Maintenance managers should refuse work orders that are less than completely executed—at least to the limit of the originator's knowledge. Work order identification is essential to preventing a job from being "lost in the system." Particularly in larger maintenance organizations, it is not at all unusual to find work requests that are months old and still not completed. When work orders can be easily identified they can be constantly accounted for.

Work order identification is accomplished by using a work order number and a work order log. Work orders may be prenumbered. Thus, the originator knows the number and is able to refer to it when discussing the work order with maintenance personnel.

The work order may also be numbered at the time of logging in. The advantage of this approach is that the number reflects the age of the order. Work orders of the same priority may be scheduled by number, completing the older, smaller-numbered orders first. In addition work orders logged in numerical order make it easier to locate an individual work order on the log. Job priorities assignments are vital to the effective flow of maintenance work. Whether the system is formal or informal, all maintenance departments use a priority system. However, if the system is informal, the priority assignment may be made by someone unqualified to make a proper judgment—a maintenance foreman, or even a maintenance craftsman. Through a formal priority assignment procedure, the person best qualified, the maintenance manager or his delegate, makes the priority judgment that is in the best interest of the total operation.

Finally, maintenance cost accounting by job is essential to proper maintenance control. Without knowledge of maintenance labor and material costs effective control is impossible.

JOB PRIORITIES

As previously stated, all maintenance work is subject to priority assignment. Although this assignment may be as uncomplicated as the foreman telling the maintenance craftsman "Get this job first," a judgment is being made. However, when the judgment is based on someone's personal preference, on "the squeaking wheel principle," or on some other such factor, results can be disastrous. For effective maintenance operation, priorities must be based solely on the impact of the work on the overall plant operation. It is a good idea to encourage the work order originator to include a suggested priority assignment when submitting the work order. However, as all jobs must be evaluated in terms of the overall operation, these suggested priorities must frequently be changed.

WORK ORDER CONTROL

When a work request is received by the maintenance department, assuming that it is not an emergency job, it is recorded on the work order log. Figures 2, 3, and 4 show log sheet formats which may be used. The number of work orders processed and the amount of control to be exercised over the system determine whether a very simple log (Fig. 2) should be used or whether a comprehensive log (Fig. 4) would be better.

When a priority is assigned to the work order, it should be indicated on the log sheet following the work order number. Thus a critical job on work order number 12345 would be entered on the work order log as number 12345C.

Emergency jobs that must be worked on immediately, prior to writing a work order, need not be entered on the log. However, many maintenance managers include emergency orders in the log to account for total departmental workload.

Foreman's W/O Scheduling
WORK SHEET

W/O number	Date received	Date assigned	Assigned to	Date completed	W/O number	Date received	Date assigned	Assigned to	Date completed

Fig. 2   Simplest work order log.

MAINTENANCE WORK ORDER LOG

Sheet No._____

Date entered	W/O No.	Work description	Date completed

Fig. 3   Median work order log.

A.B.C. COMPANY

WEEKLY MAINTENANCE WORK ORDER LOG
Week ending_____
Sheet No. _____

W/O No. & priority	Date received	Date written	Initiated by	Work description	Date released	Resp. supervisor	Date completed

Fig. 4   Comprehensive work order log.

JOB PLANNING

After a work order has been logged and a priority assigned, the order is reviewed to determine if the ordered work may be scheduled for completion without preplanning or if it is so complex that is must be planned.

Figure 5 shows a job planning sheet that provides an effective maintenance job layout.

MAINTENANCE DEPARTMENT

PLANNING AND SCHEDULING SHEET

W/O No.	Dept.	Bldg.	Floor	Date prepared

Manpower needed				Work description
Craft	No.	Craft	No.	

Manpower schedule				No. / hrs.	Materials − Tools	
Date	Craft	1st	2nd	3rd	Quantity	Description

Date scheduled _____ Date completed _____ Signed _____

Fig. 5 Job planning sheet.

Using this planning sheet assures that the work will be done at the scheduled time (with no interference from production operations), that sufficient craft skills manpower is available, and that the required tools and materials are on hand. It also allows for assembly of necessary tools and materials before the job is started. This preassembly of tools and materials aids in reducing job costs, as these tasks can be accomplished by personnel with

MAINTENANCE DEPARTMENT

Daily Work Schedule

Foreman _____   Date _____   Shift _____

All work orders on this schedule shall be assigned in the order in which they are listed on this schedule for each craft classification.

W/O No.	Craftsman assigned	Status at end of shift	Remarks

Signature _____

Fig. 6 Daily work schedule.

hourly rates lower than those of the craftsmen (such as apprentices, helpers, or stockmen). Also, if the work is scheduled for overtime, tool and material assembly may be accomplished during straight-time hours.

When work is scheduled for overtime, an additional advantage is gained from using the planning sheet. The maintenance manager or the maintenance planner can determine the total number of working hours scheduled for each craftsman required for overtime. If the total working hours do not equal a full shift for any craftsman, that craftsman can be released from work at the completion of the assignment. If work rules require that the worker be paid for a full shift, then additional work can be scheduled to fill the remaining hours.

Criteria for planning a maintenance job will depend on the maintenance department's method of operation. Some maintenance managers establish arbitrary guidelines, such as requiring that all work, costing more than $200 be planned. Others stipulate that all jobs requiring more than 8 man-hours be planned. An essential guideline is to plan and schedule all overtime work.

DAILY WORK SCHEDULES

Formality in daily work scheduling is dictated by local departmental environment. Scheduling may be as informal as issuing a pack of work orders to each maintenance foreman at the beginning of each shift. Or it may be as formal as issuing a preprinted form listing all work orders, the order in which they should be worked, and providing space for the foreman to report the status of each job at the end of the shift. Figure 6 illustrates such a formal work-scheduling form.

In preparing this schedule, the maintenance manager or the manager's delegate shall assure that there is at least a full shift of work for each craftsman assigned to the shift. It is frequently a wise practice to include more than a full shift of work for each craftsman. This provides a full crew schedule, even if conditions occur which prevent some of the scheduled jobs from being worked.

Selection of jobs for inclusion on the daily work schedule is not a simple matter of listing all the in-process jobs, all the critical jobs, and all the routine jobs and then filling the schedule with backlog jobs. Obviously, if this practice were followed, most backlog jobs would never appear on the schedule until they were upgraded to the routine category. Further, as backlog jobs are upgraded to routine category, some routine jobs would not be placed on the schedule and would have to be upgraded to critical. In time, the ultimate effect of this type of scheduling would be a negation of the entire priority system. To effectively assure that all work orders will eventually be placed on the schedule without the constant necessity for upgrading of priorities, some other means of selecting work orders for scheduling must be used.

One effective means for accomplishing this objective is to schedule all in-process jobs and all critical jobs ready for scheduling. Some critical jobs may be held over for several days. Next, include sufficient backlog jobs to assure craftsmen work days are completely scheduled with addition of routine work orders.

Enforced scheduling of backlog jobs assures that backlog jobs are scheduled and a pool is created from which manpower can be drawn to cover emergency jobs that arise during the shift. Thus, when an emergency job has to be worked, essential jobs of critical or routine priority do not have to be interrupted.

SCHEDULING REPETITIVE JOBS

In all maintenance operations, there are a number of jobs that recur at regular intervals. Examples of these repetitive jobs are preventive maintenance inspections and/or overhauls, lubrication, and the checks and inspections required (or suggested) by the standards established under the Occupational Safety and Health Act of 1970. Not only must these jobs be integrated into the daily work schedule but a procedure must be implemented to assure that all jobs are scheduled at the proper time.

Traditional methods of scheduling repetitive jobs—such as the use of a calendar pad, notebook, or someone's memory—are not adequate. Too frequently, a page is not turned or a job is forgotten. The same is true of card systems that require frequent card file scanning.

The system that meets basic requirements is one that requires little attention on a regular basis but one that schedules jobs at proper intervals "automatically."

There are a number of systems that meet these requirements. They range from manually programmed selections, to mechanically programmed selections, to electronically programmed selections. The common factor in all these systems is that each time a job selection is made, all jobs to be scheduled during the period will be scheduled. The prime differences lie in the time required to schedule, the form in which job information is furnished, and system implementation cost.

Manually programmed systems have low initial cost, but they require more time to retrieve jobs from data storage. Jobs are furnished in a form that either requires additional processing to prepare work orders or to replace job data in storage.

Required job data can be retrieved with electronically programmed systems in short time periods directly on work order forms without removing data from storage banks. However, these systems are costly and, in general, are usually justified by time sharing automatic data processing support with other plant functions.

Mechanically programmed systems provide all the advantages of the other systems without any of the disadvantages. While data retrieval times are not as short as is the case with electronic systems, they are far shorter than for manual systems. By comparison, if a manually programmed system requires a full-time clerk, the mechanical system will require only a few clerical hours each week. Electronic programming further reduces the required retrieval time, but not sufficient to justify the higher cost of system implementation except at large plants.

Manually programmed systems furnish work instruction data on cards with no machine assistance in retrieval (card sorting) of the stored data. Retrieving (sorting) data include edge coding and spot coding for visual scanning and key sorting. Work instruction data must be manually transferred to a work order.

Mechanically programmed systems furnish work instruction data on a reprintable medium, such as metal or plastic plates, with machine retrieving the stored data. The reprintable medium is coded by means of edge tabs, notches, or bar codes. When the machine is programmed, it senses the coding and selects required jobs. Further, when the machine selects stored data for retrieval, it also prints those data out on any appropriate form, such as a work order, eliminating the need for manual transfer.

Electronically programmed systems are systems using electronic data processing (EDP) or automatic data processing systems (ADP).

Repetitive Job Administration

The key to successful repetitive job scheduling is regularity. Once all the technical details have been completed—such as deciding jobs to be included (data input) and scheduling frequencies—time should be set aside on a regular basis, usually weekly, to review all jobs. Those jobs to be scheduled are retrieved and placed on work orders. When regularity is established, then all necessary repetitive jobs will be scheduled at the proper time. The need for regularity points to one shortcoming of electronically programmed systems. When EDP is used and shared with other functions, frequently scheduled maintenance times will be preempted by other functions, and the system fails to work properly.

Similar Multiple-Location Jobs

When a number of similar short-time-span jobs are to be scheduled, another technique can be used to improve maintenance efficiency. A general work description can be printed on a single work order, omitting job locations from the order. These locations, along with any special instructions for any specific location, can then be printed on an additional sheet.

Thus, multiple-location jobs are provided with full job instructions without need for multiple work orders. Further, by providing a routing order, a minimum of craftsman travel time will be required between job locations.

Examples of repetitive maintenance work that lends itself to this type of programming are lubrication schedules, fire extinguisher inspections, sprinkler system valve and alarm checks, and emergency lighting unit checks. The two requisites which qualify work for this approach are (1) like jobs in multiple locations and (2) short time requirements for each location.

Priorities for Repetitive Jobs

Priorities must be assigned for repetitive jobs to ensure proper progress through daily maintenance work schedules.

If a job is worthy of being placed on a fixed-frequency repetitive schedule, it is a critical job. This is particularly true of jobs scheduled at weekly through monthly frequencies. Given a less than critical priority these jobs could be ready for the next scheduling period before they are actually completed, thus defeating the purpose of repetitive job scheduling.

However, some maintenance managers deviate from this general rule by assigning routine priority classifications to all repetitive jobs scheduled for frequencies of quarterly or longer. As routine priority jobs are scheduled for completion within 15 working days of scheduling, this priority classification assures that quarterly or less frequent jobs will be completed in sufficient time to prevent abrogation of a repetitive work scheduling system.

By definition, repetitive jobs should never be assigned a backlog priority.

SUMMARY

Each maintenance manager should implement a scheduling system for all maintenance work. Effective scheduling is vital to the attainment of efficient and economic operation of any maintenance function.

Chapter 6

Management Reports

DON L. STIEGHAN
Harvey Technical Center, Atlantic Richfield Company

WHY MANAGEMENT REPORTING IS IMPORTANT

For many years maintenance was considered a necessary evil. The enterprise made money only when production facilities were operating, but the facilities were usually out of service when maintenance work was being done. In fact, hardly any maintenance was done until *after* a breakdown of the equipment had occurred. In most instances, the same person who operated the equipment while it was producing also performed all the maintenance tasks.

The managements of most companies have now recognized the significance of their maintenance operations. The cost of maintenance can distinctly affect the profits generated by an enterprise; therefore, the effect of maintenance costs on profits has been getting more and more attention by upper management. The effect is twofold. First, the costs of performing maintenance have been rising rapidly. Production equipment has become more complicated and, in many instances, much larger. The technology and methods that must be applied to repair and otherwise provide for the upkeep of this equipment have also increased in complexity. The personnel skills required are expensive. Increased wage rates and materials costs have certainly added to the direct cost of maintenance. Second, it has been recognized that maintenance can have a very significant effect upon the availability of the equipment and facility for productive uses. Upper management has begun to realize that maintenance operations are more than a fix-it activity but also can provide services that can substantially increase the on-stream time of the production equipment.

Management interest in maintenance operations has caused an emphasis on reports. In order to exercise the functions of management (planning, organizing, leading, and controlling), upper management needs information about the maintenance operations. For that matter, the managers of maintenance operations need that information also. It is important to realize that all levels of management produce reports, and the plant engineer is no exception. Even the president and chairman of the board report to the board of directors, stockholders, the general public, and their employees.

Reports can, of course, serve many purposes. Good reports to management generally include the characteristics listed below:

Operations history record Reporting provides historical records for the recall of past performance. In most instances, the continuation from the past to the present provides a trend that is helpful. The reporter should be careful not to overdo this aspect, however. Insignificant detail can be boring, and it can also obscure significant components of the report. Detailed equipment history may be very important for the effective control of maintenance costs, but it should not be included in the reports to upper management. Perhaps the very significant items would be included in the report, but too much detail certainly gets in the way of effective communication.

Performance measures Simple performance measures for maintenance are difficult to devise because maintenance itself is not a simple activity. Successful accomplishment of maintenance work requires effective application of special techniques within an environment of complicated relationships and pressures. It is even difficult to separate the performance of maintenance from the performance of other functions, such as production; and unfortunately, there is no single performance measure for maintenance that has achieved anything near universal acceptance. Even though this is true, it is still necessary to try to devise some measures that are indicative of the performance being achieved.

These are important statements about performance measures:

Performance measures are indicators that managers use to determine progress toward objectives and to influence decisions about future strategies and programs to achieve those objectives. The surveillance of progress and the corrective actions generated are part of the control function of management.

An organization with an objective to reach cannot simply rely on a series of random events to occur at the right time and in the proper sequence to attain the goal desired. Instead, the managers of the organization seek measures that indicate progress toward accomplishment of the objective. If signs of deviations appear, the managers will try to find ways to influence future events to return to the planned path.

Comparison to a feedback control loop is helpful. Some form of the system output is measured. This measurement is compared to the desired value. If the output does not agree with our expectation, we try to change the input to the system in a way that will adjust the output toward our expectation.

Later in this chapter, examples of performance measures are provided; but it should be recognized that each application may require some modification of the performance measures to be strictly applicable. In addition, since no single measure has been universally accepted, it probably will be necessary to report several measures.

Status of programs Programs are established to reach objectives. It is important to consider the status of the programs regularly. The persons in charge of the programs will want to know the results of their own actions and decisions. Also, upper management will want to be able to determine effects on overall objectives. Without some form of status reporting, it is impossible to know if past decisions and actions have led to the desired results. Checkpoints provide the opportunity for corrective action to be taken.

Projections Reports to management should include projections of future operations based on the information being reported. The regular report to management provides a good opportunity to express expectations about future operations. It is always wise to avoid surprising the boss. The regular reports can be a part of a good early-warning system.

FACTORS AFFECTING REPORTING

Different report formats and techniques are required for different kinds of maintenance operations. A standard report format or set of components for all maintenance operations is undesirable, because there are substantial variations among the operations that require different kinds of reports. The major factors that cause differences are size of operations, type of operation, management wishes, responsibilities of maintenance, and the data sources.

Size of operation   A small operation is quite different from a large one, and multiple locations increase the variation. Larger operations generally require more reporting; however, summaries and exception reporting should be employed to avoid an overlong report. Combined reports for multiple locations may include comparisons of the various operations, and this can be a cause of inaccuracies. To achieve consistency in such reports, it will be necessary to monitor the data collected from multiple sources.

Type of operation   The kind of information reported will certainly be affected by the types of operations involved. A job shop is different from a continuous processing plant, and these two are both different from a manufacturing operation. In general, reporting for all the different types of operations have similarities, but emphasis and other characteristics are different. For instance, availability of the production equipment will be important in the reports for all kinds of maintenance operations, but the on-stream time for the machine tools of a manufacturing plant may be extremely important. Because of this importance, this characteristic would be strongly emphasized in the management report.

Management wishes   Upper management sometimes provides a format for reporting by subordinate functions. If this is so, maintenance management still has the responsibility to be sure that the report is as effective as possible. In some instances, this will even include proposals for changing the report to provide a better picture of maintenance operations performance.

Also, upper management quite frequently would like to have a single measure of performance. As stated earlier, no single performance measure for maintenance has been universally accepted. Most frequently, several performance measures are necessary to describe more completely the many facets of maintenance operations. Although it is probably not desirable to report only a single performance measure, the temptation to include more than a few should be resisted. If you can find a single one that adequately depicts your performance, consider yourself lucky.

Responsibilities of maintenance   Reports are different for maintenance organizations whose responsibilities are not the same. For instance, a maintenance operation that is responsible only for fixing breakdowns certainly is different from one whose responsibility includes the reduction of equipment downtime. Unless responsibilities have been established and understood (by superiors, peers, and subordinates), it will be difficult to devise a report that will satisfy management. Reports should be related to the status of programs, the accomplishment of objectives, and the fulfillment of responsibilities. This cannot be satisfactorily accomplished unless there is a good understanding among the parties involved.

Data sources   After the content of future reports is decided, it is necessary to establish procedures and techniques for the accumulation of the necessary information. Especially if data are collected from several sources, clear definitions and rules are necessary, and usually the person responsible for compiling the combined report will have to monitor the input to be sure that the guidelines continue to be used. Data should be accurate enough, and consistent, to avoid distortion of the report.

Timeliness is an important factor. Reports that are produced after a considerable time period has passed are of little interest except as historical documents. In particular, ongoing programs need regular, timely reporting to achieve effective control.

TYPES OF REPORT FORMATS

The subject matter is of primary importance; but grammar, neatness, and arrangement of the report affect its ability to communicate. Also, these characteristics tell something about the reporter. The time spent preparing and editing the report will pay dividends. This is especially true if it is directed to upper management.

The reporter should also consider the needs of the readers. The report should be concise and easy to read. Charts and tables should not be too complicated. The writer should remember that the reader is probably not as intimately knowledgeable about the data as the writer. There is a tendency for reports by engineers to be too detailed and complicated. It is probably better to separate information intended for historical recordkeeping from the reports sent to managers. Generally, reports to managers should emphasize exceptions from plans—both good and bad—and activities that have substantial effects on present and future operations. Report formats most generally will include tables, graphs, bar charts, and narrative.

Tables Tables are generally used to report information that either needs to be shown very accurately or provides a comparison of data points. For example, Fig. 1 is a table of personnel head counts, and Fig. 2 is a comparison of maintenance cost figures for different companies. The reporter should be careful to avoid trying to display too much in one table.

WORKER/SUPERVISOR RATIOS

Locations	Number of workers	Number of supervisors	Average number of workers per supervisor
Location A	340	44	7.7
Location B	332	30	11.1
Location C	233	14	16.6
Location D	133	10	13.3
Location E	131	8	16.4

Fig. 1 Example of a table of head counts.

MAINTENANCE COSTS FOR SOME CHEMICALS COMPANIES

	Maintenance cost* as millions of dollars	Percent change from '72
duPont	$275.3	9.7
Union Carbide	219.1	7.6
Dow Chemical	167.6	7.4
Monsanto	135.7	6.2

* Maintenance and repairs (S.E.C. definition) charged directly to profit and loss.

Fig. 2 Example of a table for maintenance cost comparison (adapted from *Chemical Week*, July 18, 1973, p. 33).

Graphs Graphs can be very effective for showing trends of the data points. Comparisons to standards such as budgets, control limits, plans, etc., are easy to show on a graph. However, graphs can be made very difficult to read, and even misleading, unless some rules are followed. The usual graph paper that engineers use has too many grid lines for effective presentation of data in a management report. The reader is not going to be extracting a value from the graph for use in a calculation, so the close grid lines are not necessary.

Also, the choice of scales for graphs is important. If the trends of two or more graphs will be compared, then the scales for those graphs should be the same or the trends will be misleading. If the scale does not begin at zero at the graph baseline, the effects of changes in the data can be overemphasized and the values of the data points misunderstood. Titles on the graphs should be complete enough to describe the graph for the reader, and there should be breaks in the grid lines if the title is on the graph itself.

Bar charts Bar charts (sometimes called column charts if the bars are vertical) can be used instead of graphs for discrete data points. For instance, if there is one data point for each week or month, either a bar chart or graph could be used for the display. Sometimes average data for a period are better displayed in a bar chart because then the data are represented as having that value for the entire period (the variation of the line of the graph tends to give the impression of continuous change). Bar charts are usually more difficult to prepare, however.

Bar charts can be very effective to show comparisons. Figure 3 shows a comparison of maintenance cost for three different departments for the months of January, February, and March.

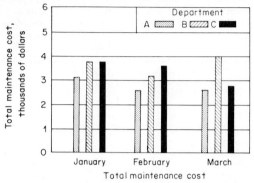

Fig. 3   Example of a cost comparison bar chart.

Narrative   The measures reported in tables, graphs, and bar charts will usually require narrative for explanations. Variations from plans and standards should be explained. The reasons for trends or changes in trends should be provided. Managers want to know not only the status of the operation but also the reasons why.

In addition to the explanations concerning performance measures, there should be some information about the status of programs and objectives. Reports to management are a good means of attaining a common understanding and agreement concerning the use of the resources in the maintenance department. The objectives and programs were probably established in the first place after consultation and agreement with management. Regular reporting confirms that the delegated responsibilities are being handled properly. Also, it helps avoid the surprises that can occur when a systematic approach is not followed.

EXAMPLES OF CHARTS, GRAPHS, AND TABLES

The examples that are included here are only some of the data elements which can be reported. Many others are possible—some of these are quite similar and some could be very different. The examples are intended to help you find the data elements that you would like to report, whether that data element is included in the examples or not. One bit of advice: Do not try to use all the data elements that are shown in this section. Choose one or more of them to present in your report. You should decide which ones are most important for your operation. Different presentation methods are used to display the examples; this is done in order to provide an opportunity for you to see how they might appear.

Consistent data are more difficult to achieve than you might imagine. If trends are to be valid, the data elements being reported must be consistent from time period to time period. If data from one source are to be compared with data from another source, input from the two sources must be consistent. Even the rules that are established for consistency can be interpreted differently. You will need to establish common definitions and monitor the data to be sure that the guidelines are being applied for every data source.

Many data elements that are reported, especially performance measures, are ratios. Ratios can present some vexing problems. You usually want to consider a maintenance data element, such as maintenance costs, compared to some other data element, such as production output. The primary problem is that the other data element may change for reasons unrelated to maintenance performance. Therefore a change in the ratio may be caused by conditions outside the maintenance operations. If only the ratio graph is included in the report, then it will be necessary to explain the causes for changes in the ratio.

Safety statistics   Almost all managements are concerned about safety performance of the operations they are managing. Most management reports will include some kind of safety statistics. There are several well-recognized elements to report: injury frequency rate, severity rate, number of lost-time accidents, number of serious accidents, number of dispensary visits, etc.

Ratio of maintenance cost to production output   This is an important measure, and the use of it is widespread. Usually the trend of the ratio is considered most important, but the absolute value can be an important financial measure: if manufacturing costs become too high as a percentage of the sales value, then the product is not profitable. This is certainly an important consideration for management. Either total maintenance costs or net maintenance costs can be used in the ratio. Net maintenance costs will include only those costs for maintaining the production units that produce the product. Figure 4 is a graph which displays a summary of past performance averages, for past years, monthly performance for this year, and the plan for the year.

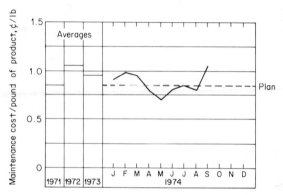

Maintenance cost/ pound of product

Fig. 4   Example of a graph showing history, trend, and plan for maintenance cost per pound of product.

Ratio of maintenance cost to investment   This is also fairly commonly included in maintenance reports. Since maintenance cost is the result of the investment in production equipment and other facilities, it would seem to be an important ratio. However, because of changes in the value of money, the investment figures should be adjusted to present value; that is, they should be treated as if the investment were made today. Then maintenance costs of today will be compared to investments valued in today's currency. The ratio is good for trends and comparisons. As with other ratios, this one can be misconstrued because of factors beyond the control of maintenance. Equipment with very poor reliability can be bought to keep investment cost low, but maintenance costs will be relatively higher because of it. This would cause the ratio to be high even though maintenance performance was good. Figure 5 is a graph of this ratio, displayed as percentages of the investment (adjusted to present value). The trend is probably a better measure in the long term than it is in the short term.

Budget variance   The budget plan provides a standard for evaluating actual performance. Expenditures over and under the budget are both significant. When expenditures are over, profits in the present period may be penalized. On the other hand, expenditures under the budget may only result in deferred and even more costly maintenance. Figure 6 is a fairly standard con-

Fig. 5   Example of a graph of maintenance-cost-to-investment ratio.

trol-type graph showing both under- and overbudget variances. Figure 7 shows the same budget figures plotted on a different kind of graph. This format was shown to the author by Mr. W. E. Chandler, a maintenance consultant.* He has found it to be effective.

Overtime ratio   Most managements are interested in reports of overtime work. I prefer a ratio of overtime hours divided by straight-time hours. Only those hours actually

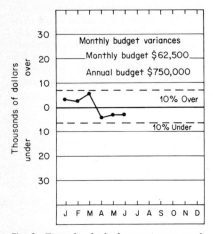

Fig. 6 Example of a budget variances graph with control limits.

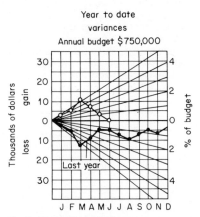

Fig. 7 Example of a budget variances graph in the W. E. Chandler format.

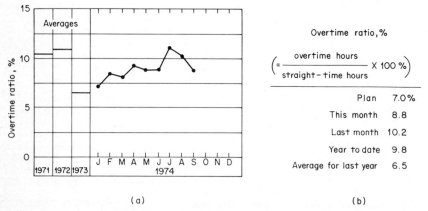

(a)   (b)

Fig. 8 Example of overtime ratio graph and table.

worked outside the regular schedule are included as overtime hours. The use of straight-time hours for the comparison provides an easy reference. For instance, if the regular work week is 40 hours and 10 percent overtime is worked, then an average of 4 hours overtime per week is being worked by each worker. Both upper and lower control limits are important. The upper limit should be set where worker productivity is adversely affected. (Also, personnel are more apt to have accidents when overtime is high.) High overtime usually indicates a lack of sufficient manpower for the workload being imposed. Conversely, an overtime ratio near the lower limit may indicate that there are too many people in maintenance for the workload that is available. In this situation, the workers may slow down, and productivity will suffer. That reduction in productivity is very difficult to recover at a later date when conditions change. Figure 8 shows two different ways of displaying overtime ratio.

* Personal communication from Mr. W. E. Chandler of Brentwood, Missouri.

Availability   This is a report of the on-stream capabilities of production equipment. It may be necessary to consider availability as a percentage of capacity or of hours available.   We must also recognize that maintenance is not the only cause for the lack of production; we should only consider the time that the equipment is available to produce, not necessarily the time that it is actually producing.   Usually, very high availability can only be achieved with relatively high maintenance costs.   Low availability certainly is costly because required product cannot be produced.   Usually a table is best for this element, because even small changes are important.   The slight variations are not very easily seen on a graph or bar chart.   A narrow band of the scale can be used, but then one or both of the reference points, zero percent and 100 percent, will not be included.   This can cause misconceptions.

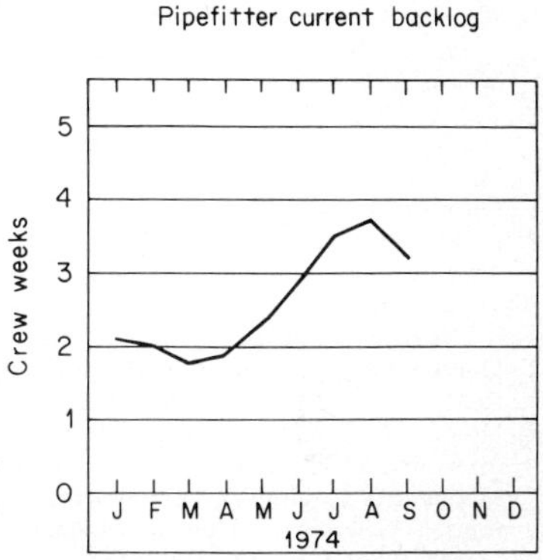

Pipefitter current backlog

Backlog   Efficient use of manpower requires that enough workload be available for the work force at all times.   Current backlog is the workload of jobs that are ready to be done when workers are available.   The trend of backlog can help determine if a maintenance force or a specific skill group will run out of work, if the available work to be done is stable, or if the workload is increasing to the point where job completion will

Fig. 9   Example of a backlog graph.

be unduly delayed.   Backlog helps determine if staffing is satisfactory or not.   Figure 9 shows how backlog might vary for a specific skill group—in this instance, pipefitters.

Maintenance overhead   Maintenance overhead can be ratioed to many other elements or shown as an absolute value.   It might be ratioed to total maintenance cost, total labor cost, or the number of workers.   However, there are so many ways to achieve good results that any of these can be misleading.   Some maintenance operations achieve good results with very little supervision and staff, while others can achieve good, economical performance with more supervision and staff.   One way to show the trend without showing the absolute value is to plot an index of the value.   In this way you compare today's performance with that of some time in the past.   This is especially convenient because the values reported are percentages of the base value.

Personnel head count   Sometimes the number of persons involved in maintenance operations is a good guide.   A table of head counts appears especially helpful for comparisons of operations.   Most of us have a better "feel" for numbers of people than we do for the costs that represent those persons.   Figure 10 is an example of a table of personnel head counts in different categories for multiple locations.

MAINTENANCE PERSONNEL
NUMBER AT END OF PERIOD

Locations	Technicians, skilled personnel, and laborers	Supervision, staff, and administration				Total maintenance personnel
		First line	Staff	Admin.	Total	
Location A	340	44	41	11	96	436
Location B	332	30	34	5	69	401
Location C	233	14	11	7	32	265
Location D	133	10	10	4	24	157
Location E	131	8	8	3	19	150
Totals	1,169	106	104	30	240	1,409
Previous period totals	1,183	107	106	30	243	1,426

Fig. 10   Example of a table of head counts.

REFERENCES

1. Charles V. Engle: "A Computerized Facilities Management and Maintenance System," paper presented at the Plant Engineering and Maintenance Conference of The American Society of Mechanical Engineers, Fort Worth, Tex., March 16–18, 1970.
2. Donald F. Hepburn: "Management of the Total Maintenance Function," paper presented at the NPRA Refinery Maintenance Conference, Houston, Tex., January 17–19, 1973.
3. Raymond McFarland: "Maintenance Cost Analysis for Performance Improvement," paper presented at the 22nd National Plant Engineering and Maintenance Conference, Cleveland, Ohio, March 22–25, 1971.
4. F. J. McGrath: "A Plant Maintenance Organization: Modern Maintenance Management Concepts Applied to a Large Aluminum Rolling Facility," paper presented at the Plant Engineering and Maintenance Conference of The American Society of Mechanical Engineers, Fort Worth, Tex., March 16–18, 1970.
5. E. F. Newbrough and the Staff of Albert Ramond and Associates, Inc.: *Effective Maintenance Management,* New York: McGraw-Hill, 1967.
6. Don L. Stieghan; "Reporting Maintenance Performance Factors," *Oil & Gas Journal,* vol. 72, no. 6, February 11, 1974, pp. 66–67 and 70–71.
7. Don L. Stieghan: "Selection of Appropriate Performance Measures," paper presented at the NPRA Refinery Maintenance Conference, Houston, Tex., January 17–19, 1973.
8. Howard L. Sunderland: "A System Approach to Planning and Controlling Maintenance," paper presented at the Plant Engineering and Maintenance Conference of The American Society of Mechanical Engineers, Fort Worth, Tex., March 16–18, 1970.
9. John J. Wilkinson: "How to Manage Maintenance," *Harvard Business Review,* vol. 46, no. 2, March–April 1968, pp. 100–111.

Chapter **7**

Appraisal of Shop's Performance

STEVEN ALTMAN and EFRAIM TURBAN
School of Business and Organizational Sciences, Florida International University

INTRODUCTION

Organizations exist to meet a variety of institutional and individual objectives. These objectives are met through a concerted effort by people to convert resources and to implement programs and activities. To ensure steady attainment of objectives, a maintenance manager must be able to know how well the maintenance shop and its personnel are doing. The measurement and evaluation of how well shops and individuals are performing is known as *performance appraisal.*

Performance appraisal has received a great deal of attention over the last 30 years. A variety of terms have been used to describe basically the same process. Among those most frequently mentioned are "performance measurement," "performance evaluation," "merit rating," "periodic review," and "periodic assessment." The subject of performance appraisal is one that often carries negative connotations in organizations. We all enjoy hearing favorable words about our actions but try to avoid those that are not favorable. Honest appraisal, however, generally contains a little of both.

Performance appraisal is a standard ingredient of all organizational life. The question, really, is not whether there will be any performance appraisal or not but rather what method of appraisal will be used. Evaluation takes place, in some form or another, in every human encounter. We make judgments about other people in terms of how consistent their behavior is with our own or society's beliefs, norms, and values. The same thing happens in organizations. Smaller companies may utilize a casual, unsystematic approach with little or no documentation, but the process takes place anyway. Larger firms (and many small ones also) tend to use a more formal method of performance appraisal. These firms have recognized the value of information on the status of their most important resource—people. In addition, employees more actively demand to know where they stand in the organization and how, specifically, they can achieve their career objectives. Pressure from unions to document personnel actions provides a stronger boost for the need to have a formal appraisal system.

In order for a machine to carry out its purpose, every single part must perform to specifications. The same is true with the personnel in the maintenance department. Therefore, a true appraisal of the maintenance department must include the assessment of individuals and also of the shop as a whole.

This chapter is divided into two major parts. First, we discuss the appraisal of individuals in the shops; second, we discuss the appraisal of units such as work groups, shops, and the entire maintenance department.

PERFORMANCE APPRAISAL OF INDIVIDUALS

Purposes

Performance appraisal systems exist in organizations to provide information which can be used to facilitate rational decision making about employees. It is used also for planning, scheduling, and control purposes. Performance appraisal seeks to carefully identify and evaluate salient characteristics of an employee's performance on the job and the manner in which this performance is executed. In addition, it may be used as a basis for incentive schemes or bonus plans.

Some performance appraisal programs are designed to provide a great deal of information regarding the future of any given employee. Certainly among the most frequent uses are input for retention, promotion, and compensation decisions. As a general measure of the value of the individual to the organization, the appraisal provides the backup data to justify these decisions. Similarly, such information is used for a variety of other personnel decisions, including transfers and general assessments of job competence. In many cases, the emphasis has been as much on the potential value to the company as on actual performance, and the objective is to provide information in advance of the time that it is needed.

Beyond the fairly obvious uses mentioned above, performance appraisal serves several other purposes for a company. One of the most important of these is that it provides an opportunity for the employee to receive feedback on performance. Formal appraisal helps the supervisor, too. Being required to perform an evaluation on each subordinate, the supervisor is forced to take the time to get to know all the employees and their activities individually. Since an appraisal is relatively empty unless it is judged against some standards, it is incumbent upon each supervisor to identify performance standards. In the process of developing such standards, the supervisor is forced to take a hard look at what is really required and how jobs may be performed more effectively.

It is hard to expect outstanding performance if the worker does not know clearly what is expected. It is hoped that each worker will be informed prior to starting work by conferences with superiors and peers and by studying policy manuals prepared for the job in question. Once an individual has started work, the appraisal process allows the supervisor to provide the necessary coaching and training so that the employee may continue to perform better and contribute to the company's objectives more effectively. If the supervisor can create a situation where the goals of the individual and the company are relatively consistent, chances are there will be fewer problems with employee motivation.

A performance appraisal system also allows a company to make better decisions in terms of long-run personnel planning. Since each person is evaluated on the same basis as every other person, the company has valid grounds for objective comparisons between people. Such a process makes it easier to determine who should be promoted now, who should be promoted after more experience and training, and who would probably not be likely to be promoted in the future. At the same time these decisions are made, a company can evaluate its own program for employee development and selection.

Scope

Since all employees are continually evaluated in one form or another, a formal appraisal attempts to reduce the bias found in "overall impressions," gossipy discussions of the worth of certain workers, or favoritism because an employee plays golf with the boss.

Only few of the maintenance employees perform routine, highly repetitive jobs, such as those performed by production employees. Therefore an assessment which is based solely on work measurement is generally not feasible. Nevertheless, whenever possible, maintenance work should be measured and performance compared to standards. Chapters 4 and 5 of this section deal with the question of measuring the maintenance work. A good reference is cited at the end of this chapter.[12]* However, measuring the quantity of maintenance work and even its quality is only one dimension in the performance assessment of maintenance employees. Maintenance work by nature is rather complicated; it involves diagnosis and decisions on the proper tools, materials, and parts to be used. The sequence of performing the work is, in many cases, up to the employee. Therefore, the overall assessment of a maintenance worker involves many factors that vary from job to job. Thus instead of a job-by-job evaluation, it is more suitable to talk about periodical evaluation (i.e., semiannually or annually). In this respect the performance evaluation of maintenance employees is similar to the performance evaluation of other services as well as to the performance evaluation of the so-called white-collar employees, such as supervisors and engineers. For this reason, we will describe in this chapter only those appraisal methods that are relevant to service-type employees.

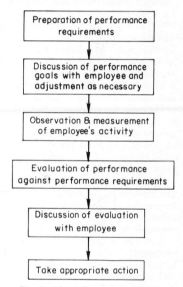

Fig. 1 The individual appraisal process.

The performance appraisal process must be consistent throughout the organization. This does not mean that the same evaluation instrument must be used for all employees but rather that the coverage should be companywide. In addition, many companies find their appraisal programs ineffective because they often select indiscriminately from the wide battery of available performance measures without really thinking through which particular technique is best suited to a particular appraisal objective. (For example, see Oberg.[17])

Another point involves who is to be rated. Again, this is a matter of the organization's objectives and the use to be made of the appraisal once completed. If salary decisions are not dependent on a performance appraisal, then it is not necessary to administer an evaluation for salary purposes. If the purpose of the evaluation is to screen employees for promotion, then only those who are eligible for consideration should be appraised in this way. In short, the appraisal program must measure the relevant things.

The General Process

What happens in an organization to effectuate the performance appraisal process? Our objective here is to identify the activities that take place during the process itself.

A general model of the performance appraisal process is illustrated in Fig. 1.

---

* Superior numbers refer to numbered references to be found at the end of this chapter.

Step 1: Preparation of performance requirements   The process begins with the specification of performance requirements for each particular job. This usually takes the form of a job analysis. However, the description in the job analysis is often too general. Therefore, when outlining performance requirements, the supervisor may want to indicate more detailed qualitative factors such as output levels, quality specifications, attendance records, and quantitative aspects such as relationships with others and general attitude. It is important, however, to be as specific as possible so as to ensure that performance of a job in a particular manner will provide progress toward company objectives. At the same time, the standards set must be realistic enough that they may actually be accomplished by an individual.

Step 2: Discussion of performance goals with employee   No matter how detailed or clear the wording of performance requirements may be, they are of little use unless they are communicated to the employee. It is imperative that both parties agree that the expectations are reasonable.

Step 3: Observation and measurement of employee's activity   Once the requirements for a job are laid out and the employee understands what is to be done, the supervisor *observes* the employee's performance over a given period of time. This does not imply that the manager "spies" on subordinates but rather that the manager makes mental (and written) notes based on the day-to-day interactions and performance of the employee. Many potential sources of error arise during the observation period, and good records of these become quite valuable.

Step 4: The evaluation of performance   The fourth phase of the process is the evaluation itself. It is here that the manager must measure and evaluate the employee's performance compared to the performance requirements of the job. A variety of techniques exist for summarizing employee performance, and these will be discussed in a subsequent section. The supervisor, however, must gather the data and, as objectively as possible, evaluate the strengths and weaknesses of each employee. The supervisor must be careful to set aside personal friendships and give a fair, honest appraisal of the employee's performance.

Evaluation systems may be either objective or subjective in nature. Frequently, some combination of the two is most appropriate. Wherever feasible, efforts should be made to include as much quantitative information as possible to reduce the bias inherent in subjective measures. The employee will generally place greater credence in objective measures which can be applied uniformly throughout the maintenance department.

There is, of course, a place for subjective evaluation as well. Especially where data are required to judge employee potential, promotability, or significant personality characteristics vital to the work environment, judgments are influenced by opinion and subjective appraisal. It is the responsibility of the rating supervisor to be as fair and as impartial as possible in making the evaluation to ensure fairness to the employee and the reliability of the appraisal. Comprehensive forms such as that shown in Fig. 2 are useful aids to evaluation.

Step 5: Discuss evaluation with employee   Perhaps the most difficult part of the entire process comes when the supervisor discusses the evaluation with each subordinate. This takes place in what is known as the *appraisal interview* and, more often than not, the skill used here by the supervisor has a tremendous impact on whether the appraisal process serves its purpose. Many fine appraisal programs have been dramatically weakened because the supervisor is poorly trained to conduct such an interview.

Step 6: Take appropriate action   Finally, based on the outcomes of the appraisal and the appraisal interview, the supervisor takes any appropriate action that may be necessary. This may take the form of a recommendation for promotion, a bonus, a salary increase, additional training, or adjustments in personnel. The supervisor should strive to reward outstanding performance and continually attempt to upgrade performance.

Methodological Notes
What is measured?   Determination of what is to be measured by a particular type of appraisal system is an important consideration. Many appraisal programs attempt to focus on assessments of what the employee has actually done during the appraisal period. This *performance-based* approach generally meets with greater approval where more objective criteria are available and can be used. For example, if a quality-control program can identify those employees who consistently make good repairs, it is fairly easy to rate the quality of those individuals' work as "above average" or "excellent."

Assessment of potential   The reliance on performance appraisal as a planning process directed toward future decisions, like manpower utilization or promotion, injects a second dimension—measurement of potential.   Whereas measurement of performance is usually accepted by the employee, the unknown future creates additional anxiety. Many employees resent and resist unfavorable statements about their potential. Prediction of future performance will also be tied in large measure to current performance.   Of course, other factors may be considered, such as educational background, test scores, or experience with similar situations.

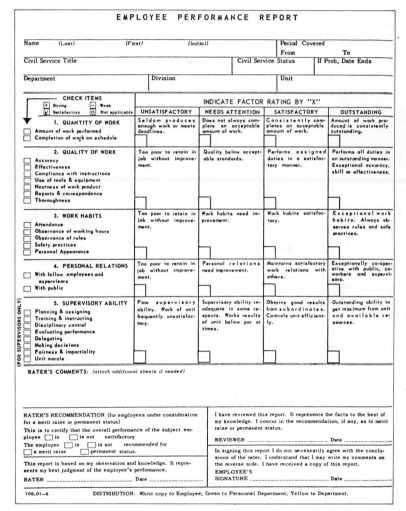

Fig. 2   Employee performance report form.

Should personality traits be considered?   Another widely debated issue is the reliance on personality traits as the basis for appraisal.   While few would deny that personality is frequently a correlate of job performance, the selection and weighing of appropriate characteristics is often a problem.   Critics of the trait approach cite the difficulty in correcting "problems."[3]   Concentration on personality characteristics leads to a perplexing situation for the employee: how one is to change a lifetime's habits.   Further, there is often little the supervisor can do to offer corrective solutions.   It is difficult to help an employee "develop a better sense of humor" or "become more creative."

The supervisor's role   The supervisor, as the person charged with the responsibility for conducting the appraisal, obviously occupies a central and critical role in the process. The skill and effectiveness by which a supervisor is able to objectively evaluate a situation and then communicate these views to subordinates frequently determines whether the process is a useful one or not. The conscientious supervisor is confronted with the need to be honest and straightforward while also respecting the integrity of the individual being appraised.

Frequency of evaluation   Most companies require that an appraisal be conducted on a regular basis. Generally, companies engage in this process either annually or semiannually. Some companies have provisions for more frequent assessments of new or probationary employees.

Who evaluates?   In addition to using the supervisor as an evaluator, some companies use systems whereby a group of supervisors do the evaluation. Others allow the individual's peers to do the appraisal. In other cases, the employees may be allowed to rate themselves. Although there are some obvious problems with this approach (e.g., higher ratings than the supervisor would give in some cases), there are also numerous benefits, including (1) more comprehensive upward flow of information, (2) more systematic thought about employee's own performance, and (3) greater motivation through increased participation in the process. This practice is not as yet widespread but does indicate that there may be more room for employee involvement in the process than is currently utilized. (For further discussion, see Flippo.[6])

Employees' reaction to performance appraisal   Performance appraisal touches on one of the most emotionally charged activities of organizational existence: the assessment of a worker's contribution and ability. The feedback the workers receive from this evaluation has a profound impact on their self-esteem and on their performance in the future. Nobody likes to hear negative comments regarding their performance, since these are taken as indictments of them as human beings.

Many employees are naturally both fearful and skeptical over evaluations. They question the right of anyone but themselves to judge their performance. They fear that the information gathered will be used against them as punishment or that their talents and abilities are not appreciated even though they work hard. Others genuinely look forward to performance appraisals as a constructive exercise in determining where they stand and how they may improve their performance. Still others look upon the whole process with indifference. In short, employee reactions to performance appraisal run the gamut of all human responses (e.g., see Eckles, et al.[4]). Employee reactions often take the form of a response to a supervisor's uncomfortable feelings. The supervisor who cannot deal with human encounters where criticism is involved will often trigger feelings of hostility and aggression in the subordinate.

In many cases, a sensitive problem arises when criticisms of an employee's performance point out problems with which the person has been contending for a lifetime. That person usually knows of these weaknesses already, and further reminders serve to do little but undermine an already shakey self-esteem.

Such problems are most likely to arise in companies which rely on personality traits as prime measures of evaluation. There is no one best way to avoid such reactions. Some suggestions point toward a *management by objectives* appraisal system, which minimizes excessive focus on personality factors. Another idea focuses on reporting only significant changes, either positive or negative. In this way, the supervisor can deal with specific items on an exception basis. Beyond that, supervisors who are aware of what they are doing and who genuinely care for the people they work with run the best chance of preserving the individual's self-respect. Failing to do so inevitably leads to a reversal of the stated goals of performance appraisal and a trend toward poorer overall performance. In addition, increased union influence has brought pressure on supervisors to require further justification of ratings where employees feel they have been dealt with unfairly. A union-management squabble then becomes more disruptive to the goals of the organization.

Certainly, the appraisal process can lead to very positive reactions by employees as well. Recognition of a job well done serves as a useful motivation device. Employees who feel appreciated will often continue to perform at a high level and frequently move into leadership positions. A positive rating serves to keep employees "on board" when they may have felt unsure of themselves or uncertain about what was expected of them.

APPRAISAL OF UNITS (SHOPS, CRAFTS, DEPARTMENTS)

The maintenance function is normally provided by at least one group, and in many organizations by several groups such as shops or crafts. Generally a large maintenance organization may be composed of divisions, each of which is divided into departments, which in turn are composed of work groups. The methods of evaluating a shop, department, division, or an entire maintenance organization do not differ much. In virtually all such cases, a collection of individuals headed by a manager is the subject of concern. Therefore, in this section, we will speak about evaluating a maintenance unit which can be any of the above mentioned. We will use the terms "shop," "department," "unit," and "group" interchangeably.

Purposes and Scope

The purposes of measuring the performance of the maintenance department are similar to those mentioned in discussing the appraisal of individuals' performance. Management is interested in measuring the performance of the maintenance unit for several reasons:

1. Analysis of possible improvements in performance
2. Comparison of the performance of the maintenance department versus the possibility of subcontracting maintenance services
3. Comparison of performance with other departments in the organization
4. Assessment of performance of the maintenance manager and the foremen against established standards
5. Assessment of the impact of changes in methods, materials, or personnel on the objectives of the maintenance department

In general, the evaluation of the maintenance department is strongly related to the maintenance control system. Any discussion on evaluation should be viewed, therefore, in light of the overall maintenance control system.

One question that people may ask is: Would it be possible to use the personnel performance appraisal to make inferences about the shop's performance? In other words, can the shop's performance be viewed as the sum of the performances of the individual employees? In some cases one may find it to be true that a collection of effective employees results in an effective group. However, there are many cases where, individually, each maintenance employee might be technically competent and a great performer, and yet collectively the maintenance department might be rated poorly in accomplishing its mission. The reasons for such a difference may be attributed to the need for coordination, efficient use of resources, and better planning and control at the managerial levels. In addition, the individual's objectives do not exactly coincide with the shop's objectives. Therefore it is necessary to conduct a performance appraisal at the shop's level in addition to making individual evaluations. As a matter of fact, each maintenance group with its supervisor or foreman should be evaluated, as well as the entire maintenance department.

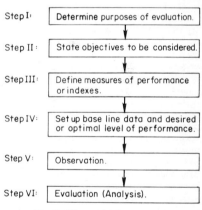

Step I: Determine purposes of evaluation.

Step II: State objectives to be considered.

Step III: Define measures of performance or indexes.

Step IV: Set up base line data and desired or optimal level of performance.

Step V: Observation.

Step VI: Evaluation (Analysis).

Fig. 3 The evaluation process.

The General Process

An evaluation plan takes the following steps (see Fig. 3):

Step 1: Determine the purpose of evaluation First, the purpose of appraisal should be specified. This step is necessary for decisions about what to measure and how, who should be observed and when.

Step 2: State objective(s) to be considered Once the purpose of the evaluation is decided upon, then the objectives and goals whose attainment will be measured must be spelled out. For example, let us assume that a new preventive maintenance program is installed in order to improve maintenance effectiveness (Step 1). Here we will state objectives such as minimize total maintenance cost, increase production employees' satisfaction, and decrease cost of downtime. These are expected to result from the new preventive maintenance systems.

Step 3: Define measures of performance Each of the above objectives may be attained through one or more attributes or indicators. For example, total maintenance cost may be measured by the cost of labor, cost of parts and materials, cost of maintaining related inventories, and cost of capital equipment.

Step 4: Set up baseline and target data Once the indicators have been specified, a target level for each should be determined. Also current (or last period's) observation should be recorded so there will be a baseline for comparison. For example, we may observe that the existing cost of labor is 7 percent of value of equipment, while a target figure for the next period may be 5 percent.

This information, as in the case of an individual's appraisal, should be communicated to all employees in the unit under evaluation.

Step 5: Observation During the period of concern (e.g., a month or a year), information should flow and data accumulate so that analysis can be done at the end of the period. The existing accounting system is usually a poor source for such data. Thus, special reports should be established to assure that all relevant data are collected.

Step 6: Evaluation At the end of the period, a formal evaluation is conducted. The evaluation may appear on a chart that shows the trend. It can be in the form of a routine, periodic report, or it may take the form of a special report prepared for a specific purpose.

Types of Appraisal Methods

Appraisal systems have been developed largely to meet particular needs of the organizations that use them. Here are brief descriptions of the most commonly used traditional methods.

Rating scales Rating scales consist of a series of questions about the employee which are to be checked off or answered in the appropriate space corresponding to the degree, frequency, or quality which best describes the employee. Frequently such scales make use of an overall score which is determined by adding up scores attributed to specific factors. This type of system allows a large number of employees to be compared, and at the same time enables the supervisor and the employee to easily identify specific areas where further improvement is necessary.

Rating scales take on a variety of forms. Those most frequently used are: *graphic scales, frequency scales, forced distribution, forced choice,* and *rankings.* Each will be discussed in turn.

Graphic rating scales Probably the most frequently used system with blue collar employees is a graphic rating scale. A graphic rating scale usually consists of a list of five to forty qualities that an employee may have, and a range of degrees for each quality. The scale may consist of numbers representing a range from poor to outstanding, or a series of descriptive words or phrases corresponding to the achievement of a particular attribute. For example, one quality may be "initiative." The extent to which the employee demonstrates initiative on the job may be graded as "excellent," "above average," "average," "fair," or "poor." Similarly, these terms may be coded so that a 5 means "excellent," 4 means "above average," and so on. The rater merely selects the phrase or number which most closely corresponds to the particular attribute of the employee. An example of one such graphic scale is provided in Figure 2.

In summarizing an employee's evaluation, the rater may then total the point values for each attribute to obtain an overall score. However, the realization that some factors are more important than others has led to the development of weighting systems. For example, if "quality of work" is judged to be more important than "creativity," the former would receive more weight in the overall summary. This allows the most important items to assume the greatest relative significance in the overall rating.

Some companies try to help raters apply uniform standards with respect to each of the several attributes. This is done by describing in more detail both what is meant by the attribute and by the particular judgments which are possible in evaluating each attribute. For example, for the attribute "initiative," there may be a descriptive phrase such as "self-starting ability, able to start new projects and carry them through." The possible choices may read "excellent-energetic self-starter, continually develops new ideas and is very reliable," "above average—often demonstrates initiative and willingness to get involved," average—"occasionally develops new plans and ideas," "fair—usually needs direction," or "poor—always must be told what to do."

Frequency rating scales   Frequency rating scales are very similar to graphic scales with the exception that quantitative choices are offered for each attribute of descriptive phrases.   For example, in response to the attribute "initiative," the choices may be to indicate whether the employee is in the "top 10 percent," "top 20 percent," "middle 40 percent," "bottom 20 percent," or "bottom 10 percent" of all employees, rather than the phrases "excellent," "above average," etc.

Forced distribution scales   Forced distribution scales involve the supervisor giving an overall rating to each subordinate, by class, and limiting the number of people who may fall into a particular class within certain guidelines.   The major difference between this method and the frequency rating scale is that no attempt is made to differentiate between performance on specific attributes.   Rather, with a forced distribution scale, overall ratings for all attributes combined are given.   For example, there may be classes for superior performance, good performance, average performance, fair performance, and unsatisfactory performance.   Continuing with the example, there may be provision that approximately 10 percent of the people may fall in the "superior" class, 20 percent in the "good," 40 percent in "average," 20 percent "fair," and 10 percent "unsatisfactory," and the supervisor is forced to choose which employees are identified with each class. Since only one overall rating is given, the chance that standards will be interpreted differently by different supervisors is largely reduced.

This relatively simple approach runs into trouble, though.   The method assumes that all groups have the same proportion of superior, good, average, fair, and unsatisfactory employees.   This assumption is tenuous at best, especially if the number of people who are being rated is small.   For this reason employers who use this approach usually work on the basis of ranges rather than a given strict percentage guideline.   This allows the supervisor more flexibility in assessing his particular work group.

Forced choice ratings   Forced choice ratings consist of a series of four possible statements about the employee.   Within each series of four statements, the rater must indicate the one statement that is *most* descriptive of the person, and the one statement that is least descriptive.   Generally two of the four statements are positive, and two are negative.   However, only one of the positive and one of the negative statements actually give credit toward the overall score.   Those statements which do not affect the rating (either positively or negatively) are usually resultant from tests which show relatively low correlation with efficiency of performance than the two that give a score.

The catch with the forced choice method is that the rater does not know which items count and which items do not count.   Therefore, rater biases are minimized.

As an example of the forced choice method, the rater may be confronted with the following statements regarding an employee:

	Most	Least
1. Deals well with others	____	____
2. Doesn't consult superiors	____	____
3. Always prompt	____	____
4. Not very creative	____	____

The rater then must check one statement as most descriptive and one as least descriptive.   But depending on the particular organization, only one of the positive statements 1 and 3 and one of the negative statements 2 and 4 would count toward a final score.

While on the surface forced choice methods are quite good in reducing rater bias, its popularity has not been widespread.   The system is very expensive to install because the statements used must be designed specifically for each job situation.   This entails a potentially lengthy validation process to insure that the questions are really measuring what is intended to be measured.   Further, forced choice methods are often resented by raters as demeaning to their responsibility.   Since the rater is not familiar with which attributes are significant, he often feels like a processor or a machine, with no helpful input into the process.   In addition, raters think that because the significance of items are withheld from them, the company does not trust them to rate people fairly.

Ranking systems   The frequently used ranking system is simple in that it involves ordering each employee in a group in descending order from the most outstanding to the poorest. Every person is considered in his totality, and then compared to every other person. This method has some intuitive appeal in that managers tend to rate or compare their employees anyway. The approach can become quite tedious, however, when one considers the number of comparisons that must be made. The formula for the number of comparisons is $[N(N-1)]/2$ where $N =$ the number of people to be ranked. With a large department, the numbers can become large. For example, with 20 people, there would be 190 comparisons required for a final ranking to be generated. Another drawback of this approach is the lack of specific feedback that is possible to help the individual improve his performance. Since rankings are based on aggregate, subjective evaluations, it is difficult to pinpoint areas.

Critical incident method   The essence of the critical incident method is that the supervisor records incidents which are either very good or very poor relating to the employee's performance. The rater has now developed a data base upon which decisions can be made consistent with the system in use. The critical incident method then is used to substantiate other appraisal methods, and does not replace them.

The selection of what to record as a critical incident is obviously a key factor. It is important that all observers of performance agree on what is critical, or else the familiar problem of rater bias emerges again. One of the advantages of the critical incident method is that subsequent ratings are based on evidence, rather than subjective judgment.

The critical incident method provides the raw data for use in other types of appraisals and is used as a supplement rather than a substitute in many cases.

Management by objectives (MBO)   Management by objectives (MBO) is a motivation and appraisal method that shifts the focus of attention from the past to the future, from work to the results of work. Perhaps the most significant deviation of MBO from other appraisal systems is the employee's responsibility to establish goals for himself. These goals are established to be consistent with the organization's goals. Employee goals are usually developed after consultation with the supervisor to insure that the responsibilities of each job position are fulfilled.

A key element in the employee's formulation of his goals is that the goals, to the greatest extent possible, should be measurable. The employee must be specific about the target (maintenance cost reduction of 10 percent, waste cut by 5 percent, etc.) and his plans for how he will achieve these targets in a given time period. The supervisor and the subordinate then confer to modify, clarify, and mutually agree on the objectives document. Often forms are developed to help guide the employee in the preparation of his objectives in specific areas. The final document is often referred to as a *performance agreement* or *performance contract.*

The supervisor then adopts a coaching role. He can help the employee stay on target and assist him in meeting his goals. At the end of the agreed time period, the supervisor again confers with the employee to appraise accomplishments related to the goals previously identified. The employee then prepares his own assessment of his results and substantiates his evaluation with factual data wherever possible. This process allows him to develop insight into his own needs for improvement and adjustment of tactics.

Kindall and Gatza[9] believe that MBO (1) tends to help people set targets which are both challenging and more realistic, (2) provides a method of detecting training needs, and (3) treats as a total process a person's ability to see an organization's problem, to devise ways of attacking it, and to translate his ideas into action.

Limitations of MBO   Although management by objectives provides a strong mechanism for performance evaluation, it has been widely criticized for several of its weaknesses.

The goal-setting activity of the employee is very difficult and often only a projection of what the supervisor wants in the first place. The freedom given the employee may lead to goals which are vague, or deliberately low. The emphasis should be on goals which are desired by the organization, and it therefore becomes difficult to prepare goals which are desired by the individual as well.

Instituting a proper MBO system takes a large amount of time. Critics maintain the trade-off in time required to make the system effective outweigh the increased levels of performance.

Kindall and Gatza[9] suggest other weaknesses of MBO:

1. It leads many managers to assume that there is now less need for them to counsel employees because the figures give each man a running check on how he had done

2. It may be questioned whether the understanding that is supposed to develop between supervisor and subordinate really comes about.

A final dilemma regarding MBO involves the determination of who is to receive salary increases, or promotions. MBO usually measures how a man has performed a specific job, but it provides little information on how he might do on other jobs. Since each individual's objectives will differ, some determination is required on the relative weight of each person's performance. For example, a person who sets low goals for himself and completes them all should not necessarily be rewarded more than a person who has established very high goals, but fails to reach all of them. The latter's contribution to the organization is likely to be far superior to the former's.

To avoid some of these problems, some companies have introduced an MBO system which stresses employee development rather than formal evaluation, per se. Used in conjunction with other rating systems, a broader approach to organizational and individual development can be utilized.

Limitations of Appraisal Methods

There are multiple obstacles and sources of error inherent in virtually all appraisal methods, beyond those mentioned in the preceding section. Most concern the rater and how he performs his job of appraising others. A brief discussion of common sources of bias and error follows.

1. Poorly defined performance standards: If standards are not explicit or if the employee does not know what is expected of him, raters are evaluating against their own subjective value systems and the worker can be at a disadvantage.

2. Insufficient data: If the supervisor does not have enough or all of the information to make a decision, the quality of his output is severely limited.

3. Leniency or strictness: Some raters have lower standards, and some have much tougher standards. This obviates the comparability between employees.

4. "Halo" effect: Frequent tendency to rate an individual highly based on some nebulous "general feelings and impressions" toward the worker. Often one factor is given much more significance and all other factors tend to be evaluated in the same way.

5. A person's performance appraisal is designed to evaluate how well an employee does on a particular job. However, the common tendency is to rate a person higher who holds a higher paid (or higher status) position just because of his position.

6. Recency: The last few months prior to the appraisal tend to exert undue influence on the rater. Impact may be positive or negative.

7. Exceptional performance: A subjective review of the past appraisal periods events may focus too narrowly on a few peaks or valleys.

8. Central tendency: Central tendency problems arise when the rater marks almost everyone as average. This usually occurs when the rater wants to avoid sticking his neck out, or when he is in doubt because of inadequate data.

9. Playing the "rating game": Another source of bias emerges where raters, confronted with a formidable task to complete, make light of the process and try to outguess the system. Certainly, the unpleasantness that performance appraisal often contributes to this feeling as well as a lack of information about what they are really supposed to do. So the rater tries to beat the game and convey his general impression of the employee despite the complications of scales, and special definitions.

10. Supervisor resistance: Supervisors sometime feel that the appraisal instrument is invalid, or mistrust the entire process.

Certainly other factors may come to mind when criticizing performance appraisal techniques, and probably no system successfully eliminates all of them. By becoming aware of the problems, however, supervisors should be in a better position to evaluate their own actions and improve their effectiveness.

The Appraisal Interview

The appraisal process is not complete until the employee is informed of the results of his evaluation by his rating supervisor. The appraisal interview is the time when the employee receives direct feedback on his performance, has a chance to discuss where he stands, and has the opportunity to begin planning for the next period. Further, the interview may form the basis for subsequent personnel actions.

Much of the anxiety associated with performance appraisal stems from the prospect of the appraisal interview. Many supervisors make the mistake of playing down the session because of the uneasiness they have in communicating negative comments, fears of argument, a lack of confidence in their evaluation of the subordinate, or a personal sense of inadequacy over their own interviewing skills. It is the appraisal interview, however, that may make or break the entire process. If performance appraisal is to achieve its stated goals, honest communication between supervisor and worker must take place.

The appraisal interview uses the performance evaluation instrument or form as the focal point of discussion. The purpose is to explain and discuss with the employee the supervisor's evaluation of the employee's work. Further elaboration on significant factors gives the employee additional feedback on where he is going—right or wrong. The typical interview lasts between 30 to 90 minutes, depending on the complexity of the situation.

Conducting the interview   Several companies utilize training programs to upgrade the quality of supervisory interviewing. They have developed standardized guidelines on how to conduct such an interview.

A typical script (see Trull[24] and Strauss and Sayles[21]) would be as follows:

1. Welcome the employee, and attempt to put him at ease by discussing a mutual interest.

2. Indicate the purpose of the interview, and outline the format of the discussion.

3. Present the formal evaluation, highlighting strong points first. Give examples of reasoning behind decisions, and perceptions of overall performance.

4. Give the interviewee an opportunity to respond to the evaluation, and make general comments. Remember that most people will act defensively to negative feedback, so try to provide time for the employee to save face. Encourage him to present his own evaluation of his progress, the problems he faces and suggestions for resolution.

5. The interview ends with a discussion of means for improvement, including specific steps to be taken by both the employee and the supervisor. Plans should be specific and directed toward opportunites for growth, aimed at the employee's strengths, and goal oriented.

6. Where the fault is difficult or impossible to correct, there is no point in discussing it at all.

7. If a man has faults that are correctable, it may be better to let him bring them up himself where he sees fit. It may be necessary to wait until the next periodic appraisal, but as long as gradual progress is being made the supervisor can assist by his coaching efforts.

8. In some cases the employee's performance may be so poor as to raise the possibility of his being discharged. Under such circumstances it is only fair that he be given warning, even though there is little chance of changing his behavior.

Certainly, the preceding points are not meant to be taken as a magic formula for success, but they can aid in the process.

Methodological Notes

The supervisor's role   Any maintenance productivity measurement program will fail without the wholehearted support of the maintenance supervisors. Therefore they should participate, to the utmost degree possible, in the above process. For example, consider a possible implementation model:

TRAINING PROGRAM FOR SUPERVISORS (THREE 2-HOUR SESSIONS).   A training program should precede any evaluation. Topics to be discussed are as follows: Who is responsible for improvements? What indexes are to be used? Where will information come from? What are the objectives of the evaluation plan? What are the targets for improvement? What will be done with poor performers?

What is measured   The performance appraisal system may attempt to measure the cost of rendering maintenance services (at a satisfactory level), attitudes of the clients, the quickness of response, or other measures of effectiveness. As in the individual appraisal case, an attempt is made to focus on assessments of what the department (or group) has actually done during the appraisal period. Depending on the objective of the appraisal and on the availability of data, a decision has to be made on what other variables may be considered.

Who will conduct the appraisal?   Shop appraisals can be done by the maintenance manager for self-evaluation purposes, by the plant engineer, by the controller, or by the research department.

Frequency of evaluation   Depending upon their purpose, appraisals for the shop as a whole are conducted anywhere from daily or weekly (mainly for labor analysis) to once a year.   Monthly evaluation is probably the most common.

Employees' reaction   It is reasonable to believe that employees' reactions to a group or shop evaluation will be generally milder than to their own evaluation.   An exception to this will be the maintenance manager and foremen.   The appraisal of a unit or department reflects on them much more directly than on their subordinates.   Therefore they will probably react to the shop's appraisal in a similar manner that employees will react to an individual assessment.

Types of Appraisal Systems

The appraisal of the performance of the maintenance department is much more complicated than the personnel appraisal.   The major reason is that the performance of the maintenance department is expressed by a large number of attributes; several are objective, the remainder are subjective.   For example, cost of maintenance, level of service, downtime cost, and employees' satisfaction are all attributes of the overall performance.   Therefore, almost any appraisal system must be multidimensional in nature.

Subjective (attitudinal) evaluation   All methods for measuring individual's performance are subjective in nature.   That is, they expressed the opinions or attitudes of people.   A similar approach can be used in shop performance evaluation.   Through the use of forms or questionnaires, one can collect information on the performance of the maintenance department.   A most acceptable tool for such a purpose is the *checklist*.   A maintenance checklist or a checklist appraisal is an instrument that poses a series of questions to the maintenance managers or employees (see Fig. 4) and/or to those who are served by the maintenance department (see Fig. 5) regarding the performance level of the

		Yes	No
1.	Do your equipment records represent an accurate inventory and a permanent record as essential planning tool?	___	___
2.	Do you schedule your preventive maintenance?	___	___
3.	Do you have time standards for routine work?	___	___
4.	Do you use a mathematical analysis to determine frequency of preventive maintenance?	___	___
5.	Do you prepare daily assignment sheets?	___	___

Points: Question 1: Yes = 2, No = 0; Question 2: Yes = 4, No = 1, etc.
Rating: 90–100 is excellent, 80–89 is good, etc.

Fig. 4   Sample questions to a maintenance manager.

		Very poor	Poor	Average	Good	Very good
1.	Quality of repairs	___	___	___	___	___
2.	Promptness of service	___	___	___	___	___
3.	Attitudes of maintenance foremen	___	___	___	___	___
4.	Attitudes of maintenance employees	___	___	___	___	___
5.	Reasonableness of cost of repair	___	___	___	___	___
6.	Downtime situation	___	___	___	___	___
	Points	0	1	2	3	4

Subjective evaluation can be used in conjunction with objective evaluation methods for an overall performance appraisal.

Fig. 5   Sample questions to a maintenance client.

maintenance department. Answers can be yes or no or may be arranged in a multiple scale structure (e.g., one may choose from among five possible answers).

Points can be assigned to each answer, and an overall point value is then computed. Interpretation is made of total points, indicating excellent, good, fair, or poor performance.

Attitudinal questionnaires can generally check the satisfaction of the maintenance employees from their work and their job, the perceived effectiveness of communication and leadership, and several other characteristics of what is known as "climate analysis." (For further information, see Litwin and Stringer.[13])

Objective evaluation   The major difference between appraising the performance of individuals and the performance of maintenance units is the availability of considerable amounts of objective data in the latter case. Information about cost, downtime, overhead, idletime, delays, promptness, and backlog is available in most maintenance units and can serve as an indicator of performance. This information is usually analyzed in a comparative manner, using ratios (such as maintenance cost as a percent of value of equipment). In addition, trend-line analysis is used, as are comparative studies with industry averages. A major difficulty is the existence of a multiplicity of measures to be considered. Details are presented below.

Maintenance Indicators*

As efforts are made to control and/or reduce maintenance cost and to increase effectiveness, numerous objective indexes (or indicators) are being used by management in an effort to relate the performance of maintenance to other factors. For example, the cost of maintenance as related to the cost of sale is an index. Such an index can be viewed as a single indicator or can be a part of a wider performance overview. For example, assuming that the service given by the maintenance unit is adequate, then analysis of such an index over time can indicate the changes in performance (up or down) of the maintenance department. Further, a comparison to nationally published indexes† (usually by industry) can give some comparative idea about the relative performance standing of the maintenance department. In addition, such an index will contribute to a multiindex evaluation, as we will see later.

Maintenance indexes in general should be used only as a first approximation for appraising performance. The reason is that several of these indexes are very broad and subject to the interaction of many variables not directly associated with effectiveness. Despite their shortcomings, they are usually easy to monitor and explain. Further, in some cases the combination of several of these indexes may result in a validated overall measure of performance.

To accomplish its trend-indicating function, the appraisal of maintenance performance must be based upon factors of reference which are comparatively stable. As with any indicator or index, a baseline must be established. If the sole purpose of the analysis is to see trend over time, then the first year is considered as the baseline year. If the index is being used for comparative analysis—e.g., with similar plants—then some kind of a "base plant"should be decided upon before a comparison can be made.

Types of indexes

1. *Ratio of maintenance cost to sales.*

2. *Ratio of maintenance cost to the value of facilities.*

3. *Current backlog.* This includes the total amount of work to be done, expressed in crew weeks. Only work for which resources are available is considered. If we also include work for which resources are not currently available, we will get the total *backlog* index.

4. *Ratio of preventive maintenance.* This denotes the percent of man-hours spent on preventive maintenance compared with the total man-hours spent on maintenance.

5. *Ratio of repair work to total maintenance.* This denotes the percent of man-hours spent on repairs compared to the total man-hours spent on maintenance.

6. *Percent of jobs completed on schedule.* This index shows the percent of jobs (or hours) scheduled that were completed on schedule.

* This section is based on Chapter 18 in Newbrough,[15] on Johnson and Sharp,[8] on Almack,[1] and Ramond.[18]

† See *Moody's Industrial Manual* published by Moody's Investors' Services, Inc., New York, and *Factory*, published by Morgan-Grampian Publishing Co., New York.

7. *Maintenance hours planned.* This index points out what portion of the maintenance work is planned ahead of time and what portion is done on an emergency basis.

8. *Ratio of overtime to regular time.*

9. *Percent of work for which time standards are developed as compared to total work.*

10. *Ratio of downtime.* This index measures the percentage of breakdown as compared to total equipment hours. Alternatively, it measures the cost of downtime as a percent of the total maintenance cost.

11. *Manpower productivity level.* This index measures the percent of hourly maintenance personnel actually working at a given point of time (usually determined by work sampling).

12. *Labor effectiveness while working.* This is usually expressed as a percent of a standard where the standard is available. This ratio is more applicable to an individual worker; however, it can be applied, as an average, for a group too.

13. *Maintenance labor turnover* (as compared to the average plant's turnover).

14. *Maintenance labor cost compared with maintenance material cost.*

15. *Absenteeism rate in the maintenance department.*

16. *Maintenance cost per unit of production.*

17. *Complaints rate* (written, by those served by maintenance).

18. *Percent of maintenance overhead cost.*

19. *Ratio of direct to indirect maintenance cost.*

20. *Actual maintenance cost compared to the budgeted one.*

Maintenance performance when assessed for a unit or a shop clearly involves multiple attributes. Therefore, a true appraisal of performance must take all the significant attributes or measures of performance into consideration. Two practical approaches are described next.

The multi-index profile* A practical way to handle situations with several measures of performance of maintenance is to develop a multi-index profile. Basic to the use of the profile is the selection of a relatively few practical and reliable indexes for which optimum points can be established. These optimum points become goals or targets against which actual results can be measured periodically.

In a typical situation, the following eight indicators might be chosen and an optimum point selected for each:

1. Forecasting effectiveness, expressed as a percentage of actual hours compared with the hours forecast. This factor measures the ability to man according to the forecast plan.

2. Backlog of maintenance work, expressed as the number of crew weeks of scheduled work awaiting accomplishment.

3. Overtime hours, expressed as a percentage of total maintenance man-hours.

4. Downtime, expressed as a percentage of equipment hours lost because of mechanical failures for which maintenance was responsible.

5. Budget variance, expressed as the percentage that actual costs were over or under the budgeted costs.

6. Labor performance, expressed as a percent of standard.

7. Maintenance cost, expressed as a cost per unit of production.

8. Administrative cost of maintenance, expressed as a percentage of the maintenance payroll.

An example of these eight factors are shown in Fig. 6. The various scales for each factor have been related to a master scale, with all optimum points at the bottom of the table. An example of the results of a performance survey for each factor is shown in Fig. 7.

By plotting these results on the graph and connecting the points, a profile of the eight factors is drawn, showing the deviations from the baseline or objectives.

Good performance would show up in a lowering of the profile toward the bottom of the graph, poor performance would show up in a high profile line. Weak spots will show up as peaks on the profile line (e.g., downtime in Fig. 7).

Composite index The multi-index profile expresses performance on various dimensions, but it does not show the relative importance or weight of each measure of performance. Further, in comparing performance over time, one can find that some of the

---

* Based on Newbrough,[15] p. 350.

measures of performance may climb while others decline; thus, an overall comparison of performance with the multi-index profile may be difficult or even impossible. The composite maintenance index is an attempt to include in one measure of performance all relevant performance attributes. The basic idea is borrowed from economics and finance, where composite indexes have long been in use. The Dow-Jones industrial average and the Index of Economic Activities are each composed of several components. (For example, the Index of Economic Activities includes such components as the rate of unemployment, retail sales, and new construction.) Each component may get a different weight, depending on its importance. In the example presented earlier, we can assign

Master scale	Forecasting, %		Backlog, weeks		Overtime, %		Downtime, %		Budget variance, %		Labor performance, %	Cost per ton, dollars	Administration, %	
Poor (excessively high or low values) 0	120	80	4	0	10	0	4.0	1.0	+ 10	− 10	0	10.50	20	0
1	118	82			9½	½	3.9	1.2	9	9	10		19	1
2	116	84			9	1	3.8	1.4	8	8	20	10.00	18	2
			3½	½										
3	114	86			8½	1½	3.7	1.6	7	7	30		17	3
4	111	88			8	2	(3.6)	1.8	6	6	40	9.50	16	4
5	110	90	3	1	7½	2½	3.5	2.0	5	5	50		15	5
6	108	92	(2.7)		7	3	3.4	2.2	4	4	60	9.00	14	6
7	106	(94)			6½	3½	3.3	2.4	(3)	3	70		13	7
			2½	1½										
8	104	96			(6)	4	3.2	2.6	2	2	(80)	8.50	(12)	8
9	102	98			5½	4½	3.1	2.8	1	1	90		11	9
10	100		2		5		3.0		0		100	(8.00)		10
Optimum value														

Fig. 6   Multifactor profile.

	Optimum	Observed
Forecasting	100%	94%
Backlog	2 weeks	2.7 weeks
Overtime	5%	6.0%
Downtime	3%	3.6%
Budget variance	0%	+3.0%
Labor performance	100%	80%
Cost per ton	$8	$8
Administration	10%	12.0%

Fig. 7   Example of results.

	Objectives (optimum)		Observed	
Components	Value	Points	Value	Points
Forecasting	100%	10	94%	7
Backlog	2 wks.	10	2.7 wks.	6
Overtime	5%	10	6.0%	8
Downtime	3%	20	3.6%	8
Budget variance	0	10	3%	7
Labor performance	100%	20	80%	16
Cost per ton	$8	10	$8	10
Administration	10%	10	12%	8
Composite index		100		70

Fig. 8   Computation of composite index.

weights to each component. The sum of these will total 100 at the objective (optimum) level (see Fig. 8).

For example, downtime and labor performance are twice as important as all other components. Next, we decide what observed value is worth in terms of points; for example, 94 percent forecasting success is valued at 7 points (assuming linear relationship), and 3 percent budget variance is valued at 7 points. Thus, in the example, the overall performance is rated at 70 of a possible 100. This approach enables us to assess and compare the overall performance at any desired times. Attitudinal results may be incorporated here too, simply by adding the overall results of an attitudinal survey as an additional component.

REFERENCES

1. L. Almack: "Managing Plant Maintenance," *Plant Management and Engineering,* October 1972, pp. 35–37.
2. Glenn A. Bassett, and H. H. Meyer: "Performance Appraisal Based on Self Reviews," *Personnel Psychology,* vol. 21, no. 4, Winter 1968, pp. 421–430.
3. J. C. Conant: "The Performance Appraisal—A Critique and an Alternative," *Business Horizons,* June 1973, p. 75.
4. R. W. Eckles, R. L. Carmichael, and B. R. Sarchet: *Essentials of Management for First Line Supervision,* Wiley, New York, 1974.
5. J. C. Flanagan and R. K. Burns: "The Employee Performance Record: A New Appraisal and Development Tool," *Harvard Business Review,* September–October 1955, pp. 95–102.
6. Edwin B. Flippo: *Principles of Personnel Management, 3d ed.,* McGraw-Hill, New York, 1971, pp. 256–257.
7. W. J. Jamieson: "Measuring Maintenance Work," *Plant Management and Engineering,* May 1972, pp. 30–32.
8. J. J. Johnston and W. E. Sharp: "How to Analyze Maintenance Cost," *Factory,* July 1973.
9. A. F. Kindall and J. Gatza: "Positive Program for Performance Appraisal," *Harvard Business Review,* November–December, 1963, pp. 52–59.
10. B. T. Lewis and W. W. Pearson: *Maintenance Management,* J. F. Rider Publisher, New York, 1963.
11. B. T. Lewis and J. P. Marron (eds.): *Facilities and Plant Engineering Handbook,* McGraw Hill, New York, 1973.
12. B. T. Lewis: "Work Measurement," in B. T. Lewis and J. P. Marron (eds.), *Facilities and Plant Engineering Handbook,* McGraw-Hill, New York, 1973.
13. G. H. Litwin and R. A. Stringer, Jr.: *Motivation and Organizational Climate,* Division of Research, Graduate School of Business, Harvard University, Cambridge, Mass., 1968.
14. H. H. Meyer, E. Kay, and P. French, Jr.: "Split Roles in Performance Appraisal," *Harvard Business Review,* January–February 1965, pp. 123–129.
15. E. J. Miller and J. W. Blood: *Modern Maintenance Management,* American Management Association, New York, 1963.
16. E. T. Newbrough: *Effective Maintenance Management,* McGraw Hill, New York, 1967.
17. Mitchell Novit: "Performance Appraisal and Dual Authority: A Look at Group Appraisal," *Management of Personnel Quarterly,* vol. 8, no. 1, Spring 1969, p. 3.
18. W. Oberg: "Make Performance Appraisal Relevant," *Harvard Business Review,* January–February 1972, p. 62.
19. A. Ramond: "Maintenance Cost Ratios Dropping, Survey Shows," *Factory,* September 1971.
20. H. E. Roadman: "An Industrial Use of Peer Ratings," *Journal of Applied Psychology,* vol. 48, no. 4, August 1964, pp. 221–214.
21. G. Strauss and L. R. Sayles: *Personnel: The Human Problems of Management,* Prentice-Hall, Englewood Cliffs, N.J., 1972, pp. 516–520.
22. Paul H. Thompson and Gene W. Dalton: "Performance Appraisal: Managers Beware," *Harvard Business Review,* January–February 1970, pp. 149–157.
23. Henry L. Tosi and Stephen J. Carroll: "Managerial Reaction to Management by Objectives," *Academy of Management Journal,* vol. 11, no. 4, December 1968, pp. 415–426.
24. S. G. Trull: "Strategies of Effective Interviewing," *Harvard Business Review,* January–February, 1964, pp. 19–24.
25. "The New Emphasis on Preventive Maintenance," *Plant Operating Management,* special issue, January 1972.

Section 5

Utilities Management

Chapter 1

Production Cost Analysis—Utilities

EDWARD F. WEHLAGE, P.E.
Edward F. Wehlage and Associated Engineers
and

J. WITMEYER, P.E.
Naval Facilities Engineering Command

COSTLY ENERGY NECESSITATES UTILITY COST ANALYSIS

Sharply convulsive energy supply problems, which became clearly apparent after 1973, will result in continually escalating prices for fuels and electrical energy in the forseeable future. These, in turn, will force management to seek more detailed analysis of all utilities used for industrial plant, commercial, and institutional business enterprises. The critical appraisal of purchased utilities like electricity, gas, oil, coal, water, and other utility-type services will be enhanced and extended to site-produced utilities ranging from hot water, steam, lighting, compressed air, etc. The application of "in-plant" and "on-site" services will undergo more rigorous scrutiny to establish *real costs* for production and utilization.

The production and use of many in-plant and on-site services in the past have been the result of subjective reasoning to such an extent that acknowledgement of the true cost for producing these utilities has often been overlooked while merely meeting the exigencies of plant operation. It appears that continued substantial increases in cost of the raw energy materials for plant utility services will force managers and plant engineers alike to study more thoroughly the extent to which these services may be committed for production and operation. Such study must be followed with analysis of the essential costs from figures for input, output, production, and financial values.

TYPES OF ANALYSES EXPECTED

The required data will be developed from analyses that fall into two general classes: (1) engineering analysis and (2) cost analysis.

Many times during design stages, too much time is spent analyzing engineering operations without performing an economic analysis of the total utility system to establish real costs that will include amortization, interest, taxes, etc. These may frequently outweigh the cost of operating and maintaining the system. Likewise, first costs rather than life-cycle economics have been the prime selection factor, but increasing energy costs can now easily influence the need for reanalysis to determine long-range operation costs before as well as after initial operations. Changing conditions caused by the energy and environmental impacts create a need for more precise utility analyses.

Engineering Analysis

The engineering analysis of utility production costs in any commercial, industrial, or institutional plant will usually include a substantial balance between hindsight and fore-sight, since the investigation will concern an existing, rather than a forecast, set of conditions. Although the installation may have gone well into its expected normal operating life, the analysis will still develop at least four important factors.
1. Appraise the whole application
2. Determine existing efficiency
3. Need for increased efficiency
4. Show the true operating costs

Where fuel, water, or electric power costs are a significant part of the overall operating cost, an appraisal of the ultimate application becomes increasingly important as a measure of performance and financial impact. A balance of the impacts of energy, economics, and environment upon the utilities systems and the total plant application must be determined. From this the following decisions should be made:
1. Elimination of wasteful processes
2. Replacement of high energy users
3. Use of alternate energy approaches
4. Reassessment of process practices

New and altering conditions require a continuous analysis of utilities costs.

With the creation of high energy-cost situations, there is greater need for expressions of efficiency in terms of use and end product than a simple basic expression of utilization for any single component in the chain.

$$\text{Efficiency} = \frac{\text{output quantity of service or product}}{\text{input in terms of units of source energy}}$$

An expression of boiler efficiency is an excellent control measure for a single component in a chain; but the expression in terms of useful production units, cost per square foot of heated space per thousand degree days, etc., may produce figures more revealing than others as a measure of financial performance and the position for a business entity.

Too frequently, the plant engineer is unable to relate the true cost of utilities to the cost of the end product. The distribution of source energies (e.g., purchased electricity), the transformation of source energies to other energies and their distribution to all components of the organization, the costs of operation and maintenance of each utility system, and the "ownership" costs of the utilities plants and systems are all needed to establish the true utilities cost. This can only be achieved through the availability of cost and quantity records and the establishment of metering procedures.

Purchased Utilities

There are a number of factors for consideration in the examination of purchased utility costs. The effect of loading of a system on the basic rate structures may sometimes justify major engineering rearrangements for beneficial cost reduction. This often enters a specialized field of engineering analysis, but each plant engineer must be aware of whether purchased power cost is influenced by:

1. A basic power rate
2. A basic rate with modifiers
3. Special application rates
4. Off-peak rates

An overall efficiency analysis, a departmental analysis, or a unit output determination made on a continuing basis becomes an important engineering control function for purchased utility services.

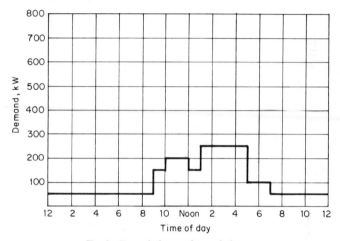

Fig. 1 Typical electric demand chart.

Demand rates for all utilities are usually justified, but they also are an important criterion in utility cost analysis. System load factors are often so poor that, when coupled with demands for reliability (avoiding downtime), they result in large and unwieldly installations which incur higher utility charges because they are poorly utilized.

For such utilities as gas, water, etc., or electric power used to produce compressed air, the demand and load factors do not receive the same analysis because the money value of the utility charge is not in evidence. Consequently, each type of service that is subject to utility analysis should be reviewed for demand and load factors with a simple graphic representation as shown in Fig. 1. Building area is 50,000 square feet, connected lighting requires 5 watts per square foot, connected motors require 80 kW, other loads amount to 60 kW, and institutional hours are 9 A.M. to 5 P.M. Monday through Friday with no variations.

The basis for similar charts is shown in Fig. 2, based upon a percentage of capacity versus time. Charts for any specific type of analysis can be developed for use in varying types of utility analysis.

In the analysis of purchased utilities with rates in steps at varying costs, a useful graph can be developed for rapid and relatively accurate determination of the cost for different amounts of power. These are usually termed *energy rate blocks*.

DETERMINING REAL COSTS

In all business and corporate structures today, because of the rising energy costs which affect all utilities costs, executives are faced with the need for sound understanding of total plant utilities costs. In developing the required information to determine these costs, the engineering analysis should precede the cost analysis, so that actual utilities needs and total utilities costs are used to establish the *real costs*. The final determination of costs for utilities services may often be staggering to management when the combined engineering and cost figures become available. There are many instances where the cost to generate steam (e.g., 75 cents per thousand pounds) was used to determine factory production costs, whereas the real cost was nearly double the generation cost.

FINANCIAL ANALYSIS

A financial analysis will be the second step in a determination of *real costs*. This involves the calculation of the burden imposed as the result of a money expenditure which is termed *ownership costs* and sometimes *fixed costs*. These are important charges for any utility analysis. Frequently, however, they are not a direct concern in plant engineering

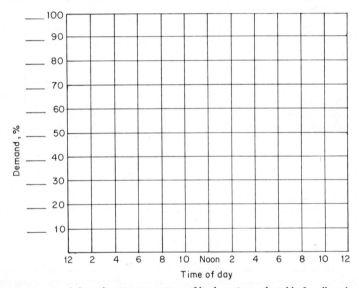

Fig. 2 Sample of chart showing percentage of load vs. time, adaptable for all analyses.

studies, because in any given operation, this may be considered entirely an accounting matter.

The basic organizational policy for financial analysis can result in wide variations in the relative value of in-plant and on-site utility operations, particularly for cases where "total energy" is concerned. Fully as many operations have encountered trouble from financial misplanning as from technical shortcomings. There is a need for the fullest cooperation between engineering and accounting operations in all utility matters, whether the case involves the generation of steam or electricity; the distribution of water, gas, or refrigeration; or the delivery of compressed air.

There are values that influence a decision to purchase in a certain manner. These influence institutional, commercial, and industrial utility operations and include:

1. Tax considerations
2. Cash flow
3. Profit and loss
4. Initial investment costs
5. Ownership costs
6. Operating costs

Cash flow The flow of cash is a measure of the stream of dollars going in and out of a business and available during a given period. This stream is important to every business decision. Every business and institution must maintain it in order to operate.

Profit and loss   A regular statement of the operating position of a business at any given time reveals the financial course, determines its performance, and thereby influences decisions.

Initial Investment Costs

The total cost of generating equipment, auxiliaries, controls, separate housing facilities, distribution lines, supports, pumping stations or substations, valves, etc., necessary to generate and/or distribute a utility is the initial investment cost; the cost of subsequent additions to a system will become a part of the investment cost.   Too frequently this cost, rather than life-cycle considerations, is the motivator in equipment selection.   Initial cost should be balanced against:

1. Operating life
2. Efficiency
3. Energy availability
4. Maintainability
5. Operating costs

An analysis of fund availability, interest rates, initial investment costs, and depreciation allowances will determine which of the following methods of acquisition is best suited for the business, institution, or industry.

Low-equity end:

1. A lease
2. Loans, bank, manufacturer, securities
3. Loans guaranteed by others
4. Conditional sales contract
5. First and second mortgages
6. Chattel

High-equity end:

7. Full payment from available funds

Ownership Costs

The financial analysis of utility costs must consider that certain costs start at the moment of acquisition and continue as long as the plant or equipment is in the possession or service of the business and sometimes thereafter.   These include:

1. Insurance and taxes
2. Interest
3. Amortization
4. Depreciation

Insurance and taxes   These costs are usually on a prorata basis from overall billings. Special insurance items like boiler and compressor insurance may be applied directly. These may be substantial costs and should not be overlooked in any analysis.

Interest   This represents "rental" on the money involved by investing in the utility installation.   It becomes an extremely significant part of the cost for any system, equipment, or production facility.   If the installation had not been made and the same sum of money had remained in a bank account or were invested elsewhere, it would have earned a return according to the current money market.   Therefore replacing it becomes an expense for the operation.

As the principal sum is reduced by payments, the amount of interest changes from a high figure initially to a lower amount toward the end of the payout period.   A handy calculation in a typical analysis is the determination of "average interest" which, when combined with straight-line depreciation, gives a uniform sum for each year of the cost basis.   An approximate formula for computing average interest is:

$$\text{Average interest} = \left(\frac{Pi}{2}\right)\left(\frac{n+1}{n}\right)$$

where P = amount of investment
    i = interest rate used
    n = number of year for period used

The average interest values can be also obtained from standard financial data like those given in Fig. 3.

n	i 2%	3%	4%	5%	6%	7%	8%	10%
1	0.0200	0.0300	0.0400	0.0500	0.0600	0.0700	0.0800	0.1000
2	0.0150	0.0225	0.0300	0.0375	0.0450	0.0525	0.0600	0.0750
3	0.0133	0.0200	0.0267	0.0333	0.0400	0.0467	0.0533	0.0667
4	0.0125	0.0188	0.0250	0.0313	0.0375	0.0438	0.0500	0.0625
5	0.0120	0.0180	0.0240	0.0300	0.0360	0.0420	0.0480	0.0600
6	0.0117	0.0175	0.0233	0.0292	0.0350	0.0408	0.0467	0.0583
7	0.0114	0.0171	0.0229	0.0286	0.0343	0.0400	0.0457	0.0571
8	0.0113	0.0169	0.0225	0.0281	0.0338	0.0394	0.0450	0.0563
9	0.0111	0.0167	0.0222	0.0278	0.0333	0.0389	0.0444	0.0556
10	0.0110	0.0165	0.0220	0.0275	0.0330	0.0385	0.0440	0.0550

Fig. 3 Average interest factors for use in approximate method of determining annual cost of capital recovery.

Amortization This represents the repayment of money against the amount expended for an installation. The debt is usually repaid in monthly, quarterly, or annual installments. Payments can be calculated with formulas available in standard financial or economics references. The payments, although identical for each period, change in proportion to the amount that goes toward reducing the principal and the portion that pays the interest. Under certain circumstances, amortization becomes a utility system cost.

Depreciation This is a very essential part of any utility financial analysis since it provides for the ultimate replacement of equipment and facility (management of the reserves also is of major significance). Depreciation is an allowance for wear and tear on equipment, machinery, and buildings. Basically the rules for time and rate are set by the U.S. Internal Revenue Service, which allows the deduction of depreciation allowances against taxable income. In this fashion, depreciation puts dollars into the business bank account.

Depreciation calculations are equally applicable for institutional operations, even when not taxable, because equipment must ultimately be replaced. However, government operations may be required to accomplish repayment of bonds or other forms of obligations used to finance the original installation without provision for any reserve for replacement. The bond repayments are calculated as amortization.

An accounting department may have selected one of four usual methods of calculation of annual depreciation charges, which are as follows:

1. The straight-line method, over a number of years
2. The 150 percent declining-balance method
3. The double-declining-balance method
4. The sum-of-the-years digits method

Year	*Straight line*	*Double declining balance*	*150% declining balance*	*Sum-of-the years digits*
1	$100	$199	$149	$182
2	100	160	127	163
3	100	128	109	146
4	100	102	92	127
5	100	82	78	109
6	100	66	63	91
7	100	52	54	73
8	100	42	46	54
9	100	33	39	37
10	100	136	243	18

Fig. 4 Comparative depreciation figures.

The most simple method for calculating depreciation is the straight-line method:

$$\text{Annual depreciation} = \frac{\text{depreciation basis*}}{\text{depreciation life}}$$

The other methods are called *accelerated,* which means that there is more depreciation taken in the earlier years after installation is made. Figure 4 shows the comparable depreciation using each method for a piece of equipment that cost $1,500 installed and having an estimated salvage value of $500 (i.e., a depreciation basis of $1,000).

Regardless of the method of depreciation used for accounting purposes, the use of straight-line depreciation in life-cycle costing is recommended to establish the fixed-cost factor. Figure 5 illustrates the use of a capital-recovery factor (CRF) to combine straight-line depreciation with average interest for analysis used.

Operating Costs

The basic data for determining the operating cost of any plant utility will include:
1. Fuel input
2. Purchased utilities
3. Other utility input (water, steam, electricity, etc.)
4. Supplies and materials
5. Labor and related costs
6. Supervision and overhead
7. Maintenance, preventive and emergency
8. Rent, contract costs, etc.

The costs of these items should be grouped for each utility as (1) generation/purchase costs and (2) distribution costs.

Cost analysis forms   Basically all that is required to make a cost analysis is the real costs and the units of utility delivered. In a simple operation (e.g., heating a building directly), the cost-analysis form is as shown in Fig. 6.

Where the cost of several utilities is to be incorporated into more than one product, the plant engineer should refer to economic texts to better understand the complex procedures required by some accounting practices to establish cost distribution. Annual fixed costs for each utility can be prorated for each product and unit cost can be established based on planned production (See Fig. 7).

However, accelerating energy costs require more frequent than yearly evaluation of unit costs; monthly analysis of the unit operating cost will assist in the management of the utilities system, but reestablishment of the simplest form for cost analysis is shown in Fig. 8; but however simple the form, all costs must be included and rates should be made only quarterly. The degree of management of the utilities systems desired dictates the degree of detail in the collection of costs. Only quantities of utilities delivered are used to establish unit cost.

Value of Cost Analysis

To establish the utility cost for a unit of product, the following formula is applicable:

$$\text{Total unit cost of product} = \frac{\text{sum(unit cost of each utility} \times \text{quantity used)} + \text{fixed cost}}{\text{no. of produced units}}$$

This tool will assist the production engineer and plant manager to determine:
1. The impact of utilities costs on product cost
2. Advisability of retaining marginally competitive products
3. Production scheduling
4. Efficiency of utilities in production

The establishment of real unit costs and operating unit costs will assist the plant engineer to evaluate:
1. The efficiency of each utility system
2. The impact of environmental and energy cost on utilities

* Depreciation basis = total installed cost − estimated salvage value

Rate of return or interest rate, percent

Years	3½	4½	6	8	10	12	15	20
2	0.52640	0.53400	0.54544	0.56077	0.57619	0.59170	0.61512	0.65455
4	.27225	.27874	.28859	.30192	.31547	.32923	.35027	.38629
6	.18767	.19388	.20336	.21632	.22961	.24323	.26424	.30071
8	.14548	.15161	.16104	.17401	.18744	.20130	.22285	.26061
10	.12024	.12638	.13587	.14903	.16275	.17698	.19925	.23852
12	0.10348	0.10967	0.11928	0.13270	0.14676	0.16144	0.18448	0.22526
14	.09157	.09782	.10758	.12130	.13575	.15087	.17469	.21689
16	.08268	.08902	.09895	.11298	.12782	.14339	.16795	.21144
18	.07582	.08224	.09236	.10670	.12193	.13794	.16319	.20781
20	.07036	.07688	.08718	.10185	.11746	.13388	.15976	.20536
25	0.06067	0.06744	0.07823	0.09368	0.11017	0.12750	0.15470	0.20212
30	.05437	.06139	.07265	.08883	.10608	.12414	.15230	.20085
35	.05000	.05727	.06897	.08580	.10369	.12232	.15113	.20034
40	.04683	.05434	.06646	.08386	.10226	.12130	.15056	.20014

Fig. 5 Table of capital recovery factors (CRF).

A. Fixed costs
    Ownership cost (cost recovery factor × investment)   _____
    Insurance and taxes   _____
    Interest   _____
    Total   _____
B. Operation costs
    Fuel cost   _____
    Purchased utilities: Water   _____
                    Electricity   _____
                    Sewage   _____
    Labor   _____
    Supervision and overhead   _____
    Maintenance   _____
    Supplies   _____
    Miscellaneous (contracts, etc.)   _____
    Total annual utilities cost   _____

Fig. 6 A simple cost anlaysis form.

1. Ownership cost (CFR) (IC)   _____
2. Interest   _____
3. Insurance and taxes   _____
4. Annual fixed cost (AFC) of utility
   (sum of lines 1, 2, and 3)   _____
5. Percentage of utility used in
   product*   _____
6. AFC of utility for product
   (line 4 × line 5)   _____
7. Total units of product per annum
   (planned or historical mean)   _____
8. Fixed cost per unit of product
   (line 6 ÷ line 7)   _____
9. Total fixed cost per unit of
   product (sum of line 8 for all
   columns)   _____

* When metering of a utility is unavailable, engineering estimates may have to be used.

Fig. 7 Unit fixed-cost form.

Item utility	*Heat,* 10^6 *Btu*	*Electricity,* *MWH*	*Water, etc.* *kgal*
1. Quantity produced			
2. Less quantity used in production			
3. Net production			
4. Quantity purchased			
5. Produced and purchased			
6. Line loss			
7. Quantity delivered			
8. Fuel cost			
9. Labor cost			
10. Maintenance			
11. Supplies			
12. Supervision and overhead			
13. Contracts, etc.			
14. Cost of other utilities			
15. Total utility cost (lines 8–14)			
16. Less utility transferred out			
17. Net utility cost			
18. Unit cost (line 17 ÷ line 7)			

Fig. 8 Simple operating cost analysis form.

3. The advisability of in-house versus purchased utility

It will provide the plant engineer with a realistic management tool for decision making, conservation efforts, and cost control.

REFERENCES

1. *ASHRAE Handbook and Product Directory, 1973 Systems,* American Society of Heating, Refrigeration and Air Conditioning Engineers,
2. Norman N. Barish: *Economic Analysis for Engineering and Managerial Decision Making,* McGraw-Hill, New York
3. W. Grant Ireson and W. L. Grant, eds.: "Engineering Economy" by Paul T. Norton, Jr., *Handbook of Industrial Engineering and Management,* Prentice-Hall, Englewood Cliffs, N.J., 1971.

Chapter **2**

Energy Source Selection Studies

ROBERT G. CAUGHEY
The H. K. Ferguson Company

DESCRIPTION OF THE PROBLEM

The energy used in an industrial facility can be a significant part of the total operating cost. Its cost can vary from 5 to 10 percent of the total in a light manufacturing plant to 40 to 50 percent in such large energy consuming processes as electric-furnace steel-making and aluminum refining. In these latter cases, the cost of energy may determine the plant location. (Note that aluminum refining plants are concentrated in the Northwest, where economical hydroelectric power is available.) In all cases, the cost of energy must be established as an aid in determining manufacturing costs; this is an absolute necessity in making a selection from the various types of energy available at a particular site.

The degree of accuracy required in estimating energy costs will, of course, depend on the relationship of energy costs to other manufacturing costs. In the light manufacturing plants mentioned above, energy costs will be less significant; in the heavy-use industries, however, it will be most important to determine energy use accurately.

The first step in the selection of energy is to determine the amounts that will be used of each type, such as electrical or heat. This estimate must consist of two parts: the first is the maximum rate at which energy is used, which is called the demand. The second part is the total units of energy consumed; this depends upon the times at which the maximum demand is required or the amount of partial utilization of the maximum demand.

The next step is to determine the initial costs of the facilities necessary to utilize each form of energy. These costs are determined by two factors: the demand and the form of energy utilized.

Finally, maintenance costs must be estimated for each type of facility. Then the total cost (initial, operating, and maintenance) can be determined. This provides the basis by which types of energy may be selected.

ESTIMATING DEMAND

Manufacturers of process equipment always include in their specifications the energy requirements. These are the best source of data for estimating demand. After a total is arrived at, a demand factor is applied. This demand factor is most often the result of experience in the field and knowledge of manufacturing techniques. A plant with continuous flow of product will usually have a high demand factor (0.75 to 0.95), while a job-shop-type operation may have low factors (0.30 to 0.60). In the latter case, the larger the number of separate machines, the smaller the demand factor.

Often a plant engineer is asked to make an energy selection before a plant layout is available; in this case, data from similar operations are necessary to make an estimate. For this discussion, we will assume that the electrical demand will be in kilowatts (kW) and the heating and cooling demand in thousand of British thermal units per hour (MBH), which we will assume the same as pounds of steam per hour (1 lb/h steam ≈ 1000 Btu/h). For small machines, assume 1 horsepower ≈ 1 kW; for larger machines, the actual kW load should be obtained from manufacturers' data. For industries in which there is a byproduct which can be utilized as fuel, the amount should be estimated (in MBH available) for use later in the selection process.

Ventilation requirements may produce heating and cooling demands greater than any other single requirement, especially where there are extremes in outside temperatures. Local or national (OSHA) codes, as well as operating experience, will determine the exhaust air requirements. Wherever possible, outside air should be brought directly to the process requiring exhaust. In most cases, this will not be possible, and makeup air must be introduced into the space: to do this it must be heated or cooled, depending upon the space requirements. The amount of heating required may be calculated by the equation:

$$MBH = \frac{(cfm) \ (1.08) \ (T.D., °F)}{1,000}$$

where cfm is the cubic feet per minute of makeup air and T.D. is the temperature difference between the outside air and the space condition. The minimum outside air condition at which the maximum load occurs may be obtained from the local weather bureau. For cooling requirements, 1.08 times the T.D. must be replaced by the difference in total heat of air (in Btu/lb) times 4.5.* Because the ventilation load may be most significant, it is important that it be accurately estimated.

Loads due to heating and cooling requirements should be estimated using generally accepted methods for transmission heat loss and gain and solar and interior heat gain.† This requires a relatively complete set of building plans and a plant layout. When such information is not available and it has been ascertained that the resultant load will not be a significant part of the total, it is possible to estimate these loads in a very broad sense. For temperate climates, the heating load will be about 0.040 MBH per square foot and cooling load, 0.020 MBH per square foot. For southern and northern climates, these figures should be changed in an appropriate direction by about 50 percent.

ESTIMATING CONSUMPTION

Consumption of energy will depend directly on the time of use. The term "load factor" is used to show the ratio of time that energy is used at the maximum demand rate to the total time. For example, when process equipment is used at its maximum demand

---

* See ASHRAE *Handbook of Fundamentals 1972*, p. 422 (51).
† Op. cit., chaps. 21 and 22.

for one 8-hour shift for 5 days a week, the load factor would be $(8/24)(5/7) = 0.24$. The higher the load factor, the greater will be the utilization of plant equipment. Another item related to the load factor is the average demand: this is the total consumption for a given period of time divided by the time. It is obvious, then, that the load factor is also the ratio of the average demand to the maximum demand for a given period of time.

The consumption of energy for a given interval of time for process equipment is then the product of the maximum demand, the load factor, and the interval of time. It will be expressed as kWh, 1000 Btu, or pounds steam. The consumption of energy for ventilation and heating will be complicated, for it will depend not only on the time of operation but also on the outdoor conditions. Outdoor conditions in a particular area are usually well recorded by the weather bureau and expressed in degree days. Degree-days (D.D.) are defined as the number of days times the amount by which the outside temperature falls below 65°F. Therefore the heat energy required will be

$$1000 \text{ Btu} = (\text{MBH/T.D.}) \text{ (D.D.) (24)}$$

where MBH/T.D. is the maximum demand as previously calculated for ventilating and heating divided by the degree temperature difference. The amount of fuel used to provide this consumption can be determined by utilizing the energy value and its efficiency of utilization. For instance, the electrical consumption would be determined by using the relationship 1 kWh = 3400 Btu with an efficiency of 100 percent. For natural gas, use a heating value of 1000 Btu/ft³, and an efficiency of 80 percent; for fuel oil, the heating value will be between 140,000 and 160,000 Btu/gal, with an efficiency of 60 percent.

UTILIZATION FACILITIES

Utilization facilities are defined as the means by which the raw fuel or energy source is transferred into a form which can be used in the plant. Before the advent of the public utility, the utilization facility was a central power plant which burned coal or oil and transferred this into steam, shaft horsepower, or electricity. Today, such a plant is necessary only when no form of energy other than fuel is available. When electrical energy is available, an analysis still should be made to determine whether it would cost less to generate the electrical power than to purchase it from a utility. This is particularly true if the plant process produces a byproduct which can be used as fuel, as was previously mentioned.

Some plant processes can utilize the fuel directly as heat energy, while others require the conversion of fuel energy into heat energy, as steam, in a boiler. Steam is then used in the plant process, to generate electricity or for absorption refrigeration. Hence we will consider the boiler plant as the main central plant facility, and we will discuss the various ways in which this plant may be provided with fuel. As was mentioned earlier, first consideration must be given to any waste product or byproduct from the manufacturing process which can be used as fuel. Even though exotic methods may be necessary to burn such materials in the boiler and to eliminate ash from the products of combustion, use of these products will normally result in a minimum fuel cost.

Next to consider as a fuel is coal. This first-used fuel has been overshadowed in the past by petroleum products, but it is now in the limelight because this country does have an adequate coal reserve. Coal burning equipment does have the highest initial cost, especially when the pollution-preventing equipment, which is usually required, is included. Therefore the low fuel cost is offset by the high initial cost as well as a higher cost due to manpower operation and maintenance requirements.

Fuel oil is generally available in two categories: heavy and light. There are many names given to different grades of oil; but the heavy types all require some pretreatment. The lighter oil may be burned immediately, in a pressure atomizing, air atomizing, or rotary burner. Heavy oil usually has a higher heat value in Btu/gal and a lower cost, but estimates of this cost must be raised to account for the cost of heat and circulation necessary to burn the oil effectively. Recent antipollution regulations make necessary some additional equipment and in most cases require a low-sulfur fuel oil, the costs of which are likely to rise repeatedly because of increasing demand. The local cost situation must be accurately determined and the future costs estimated for any type of fuel oil.

Gaseous fuel is available in several types: liquified petroleum (LPG), natural gas, and many varieties of manufactured gas. The cost of LPG usually restricts its use to standby or emergency conditions. Manufactured gas comes in so many varieties that it is difficult to describe, and since its use is definitely minimal, we will consider only natural gas. However, recent shortages have limited the use of this also. If natural gas is not available, it is probably wiser to consider oil or coal as a fuel rather than other types of gaseous fuel. Natural gas requires only the absolute minimum of fuel-burning and pollution control equipment, so its initial cost will be less than that of any other fuel. Most utility companies offer an interruptible gas rate to large users and require such a rate if the demand exceeds a certain figure. This means that standby fuel is necessary. In the case of a boiler plant, this is relatively easy, for combination-type oil-gas burners and fuel oil storage are both easily obtainable and of minimal cost.

The central plant requires forms of energy other than fuel to operate the auxiliary equipment and/or for electrical generators. Fuel burners, circulating and feedwater pumps, draft fans, and pollution control equipment may use high-pressure steam, in most cases, or electrical energy; this can amount to about 5 to 15 percent of the total plant energy capability.

With a central plant, one of the major decisions will be whether to purchase electricity or generate it. Purchase of electrical energy from a utility company will normally be most advantageous because they have the advantage of economy of scale and greater diversity of load. However, there are two instances when the purchase of electricity will probably cost more than local generation: one has been mentioned before, when fuel is available from the plant process. The other is when medium- or low-pressure steam is needed in the plant process. In this case, the plant can use exhaust steam from the turbine which drives the electrical generator, therefore acting as the condenser and increasing the thermal efficiency of the plant.

In the range of quantities that normally interest the plant engineer, the electric utility uses a demand rate; i.e., costs are determined not only by the energy consumed (in kWh) but also by the maximum demand (kW) within the billing period. Utilization facilities for the use of outside electrical power are minimal; at the most they could include stepdown transformers, which will allow a lower electrical rate. Also, complete monitoring facilities should be provided (if not part of the utility company equipment) to determine the extent and time of peak demand. If demand peaks are excessive and load factor is low, effort should be made to schedule operation, so they do not contribute to the peak demand. Equipment is available to do this automatically; its cost and that of revised production schedules can very often be paid by the savings in electrical utility rates. One item should also be mentioned here in connection with utility company electric power supply: In some localities, the reliability of supply is not sufficient for the manufacturing process. If study of past performance of the utility company indicates a problem, this could be a reason for in-plant generation of power. Otherwise, it would require some standby generation equipment, which would involve additional initial expense.

In many localities steam is available as a utility, and its purchase may offer significant savings over plant-installed and plant-operated steam production facilities. It will always allow less initial cost, but its total cost over many years must be carefully evaluated and compared with in-plant production. In like manner, chilled water may be available for refrigeration, so its cost must also be carefully evaluated.

In some plant processes, fuel is required as a part of the process in addition to, or instead of, its use in the central plant. If gaseous fuel is required and an interruptible gas rate is required by the utility (as was previously mentioned), the standby fuel can be quite costly and require extensive equipment to assure quick changeover. At the present time, the reduction in gas supply and rising cost of LPG make such interruptible rates more expensive. A thorough analysis should be made of these costs, as they will, of course, affect production costs.

It is apparent from the preceding discussion of equipment necessary to utilize different types of fuel or energy supply that many choices are available to the plant engineer. Some choices may be eliminated by the plant process requirements and by local conditions of supply, but a thorough study of the remaining choices must be made to establish the initial costs of the plant energy utilization facilities.

TOTAL COSTS

We have now discussed that part of the operating costs due to the consumption of energy and the initial costs that are dependent on the rate at which energy is consumed (the demand) and the type of energy involved, which determines the type of facility required. The facility type also determines the maintenance cost, which usually is the most difficult to estimate. Maintenance cost is not always a function of initial costs, although the most expensive equipment is most often the least expensive to maintain, but under special circumstances there are notable exceptions to this rule. There is some published information on maintenance costs,* but the best source is experience. Also, local contractors who specialize in maintenance work are a good source of estimates of maintenance costs.

Also important to determine are the initial costs of the various types of equipment necessary for energy utilization. Some published information is available** on initial costs of various pieces of equipment, although these sometimes are too general and do not include some particular items of fuel utilization equipment. Suppliers are then the most satisfactory sources for estimates of equipment. Once the initial costs are established, the yearly cost of ownership can be found by using procedures well described in engineering economics textbooks.† These procedures unfortunately require the engineer to establish the cost of money, or interest rates, which should better be determined by the company's financial department. It is, therefore, most necessary to check with these other authorities before making decisions based on owning cost.

Operating costs are now defined as those dependent only on the amount of energy consumed. The cost of purchased energy sources can easily be determined by using published utility rates or asking for proposals from nonregulated suppliers for the amounts of energy previously determined. The yearly costs so estimated can then be added to the owning and maintenance costs to arrive at the total cost.

FINAL SELECTION

Final selection of energy sources will be made on the basis of total costs as well as other factors for which it is most difficult to establish cost. As was noted, total costs depend significantly on economic factors such as cost of money and cash flow requirements. Differences in initial cost of equipment, which produce differences in operating costs, must always be examined in view of the expected depreciation of initial investment. In some instances, higher initial costs cannot be justified by lower operating costs alone.

Other factors that can affect the energy selection are the process requirements (as noted previously), the time stability of the process involved, and market considerations. The importance of these factors can outweigh pure cost considerations, so that selection can become more subjective than objective. In either case, the guidelines established here can be used as the basis of selection.

* Steam-Electric Plant Construction Cost and Annual Production Expenses, Federal Power Commission, issued annually. Also *ASHRAE Handbook—1973 Systems,* chap. 44.

** *Building Construction Cost Data,* Robert Snow Means Co., Inc., P.O. Box 36 Duxbury, Mass. 02332, published each year, and *Current Construction Costs,* Lee Saylor, Inc., 1541 Palos Verdes Mall, Walnut Creek, California 94596, published each year.

† Grant and Ireson, *Principles of Engineering Economy,* Ronald Press, New York.

Chapter **3**

On-Line Scheduling
of Generating Equipment

J. R. WITMEYER, P.E.
Utilities Division Staff
Naval Facilities Engineering Command

PLANNING UTILITIES OPERATION

Historically, the scheduling of utilities generating equipment was a luxury. Few plant engineers were able to supply utilities upon request, and the older installations lacked the flexibility to meet requirements at maximum efficiency. As long as energy was cheap and abundant, this situation was permitted to continue; but environmental impacts and the availability of domestic fuels have limited the choice of fuel and escalated the cost of energy.

The true cost of utilities has become a significant part of the product cost and must be controlled. The choice of which equipment to use (for heat and electric generation, air conditioning and refrigeration, etc.) and the coordination of the utility with production requirements necessitate the planning of utilities operations.

FACTORS INFLUENCING SCHEDULING

The plant engineer must consider the efficiency of the generating equipment, the cost to operate, and the demand for each utility in order to establish operating schedules.

    ● Efficiency—the ratio of input energy to output energy over the normal operating load range

    ● Cost—the sum of the fixed and variable cost to operate the equipment and system in order to provide the required amount of that utility

• Demand—the amount of each utility (i.e., kilowatts of electricity, tons of air conditioning, etc.) needed for any particular hour

Demand

A complete profile of utility requirements is a primary prerequisite for load scheduling. In office buildings and shopping centers, the requirements (demand) for heating, cooling, and electricity are directly associated with working schedules and climatic conditions; however, in industrial complexes, the production loads add an additional parameter. Therefore the plant engineer should develop hourly demand curves for each utility for different periods of the year and for different production schedules. Figure 1 shows

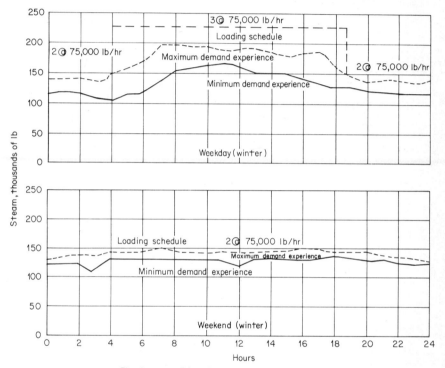

Fig. 1 Typical hourly steam demand profile.

typical steam-load curves for two different days based on hourly demand. This information can then be assembled into a forecast, as shown in Fig. 2, for yearly requirements.

Profile curves for electrical requirements (shown in Fig. 3) should be separated to show both demand and usage for in-house generation and purchased power (Fig. 4). Requirements for other utilities (i.e., air conditioning, compressed air, etc.) can be collected and graphed in a similar manner. The plant engineer will then be able to determine how many production units will be required and for what periods of time.

Efficiency

There has been a tendency to assume that the manufacturer's rated efficiency (MRE) is valid for the greater part of the life of the equipment. In most cases the actual efficiency is lower, due to improper calibration of controls, minimum maintenance of equipment, or operating ranges. The actual efficiency of each piece of generating equipment under operating conditions should be plotted and the most efficient operating ranges determined. The plant engineer should replot his efficiency curves whenever controls are recalibrated or any major maintenance is performed on the equipment.

Scheduling of specific units in a multiunit operation should consider what operating range will be required of each unit and the efficiency of the unit in that range. Maximum efficiency of the combination of units selected is more important than the efficiency of an individual unit.

Cost

While the cost to produce a utility (steam, electricity, etc.) consists of both fixed and variable costs, the selection of which unit to use under specific conditions should be based on the variable cost. Figures 5 and 6 depict cost curves over the normal operating range.

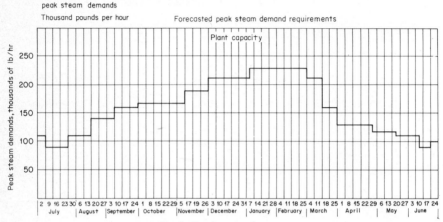

Fig. 2   Yearly steam forecast.

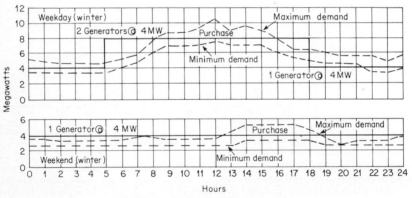

Fig. 3   Hourly electrical demand profile.

These curves were developed for specific efficiencies, and energy cost and the shape and relationship will vary only when efficiencies change. The values of the ordinate (y axis) are dependent on energy costs and will need periodic adjustments, while the abscissa (x axis) will remain constant.

Scheduling

Having determined load requirements, generating unit efficiencies, and the variable cost to operate, the plant engineer has the necessary elements to schedule on-line generation. For a particular period, the engineer will be able to determine the projected requirements, the number of units necessary to meet the requirements, and which units will be most cost-effective to operate. The following example shows how this information can best be used:

A plant has five boilers, each of which delivers 75,000 lb/h. Which boilers should be scheduled for use during the month of December?

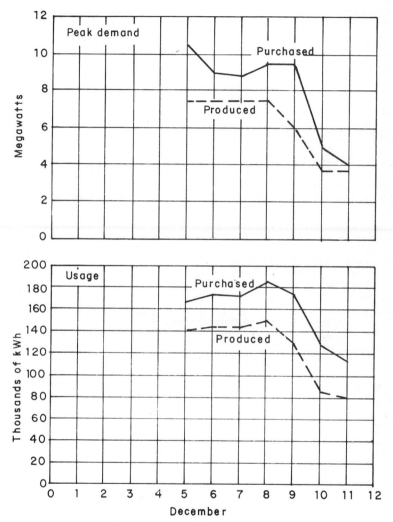

Fig. 4 Electrical demand and usage profiles.

1. From Fig. 2, the forecast for December is 210,000 pounds of steam per hour of maximum demand.

2. From Fig. 1, it becomes evident that three (3) boilers will be necessary during peak periods and two (2) at night and during weekends.

3. From Fig. 5, boilers 2, 4, and 5 should be scheduled during the peak period and boilers 4 and 5 during the nine (9) hours of lower loading at night.

The question that now arises is what the schedule should be for weekends and prolonged

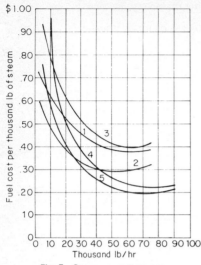

Fig. 5   Steam vs. cost curves.

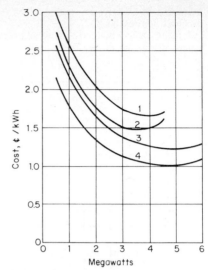

Fig. 6   Electricity vs. cost curves scheduling.

holiday periods.   It is obvious that additional information such as the cost of an idle piece of equipment must be determined.

4. From Table 1 the cost to bank boiler 2 for the 55-hour weekend would be $154 versus $77.80 to shut down and start up.   Since fuel costs have escalated over 300 percent since these charts and tables were prepared, the choice becomes more obvious.

The profile shown in Fig. 2 can also be used to determine when equipment can be made

TABLE 1   Banking and Startup Cost for Boilers and Turbines

	Boilers		Turbines
Unit	Banking cost per hour*	Startup cost†	Startup cost
1	$1.40	$121.70	$14.64
2	2.80	77.80	10.19
3	3.90	65.90	11.20
4	3.70	92.00	13.60
5	4.50	113.20	

* Banking cost per hour is determined on basis of fuel cost.
† Start up costs are determined on basis of fuel inefficiencies and additional maintenance resulting from startups.

available.   Similarly, scheduling decisions such as that developed in the example will determine the feasibility and cost of making minor repairs during weekends versus replacing on-line equipment with units that are more costly to operate.

The need to develop a scheduling plan becomes more urgent as fuel cost escalates. The development of costs, requirements, and efficiency charts and graphs is time-consuming.   But the result is an efficient and cost-effective operation and a reduction in energy requirements.

Chapter 4

Energy Use Factors

F. J. PACKARD
The H. K. Ferguson Company

INTRODUCTION

A factor of increasing importance in the successful design and operation of a modern plant is the assessment of energy demands. All products require some degree of energy expenditure before they reach the consumer in usable form. The Btu's or kilowatthours per ton, pound, or unit have constantly increased over the years as production has become more automated. Abundant energy has permitted the expansion of our economy and the increase of our gross national product to seemingly limitless proportions. Unfortunately, with the depletion of some of our energy sources and the delayed technology in the development of new sources, we find ourselves faced with limitations on energy that are sure to affect operation, expansion, and consideration of new manufacturing facilities. We have come to regard electrical energy as among the lesser of the many problems involved in plant operation. Power has been available, inexpensive, and dependable. It is now a fact that the supply of electrical power is becoming increasingly short and we can expect to pay more for what power will be available. If kilowatts are to become a precious commodity, then, we must be more respectful of their use. Watt wasting must be halted. Our energy must be put to the most efficient use.

The following discussions, recommendations, and suggested procedures are provided to aid the plant engineer in properly evaluating electrical energy requirements and to generally reduce the cost of electrical systems. They are intended to be used as a guide or checklist and do not preclude the use of the engineer's judgment or knowledge in specific industry applications.

REVIEWING EXISTING INSTALLATIONS

Finding and correcting energy-wasting conditions in most plants is like "shooting fish in a barrel," according to an expert who has been engaged in such investigations for many years in a large, multiplant company's plant engineering department. Watt wasters are so prevalent in most plants that one hardly knows where to begin.

Power Factor Correction

A good place to start is at the plant's incoming electrical service. Most utility rate schedules place some sort of penalty on low power factor. In many cases, the penalty charges are avoided through the use of large banks of static capacitors connected to the main distribution bus at such voltages as 13,800, 4,160, or 2,400 volts. The capacitor banks are generally rated to provide leading reactive kVA sufficient to satisfy the utilities requirements, and their cost is reimbursed over a comparatively short period of time. But what of all the wattless power downstream? The proper place to correct power factor is at or as near as possible to the load. Capacitor units may be placed at the motor, as permitted by the National Electrical Code. Here, the capacitors will be switched with the load, an ideal situation. Capacitors may also be connected to motor control center or starter rack buses. In these cases, the benefits of smaller feeder requirements and release of additional transformer capacity may be realized. The type, location, and rating of capacitor banks may be determined using conventional methods that are readily available.

Excess Switchgear

It is not unusual to find distribution voltage switchgear installations with a multitude of expensive circuit breakers feeding relatively small loads on a one-breaker–one-load center design concept. It is wasteful of initial cost, maintenance dollars, and space to permit such conditions. For example, a 1,200-ampere circuit breaker should be carrying a minimum of 8,000 kVA at 13,800 volts. A large lineup of circuit breakers servicing light loads in a plant distribution system is a needless waste of equipment and poor economy.

Retired switchgear may be used for expansion in other areas of the plant. Every piece of excess equipment on plant property is an added expense and a possible source of trouble.

Metering and Billing of Power

To find wasted power, it is necessary to provide adequate metering throughout the plant distribution system. Portable meters may be temporarily connected for survey purposes. The plant engineer should add load surveys to the scheduled maintenance list and maintain up-to-date load information and single-line diagrams for the entire plant system.

It may be desirable to install demand-limiting devices, such as an alarm that goes off when the rate-of-demand increase indicates a possibility of exceeding the established demand. Then nonessential loads can be manually dropped. A more sophisticated system may also be used, one that will automatically reduce load on a programmed basis as well as signal the urgency of a demand overrun. Plant engineers may be shocked to know that many utilities determine maximum demand, and the ensuing charges, by "eyeballing" a strip chart once a month. Having your own recording demand meter keyed to the utility's demand period, including a reactive kVA chart, on the incoming line power will allow you to check your power billing. The utility will not accept your readings for billing, but they may be willing to review their charts and, if warranted, make an adjustment in your bill.

Before renewing a power contract or entering into a new contract, the engineer should review the utility's applicable rate schedules to make sure that an alternate schedule may not be more beneficial to the company. In some cases, a *primary* service may offer advantages over a *secondary* service, or even vice versa. The engineer must be properly prepared to provide all necessary information before the company begins negotiation.

A load study of the type described herein will be of value in apprising the utility of the type, magnitude, and general nature of the service required.

Overmotoring

A villain in the wasted power melodrama is often the motor that is rated far in excess of the brake-horsepower needs of the driven equipment. It may be like the shoe sales-man's customer whose feet were size nine, but tens felt so good that he wore elevens. There are machinery manufacturers who deliberately oversize motors to ensure positive operation of the machine under conditions your plant may never experience. In other situations, it may have been expedient to use a spare motor or a pump that was sized for conditions that never materialized and is now operating at considerably reduced capacity. A number of motors loafing along at half load or less can have a significant effect on efficiency and power factor. You may now have suitable motors in stock to correct these misapplications.

Lighting

Most existing plants have at least one case of wasteful lighting. 1,000 watt high-bay incandescents can be replaced with a lesser number of 1,000-watt high-intensity dis-charge (HID) lamps in suitable fixtures. Incandescent yard lighting can be replaced by fewer wide-distribution fixtures with HID lamps, resulting in better lighting at less power and reduced maintenance.

Corridors, locker rooms, lavatories, and other areas that must be lighted at all times should be illuminated with fluorescent rather than incandescent lamps.

Electric Heating

Ovens, furnaces, and jacket heaters should be equipped with "watt saver" controls that will cut the power to such a point that only losses will be covered while maintaining temperature but that will provide adequate recovery power when needed. Insulation should be checked to make sure that heat losses are kept to a minimum. Even the brightest operators can be found leaving pipe-tracing circuits energized the year around so as not to be caught by an "early freeze." Where extensive heat tracing is used, suitable panels with thermostatic controls, contactors, and indicating lights will pay for them-selves in a relatively short time.

Any of the above power wasters may not appear to be significant when considered individually; however, collectively they may account for a considerable amount of poten-tial power saving.

DESIGNING NEW INSTALLATIONS

Once management considers the possibility of building a new plant or expanding an existing plant, the plant engineer begins the preparation of feasibility studies, flow sheets, and preliminary plant layouts. Energy requirements for the new facility may be based on material balance diagrams; estimated kilowatthours per ton, pound, or unit; or other pertinent data. Cost of power may be a deciding factor in the location of the plant, as is the case with aluminum reduction, chloralkali, phosphorus, and similar large power-consuming plants. Availability and cost of electrical power will become a prominent factor in locating the plant site, as the effect of ecology requirements, fuel, and operating costs drive the cost per kilowatthour upward.

Load Factors

Estimating electrical load requirements involves the use of certain factors. An under-standing of the factors and their application is essential.

Connected load is the sum of the full-load ratings of all electrical power-consuming equipment and devices connected to the system.

Average load is the average electrical load on the system over an extended period of time, usually 24 hours.

Peak load is the maximum rms power required over any period of time.

Demand is an average of the electrical power required for a specific load or group of loads on the system during a specified period of time. Utilities generally refer to 15- or 30-minute intervals of time in establishing demand requirements.

Maximum demand is the highest of all demands.

$$\text{Demand factor} = \frac{\text{maximum demand}}{\text{connected load}}$$

$$\text{Diversity factor} = \frac{\text{sum of individual maximum demands}}{\text{system maximum demand}}$$

$$\text{Load factor} = \frac{\text{average load for a period}}{\text{peak load for same period}}$$

Load Studies

A practical and fairly accurate method of estimating electrical load requirements is needed by plant engineers to establish utility demand, select equipment, calculate es-

THE H. K. FERGUSON CO.

JOB TITLE _____ W. O. NO. _____

LOAD STUDY FORMAT

DESCRIPTION _____

_____ SHEET NO. _____

MADE BY _____ CHECKED BY _____ DATE _____

Equip. No.	Description	H.P. Con-nected	H.P. Run-ning	A.L.	B.H.P.	Eff.	P.F. COS	TAN	kW	KVAR	Remark
A-207-M	CRYSTALIZER CIRC.	5	5	0.8	4	.83	.71	.99	3.60	3.56	
P-235-M	FEED PUMP	25	25	0.8	20	.89	.80	.75	16.76	12.57	
P-240-M	C.W. CIRC. PUMP	50	50	0.8	40	.92	.76	.86	32.4	27.7	
P-230-M	SALT SLURRY PUMP	1.5	1.5	0.8	1.2	.75	.64	1.20	1.19	1.43	
F-208-M	SALT CENTRIFUGE	25	25	0.8	20	.89	.80	.75	16.76	12.57	
P-212-M	CENTRATE PUMP	50	50	0.8	40	.92	.76	.86	32.4	27.7	
P-231-M	SALT PUMP	5	5	0.8	4	.83	.71	.99	3.60	3.56	
P-204-M	FLASH COOLER CIRC.	75	75	0.8	60	.915	.82	.70	48.9	34.1	
DA6000-1	POWER PANEL X-1	15KVA	15KVA	1.0	--	--	.90	.48	13.5	6.48	
A-202-M	CENTRATE PUMP	10	10	0.8	8	.86	.76	.87	6.94	6.04	
P-231-MS	SPARE	5	--	--	--	--	--	--	--	--	
P-249-M	CIRCULATING PUMP	10	10	0.8	8	.86	.76	.87	6.94	6.04	
P-209-M	FEED PUMP	75	75	0.8	60	.915	.82	.70	48.9	34.1	
P-209-MS	SPARE	75	--	--	--	--	--	--	--	--	
P-215-M	CENTRATE PUMP	30	30	0.8	24	.90	.80	.75	19.89	14.92	
Total		456.5	376.5						251.78	190.77	

Fig. 1   Load study format.

timated operating costs, and complete the design of the distribution system. Such a method is outlined herein. Prerequisites are a plant layout showing general locations of process or manufacturing areas in their relatively final arrangement, a motor list, and equipment and system operating data. A formal description of operation in all departments or process areas must be compiled at some time during design, and the sooner the better, since these data will help in eliminating false starts and reworking of the load study.

Figure 1 shows a typical tabulation which includes:

Equipment description
Brake horsepower (machinery builder's data or estimated)
Motor horsepower (as above)
Average load (estimated)
Calculated kW
Power factor (estimated)
Efficiency (estimated)
Calculated kVA
Lighting and heating loads—kW

Tabulations are set up, first, on a department or process area basis and, finally, on a load-center or motor-control-center basis.

Total connected brake horsepower, motor horsepower, lighting and resistance heating (kW), kVA loads (vector sum), and overall power factors are obtained from the tabulation. Note that the *average load* allows for real loads on motors, heating, or lighting.

Using calculated kW, kVA, and power-factor figures, total connected loads and estimated demands for each sector of the plant can be determined. True spares and alternately operated equipment are not counted.

At this point, a single-line distribution diagram may be roughed out and switchgear, transformers, and feeders located on a load-center approach. The load tabulation is revised and updated to conform with the resulting distribution system design.

Motor-control-center layouts may now be prepared, keeping in mind the use of standard units, bus ratings, and internal wiring arrangements wherever possible.

Next, load-center transformers and desired features may be selected, again keeping in mind the use of standard types and ratings.

A *diversity* can be factored into the sizing of a transformer serving two or more motor-control centers, since varying loads on individual centers are not likely to reach maximum simultaneously. The extent of *diversity* will depend on conditions of operation for any particular facility. Another diversity can be considered between load centers at the distribution level to allow for load variations between two or more load centers.

Adjusted load figures can now be used to size feeders at all voltage levels and feeder loads distributed over the properly rated switchgear (fused switches or circuit breakers).

In some cases, a power transformer is required to reduce the utility service voltage to plant distribution voltage. The power transformer capacity is based on the adjusted load at that point in the system. In a utility contract of the *primary*-service type, the transformer is generally selected and furnished by the customer. In a utility contract of the *secondary*-service type, the transformer is usually selected and furnished by the utility. Where it is the customer's responsibility, the suggestions given herein should be considered.

With properly prepared load data, the engineer may calculate any or all the conditions generally involved in system load studies.

Selection of Equipment

Switchgear Standard units properly rated for short-circuit requirements (including momentary ratings) should be used. Draw-out or stationary, fused-switch or circuit-breaker type may be selected, depending upon system requirements and economic considerations. Either type will provide adequate switching and protection when properly applied. Avoid using overrated gear due to ignorance of actual short-circuit requirements; however, avoid using current-limiting reactors wherever possible in the design of new systems. Provide adequate protective relays such as undervoltage, overcurrent, and ground sensing as required. Avoid sophisticated and complex relaying and transfer systems that require sensitive coordination and the "belt and suspenders" approach. Use standard backup protection where necessary. Relay operation should allow for prompt detection and disconnection of faults and quick, safe restoration of power. Avoid "bells, lights, and whistles" annunciator systems. One suitable signal operated by circuit breaker auxiliary "trip" contacts covering the entire switchgear lineup will indicate trouble in an unattended control room. The trouble can be pinpointed by checking individual relay targets or trip indicating lights. Keep it simple!

Buy the best control battery you can afford and maintain it as recommended by the manufacturer. Stick to 125- or 250-volt control. Locate the battery in a clear, ventilated, accessible area near the switchgear, so that the operator or maintenance worker will see it every time the gear is checked. Avoid low-voltage batteries mounted inside the switchgear compartments. These are easily forgotten during maintenance checks.

Switchgear should be located in accessible, ventilated, adequately lighted areas with sufficient space for working on draw-out units, cable connections, cable reels, tools, etc. This need not be a fancy room or building. Suitable switchgear is available for outdoor or "shelter-type" installations in almost all climates. Remember, plant space is expensive!

Power transformers Standard, load-center-type units are preferred for supplying utilization voltage power to equipment located throughout the plant. The "package" generally includes a distribution-voltage disconnect switch or cable terminating compartment directly connected to the transformer primary, the power transformer, and close-connected secondary switchgear to provide an integrated, coordinated, factory-assembled unit. Smaller units, 225 to 500 kVA, may be completely factory-assembled, ready to drop into a suitable location in the plant with a minimum of installation work. Larger units, up to 2,000 kVA, require some assembly of components at the site, but this is simple and the units go together neatly and quickly. The "load-center" type of distribution is extremely flexible and economical for the majority of plants.

Load centers can be located just about anywhere that adequate space is available, including outdoor pads, rooftops, indoor plant areas, mezzanines, electric rooms, etc. As with other electrical gear, proper lighting, accessibility, ventilation, and—in open areas—protection from fork trucks and other plant operating mobile equipment are required.

Transformers should be sized for the load they are intended to carry and for best efficiency, regulation, and power factor. They should be operated as close to full rating as possible. Large allowances for future loads "just in case" should be avoided. Provisions for forced-air and, if necessary, forced-oil cooling may be specified, which will permit adding loads at some future date. Some plant policies on excess transformer capacity border on the ridiculous. Carrying a cup of water in a 10-quart bucket is wasteful as well as poor economy in initial investment. Careful distribution of loads and use of double-end load centers and secondary bus ties are recommended to ensure against loss of power to essential loads. One of the advantages of the load-center concept is the ease with which units can be added or relocated in the plant distribution system as required.

Load-center transformers may be ventilated dry type, sealed dry type, askarel-insulated self-cooled, or oil-insulated self-cooled. Ventilated dry type are usually lowest in cost. Oil-insulated, askarel-insulated, and, finally, sealed dry type are progressively more expensive. Oil-insulated transformers should be located outdoors to avoid vault requirements.

Ventilated dry-type transformers are now available in higher BIL (Basic Insulation Level) ratings equivalent to oil and askarel units and are adequate for clean, dry ambient conditions; however, they must be kept clean to permit proper ventilation. Askarel-insulated transformers are widely used in dusty, damp ambients. It should be noted that askarel (a nonflammable liquid) is a corrosive medium and requires strict precautionary measures in handling and containing it. Sealed dry-type transformers are desirable for dusty, abrasive, or mildly corrosive areas, require the least maintenance, and present the least operating hazards.

In recent years, there has been a measure of standardization in larger power transformers. Computer programming of design requirements and standardization of core and tank designs—together with NEMA standards for characteristics, testing, and accessories—make repetitive manufacture of large transformers feasible on a production-line basis, thus reducing the cost and production time substantially.

Large power transformers are generally oil-insulated and best located outdoors, properly protected and isolated to prevent the spread of fire in the event of a serious and damaging failure.

Dikes and/or oil sumps and drainage arrangements must be provided to contain insulating oil should a tank or radiator rupture occur. Fire walls may be used between transformers where sufficient space is not available for isolation by space. Fog systems may be used for fire protection for outdoor installations. Sufficient space must be provided to properly service and maintain large transformers. Roadways wide enough to accommodate a lowboy truck, mobile crane, and filtering equipment must be provided. Sufficient height and provisions for untanking in place should be considered. When large transformers must be located indoors, expensive vaults and their accessory provisions may be required. CO_2 systems are sometimes used for fire protection with indoor oil-insulated transformers.

All power transformers should be equipped with a thermometer, and those using a liquid insulating medium should have a level gauge. Alarm contacts can be provided on both devices if desired. Drain and sampling valves for the insulating oil are standard, as are jack pads, lifting eyes, ground connection lugs, etc. Provisions for forced-air and forced-oil cooling must be specified if desired. Larger transformers may carry a triple rating OA/FA/FOA (oil to air/forced air/forced oil and air) to provide for future additional loads.

No-load primary taps are usually provided on most power transformers; however, the number and voltage range are not standard. Generally, five fully rated primary voltage taps including two 2 1/2 percent above and two 2 1/2 percent below nominal line voltage are adequate. Careful consideration must be given to what is to be considered *nominal* line voltage before specifying taps. A large, clearly legible nameplate should be provided and maintained legible, listing kVA rating, primary and secondary voltages and currents, internal coil connections, terminal designations, impedance, reactance, insulation type and temperature rating, insulating medium (number of gallons required), and total operating weight including bushings, radiators, and all accessories.

Motor controls Motors for use on a 480-volt three-phase 60-Hz system are generally what are referred to as standard NEMA frame type, squirrel cage, induction, normal starting torque, normal starting current. These motors usually require a simple across-the-line full-voltage nonreversing starter with running current and short-circuit current protective devices and disconnect switch. These components are normally provided in single enclosures and referred to as *combination across-the-line motor starters.* The starters may be located adjacent to the motors or grouped together at convenient locations within the general area where the motors are located. The grouping may take the form of individual units mounted on a rack with an enclosed bus using ducts and conduits for interconnections or a specially designed series of sectionalized cabinets incorporating horizontal and vertical bus arrangements which permit an accessory combination starter unit to be "plugged in" to the vertical bus. Since the starters are of various sizes, cabinet openings of varying size can be arranged to accept the plug-in units. Spacers are provided to fill in unused spaces. Space is provided for a main switch or circuit breaker, small transformers, current-limiting reactors, lighting panels, relay control panels, and individual circuit breakers or fused switches.

Internal wiring is available in various arrangements including complete factory wiring to master terminal boards.

In all, it is a neat, tidy arrangement that fits in with the load center concept, is easy to assemble and maintain, and is generally cost competitive with other types of motor control arrangements that require considerably more field labor and do not provide many of the desirable features.

Control units are available for reversing, multispeed, multiwinding, reduced voltage, and wound rotor motors within the capacities of conventional horsepower ratings.

Larger motors may be controlled for across-the-line starting by properly equipped circuit breakers at 480 volts provided frequency of operation is not excessive. Transformer, reactor, and resistance-type reduced voltage starters are available for control of large motors at 480 volts.

Motors in the range of 400 to 3,000 horsepower will require an intermediate voltage such as 2,400 or 4,160 volts in the case of a 13,800-volt distribution system. 4,160 volts can often be used for the distribution voltage in plants not exceeding 15,000-kVA demand, making use of that voltage for utilization as well as distribution. It is best to stick to standard voltages such as 480, 2,400, 4,160 and 13,800 volts in the average industrial plant, up to approximately 30,000-kVA demand. Higher voltages involve station-type distribution switchgear and are much less convenient as far as space and equipment maintenance are concerned.

Pushbutton controls, selector switches, and indicating lights may be installed in the individual or grouped starter units.

Although motor control centers and starter racks may be located on the production floor in reasonably clean ambients and with proper protection, they are generally located in a control room which must be accessible and provide proper space, ventilation, and lighting. In dusty, hot, hazardous, or corrosive areas, isolation in a separate room away from the operating area may be a requirement. Motor starting equipment of the proper type may be located in hazardous areas in some cases; however, the cost is extremely high. Explosionproof control devices may be racked to provide centralized grouping, but the high cost of necessary fittings, labor, and maintenance indicates that serious consideration be given to providing a control room outside the hazardous area.

Location and housing of electrical equipment It is indeed a sad fact that in most plants electrical equipment gets the least consideration. As layout of equipment proceeds, space allotted to electrical equipment grows smaller and smaller. As a result, cramped, poorly arranged, inadequate facilities are not uncommon in many otherwise well-designed plants. Often, buildings are designed on the basis of early estimates of space requirements, and the equipment must be arranged to fit the building. Unbelievable as it may seem, sometimes the building size and the type of construction are chosen on the basis of price, resulting in an increase in cost of mechanical and electrical work that far exceeds the savings in building shell costs. Poor column spacing, inadequate clear height, structure arrangements that inhibit clear areas for running overhead piping, ductwork, and conduit are just a few of the problems encountered when building and plant layout requirements are not coordinated.

In a multibuilding plant, electrical substation load centers and even motor control centers may be located on pads outdoors. All the equipment involved is available for outdoor installation. In the warmer climates, this approach is becoming more and more popular. So-called *shelter*-type outdoor equipment provides protection for maintenance personnel during inclement weather. Properly designed, significant savings in building costs and space can be effected.

Where outbuildings are used to house electrical equipment, the construction may be simple, such as concrete block walls with a precast concrete plank roof and built-up roofing.

Prefabricated buildings may also be used. Almost any type of construction that will provide adequate protection for the equipment is acceptable. The building should have adequate clear height to permit running of conduits, cable trays, and interconnecting buses overhead. This arrangement is preferable and more economical than using pits and trenches. Buildings should have adequate doors—at least two—arranged for safe egress in event of an emergency and of sufficient size to permit passing of the largest shipping unit of equipment contemplated. Windows may be provided if it is desirable to view the general condition of equipment without entering the building. Adequate ventilation should be provided, preferably on a positive pressure basis.

Good lighting and receptacles for the use of portable tools should be provided. In many instances, heat is necessary to prevent condensation in the gear due to outside temperature variations or when equipment is deenergized.

Electrical equipment rooms within plant buildings should be located so as to provide ready access. If elevated, stairways should be provided. Maintenance personnel should not be required to climb a vertical ladder to get into a room housing vital electrical equipment. At least two doors, preferably one at either end of the room, are necessary for egress in case of emergency. There should be no "pockets" or areas where a worker could be trapped in case of an emergency. All electrical equipment is subject to explosion and fire when it is energized. Adequate space is required in which to work on equipment, especially drawout types. No person should be required to work on equipment in a cramped or unnatural position. Most electrical equipment is designed to be accessible provided that there is sufficient surrounding space.

Rooms should be properly lighted, ventilated, and heated if necessary. Mechanical ventilation is recommended in such a manner that the room is kept under a slightly positive pressure. Most electrical equipment is designed to operate in a 30°C (maximum) ambient. If this ambient temperature is exceeded, trouble can be expected.

Electrical rooms should *not* be used for storage, as workshops, or as lunchrooms. Doors should be kept locked and rooms accessible only to authorized personnel.

System design—keep it simple! Simplicity of design in all electrical systems is preferable, but especially so in plant distribution systems. Straight radial systems are generally adequate for most plants, are cheaper in initial cost, and require less maintenance. A

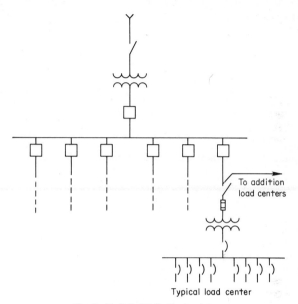

Fig. 2   Radial distribution system.

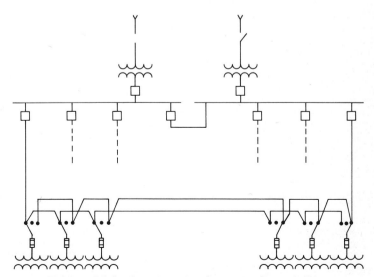

Fig. 3   Radial distribution system with primary selective feeders.

multiple bus arrangement with primary selective radial feeders will enhance the reliability of the system. Ring buses, loop systems, and secondary networks should be avoided wherever possible. At first blush, every plant seems to need absolute continuity of service; however, a detailed analysis of plant operation will usually reveal that a short outage to replace a faulted cable or isolate a damaged switch or circuit breaker will not really affect production that much. Of course, there are exceptions. In these cases, a small engine-generator or a UPS (uninterruptible power supply) unit may be all that is necessary to keep critical circuits energized.

Additional costs for redundant equipment seem to follow a logarithmic curve; that is, you pay a considerable price to obtain a little more insurance against a power failure that appears less likely to occur. The trouble is, sophisticated and complex systems sometimes defeat their very purpose. False operation of a sensitive relay can cause an outage that will last for hours before someone finally figures out where it is. In the heat and anxiety of a power failure, there is little time to bone up on how that special arrangement really works. "Close circuit breaker B after opening circuit breaker A but before closing breaker C which temporarily parallels transformers 6 and 8" can spell disaster, especially if the boss is on vacation and the chief electrician is off attending his daughter's wedding. But even the marketing manager can understand a straight radial system. Complex automatic transfer systems sometimes hang up just when they are most needed, and then someone says, "I dunno, Charlie was the only one who knew how it worked." Charlie—the chap who retired last year.

It is important that all authorized personnel know the operation of the equipment involved.

Codes and standards Your installation may be covered by certain fire, building, and safety codes. If you are in doubt about which codes and ordinances cover your plant, a call or visit to the local city building inspector is a good starting point in learning what requirements may apply. You may employ an architect/engineer to design your plant, in which case he will most likely accept responsibility for meeting code requirements. Do not depend upon vendors and salesmen to cover you on this point. A "catch all" clause or weasel-worded paragraph on a purchase order may not provide proper protection in a legal sense. Most city and state electrical codes are adaptations of the National Fire Protection Association's *National Electrical Code (NEC)*, which is revised and reissued periodically. The purpose of the code is the practical safeguarding of persons and buildings from the hazards arising from the use of electricity for utilization equipment. City and state authorities may base their codes on obsolete editions of the *NEC.* They also may list supplemental requirements. There are also national and federal safety codes which may relate to your installation. Plant engineers should be conscious and alert to any and all codes that apply to their plants.

Codes are not intended to be design manuals and should not be used as such. An installation is not designed in accordance with a code or codes but is designed to *meet* the requirements of such codes as are applicable. Much has been said and written regarding the interpretation of code requirements. In the final analysis, it is generally the local inspector who is charged with the responsibility of enforcing the code and who must be satisfied that all requirements are met. This inspector, being generally experienced in local conditions that may bear on the safety of the installation, will judge all facets of the installation; and these judgments will result in the *official* interpretation of the code for any specific installation. It is good practice to discuss the proposed installation with the governing inspector before proceeding with engineering. This is particularly true in the case of an unusual installation. The inspector's advice may save you money in the long run. You are more likely to breeze through the final inspection if the inspector has been consulted and the resulting advice has been followed. A costly delay and rework can be avoided in most cases. Sometimes engineering drawings are required to be submitted for review and approval. Drawings should be neat and legible and should properly illustrate those areas of the installation that are the concern of code authorities.

The Occupational Safety and Health Act (OSHA) requirements are likely to apply to your plant. Plant design should meet these requirements without going overboard as the result of not taking the time to determine what requirements apply and to what extent. If you have an unusual installation, state your case, giving complete information and detailed data on the design and operation, including the procedures you intend to follow in the operation of the facility and how you have planned to meet emergencies in this area. Include a description of your safety program, its enforcement, and employee education features. This preplanning may result in a twofold saving on initial installation and violation penalties.

If your plant is like most others, it will be insured. In addition to meeting all applicable codes and ordinances, the insurance company will advise you of certain requirements relating to the type(s) of insurance covering your plant and its operation. Fire insurance is the most common. The insurance company will want to know, for example, if you intend to store large quantities of inflammable materials and their proximity to other facilities that may be damaged in event of fire or explosion resulting in fire. Insurance companies are generally associated with organizations that make a speciality of setting up requirements and inspecting installations for hazards. The two organizations most often encountered are Factory Mutual (FM) and Factory Insurance Association (FIA). Generally, plant layouts are submitted for review and comments before the insurance is written. FM and FIA employ engineers who are expert in the fields of protection from fire, explosion, and other hazards to the maintenance and operation of all kinds of commercial and industrial facilities. They are recognized authorities who will work with you to mutual advantage in design of your new plant or expansion. Again, here is another place to completely evaluate your requirements so that you can state your case in detail and avoid unnecessary insurance penalties wherever possible.

Your attitude toward codes and safety ordinances should be positive. Those who set out to beat the codes usually end up defeating their purpose and, nowadays, may even end up in jail.

Chapter **5**

Procurement by Contract

J. KILROY
Consultant

INTRODUCTION

The procurement of utilities services by contract is a plant engineering function that receives little attention but which could result in a large payback. Rate development and regulation is remarkably similar throughout the country, but there are significant differences for different types of service. A prime example is that generally electric power requirements are procured by a rate selection process from a utilities supplier who is normally regulated by a state commission. On the other hand, water and sewage services are more generally obtained through public facilities such as cities or municipal authorities that are not subject to commission approval. The most complex rate schedules and the largest dollar value applicable to most industrial plants is in the electrical utility. Telephone services are high-cost items, but they are not the subject of this analysis. For this reason, rate analysis examples shown will make use of the electric energy rates and rate making process.

Rates are generally developed with the aim of returning to the company its expenditures plus a return on its capital investments to permit the utility company to compete in the financial market when additional capital may be required. Other goals of rate making are (1) to minimize the effect of variables, such as fuel costs, and (2) to allocate costs to the customer causing such costs. However, to achieve the aim and apply the premises precisely, it would be necessary to have a rate tailored to each customer of the utility—a rate reflecting instantaneously all changes in the marketplace. This would be an impossible administrative task, even with present-day computer technology.

Compromise is the name of the game and, generally speaking, it has resulted in several types of rate schedules developed to assure costs return for various levels of service. It is in these compromises that the opportunity exists to attain certain economies if the plant engineer recognizes, through rate analysis, the breakpoint in the rate classification levels and also applies his cost analysis knowledge to modify plant operations so as to permit the use of another rate.

Rates are quite similar throughout the country. A given company will have a rate for residential use, a rate for commercial users, and a rate or rates for high-volume users, such as industrial concerns. Some companies will have rates for intermittent or summer use and others for water heating or other special uses. This section is oriented toward commercial-industrial and other large-volume users and will, therefore, provide simplified procedures for analyzing effects on these customers.

There are several methods in use to simplify rate structure evaluation, such as a substitute equation and hyperbolic graphing. All rate schedules equate to the following formula: total cost equals the number of units purchased multiplied by the cost per unit. This is the equation of a hyperbola. It is readily apparent that a graphical representation of the rate structure provides a convenient, simple tool for studying or comparing rates. Through the use of hyperbolic graph paper, the plotting of the rate will be a straight line or a series of straight lines.

The first step in developing the graphs is to determine the schedules that would apply to the service requirements. The following rate schedules are actual schedules taken from a rate book for a private company. They are simplified by omitting tax adjustment, comments on certain regulations, and items not really affecting the schedule itself. The fuel adjustment clause has also been omitted, as it will be covered separately.

In developing the hyperbolic graph, any hyperbolic graph paper can be used, although there are special graph papers available commercially for the plotting of rates. To permit more precise calculation for a given size graph, the example starts with 200 hours of use of the demand. This equates to a load factor of about 0.027, which is a low load factor. Load factors in excess of 0.027 will cover virtually all industrial users. However, it is a simple procedure to extend the graph below this 200 hours of use.

The following schedules will be identified as rate A, rate B, and rate C.

GENERAL SERVICE—RATE A

Applicability

To any customer for any purpose not included under applicable provision of residential rate if all service at an establishment is supplied herewith.

Character of Service

Alternating current, 60 cycles, single- or three-phase; metering at primary or secondary voltage

Rate

4.4 cents per kWh	first 300 kWh*
1.4 cent per kWh	next 700 kWh
1.1 cent per kWh	" 7,500 kWh
0.9 cent per kWh	all additional kWh

29kWh will be added to the first energy block for each 0.5 kW of demand in excess of 5kW.

Discount

Two percent if bill is paid within 10 days

Minimum Bill

$1 gross per kilowatt of demand, but not less than 50 percent of the kilowatt capacity necessary to serve the customer

Billing Demand

Maximum 15-minute measured demand in the month taken to the nearest 0.5 kW, but not less than 1 kW for each meter

Fluctuating Load Charge

Net of 1.5 percent per month of the cost of any additional transformer capacity required to supply highly fluctuating loads

Water Heating

Separately metered, uncontrolled, utility-approved water heating will be supplied at 1.1 cent net per kilowatthour with a minimum charge of $1 net per meter per month. This service is not available for space heating.

Short-Term Service

Service for periods of less than a year is offered under this schedule if customer advances the net cost of connection and disconnection on terms arranged with utility.

Charges shall be increased 10 percent, and the minimum bill based on 50 percent of the kilowatt capacity necessary to serve customer shall be waived.

LARGE POWER SERVICE—RATE B

Applicability

To any purpose if customer's demand is 100 kVA or more for each service connection

Character of Service

Alternating current, 60 Hz, three-phase; metering at primary or secondary voltage

Rate

3.5 cents per kWh	first 70 kWh per kVA demand
0.60 cent per kWh	next 140 kWh per kVA demand
0.35 cent per kWh	all additional kWh per kVA demand

Discount

Two percent if bill is paid within 10 days; 5 percent on the total kilowatthours when service voltage is between 1 and 15 kV; 10 percent on the total kilowatthours when service voltage is over 15 kV. When these discounts apply, a 5 percent discount shall be allowed on the minimum bill.

Minimum Bill

For not less than 25 kVA nor less than 50 percent of the demand contracted for, $1.25 gross per kilovoltamperes of demand.

* For each 0.5 kW, of demand in excess of 5 kW, 29 kWh will be added to the first energy block.

Billing Demand

The average of the weekly demands established during the calendar weeks within the billing month, but not less than 25 kVA. No weekly demand shall be taken at less than 15 percent of the highest weekly demand in the month.

The weekly demand shall be the highest of the following amounts determined from measurements during each calendar week ending Saturday midnight:

Rate A The maximum 15-minute kVA demand during the on-peak period

Rate B Fifty percent of the maximum 15-minute kVA demand during the off-peak period

Rate C Forty percent of the maximum instantaneous kVA demand during the on-peak period

Rate D Twenty percent of the maximum instantaneous kVA demand during the off-peak period

Power Factor

Customer's demand in kilovoltamperes shall be determined by increasing the kilowatt demand 0.5 percent for each 1 percent the lagging power factor is below 100 percent. If, at the time of all weekly demands, customer maintains a leading power factor of 95 percent or less, the kilowatt demand shall be decreased 1.5 percent. For leading power factors between 100 and 95 percent, the demand shall be taken at its kilovolt value.

Off-Peak Hours

The off-peak period will be from 4 P.M. to 7 A.M. daily and from 12 noon Saturday until 7 A.M. Monday. The following are off-peak days: New Year's Day, Washington's Birthday, Memorial Day, Independence Day, Labor Day, Armistice Day, Thanksgiving Day, and Christmas Day. The on-peak period shall include all other times.

HIGH-TENSION POWER SERVICE—RATE C

Applicability

To any customer for general power purposes when the demand is 2,000 kVA or greater and all service is taken at one point of delivery. Lighting incidental to the use of power is permitted.

Character of Service

Alternating current, 60 Hz, three-phase; 25,000 volts or higher

Rate
  Demand charge
  $2.61 per kVA   first 2,000 kVA demand
  $1.83 per kVA   all additional kVA demand
  Energy charge
  0.375 cent per kWh   first 400 kWh per kVA demand
  0.335 cent per kWh   all additional kilowatthours
  Maximum rate Charges under this schedule shall not exceed the above demand charge, including 125 kWh per kilovoltampere of customer's demand, plus 0.9 cent gross per kilowatthour for additional use, except by reason of the transformer charge.

Discount

Two percent if bill is paid within 10 days

Minimum Bill

The demand charge, but for not less than 2,000 kVA.

Transformer Charge

When customer desires to take service under this schedule at a voltage between 1 and 15 kV, utility shall provide one transformation at a charge of 17 cents gross per kilovoltampere for the first 2,000 kVA and 7 cents gross per kilovoltampere for additional kilovoltamperes of the highest on-peak or off-peak demand for any week as defined in the billing demand provision but not less than any such demand previously established during the term of the electric service agreement or less than the capacity specified therein.

Billing Demand

The billing demand for any month shall be the average of the weekly demands established during the weeks ending within the billing month. No weekly demand shall be taken at less than 50 percent of the highest weekly demand of the month. The billing demand shall not be less than the highest of the following:

Rate A   2,000 kVA
Rate B   50 percent of the kilovoltampere demand specified in the contract
Rate C   50 percent of the highest demand previously established during the term of contract

A weekly demand shall be the demand of the on-peak period plus 20 percent of the amount the off-peak demand for the same week exceeds 150 percent of the on-peak

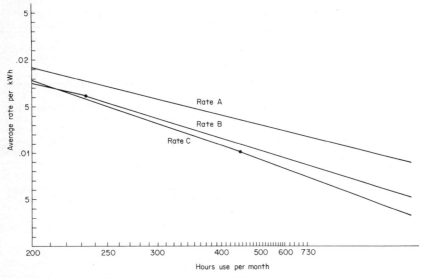

Fig. 1 Hyperbolic graph method of rate analysis.

demand. The demand of the on-peak period is the maximum 15-minute on-peak kilovoltampere demand plus 25 percent of the excess of the maximum instantaneous on-peak kilovoltampere operating peak for the same week over 140 percent of the maximum 15-minute on-peak demand. The off-peak demand similarly determined for the off-peak period from 10 P.M. to 7 A.M. daily.

Since the plotting of the schedule is to start at 200 hours of use, the first step is to calculate the unit cost for 200 hours of service for the applicable rate. The examples in Fig. 1 use a 2,000-kW demand. It should be noted that a different family of curves is required for significant changes in demand. The 200 hours of usage of 2,000 kW equate to 400,000 kWh per month. This usage is then applied to the rate schedule and the calculated unit rate is plotted on the 200-hour ordinate, providing the first point on the curve. A second point on the curve will be at infinity. At this point all preceding blocks have no effect. Therefore, this point is equal to the unit rate of the last block in the schedule. Connecting these two points will provide the graph that will show the unit rate for any load factor. Care must be exercised here, since rate schedules contain breakpoints between the 200 and 730 hours of usage. As can be seen from the plotting of rate B, a point must be plotted for each change in the relationship of demand charges and these points connected by a straight line. In the rate schedules chosen, the power factor effect is included in the relationship of the hours of use. This is not a usual procedure, but it does exist and requires more care in the plotting of the schedules, particularly where a change in the block occurs, as in rate B. Figure 1 illustrates the graphing of three rate schedules that would apply. As is readily seen, rate A would never be economical for the 2,000 kW demand above 200 hours of use. Rate C would be the most economical until 215 hours of usage, where rate B is equal to rate C and more economical for greater load factors.

The hyperbolic graphing method of rate analysis is only one method that can be used to simplify the process. Another procedure is to develop a simplified equation for each rate. Virtually all schedules can be shown in an equation composed of three parts:

$$c + x(\text{kW}) + y(\text{kWh}) = \text{total cost}$$

This provides a simple method for checking your monthly billing.

However, none of these methods has any effect on the rate itself. The rate determination procedures before the utility commissions provide the greatest opportunity to attain minimal costs. The commissions are frequently not capable of analyzing the submissions of the utility companies; when they are technically capable of doing so, they do not consider that their purpose is to assure the provision of service at minimal cost. All their deliberations and conclusions have the appearance of first assuring the stability of the utility company, particularly through the determination that its rate of return will keep it in the most desirable category in the obtaining of capital. A stable, healthy utility company is certainly required, but this should not be the primary consideration of the regulatory body. However, these attitudes will not change unless there is greater participation in the proceedings by the consumer. Very few commercial or industrial companies participate in the hearings where rate increases substantially effecting their costs are being determined. Many commissions consider this a lack of interest on the part of the customer. More recently, individual groups have come in with emotionally oriented protests which continue vigorously for a short time but have little lasting effect. Most industrial concerns do have the capability of bringing to the forum a technically correct position through their engineering know-how, a financially correct position through the use of their accountants, and a disciplined "legal" presentation through their company counsels. Realistic rate schedules can be achieved throughout the country by the participation of these three components of industrial facilities, working with the commissions. This will serve to balance the preponderance of expertise now provided by the utility companies.

FUEL ADJUSTMENT CLAUSES

One of the most interesting aspects of the rate schedules is the fuel adjustment clause. While most utility companies have fuel adjustment clauses, other companies have not felt the need and have managed to get along without them.

Fuel Adjustment

The energy charge will be increased or decreased when in any month the average cost of fossil fuels is 0.1 cent or more, above or below, 32.0 cents per million Btu. Any increase or decrease will apply to all kilowatthours billed in the month following the average cost determination. The adjustment factor for each 0.1 cent variation is 0.00130 cent per kWh multiplied by the ratio of total kWh produced by fossil fuels to the total kWh produced in the month.

The return to the company on the fuel adjustment is a function of the heat rate of the turbine generator, the efficiency of the boilers, and distribution losses. The following are the precepts in the analysis of the fuel adjustment clause:

1. Under the above rate the return to the company for 0.1 cent expense is 0.00130 cent per kilowatthour.
2. Assume a heat rate of 10000 Btu/kWh. (Most large companies approach a heat rate of 10000 Btu/kWh and many do even better.)
3. Steam plant efficiency of 89 percent
4. Distribution efficiency of 93 percent

$$\frac{\text{Cents recovered by}}{0.1 \text{ cent expense}} = \frac{a}{y} (0.89)(0.93)\ 0.00130 \text{ cent per kWh}$$

Where $a = 1$ million Btu
$Y =$ heat rate (10000 Btu/kWh)
$= 0.1076$ cent

Therefore, each unit of 0.1 cent increase in fuel cost provides 0.1076 cent return. In recent times these have been in excess of 1,000 units of increase in fuel cost, resulting in a fuel cost adjustment of 1.3 cent per kilowatthour. Applying this to a moderate-sized industrial company using 750,000 kWh per month results in a $9,750 adjustment for fuel. The excess over that needed by the utility company to come out even is $741 per month or an annual return of $8,892. If the entire utility company is considered, the sale of over 25 billion kWh in a year results in a fuel cost recovery of $325 million, of which 7.6 percent or $24.7 million is excess. There is little incentive to keep the fuel costs down under these conditions.

COST ANALYSIS

In the cost analysis associated with the procurement of utilities services, much can be done in the analysis of the uses of the power. This section will not go into the various conservation techniques, as these have been publicized in detail in virtually all media. However, associating the procurement rates to the analysis can many times result in a vary large payoff. The result of the conservation will be readily determined and can be used in the economic analysis to determine how much can be expended to accomplish the conservation goal. Referring to Fig. 1, it is evident that in every case there is a large effect associated with the electrical demand. A brief analysis shows that while performing exactly the same functions, thus using the same amount of energy, but at the same time rescheduling certain large loads, 15 percent, or about 300 kW, a significant savings, could result. It must be noted that care should be taken in evaluating the graphs. For example. Figure 1 was plotted for a 2,000-kW demand with a 0.9 power factor. A new curve should be plotted to show the 1,700-kW demand. To determine the difference in unit cost, each curve must be used, as different hours of use or load factors apply for the same energy use when the demand is changed.

A "must" requirement for determining the capability of achieving a lowered rate is the development of a daily load curve for the industrial plant. An example is shown in Fig. 2. While this figure shows a daily load curve of a typical workday, this load curve

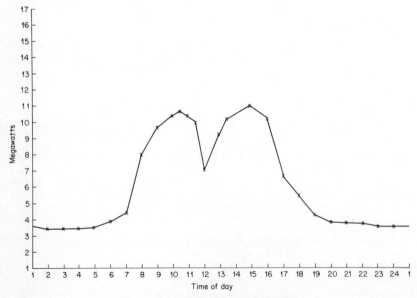

Fig. 2 Typical daily industrial load curve.

can be extended to a weekly or even monthly period and will show the time of day the peaks occur. The demand readings of the utility company are available to the customer. The concept of achieving savings by this method is simple. If a function presently being performed at peak periods of the day can be moved to a different hour, a saving can be achieved. The greater the demand of the function modified, the greater the savings. One example that most plants can use is in the testing of a fire pump. This can normally be done off peak at a significant saving. With a little analysis, many other functions can be reassigned. One item of note in the rate schedules, the "ratchet clause," has the effect of penalizing the customer for some period of months after the peak has been achieved. Most utility companies have a ratchet clause of some type. Generally it states that the demand established during the previous 12 months will apply to the billing.

Another aspect in cost analysis is the power factor penalty. Not all utility companies have power factor penalties, but even where there is no penalty, a low power will have an effect on voltage regulation and can cause overheating of circuits. Where a penalty exists, it is a simple matter to show the savings to be obtained by correcting the power factor. The other benefits to be derived are less subject to economic determination.

Regardless, if the industrial plant has a power factor of less than 0.90, serious consideration to correction methods should be given. There are numerous methods available for correcting power factor. The capacitor method generally is the most effective. The capacitors are maintenance free and of relatively low cost. They are most effective when installed closest to the large inductive units that are serving the low power factor.

SUMMARY

The procedures or tools noted above are part of a twofold action in which industrial concerns should be active participants. First, the rate analysis, if carried to the ultimate by participation in the rate approval by the utility commissions, will result in increased responsiveness by the utility company and, perhaps, a sorely needed change in the apparent goals of the regulatory bodies. Second, even under existing rates and regulations, an economic benefit will accrue to the company that follows a disciplined procedure for rate and cost analysis in utility services procurement.

Chapter **6**

Management Reports

L. T. WASSMAN
Plant Engineer, Sherwin-Williams Company

INTRODUCTION

In this age of high-cost utilities and shortages, it is increasingly important that the utilities function of the plant engineering department be effectively managed and controlled. An efficiently run utilities function that minimizes cost and usage could be the factor that tilts the scale of success and failure so that the production plant or facility served is and remains successful. Reports are a tool which can and should be used to assist in assuring the most efficient operation of the utilities function. Operation of the utilities function includes not only the operation of equipment that generates utilities—such as boilers to generate steam—but also the distribution of utilities and the conservation of utilities.

The emphasis in this chapter is on reports which are generated internally, either by plant engineering or by accounting, to report on utilities operations. Reports generated externally—such as weather forecasts and climatological data—are also management tools, but these will not be discussed.

NECESSITY FOR REPORTS

As stated earlier, reports are tools to assist in utilities management. The danger does exist, however, that reports that have no value may be generated. Reports that are not read, analyzed, and reviewed are a waste of time and paper. Also, reports that have value today may have no value tomorrow. Therefore the usefulness of all reports generated should be reviewed periodically to determine whether the necessity for each still exists. The principal reasons for making reports is to minimize the cost of utilities, establish the cost of products, plan for the future, and conserve utilities.

Minimize Cost of Utilities

Most reports which are generated in connection with utilities are cost reports. In the past, costs of various utilities have risen more or less proportionally to the economy of the country. Due to the energy shortage, costs have now jumped out of proportion compared to what they were. This makes it particularly important to minimize the cost of utilities by increasing the efficiency of utility producing operations as much as possible. Utilities must be conserved and consumption minimized to keep costs down.

Establish Cost of Products

Reports on cost of utilities are a necessity to determine the overall cost of products produced. A facility producing one product or a single closely related group of products will charge all the cost of the utilities to the single cost center. Under these conditions, it is not necessary to establish unit costs of utilities separately to determine total product cost. However, if the utilities function is to be run efficiently, then utilities costs must be segregated and analyzed separately from the other costs involved in producing a product.

Plan for Future

Constant monitoring of utilities capacity vs. consumption is necessary to be sure that consumption does not exceed capacity. This sounds easy, but an important point is that it is not enough to determine consumption in terms of average usage; peak consumption must be known to take steps to avoid problems with overloaded distribution systems and utilities generating equipment. The steps that must be taken when consumption exceeds supply are to install increased generating capacity and to expand or increase the capacity of distribution systems.

Conserve Utilities

A basic fact in any utilities conservation program is that, in order to conserve utilities, it must first be known where, how, and how much of each utility is used. The start of this knowledge is a utilities distribution report which distributes each utility on a periodic basis, usually monthly, for cost accounting purposes. As already pointed out, if only one product or a single related family of products is produced, all utility costs will be charged to the one cost center. However, even under these conditions, it is desirable to know what part of each utility goes directly into product and what part is used for heating, lighting, etc. After it is reported where and how much of each utility is used in a process or area of a production facility, the possibility of conservation can be explored. For electricity, this will take the form of reducing consumption; for water, recirculation and reducing consumption; for steam, reducing consumption and taking full advantage of pressure and temperature energy; and for fuel, reducing consumption and promoting efficient combustion. Other utilities will require these and other conservation methods.

TYPES OF REPORTS

Reports can be generally categorized by the objectives of the reports. While there is some overlap between categories, there are basically three types of reports: operational management reports, cost control reports, and utilities distribution reports. A discussion of each follows.

Operational Management Reports

Reports to monitor and to assist in the operation of equipment to generate utilities such as boilers can be roughly subdivided into two categories. Direct management of the operation requires detailed reports, which, however, are not needed by management at a higher level. For example, the logs that are commonly kept as a part of steam generation plant operations are rarely read by anyone except the lowest level of management of the operation. Higher-level management (or indirect management) requires consolidated and summarized reports.

Cost Control Reports

Controlling cost by minimizing it is an important function of management. Direct management of the utilities function requires cost reports on which various decisions regarding the operation can be based. An example of this is maintenance cost of generating plant equipment. If maintenance cost on certain equipment is higher than costs for comparable equipment, replacement or changes may be desirable, such as changing materials of construction, lubricants, design of parts, etc. Indirect management uses reports to control costs by comparing actual costs with budgets, checking efficiency reports, or by other techniques.

Utilities Distribution Reports

Distribution reports are also cost control reports in a sense, since they are the first step in conserving utilities and they are necessary to determine the contribution of utilities cost to the total cost of products. Distribution reports are necessary, not only for generated utilities but also for purchased utilities, since purchased utilities should also be charged to those cost centers where they are used.

FREQUENCY OF REPORTS

The time period covered by most reports will be approximately a month. Purchased utilities are generally invoiced 12 times a year and each covers a period of about a month. Some plants use an accounting period of 4 weeks or 13 periods a year instead of 12. This system solves a problem affecting those operations that use calendar months as the accounting period. If the last day of the accounting period is always the same day of the week (to make it convenient for payroll reporting), then 4 of the 12 monthly reports will cover a 5-week period and the other 8 will cover 4-week periods. This variation makes it difficult to compare costs from period to period, and this must be taken into account when analyzing costs. A standard cost system overcomes this problem of variable time periods. (Cost analysis reports are discussed under "Cost Control Reports" in the second half of this chapter.)

HOW TO PREPARE REPORTS AND FORMAT

To illustrate the various types of reports and a typical format for each, a steam generation plant will be used as an example. The reason for choosing a steam generation plant is that steam is perhaps the most difficult utility to report and it is usually generated in-plant rather than purchased.

The first step in setting up a report system is to make a diagram of the generation plant and of the distribution system. Figure 1 shows an arrangement of steam generation equipment that is fairly typical of an industrial installation. The diagram is simplified and shows only what is needed for illustration.

Operational Management Reports

The first law of thermodynamics (conservation of energy) is the basis for efficiency and distribution reports of utilities. Based on the fact that what goes in must come out, heat and energy balances designed to calculate efficiencies and to determine distribution are made.

Steam generation log sheets   Running logs of boiler operation are generally kept in one form or another. A typical log sheet is shown in Fig. 2. While logs are often kept in books, it is more convenient, in the case of steam generation logs, to have separate sheets for the log, each sheet covering a 24-hour period. The log sheet for the day should be kept at a desk near the control panel for the boiler shift engineers, who should fill in all readings from meters, gauges, and thermometers.

It is suggested that the log sheet be made 11 inches wide, with length to suit. A sheet

11 × 16 inches can be folded once off center to form an 8½ × 11 inch sheet, which can be punched for putting into a loose-leaf binder or filed in standard-sized files. Similarly, an 11 × 24 inch sheet folded twice will fit into the same size binder or file.

The sample log sheet is arranged so that the information logged is entered beginning at the bottom. This makes it convenient to subtract meter readings, since the last reading will be the largest number and it will be above the previous reading, which simplifies subtraction to obtain hourly flows.

The information to be logged is largely a matter of determining what information, if logged, will be helpful in determining whether boilers are operating normally. In our sample, poor efficiency will show up as abnormally high fuel consumption for the amount of steam generated. Steam temperatures need be logged only if steam is superheated. If steam is not superheated, steam temperature will correspond to the steam pressure saturation temperature, so pressures should always be logged. Dirty firesides will retard heat transfer, resulting in lower-than-normal steam temperature as it leaves the boiler.

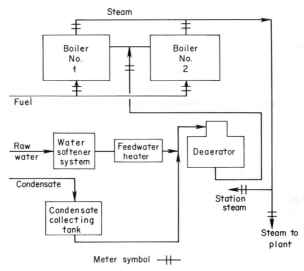

Fig. 1 Diagram of steam generation plant.

Flue gas temperature may also be an indicator of trouble. A leaking tube will result in lower-than-normal exit gas temperature, since steam will be going out the stack with the flue gas. Logs will generally not show all the information which the shift engineer has available to operate the boilers. These include draft pressures, other temperatures than those listed, water level, etc.

Boiler efficiency report In the process of generating steam in a boiler, water is pumped into the boiler and fuel and air are added and ignited to generate heat. Leaving the boiler are steam, gases formed in the combustion process, and blowdown water. The overall efficiency of a boiler is the ratio of the heat absorbed by the water inside the boiler divided by the total heat in the fuel added to the boiler. Losses due to blowdown, excess air, radiation, and heat lost in the flue gas reduce the efficiency. The quantity of feedwater, the feedwater temperature, the quantity of steam, the steam temperature and pressure, and the amount of fuel must all be measured to make the efficiency calculation. Preparing a heat balance with the information is the next step. Figure 3 shows a suggested format for a boiler efficiency report.

While it is desirable to measure the efficiency of larger boilers individually, smaller boilers can be metered as a group. Under these conditions only the combined efficiency will be known. A decision must be made as to whether the benefit realized as a result of individual metering can justify the additional cost of metering equipment.

In most steam generating plants, steam is used within the plant proper to drive tur-

STEAM GENERATION LOG

24-hour period beginning midnight: _____

Time	No. 1 Boiler						No. 2 Boiler						Total steam flow	Total fuel burned	Feedwater		Steam pressure	Load					
	Temperatures		Steam		Fuel		Temperatures		Steam		Fuel				Flow meter	Hourly flow		Station steam		Steam to plant			
	Steam	Exit gas	Flow meter	Hourly flow	Flow meter	Hourly flow	Steam	Exit gas	Flow meter	Hourly flow	Flow meter	Hourly flow						Flow meter	Hourly flow	Flow meter	Hourly flow		
12 M																							
11																							
10																							
9																							
8																							
7																							
6																							
5																							
4																							
3																							
2																							
1 p.m.																							
12 N																							
11																							
10																							
9																							
8																							
7																							
6																							
5																							
4																							
3																							
2																							
1 a.m.																							
Previous midnight																							
Average																							

Comments, midnight shift: _____

Day shift: _____

Afternoon shift: _____

Engineer	Shift
_____	Midnight
_____	Day
_____	Afternoon

Fig. 2 Steam generation log sheet.

Period: _____

1. Feedwater
   Flow   @_____°F av._____lb
   Temperature corrected   _____lb
2. Steam produced
   Boiler #1 steam flow   _____lb
   Temp. & press. corrected   _____lb
   Boiler #2 steam flow   _____lb
   Temp. & press. corrected   _____lb
   Heat out (steam enthalpy-feedwater
       enthalpy × total steam produced   _____Therms
3. Fuel consumed
   Fuel consumed   _____therms
   Alternate fuel consumed   _____therms
   Total heat in   _____Therms
4. Efficiency
   $\dfrac{\text{Heat out}}{\text{Heat in}} \times 100\% = $_____%

Fig. 3   Boiler efficiency report.

bines, preheat oil, de-aerate feedwater, etc. This "station" steam is part of the cost of running the generating plant. However, since the costs to run a generating plant are generally charged to consumers of the steam, the station steam may be absorbed as part of the total cost of steam generation. It is wise, however, to meter the station steam (1) so that the usage does not get out of line and (2) to allow cost comparisons between the use of steam and other forms of energy used to drive powerhouse auxiliary equipment. A meter for station steam is shown in Fig. 1. Another purpose of a station steam meter is to use the sum of the station steam and the steam to the plant to check against the sum of the steam from the boilers and the water added to the desuperheating station, assuming desuperheating water is metered. If the sums are not reasonably close, meters should be checked for accuracy and for proper operation.

It is not necessary to meter desuperheating water, since this may be calculated from the difference between the sum of the steam from the boilers and the sum of the station steam and the steam to the plant. Taking the difference does not allow checking of the operation by a heat balance since, one factor—amount of desuperheating water—will be missing. In a large plant, desuperheating water should be metered to allow checking.

Supplementary reports   Supplementary reports as shown in Fig. 4 are used for specific purposes. They are not necessarily kept current each month but are prepared

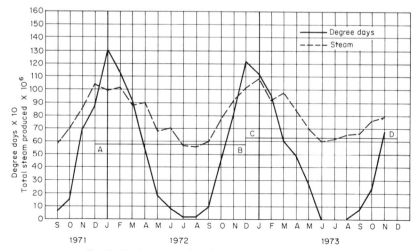

Fig. 4   Total steam produced versus heating degree days.

or brought up to date as required. Figure 4 shows a typical total heat load for a couple of years graphed against the actual heating degree-days for the area where the steam generation plant is located. Analysis of this graph gives the information needed to project actual fuel consumption by months for budgeting, ordering fuel, etc. Also, changes in process load can be studied. Summer load is process load only (unless steam is used for air conditioning). Line AB on the graph is the approximate process summer load in 1972. Line CD is the summer load in 1973. The difference in height between the lines represents an increase in the process steam load in this particular plant.

Cost Control Reports

To control cost, knowledge of where and how much is being spent is essential. Reports with this information are generally prepared by the accounting department.

Period: _____

STEAM GENERATION MONTHLY COST REPORT

	Month		Year to date	
Fixed expense	Actual	Budget	Actual	Budget
Labor				
Hourly labor				
Employee Benefits – hourly				
Overtime – hourly				
Salaries – supervision				
Employee benefits – salaried				
Overtime – salaried				
Depreciation				
Taxes – real est. & pers. prop.				
Insurance				
Miscellaneous				
Subtotal				
Variable expense				
Fuel				
Electric power				
Water				
Feedwater chemicals				
Maintenance				
Building				
Boilers				
Piping & access. equipt. in powerhouse				
Piping Outside Powerhouse				
Subtotal				
Allocations				
Purchasing				
Personnel				
Accounting				
Medical				
Security & safety				
Subtotal				
Grand total				

Fig. 5 Steam generation monthly cost report.

Steam generation monthly cost report A typical cost report is shown in Fig. 5. The categories listed in the cost report can be expanded or contracted, depending on how detailed the cost information is needed to control cost. The sample report compares actual cost per month with budgeted costs, which must be estimated. Budget preparation is complex and only a few comments will be made on the subject. Budgets are worthless if not prepared carefully. Too often budgets are prepared strictly on the basis of historical data, with a percentage increase included to allow for increased dollar costs. If budgets are not prepared on the basis of production projections, they are worthless. Budgets are a device to keep costs in line or to reduce costs. Using historical data year after year does not allow for the fact that costs may have been too high when the budget system was started. If an operational manager feels comfortable with his budget, it probably is inflated and can be reduced. On the other hand, higher management must recognize that a budget is an estimate. No one can predict the future precisely, so there must be some flexibility in allowing for unforeseen circumstances. Being unrealistic regarding budget overruns contributes to inflated budgets. Budgets are, however, an excellent tool to control costs if prepared and used properly.

Graphs of monthly cost report data   After the preparation of the basic cost report, more sophisticated reports may be prepared. Graphing projections (budget) vs. actual is a dramatic way to present cost report information in a way that allows quick absorption of the information. Figure 6 shows a typical graph for the total of all costs of steam generation. Each month the graph is extended. If more breakdown is desired, individual costs such as fuel can be graphed separately. Such a graph is shown in Fig. 7. Notice on this graph that the fuel cost curve is weighted according to the heating season,

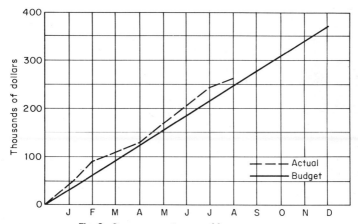

Fig. 6   Steam generation monthly cost report.

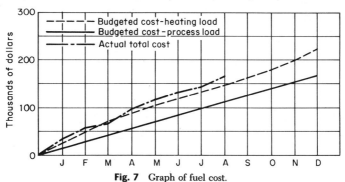

Fig. 7   Graph of fuel cost.

since fuel consumption is not linear when space heating. If budget figures on cost reports are $1/12$ of the total annual budget (easiest to program if a computer is used), this must be taken into account when analyzing monthly costs and cost variances.

Cost analysis report   A further sophistication of the cost control report is a cost analysis report, which analyzes the reason for budget variances on a systematic basis. Figure 8 is an example of a cost analysis report. Since all the information included in the basic monthly cost report is in the analysis report, the monthly cost report need not be prepared to avoid duplication. In our example, the analysis report segregates fuel cost from other costs. This was done because fuel cost is generally the largest variable cost and also the largest single cost. Referring to Fig. 8, only the spaces with lines will be filled in. Spaces with an "X" are not used. The first two columns develop a cost for steam based on budget estimates. Estimates include the amount of steam expected to be

STEAM GENERATION COST ANALYSIS REPORT

Period: _____

	Standard cost — based on budget		Comparison of budget vs. actual cost						Budget vs. actual variance			
			Budget		Actual		Per 1000# steam		Total variance		Per 1000# steam	
	Annual budget	Cost/1000#	—annual	YTD	This period	YTD	This period	YTD	This period	YTD	This period	YTD
FUEL COST												
Reg. fuel—total therms	X	X	X	X			X	X	X	X	X	X
Alt. fuel—total therms	X	X	X	X			X	X	X	X	X	X
Total fuel—therms	X	X										
Reg. fuel—cost/therm $	X	X	X	X		X	X	X	X	X	X	X
Alt. fuel—cost/therm $	X	X	X	X		X	X	X			X	X
Total fuel cost												
Steam to plant—1000#	X	X					X	X	X	X	X	X
Station steam—1000#	X	X					X	X			X	X
OTHER COSTS												
Hourly labor—incl. O.T. & benefits												
Salaried labor—incl. O.T. & benefits												
Utilities—not incl. station steam												
Maintenance												
Depreciation, taxes, insurance												
Allocated charges												
Miscellaneous												
Total costs except fuel												
Total costs incl. fuel												

*Year to date

Fig. 8 Steam generation cost analysis report.

generated for the entire fiscal year. Total annual budget figures are recorded in column 1. In column 2, the figures in column 1 are divided by the estimated amount of steam which will be sold to the consumers of the steam. The amount of station steam is recorded only as a matter of information. Since steam generation plant costs are all ultimately charged to consumers, there is no point in charging the generation operation for the station steam and then redistributing it. Columns 3 through 8 compare the actual figures with the budget figures for the period and year to date. Columns 5 and 6 compare total figures and columns 7 and 8 compare ratios by dividing the actual figures by the actual amount of steam distributed to the plant. The last four columns of budget vs. actual variances are simply the differences between the budget estimates and the actual figures for the period.

Maintenance cost reports   This subject is covered in detail in other chapters in this book, and those chapters should be used for reference. The same information needed by production departments to monitor maintenance cost is also needed by powerhouse management for the same reasons.

Utility conservation report   Since utilities consumption is proportional to many variables, it is difficult to measure the effectiveness of efforts to conserve utilities. The only method that offers a fair amount of success is to establish bench marks for utilities consumption and then to check consumption against the benchmarks from time to time.

While there are many variables affecting consumption, only major variables should be considered when setting up a report system, since consideration of all variables will only result in making a complex situation more complex. Major variables are:

1. Rate of production. Consumption of certain utilities will vary according to the number of units produced. A further complication is the fact that the ratio of utility consumption to number of units produced may not be linear.

2. Time of year. Wintertime requires heating, and air conditioning in summer requires utilities consumption to cool. Summer and winter consumption will not be the same, and transition periods—spring and fall—will approach zero consumption. Short winter days will require more lighting than long summer days. In buildings with no or few windows, this variable will not exist; but it could be a significant factor in some facilities.

Establishing consumption bench marks is done by relating consumption to variables. Consumption of each utility which is consumed directly in producing products is divided by units produced to obtain ratios. Cost should not be used in determining ratios since both utility costs and product costs change. Calculating ratios such as kWh per pound of product eliminates cost variables.

Sometimes there are two major variables that affect the consumption of a single utility. An example is the use of steam for both processing and space heating. If each consumption is metered separately, a ratio can be calculated for production and a second calculated to relate to heating degree-days. If consumptions are not metered separately, it may be possible to separate the figures some other way, such as graphically. Graphing total steam consumption—including heating steam—month by month should result in a curve similar to that in Fig. 5. Since heat is not needed in summer months in most locations, the steam consumption in summer months is process consumption and the ratio of steam consumption to units produced can be determined.

If it is not possible to separate the effects of more than one variable, the next best is to calculate the ratio of consumption to the largest variable, which, in most cases, will be units produced. A study of degree-day records indicates the danger involved in this approach, however. Consumption of utilities may have been reduced per unit produced, but extreme cold weather may have required more consumption for heating or unusually hot weather for cooling.

After the bench marks or initial ratios are established, periodically repeating the procedure should show trends. The word "trend" was used because it must be pointed out that reporting on utilities conservation is difficult. Much time and effort must be expended to make reports meaningful. This should not, however, be discouraging, because climbing utilities costs make conservation not only desirable but a necessity, and there should be a yardstick to measure efforts.

Utilities Distribution Reports

While the discussion in this section is again about steam, all utilities should be distributed. The starting point for the distribution of utilities is meter readings, either utility-company-owned meters or in-plant meters. The distribution techniques are the same in either case. After costs of steam production have been totaled, they are commonly distributed on the basis of consumption. A distribution report that accounts for all the steam leaving the steam generating plant should be prepared. Fig. 9 illustrates a form of steam distribution report. It will be assumed that each process has a meter as shown in Section 1, Chapter 6, Figure 1. Steam is a compressible fluid whose volume changes with temperature and pressure, and meters measure volume. Compensating meters

Period:_____

STEAM DISTRIBUTION REPORT

	Meter integrator readings	Diff. in integrator readings	Meter integrator factor	Actual consumption	Adjusted to main meter
Process 1					
Process 2					
Process 3					
Process 4					
Process 5					
Process 6					
Process 7					
Process 8					
Total steam from process meters					
Total steam from main meter					

Fig. 9   Steam distribution report.

correct for temperature and pressure. If compensating meters are not used, allowance for volume change of the steam—due to temperature and pressure losses in the distribution system—can be made by allowing for loss between the main meter and the process meters. The example assumes that steam leaves the generating plant at certain conditions. The main meter and the station steam meter will be calibrated for these conditions. Process meters (depending on distance from the main meter) can be calibrated to allow for average pressure and temperature drop between the main and the process meter. Steam distribution piping should be sized so that pressure drop is not excessive and should be well insulated to conserve heat. Pressure and temperature drops can be calculated initially, and adjustments can be made to meters if pressure and temperature readings taken of the system in service show considerable discrepancy between meter calibration and actual.

In the previously cited diagram (Section 1, Chapter 6, Figure 1), meters are shown on all branch lines coming off the main distribution system. This is an ideal situation, and generally there will be some unmetered branches. Usage through any unmetered lines should be calculated or estimated and added to the sum of the metered utilities to arrive at a grand total. The term "estimated" will be used for any unmetered utilities. Utility usage can be estimated various ways. The methods listed below can also be used to determine where utilities are used downstream from the process meter within the process.

1. Heat used for space heating can be estimated by determining overall coefficients of heat transfer for the building—based on type of construction, ceiling height, etc.—and with the use of average or actual heating degree-days.

2. Heat used for heating water for employee's personal use and janitor use can be estimated from handbook data per employee and then multiplied by the number of employees.

3. Multiplying the number of hours a machine (or a process) runs by the electrical consumption data.

4. If a process meter fails, historical consumption data compiled before the failure can be used to estimate consumption.

5. Temporary meters may be installed to compile usage data which can be used for subsequent estimating.

There are other methods used by accounting departments to distribute the cost of utilities. Whatever system is used, cost should be distributed fairly.

DISTRIBUTION OF REPORTS

The reason for the preparation of a report determines who shall receive the report after it is completed. Steam generation log sheets (Section 5, Chapter 7, Figure 2) are of little interest to anyone except the individual who supervises the day-to-day operation of the steam generation plant. The boiler efficiency report will be of interest to the utilities manager (See "Organization" in Section 1, Chapter 6), to the plant engineer if this individual is not the utilities manager, and to the plant engineer's supervisor. This is often the plant manager.

Utilities distribution reports generally are distributed to consumers of the utilities and to accounting groups in addition to the utilities manager and the plant engineer. Plant managers do not need to get involved with the details of distribution if distribution is done properly.

Utilities monthly cost reports are basic cost reports and are of interest to utilities consumers, the utilities manager, the plant engineer, and the plant manager. These reports are compiled by the accounting department and generally are distributed by them to interested personnel. Other cost reports are derived from the basic cost reports. These are generally prepared either by the accountants, by the powerhouse supervisor, by the utilities manager, or by the plant engineer. These supplementary cost reports present cost information in a form more easily understood than the monthly basic form. Supplementary cost reports will receive about the same distribution as the basic monthly report.

Chapter **7**

Appraisal of Performance

R. B. LEITER, P.E.
Manager of Plant Engineering

F. E. Myers Company

INTRODUCTION

You, the plant engineer, face a challenge of proof of performance in every facet of a broad panorama of responsibilities. How can you best evaluate results of a planned utilities management program?

Every phase of utilities management covered in this section has been designed to provide you with means of achieving successful results. The tools required to initiate a full-fledged program are well described and fully detailed, so that you need but adapt them to your particular situation.

But a program of this type cannot be established overnight, nor can results be expected immediately, so at least a full year's operation should be experienced before any valid evaluation can be made. During this trial period, close attention must be given to every phase of the program; weeding out unnecessary details, strengthening weak spots, checking accuracy of information, tailoring the program to the needs of the particular type of manufacturing.

So let us assume that you have gone through the many exercises of setting up a utilities management program and have now reached the time when you must determine what benefits have resulted.

Quite obviously you have to convince first yourself and, more important, your management that the program is worthwhile and should be an ongoing, continuous arrangement. Management must make a total commitment toward a successful program. What is the measure of success?

ESTABLISHING A GOAL

The successful program is one that has some goal or target. What is the target of a utilities management program? In simple terms, it can be stated thus:

1. The efficient and effective use of all types of fuel, power, water, air, and the like required in manufacturing processes

2. The resulting benefits to society, present and future, from conservative, wise utilization of natural resources

3. The complete cooperation of management and employees in carrying out a successful utilities management effort

4. A continuing contribution to profitability

The rate of industrial growth in the past three decades has been meteoric, as has been the increase in requirements for the utilities. Figure 1 shows, for example, the rise in

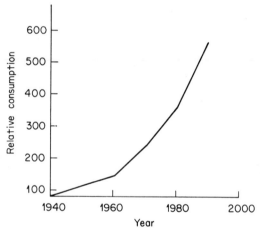

Fig. 1   Fuel resources consumption.

the usage of fuel resources during this period. The figures show, on a relative basis, the consumption of mineral fuels and electricity by industry since 1940.

Although the impending shortage of natural fuel resources has been anticipated in many circles for some time, there has also been a popular illusion of boundless supplies of natural fuel resources. Today we know that the recoverable reserves of our traditional energy sources are being depleted at such a rate that the middle of the twenty-first century will mark the end of some of our conventional supplies.

The curtailments of natural gas deliveries to industry, the allocations of fuel oils, and the "brownouts" of electrical power have now begun to alert everyone to the folly of believing in endless sources of energy.

The ever-increasing use of fresh water supplies for industrial and domestic purposes is just as significant. Figure 2 shows the rise in industrial water usage in the past three decades.

The curves show dramatically the challenge for conservation that comes with a program of utilities management.

With the use of nuclear energy and the desalinization of ocean water, there is promise for the years ahead; but the cost of these utilities is certain to become a larger portion of the industrial budget as time goes on.

Figure 3 shows the relative costs of various forms of energy available now and in the future.

In view of these facts, a target should be established that produces a realistic annual improvement in the use of utilities. Comments from industrial managers on the subject of targets for utilities management indicate the possible savings thus: "Surveys in our company repeatedly uncover potential savings of 8 to 10 percent." "A goal of 15 percent reduction in energy usage by next year has been set." "Energy conservation can reduce demand by as much as 5 percent." "A 15 percent reduction in energy consumption is well within reach." "We have the technology to recycle water, an approach that could reduce consumption by 75 percent." "A total energy system can whittle away 29 per-

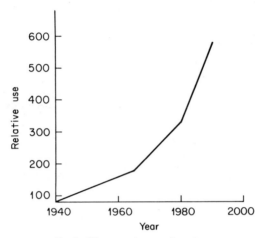

Fig. 2   Water use in manufacturing.

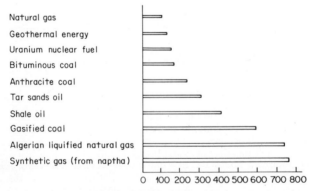

Fig. 3   Relative energy costs.

cent of our national energy consumption in buildings." "It is not unreasonable to assume that American industry wastes at least 20 percent of the electric power that it purchases." "Conservation in the use of all forms of energy can reduce demands significantly, perhaps by as much as 5 percent." Federal agencies can reduce their energy consumption by 7 percent." "We expect to reduce our energy ratio—the number of Btu consumed per unit of production—by nearly 20 percent in the coming year." "Energy usage is declining at the rate of 2 percent per year while production increases."

From these comments it would seem that a goal of somewhere between 5 and 15 percent reduction is not unreachable.

Again, the many tools of intelligent utilities management have been explained in detail in this section. It is the plant engineer's duty to put them to use.

THE FIRST CONSIDERATION

In our society, the educator and the economist seem to have been less than successful in convincing some of us that the industrial corporation does not have unlimited sums of money to spend for, among other things, the necessary utilities to operate a plant.

A vital step in a utilities management plan is development of the proper atmosphere among employees of industry. People must be made aware of the value of their ideas and efforts in conservation programs. One sign of an effective program is the number of suggestions that come from workers. Such common but often overlooked ideas as these have come from employees of industrial plants:

- Checking for compressed air leaks during off hours by plant security people
- Reporting of leaky faucets and fixtures for repair
- Care in opening and closing plant doors in weather extremes
- Shutting off unneeded heating and ventilating systems
- Turning off lights in those areas where they are not needed

An earnest effort must be made to keep all employees aware of their parts in a utilities management program. From this effort should arise a spirit of cooperation on the part of every employee. One company, for example, found it possible to conserve enough heating fuel to meet allocation limits by popularizing the wearing of heavier clothing and reducing excessive room temperatures to a comfortable 68°F.

Government agencies throughout the country have reduced energy consumption in federal offices by 7 percent by raising air-conditioning thermostat settings to 78° F. and changing custodial service schedules to take advantage of natural daylight. And management must be the keystone of the program—not only to enlist the cooperation of people but to make a strong commitment to take the bold action necessary to carry on a successful program.

So to appraise a utilities management program, one must first look at the attitudes of the involved people.

USE OF IN-PLANT RECORDS

Since every plant has peculiarities of operation which may be unique, it is important to compile historical information and to use it in appraisal of performance. One standard for a basis of comparison is the use of utilities in relation to plant labor man-hours. Such a tabulation is shown in Fig. 4. Particular notice should be taken of the changes in consumption as compared to labor man-hours.

A similar chart with utilities costs in place of quantities should be submitted annually to management with full explanation of changes and recommendations for necessary capital requests to provide improvements in utilities conservation programs. Major expenditures, planned and budgeted regularly, must be part of the program. An annual utilities cost survey will prove invaluable in appraising the performance of a utilities program.

To pinpoint trends more closely and take action to correct problems immediately, a comparison of monthly utilities consumption is helpful. In Fig. 5, a comparison of various utilities is made, with labor man-hours again used as the basis. Trend lines can be used to show the effectiveness of the program.

It must be understood that many factors must be considered in the use of these elementary comparisons. Equipment and process changes that affect usage must be noted; uncontrollable causes such as weather extremes, production schedules, and such can alter

	Plant labor, man-hours $\times 10^6$	Change, %	Gas, cu ft $\times 10^6$	Change, %	Electricity, kWh $\times 10^6$	Change, %	Water, cu ft $\times 10^6$	Change, %
Year								
1970	1.00		166.83		4.30		9.28	
1971	0.92	− 8.0	150.35	−10.0	3.76	−12.5	8.49	− 8.5
1972	1.14	+14.0	169.16	+ 1.5	4.22	− 2.0	10.28	+11.1

Fig. 4 Sample usage chart.

trends. And, obviously, lower product costs may often justify higher utilities costs. The plant engineer must be prepared to weigh all these considerations in judging the effectiveness of utilities management as shown by such comparisons.

Since the information on this type of chart is intended to trigger immediate action when required, it is important that it be kept up to date without fail.

Utilities companies for many reasons are becoming more alert to changes in demands from industrial plants. Many of them can provide up-to-the-minute statistics on individual plant consumption. Since the advent of interruptible electrical energy loads,

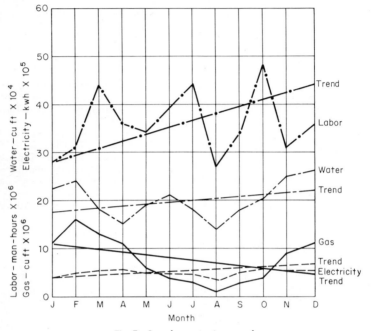

Fig. 5   Sample comparison graph.

Period	Allo-cated volume	Curtail-ment	Adjusted volume	Delivered volume	Over	Under
Nov.	6,000	—	6,000	6,260	+260	
Dec.	8,000	500	7,500	7,320		−180
Jan.	9,600	800	8,800	8,860	+ 60	

Fig. 6   Typical summary sheet.

bans on unnecessary water use, voluntary and mandatory allocations of fuels and such, some utilities are providing summaries of usage from data processing information. These, too, are valuable in the appraisal of utilities management. Figure 6 shows typical summary sheet for a natural gas allocation arrangement.

Communications between industry and public and private utilities must be maintained so that unusual conditions of usage are reported at once for remedial action. Again, the value of these in-plant tabulations lies solely in their use to spot trouble and to take remedial action.

Finally, careful daily observation of plant processes and pieces of equipment that have their own metering devices will provide useful historical data. Daily logs of usage are well worthwhile in rating the effectiveness of conservation measures. The most valuable utilities management program will be that which exercises control of usage based on knowledge of every potential improvement in utilities consumption. This knowledge can quite often be obtained only from actual experience with particular equipment and processes doing a particular type of work in a particular plant.

INDUSTRYWIDE COMPARISONS

A broader basis for evaluation of a utilities management program is a comparison of usages with those of related industries throughout the nation. Under the Standard Industrial Classification Code, it is possible to set up comparisons of utilities usage which may assist the plant engineer in appraising a program.

A series of tables have been drawn up to show the relationship between the usage of various purchased utilities and the dollar value of the product for a number of industry groups.

TABLE 1   Yearly Electrical Energy Costs

Industry code	Industry group	Electrical energy purchased, kWh × 10⁶	Cost, cents per kWh	kWh per dollar value of product
20	Food and kindred products	24,401.4	1.30	0.319
21	Tobacco	737.3	1.07	0.173
22	Textile mill products	20,264.4	0.88	1.050
23	Apparel and other textiles	3,595.1	1.86	0.169
24	Lumber and wood products	7,297.0	1.22	0.712
25	Furniture and fixtures	2,473.7	1.50	0.325
26	Paper and allied products	25,857.8	0.81	2.340
27	Printing and publishing	5,817.2	1.51	0.268
28	Chemicals	95,413.6	0.61	2.771
29	Petroleum and coal products	18,185.9	0.74	1.011
30	Rubber and plastics	10,184.2	1.15	0.844
31	Leather products	1,288.0	1.60	0.258
32	Stone, clay, and glass products	19,570.0	1.02	1.441
33	Primary metals	109,468.6	0.63	2.822
34	Fabricated metal products	14,694.2	1.41	0.428
35	Machinery except electrical	16,659.3	1.30	0.356
36	Electrical equipment and supplies	19,012.7	1.05	0.443
37	Transportation equipment	23,468.3	1.01	0.344
38	Instruments and related products	2,493.3	1.37	0.311
19 & 39	Ordnance and miscellaneous	6,583.1	1.17	0.374
	All industries, total	427,465.1	0.87	0.907

SOURCE: U.S. Department of Commerce 1967 Census of Manufacturers.

It is understood that the utilities rate may change, as may the dollar value of the product, but indications are that the relationships shown will serve as guidelines for establishing goals and evaluating performance.

Table 1 lists the cost of electrical energy by industry groups and the consumption in kilowatthours per dollar of product.

Table 2 shows the amount of water intake by industry groups and its relationship to the value of the product.

Table 3 shows the use of gas, both natural and manufactured, its average cost, and the relationship of usage to value of product.

Table 4 shows the usage of fuel oil, its average cost, and the relationship of usage to the value of the product.

Not to be overlooked is the fact that, beyond this handbook, a wealth of information for comparison of utilities management is being regularly made available to the plant engineer.

The various trade magazines actively search out information which is useful. The seriousness of the energy situation in the 1970s finds more and more space devoted to the subject of utilities management.

Many federal agencies are involved in the problems of utilities conservation and much valuable data can be secured from these sources. Chief among these agencies is the Department of Commerce Office of Energy Programs, which acts as a clearinghouse for energy conservation programs.

The technical societies of the nation are regularly offering the results of scientific research for use in utilities conservation.

TABLE 2   Yearly Water Use by Manufacturing Industries

Industry code	Industry group	Water intake gallons $\times 10^9$	Gallons of water per dollar value of product
20	Food and kindred products	811	9.7
21	Tobacco	6	1.2
22	Textile mill products	154	7.7
24	Lumber and wood products	118	10.5
25	Furniture and fixtures	4	0.5
26	Paper and allied products	2,252	107.4
28	Chemicals	4,476	106.2
29	Petroleum and coal products	1,435	65.1
30	Rubber and plastics	135	10.6
31	Leather products	16	3.1
32	Stone, clay, and glass products	251	17.4
33	Primary metals	5,005	107.1
34	Fabricated metal products	68	2.0
35	Machinery except electrical	189	3.9
36	Electrical equipment and supplies	127	2.9
37	Transportation equipment	313	4.6
38	Instruments and related products	38	3.8
39	Ordnance and miscellaneous	14	0.8
	All industries, total	15,467	27.7

SOURCE: U.S. Bureau of the Census, 1968.

TABLE 3   Yearly Gas (Natural and Manufactured) Use by Manufacturing Industries—for Heat and Power

Industry code	Industry group	Quantity purchased, $ft^3 \times 10^6$	Cost, dollars per $ft^3 \times 10^3$	Cubic feet of gas per dollar value of product
20	Food and kindred products	346,260.4	0.412	4.12
21	Tobacco	2,674.4	0.486	0.55
22	Textile mill products	55,468.0	0.447	2.80
24	Lumber and wood products	54,429.2	0.344	4.86
25	Furniture and fixtures	1,699.4	0.647	0.22
26	Paper and allied products	351,212.9	0.311	16.74
27	Printing and publishing	15,009.6	0.653	0.69
28	Chemicals	1,204,275.4	0.251	28.57
29	Petroleum and coal products	1,122,434.3	0.235	50.92
30	Rubber and plastics	42,617.4	0.474	3.34
31	Leather products	4,238.8	0.566	0.82
32	Stone, clay, and glass products	624,385.1	0.381	43.21
33	Primary metals	1,141,586.4	0.374	24.42
34	Fabricated metal products	103,736.7	0.576	3.00
35	Machinery except electrical	79,581.0	0.596	1.64
36	Electrical equipment and supplies	48,005.5	0.540	1.10
37	Transportation equipment	106,604.2	0.518	1.55
38	Instruments and related products	2,652.4	0.641	0.26
	All industries, total	5,306,862.1	0.328	9.52

SOURCE: U.S. Department of Commerce 1967 Census of Manufacturers.

The manufacturers of the many types of machinery and equipment that consume utilities of some sort are vitally interested in efficient usage.

Engineering consultants who are specialists in the many fields of industrial utilities usage offer their services to assist in utilities studies.

The utilities companies, too, are seriously concerned with energy conservation measures. Their technical representatives are responsible for keeping users informed of best

TABLE 4   Yearly Fuel Oil Usage by Manufacturing Industries

Industry code	Industry group	Quantity purchased, 42-gallon barrel $\times 10^3$	Cost, dollars per gallon	Gallons of fuel oil per million dollars of product
20	Food and kindred products	17,533.6	0.078	8,769.4
21	Tobacco	421.6	0.073	3,610.8
22	Textile mill products	6,891.4	0.067	14,607.1
24	Lumber and wood products	3,582.9	0.122	13,428.7
25	Furniture and fixtures	251.0	0.104	1,360.3
26	Paper and allied products	41,899.4	0.056	83,918.7
27	Printing and publishing	1,130.6	0.088	2,184.4
28	Chemicals	20,562.6	0.066	20,490.4
29	Petroleum and coal products	10,079.1	0.058	19,204.4
30	Rubber and plastics	3,710.5	0.069	12,214.2
31	Leather products	1,369.3	0.067	11,126.1
32	Stone, clay, and glass products	12,030.4	0.087	34,969.7
33	Primary metals	40,712.2	0.077	36,590.5
34	Fabricated metal products	4,566.5	0.087	5,546.7
35	Machinery except electrical	5,206.6	0.078	4,510.9
36	Electrical equipment and supplies	2,570.1	0.075	2,489.4
37	Transportation equipment	5,856.9	0.075	3,590.5
38	Instruments and related products	238.3	0.079	1,010.2
	All industries, total	178,613.0	0.071	13,458.5

SOURCE: U.S. Department of Commerce 1967 Census of Manufacturers.

conservation practice. They conduct seminars for industrial utilities managers to provide guidelines for energy conservation. Through the efforts of the various trade associations affiliated with the utilities companies, valuable information for appraisal of a management program is made available.

So, the plant engineer has the opportunity and the responsibility of comparing the results of the plant's utilities management program with those of many other manufacturing establishments in the nation. And this must be a continuing process to get optimum results.

DIFFERENT APPROACHES FOR SMALL, MEDIUM, AND LARGE PLANTS

Once a definite set of targets has been established and with information available as a guideline either from in-plant experience or from industrywide comparisons, the plant engineer can rate the implementation of a utilities management program.

The multiplant corporation will find it necessary to set up a group of specialists who may serve as a consulting service for all plants. Such a group might consist of persons with responsibilities for such items as emergency fuel planning, conservation programs, new equipment specifications when utilities are a strong consideration, rate structure schedules, and future utilities requirements. The wealth of information available to this group would be invaluable in appraising individual plant programs and improving and revising them. Some examples of this type of activity show its effectiveness.

One corporation achieved a savings of 10 percent in its fuel oil usage through a careful study of combustion conditions in plant boilers. This level of improvement throughout the nation would reduce the requirements by some 1½ million barrels per day of oil equivalent. This is the output of more than twenty average-sized refineries.

A study of the waste of process water and the rising cost of treatment led to the reclamation of waste oils by one corporation to the extent of 12 million gallons in one year. This oil was then used for boiler firing or re-refined for use as coolant in machining operations.

A survey team found in checking corporate plants on a yearly basis that one-sixth of the capacitors installed for power-factor improvement were inactive because of blown fuses.

Utilities rates were reduced in more than 10 percent of the plants studied by a task group.

A concerted effort to reduce electrical energy consumption in an office buildng by control of the heating, lighting, and air-conditioning operation with timers and thermostatic control interlocks resulted in a 35 percent saving.

Some of these examples required the sophisticated techniques of computer analysis to achieve results and some of them were elementary in nature, but they serve to show the potential that a group of specialists can develop.

With a group of this type inspecting single plants every three years, one corporation is reducing its utilities cost by 8 percent per year.

In the course of these inspections, every suggestion for savings is scrutinized, evaluated, and presented to the local manager for implementation. A thorough follow-up of suggestions indicates that more than 80 percent of the potential savings are actually being realized.

In the more than 300,000 manufacturing establishments in the Unnted States, however, the average employment is approximately sixty people. Hence the situation for many plants is vastly different than so far discussed.

Consider the one-location industry, with a plant engineering department of perhaps three to five people. Usually, the plant engineering manager must assume the role of specialist and single-handedly control and appraise a utilities usage program. It is hoped that the use of this handbook will provide the knowledge needed for this endeavor.

Certainly the same techniques and the same potential are available as with the large multiplant survey team. Only the scale is different.

The total utilities bill in many industrial plants may be as high as 10 percent of the cost of operation. This dictates that at least half of one man's time can be devoted to utilities management and performance appraisal with justification. Of course, management must be totally in agreement with this usage of technical skills.

An advantage in the medium-sized plant lies in the capability of quickly recognizing wasteful practices and taking remedial action more readily.

To continually appraise the value of this activity, the use of assistance from utilities representatives, equipment supplies, technical organizations, consultants, and current published reports and articles is particularly important to the smaller plant engineering staff.

A large group of manufacturing establishments are of a size or nature that may often preclude the use of even a full-time technical person for plant engineering. In this case, full dependence on outside help must prevail. As long as the top management is aware of the value of a utilities management program, the necessary help can be found.

Regardless of the size of the plant, the highest potential for savings should be sought out by some of the available means and a continuous review of the progress and results of utilities management should be made.

LONG-TERM BENEFITS

Of the major utilities, the industrial plants of the United States are obviously large users. In many cases, the industrial plants appear to also be quite wasteful users. Table 5 shows the relative uses of these major utilities and the possible savings by reduction of wasteful practices.

For the long term, the benefits of utilities management can be numerous. Consider first the reduction of waste of natural resources. There is divergence of opinion, as to the availability of energy in the form of fuels, but a reasonable estimate is shown in Table 6.

To project the requirements by industry in the future is an exercise in futility because of such unknown factors as population growth, environmental control, international affairs, economic situations, government regulation, and many, many others.

A national energy policy will perhaps dictate the use of some fuels for domestic and institutional use only. It is quite possible that the industrial plant may use electrical energy for all purposes. Thus, a management program concentrating on this utility alone might provide the most rewarding return.

It seems certain that by the year 2050, oil and gas will no longer be in use as fuels in industrial plants. Meanwhile, all measures of conservation should be stressed to provide adequate time for the shift away from these fuels.

By elimination of most of the waste indicated by Table 5, additional time would be available for the extremely complex and costly design and construction of plants to provide alternate energy sources.

A checklist in a following part of this chapter gives some helpful ideas to use in evaluating a utilities management program.

Another long-term benefit of good utilities management is the result of the need for environmental improvement.

Water usage in industry has had a great impact on the quality of our lakes and streams. Passage of the Federal Water Pollution Control Act Amendments of 1972 set a goal of 1985 for attainment of elimination of discharge of pollutants into navigable waters. This,

TABLE 5   Utilities Usage and Waste Comparison

Utility	Industrial plant usage compared to total usage (percent)	Potential savings (percent)
Electricity	43	10–25
Water	25	75–95
Fuels	30	20–30

TABLE 6   Estimated Fuel Supply

Fuel	United States	World
Recoverable coal reserves	33×10^{18} Btu	170×10^{18} Btu
Recoverable oil and gas reserves	1.8×10^{18} Btu	23×10^{18} Btu
Recoverable nuclear fuels	17×10^{18} Btu	70×10^{18} Btu

in effect, requires the plant engineer to either eliminate the discharge of process water or to provide necessary treatment to make any discharge acceptable to public waste water disposal systems. With the obvious high cost of this operation, a managment program will search out every means of reusing water supplies.

We must agree that a continued high standard of living is of great importance to everyone. Hence we must make every effort to ensure that adequate supplies of utilities are available for personal needs, yet we must also make certain that we do not restrict the supplies necessary for industrial growth, which provides the personal income from jobs to buy goods and services.

The best way to ensure these supplies in a free country is to use them efficiently. Regulatory measures are sometimes necessary under emergency conditions, but for the near and distant future a national policy should concern itself only with assuring a sufficient supply of economical utilities which can be also acceptable from an environmental standpoint.

Appraisal of utilities management must include, then, the contribution to a higher living standard based on industrial growth.

CONTRIBUTION TO PROFITS

In Fig. 3 it was shown that the costs of fuels might increase to as much as eight times the present cost. The strain on the economy to provide the capital required to develop and build the energy system of the future is tremendous. The reuse of water, previously mentioned, will certainly increase the cost at least threefold. The cost of discharge of wastes and necessary treatment will rise as ambient water quality standards become effective.

Here lies a sizable challenge in utilities management. In Tables 1, 2, 3, and 4, the uses of fuels, electricity, and water were shown for various industry groups as they related to the value of the products made by these industries. These usages indicate low costs for utilities as a part of total product cost. Table 7 shows further that total industrial utilities costs are a small part of total industrial shipment values.

However, it now seems likely that the utilities bill will rise to the point where it is at least 5 percent of the value of product shipments. In recent years manufacturing profits have averaged only a little over 5 percent of the value of product shipments. It follows that any improvement in utilities management becomes a strong contribution to profit.

Conversely, the regulatory bodies which must approve utilities rate schedules are leaning in the direction of charging a premium for large purchases. So it is imperative that the utilities purchases be held down in order to keep profits from dropping.

TABLE 7   Total Industrial Utilities Purchases

		Percent of value of shipments
Value of total industrial shipments	$557,398,000,000	
Electrical energy purchases	3,700,000,000	.67
Fuel purchases	4,000,000,000	.71
Water purchases	3,000,000,000	.54
Utilities Purchases Totals	$ 10,700,000,000	1.92

SOURCE: U.S. Bureau of the Census, 1967.

As an aid to appraisal of performance, the following list provides suggestions for a conservation program:

ENERGY CONSERVATION CHECKLIST

Improve power factor to reduce demand charges for electrical energy.
Schedule heavy loads for off-peak periods to control demand.
Reduce heating and cooling in unused areas.
Reduce air-conditioning load by setting controls higher or off during night, weekend, and holiday hours.
Use photoelectric cells to control security and parking lot lighting.
Use program controllers to start and stop heating equipment, air compressors, processing equipment.
Turn off or reduce lighting in areas which may be unoccupied for an hour or more at a time.
Increase the air-conditioning setting to no less than 77°F.
Reduce the space heating control setting to 68°F in areas where medium physical effort is required in the job.
Reduce the light level in storage areas, basements, vaults, and other such areas that are not regularly used.
Check capacitors regularly for proper operation.
Switch capacitors on large loads on and off to prevent wasted system losses.
Check to ensure that proper voltage is provided for electrical equipment.
Check for heat leaks in process equipment.
Install insulation to reduce building and process heat losses.
Check for missing or damaged insulation.
Consider replacement with more efficient lighting systems.
Provide a good effective maintenance program for plant equipment.
Consider reclamation or recovery of heat produced by machinery and lighting.
Carefully study ventilation requirements for possible savings.

Review design and specifications for new machinery and equipment to provide efficient usage of electrical energy.

Designate one person as an energy manager to coordinate and implement conservation measures and suggestions.

Avoid process heat-up losses by eliminating short runs.

Reduce temperature control settings on process equipment at nights and on weekends.

Reduce number of door openings; close doors promptly.

Use reflective heat shields on such equipment as heated ladles or forging furnaces.

Make necessary combustion analyses to ensure proper air-fuel ratios in fuel burning equipment.

Insulate all lines carrying steam, hot water, and other hot liquids.

Guard against unnecessary heating times and temperatures in such operations as heat treating, tempering, and stress relieving.

Study all possible means of recycling of hot flue gases for preheating combustion air or for space heating.

Make regular searches for and repair steam leaks.

Maintain steam traps regularly for proper steam usage.

Maintain compressed air systems at high efficiency by reducing line leaks.

Make certain all steam condensate is returned for reuse to boilers.

Conduct complete plant surveys of water usage and rectify wasteful procedures such as excessive overflowing rinses.

Check washrooms for leaky faucets, running toilets.

Reuse cooling water in process where heat is required.

Install thermostatic valves on cooling water applications to reduce consumption.

Investigate cooling tower installations for recirculating cooling water.

Make special guard rounds after end of operating shifts to shut off all equipment left running, close windows, turn off lights, etc.

Conduct supervisory meetings to keep up to date on best conservation means.

Promote conservation programs by notices on bulletin boards and through departmental meetings, house publications, and recognition of suggestions.

These and many other ideas will emerge with the development of a utilities management program and will certainly provide a means of appraising the performance.

OTHER CONSIDERATIONS

Beyond the most important phases of utilities management already discussed at some length are the consideration of effective usage of compressed air, steam, and the treatment of liquid and gaseous effluent.

From selection of the most efficient compressor, proper installation of piping system, proper pressures for a particular application, and on to regular maintenance of the entire system, the plant engineer can further improve a utilities management program. As power costs rise, so will the cost of air leaks, compressor maintenance, and equipment replacement. This again is part of utilities management performance.

The efficient generation of steam for process, space heating, and power production requires strong consideration in utilities management. Likewise, efficient distribution and usage of steam, with minimal losses and maximum condensate return, is a criterion of good utilities management. The study of steam and power plants is a field of its own, but it is also a part of good utilities management.

Another consideration of utilities management is the impact of environmental control. It was previously noted that a potential saving of 75 percent of the water intake of an industrial plant is a possibility; under federal water pollution control regulations, many industrial plants are aiming at total water conservation systems. As an indication of the rising importance of this utility, the total waste water discharge by industrial plants in the year 1968 was 13 trillion 100 billion gallons. At that time only about 50 percent of the plants were employing any form of waste treatment. It was estimated that a capital investment of over 2½ billion dollars would be required to eliminate this deficiency. The cost of this construction as well as the treatment cost must be borne by industry.

Air quality regulations too have meant the introduction of a huge industrywide program for the control of discharge from the many and varied processes.

It is beyond this discussion to consider the whole field of pollution and its control, but it must be noted that the plant engineer must consider the operation of any such systems as a phase of utilities management insofar as its effectiveness and its operating costs are concerned.

No real standards have yet been set for appraising performance in this rapidly developing area, but full consideration must be given to the state of the art as time goes by.

EMERGENCY PLANS

One final part of performance appraisal is the ability to respond to emergency conditions. With natural gas in shortest supply, standby petroleum fuels must be considered for the near future. Hence a good program will provide the capability of use of either of these fuels. In the case of new equipment, consideration must be given to such combinations as gas and electric heating systems to provide emergency backup. Likewise, under certain conditions, the electric utilities may find it necessary to reduce voltage or shed parts of their loads.

Good utilities management must prepare priority lists of important loads, both fuel and power, and provide control devices to cut off only nonessential loads in case of emergency. Further, an orderly plan of reducing these loads with the least disruption of normal operation must be prepared. Some consideration might be given to standby electrical power generating equipment for critical loads during load-dropping situations. A good program must include adequate plans for such contingencies.

In summary, the appraisal of performance of a utilities management program covers a broad and extensive panorama and offers a decided challenge to the ability of the plant engineer.

Chapter 8

Conserving Our Natural Resources—Energy and Dollars

H. HARRY PHIPPS, P.E.
Energy Systems Consultants

INTRODUCTION

The importance of conserving our natural resources surely must be recognized by almost every man, woman, and child in the country today. With the possible exception of the Watergate affair, few issues in recent years have received more widespread publicity. Even if Watergate is never put to rest, we may well anticipate that energy problems will dominate the nation's headlines with increasing frequency. Let us hope that industry can avoid comparable trials and tribulations when the energy situation really gets rough by eliminating the indiscriminate use of our natural resources that now exists.

In addition to the daily headlines, editorials, and TV news specials on some facet of energy, the energy shortage, or the pollution resulting from its use, there is evidence of an increasing awareness that industry shares responsibility for these problems. It is being pointed out that industrial and large commercial establishments account for about half of the nation's annual energy consumption. Other data indicate that:

- Industry uses 30 percent of all the oil produced annually.
- Industry uses 56 percent of the natural gas produced annually.
- Industry uses 67 percent of the annual coal production.

U.S. Interior Department statistics indicate that this consumption will increase by two-thirds by 1985.

This use of our fuel resources, of course, results in pollution. From data developed by the Environmental Protection Agency for 1969, industry's contribution to air pollution was over 60 million tons, most of which resulted from its use of energy. This was 22 percent of the total tonnage involved. But the University of Illinois has developed a new method of air pollution measurement which includes a factor for the danger and importance of each pollutant. Under this method, industry's air pollution percentage figure would more than double. In addition, industry might well be held responsible for more than half of the thermal pollution of our rivers, lakes, and coastal waters.

These figures are submitted here not to subject industry to further castigation but simply to point out the magnitude of the overall problem and to demonstrate the dire need for greatly increased conservation efforts. Both energy consumption and pollution must be reduced. Depending upon whose projections you use, there is serious question whether the amount of fuel projected to be consumed in 1985, or even in the years between, will be available. While the resulting pollution from energy usage may be controlled through the installation of very expensive equipment, the only profitable way to reduce it is simply to reduce fuel usage.

GROWTH IN ELECTRICAL DEMAND

Unfortunately, there is some indication that during the past few years residential and commercial installations and, to a lesser degree, some industrial plants have attempted to avoid the possibility of fuel shortages and to evade pollution problems by converting to the use of electricity. Many of these conversions have resulted in the inefficient use of electricity. While this may solve the user's dilemma, it simply shifts the problem to the already overburdened utility and actually adds to the overall fuel shortage.

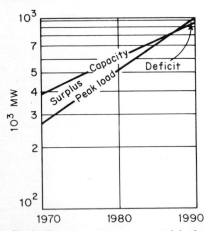

Fig. 1 Forecast—capacity versus peak load.

A recent study funded by the National Science Foundation projects electric generating capacity and the peak demand for electricity. The report shows that in 1970 the generating capacity exceeded peak demands, as shown in Fig. 1. This surplus capacity is shown to be constantly decreasing because the growth rate in electric demand is greater than the installation of generating capacity. It shows an apparent "crossover" in about 1985. It becomes obvious, then, that the electric industry simply cannot cope with the increasing demand, much of which is unnecessary and caused by the inefficient use of electricity.

Obviously, this crossover is not a phenomenon that will occur simultaneously throughout the nation at some fixed time and date. Demand will not suddenly exceed available capacity. Rather, it would begin to happen gradually, as we have already seen, and to spread with increasing frequency until such time as it became a common daily occurence to interrupt certain loads during certain times and to reject other types of loads altogether. As many plant engineers already know, the cost of such interruptions in a plant's operation is very high.

FUTURE ENERGY COSTS

While we are on the subject of economics, let us look at the role of energy conservation in relation to future operating costs. Most plant engineers have already seen significant increases in the cost of fuel oil, coal, and natural gas. As the requirements for use of low-sulfur oil and coal increase, costs will increase even more rapidly. It also appears completely realistic to anticipate a growing number of restrictions on the use of natural gas as an industrial boiler fuel.

Similarly, the Federal Power Commission has predicted that the average cost of electricity will triple by 1990. A threefold increase is significant in itself; but there are other factors involved which indicate a reason for even greater concern. An examination of existing facts and apparent trends indicates a more drastic change in the cost of electricity to the industrial user. Some of the principles involved may also be applicable to other energy sources in the future.

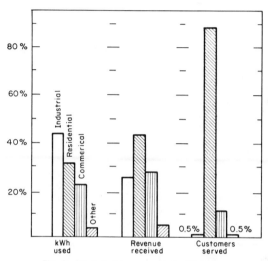

Fig. 2 Market data—annual electric sales.

Figure 2 shows that 43 percent of the electricity generated in this country is used by industrial customers as compared to 31 percent being used by residential customers. At the same time, the industrial market provides only 25 percent of the electric revenues as compared to 43 percent received from the residential market. The average cost per kilowatthour to the industrial user today is slightly less than 1 cent, while the average cost to the residential customer is approximately 2.1 cents per kilowatthour. This demonstrates the well-known principle of quantity discount. Plant engineers involved in the production of almost anything will recognize the economic validity of this type of cost structure.

Changing Philosophy of Utility Rates

However, a philosophy gaining acceptance in many circles is that this situation should be reversed, or—in these days of energy shortages—the more you use, the higher the rate should be. Thus it may not be unreasonable to expect that, while the average cost of electricity may triple by 1990, the same multiplier may not be applicable to all classifications of customers. For example, Fig. 3 shows the average cost, the residential cost, and the industrial cost approximately parallel. A closer look, however, reveals that the residential rate has increased to approximately 2½ times the 1970 rate, while the industrial rate has increased to about 4½

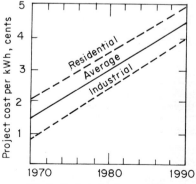

Fig. 3 Projected price per kWh.

times. This is shown more effectively in Fig. 4, which is a projection of each of the three categories as a percentage of the 1970 level.

Predicting future utility rates is a highly hazardous pastime when so many rapidly changing factors are involved. No claim is made that any special powers were bestowed from on high in the development of the data presented herein. However, based upon

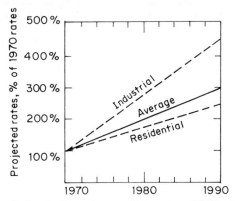

Fig. 4   Projected rates (expressed as percent of 1970 rates).

the foregoing philosophy and figures, it is possible to develop a rate schedule that will serve to provide some practical indication of the increasing value of conservation measures. To do so, let us examine a typical existing electric rate schedule and a hypothetical rate schedule that *may* exist in the future.

Typical Existing Rates

Figure 5 is perhaps typical of an existing industrial rate schedule composed of both a demand charge and an energy charge. Typically, both charges decrease as usage increases. Only the basic rate is shown here. Actual rates may include a fuel adjustment clause, a load factor discount, a power factor adjustment, state and local taxes, etc.

EXISTING RATE	
DEMAND CHARGE	
First 50 kW	@ $2.00/kW
Next 50 kW	@ $1.50/kW
Additional demand	@ $1.00/kW
ENERGY CHARGE	
First 2,000 kWh/mo.	@ 3.0¢/kWh
Next 38,000 kWh/mo.	@ 1.2¢/kWh
Next 460,000 kWh/mo.	@ .9¢/kWh
Additional usage	@ .8¢/kWh

Fig. 5   Typical existing industrial electric rate.

The lower part of Fig. 6 illustrates the point already made—that under present rates the cost per kWh decreases as usage increases, even with a constant load factor. The lower part of Fig. 7 illustrates the reduction in the cost per kWh with present rates as the load factor improves, even though usage remains constant. However, it can be seen that the cost reduction available through the improvement of load factor is relatively small.

Possible Future Rates

Figure 8 shows an industrial rate schedule which you may be faced with in 1990. Of primary importance is the fact that not only are the demand charges greater but the rate has been reversed so that the demand charge actually increases with demand, rather than decreasing as before. Furthermore, the demand charge is a significant one, justifying serious efforts in keeping peak electrical loads as low as possible.

The energy charge portion of the rate still shows a decreasing cost per kWh, but please not that a new factor has been added. A load-factor charge has been built into the rate by relating the steps in the energy rate to the kW demand.

The upper portion of Fig. 6 demonstrates that an increase in usage under the future rate no longer results in a reduction in cost, even though the steps in the rate schedule

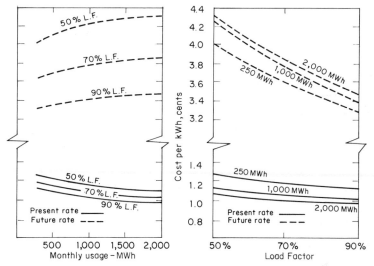

Fig. 6 Effect of increasing usage with constant load factor.

Fig. 7 Effect of improving load factor with constant usage.

FUTURE RATE	
DEMAND CHARGE	
First 200 kW	@ $3.00/kW
Next 800 kW	@ $4.00/kW
Additional demand	@ $5.00/kW
ENERGY CHARGE	
First 350 kWh per kW of demand	@ 3.00¢/kWh
Next 150 kWh per kW of demand	@ 2.75¢/kWh
Next 100 kWh per kW of demand	@ 2.50¢/kWh
Additional usage	@ 1.75¢/kWh

Fig. 8 Typical future industrial electric rate.

itself show such a decrease. Only an improvement in load factor can achieve a cost reduction. This is shown more clearly in the upper part of Fig. 7. Compared to the slope of the existing rate, it is obvious that the future rate yields greater savings in the cost per kWh when the load factor is improved. While load factor itself is not a complete indication of efficient electrical usage, it is, nevertheless, one indication that is generally reliable.

Thus we see a built-in incentive under the future rate—both to use less electricity and to use it more efficiently. It may be anticipated that cost increases will result from shortening the period of time over which demand is measured, using an annual load factor clause more frequently and imposing penalty-type taxes by various state and local taxing authorities. The principles demonstrated here may also be applied to other forms of energy.

VALUE OF ENERGY CONSERVATION EFFORTS

Based upon the foregoing, let us see whether we can get some idea of the value of energy conservation efforts. Let us assume that we have a facility using 1 million kWh per month with a 60 percent load factor. Let us further assume a rather modest objective of a *10 percent improvement in load factor* and a *10 percent reduction in usage*, although there is no direct relationship between the two. Electric usage would drop from 1 million to 900,000 kWh and demand would drop from 2,283 kW to 1,761 kW. Accordingly, monthly cost would decrease from $11,000 per month to $9,700, a saving of almost $16,000 per year. Under the future rate, the monthly cost would decrease from about $40,000 to $34,000, an annual saving of over $70,000. Assuming the rate increases were constant throughout the period, we would find that total accumulated savings in 10 years amount to $308,000 and to almost $890,000 over the 20-year period.

Based upon the same assumptions, it is possible to develop factors applicable to a rather wide range of conditions, as shown below. These factors were calculated for use in the range of 250,000 to 2 million kWh per month. The chart will help you estimate the dollar value of the savings resulting from reducing usage by 10 percent and increasing load factor by 10 percent.

To determine savings in electric cost for	Multiply present monthly electric bill by
First year	1.4 to 1.5
Twentieth year	5 to 7
5-year accumulated	9 to 10
10-year accumulated	25 to 28
20-year accumulated	70 to 84

Return on Investment

To obtain some idea of a justifiable *investment* in order to achieve these reductions, multiply your present average monthly electric cost by 10 to 11, depending upon your level of usage. The resulting figure will give you an energy conservation investment which will produce an average return of 20 percent per year for the first 5 years. The same investment will result in an average return of 25 percent per year over a 10-year period.

Obviously, the foregoing comments regarding costs and savings will vary with different existing utility rates and with what actually will happen in the future. They are presented here only to serve as general guidelines and to demonstrate the possible order of magnitude of the value of energy conservation measures. The same basic approach, however, can be applied to any specific situation to develop comparative costs on existing rate schedules. Should you be of the opinion that your own crystal ball provides a better insight into future rates, use your own figures instead of the ones shown.

START ENERGY CONSERVATION PROGRAMS NOW

The point being made is simply that efforts toward energy conservation can bring significant economic rewards today, and the return may well increase many times in the coming years. As we have seen, the reduction in utility costs alone is sizable, not to mention the resulting decreased risk of power interruptions and shutdowns from energy shortages. The important thing is to start now, because it is likely that the next 5 to 10 years may be the most serious period of the crisis. The reduction in energy requirements through more efficient usage may be the most significant contributing that can presently be made to solving this problem.

In-Plant Programs

How does the plant engineer go about starting an energy conservation program in a given facility? No attempt will be made here to cover all the details of energy systems analysis, but some general suggestions will be offered which may be of assistance in getting such a program started.

The first thing to do in any such program is simply to get "turned on." Somebody has to be motivated. Somebody has to be concerned about tomorrow—either about the *economy* or the *ecology* of your particular installation. If you are able to generate some interest and enthusiasm for the subject, you will be surprised how easily everything else will fall into line. The daily press, technical journals, and an ever-increasing number of books are giving more and more attention to the subject. Engineering societies, governmental agencies, and other groups are planning seminars on various phases of the subject. The American Institute of Plant Engineers has established a committee on energy conservation. Again, once you get "turned on," you will find that the rest will come easy.

Management Programs

Discussions with plant engineers indicate that management in some cases still shows little interest. However, perhaps a little thought may divulge both the reason for this and the solution. Stop to think that up to this time the words "conservation," "ecology," and "environment" (not to mention "pollution") have cost management a bundle, with absolutely no chance of economic return! I suggest, then, that you develop a presentation which demonstrates that efforts toward energy conservation represent a sound economic proposition. Combine economics with the effects upon ecology. You may be pleasantly surprised at the way your suggestions are received. Truly enlightened management is receptive to social as well as economic suggestions.

Your presentation for embarking on an energy conservation program might well start with an "energy inventory"—an in-depth review of all forms of energy usage and demands. Determine when and why your peak demands occur, then do the same for each of your major processes or items of major usage. Determine the reason for variations from hour to hour, day to day, and month to month. If you look closely enough, you will be surprised at the number of places where you can find large amounts of energy simply being wasted. If you do not thoroughly understand all facets of your utility rate schedules, call one of the utility's representatives and have it explained thoroughly.

Utilize Outside Help

Unfortunately, many plant engineers appear to be reluctant to utilize outside assistance on problems of this nature. While the plant engineers are among the most versatile of all those in the engineering profession, with technical knowledge encompassing many disciplines, no one can be an expert in all fields. And, with the many new and complex problems being added to plant engineer's responsibilities, certainly they should not be embarrassed to utilize the specialized skill and experience of consultants.

Expert talent is available to the plant engineer. Technical representatives of equipment manufacturers, fuel suppliers, and public utilities can frequently provide valuable assistance. It should be recognized, however, that these representatives are specialists in their particular fields and should not be imposed upon to comment on problems outside their specialty.

If the consulting engineers who designed your plant are available, they could be of particular assistance to you in achieving more efficient operation of your mechanical systems. If the design engineer is no longer available, you might call in local independent consultants who are specialists in the various fields involved. Frequently an outsider is able to take a fresh view of a situation and recognize possibilities that could be overlooked by someone working in the plant every day. Perhaps more importantly, the outside consultant does not have the interruptions and distractions with which the plant engineer must contend.

Any discussion of available talent in this field would be incomplete without mention of the growing number of consulting engineers specializing in *energy systems analysis*. They specialize in a relatively new field of engineering but one that is rapidly growing in importance. You may find them practicing as specialists in this field or as a specialized function within more conventional engineering firms. Such specialized professional expertise may be the practical answer in your efforts toward energy conservation. This assistance may be of particular value to you in selling management on an energy conservation program, in helping to get the program started, and in providing specialized assistance on specific items as well as providing continuing counsel and advice.

Results to Expect

The results to be realized from your energy conservation efforts will depend on three major factors: the initial efficiency of your plant operation, the effectiveness of your efforts, and the extent to which you complement your findings with corrective measures. Generally speaking, energy cost reductions of 10 to 30 percent may be anticipated. In our experience, very few industrial plants or large commercial installations are operating so efficiently that a 10 percent reduction in energy usage could not be readily achieved.

In addition to the direct economic benefits to be gained, there are significant ecological benefits resulting from reductions in energy usage. The drain on our fuel resources will be lessened, the strain on our electric generating capability will be reduced, and industry's contribution to air and water pollution will be decreased. A 10 percent reduction in energy usage may mean a reduction of 6 million tons of pollutants released to the atmosphere annually.

But perhaps there is an even more compelling reason. The ultimate answer to the nation's energy shortage cannot be simply to provide more energy. All indications are that it is physically impossible to build new power plants, for example, fast enough to meet the growing demands.

So even if we had the solution to the economic and ecological problems, there is still the problem of time. We may very well reach the point where nothing happens when we push the switch. And, you know that it is the industrial customer who gets shut off first when there is a gas or electricity shortage. Just what does it cost your management to shut down for an hour, a day, a week?

The approach that I suggest is the utilization of more efficient systems and equipment and enough personal concern on your part to thoroughly evaluate the total energy situation in your own plant. If energy conservation techniques are employed to the fullest extent possible, we can decrease the severity of an energy crisis, the undesirable impact on our environment, *and* achieve an economic advantage in the process.

Again, may I emphasize that this is the field in which engineers are in a position to play the leading role. Determination of the most effective systems is strictly an engineering function—one that is within the capability of practically every plant engineer. It is one of the most important responsibilities we can, and should, assume at this time to fulfill the modern day interpretation of engineering excellence.

Through engineering excellence in the field of energy conservation, we have the capability to make significant contributions toward solving the ecological problems of today and tomorrow—practically and economically. By the application of engineering expertise to existing technology, we can demonstrate that "there's a lot of economy in ecology."

Section 6

Materials Management

Chapter 1

Parts and Materials—Storage, Location, and Distribution

L. R. CALAWAY
Bonner & Moore Associates, Inc.

The storage, location, and distribution of parts and materials is unique to each plant's requirements. Many factors must be considered to develop the most economical and practical methods. These factors—for determination of the resources necessary for proper storage, location, and distribution of parts and materials—are discussed in the following paragraphs.

STORAGE SPACE

Storage space is defined as that space where parts and materials are held for future use.

Storage Categories

The first thing that must be determined is the amount and type of storage space necessary. Some of the categories that must be considered in determining storage space are the following:

Physical *An inventory listing of the parts and materials to be stored.* This should include 5- to 10-year forecast of future inventory for determining and justifying future storage space.

The mean number of individual items stored. Determined by adding half the order point to the order quantity for fast-moving materials. For slow-moving items, such as spare parts, add the order point to the order quantity.

Three-dimensional space requirements of items to be stored. The cost of storage space on a square-foot basis usually contributes more to storage cost than any other factor. The storage of material must be considered on a volume basis availability in order to reduce square-foot costs.

Weight of each item. Stock material doubles, triples, etc., floor loads proportionally. Storage bearing loads must be known for proper design of facilities.

Environmental Dry storage. Those items that must be protected against the elements and require storage in an enclosed building.

Moisture protection. Items that must be protected individually or in an assembled state, such as bearings on a shelf or in equipment and items that must be protected in bulk form, such as cement and some types of coated welding rods.

Shelf life. Epoxy paints, plastics and O-rings all must be considered against aging factors such as sunlight, high temperatures, and time.

Freeze protection. Liquid items stored in breakable containers. Items whose physical characteristics change when once frozen. Special protection for stored equipment items must be considered.

Hazardous materials Inflammables. Are the parts and materials combustible? Can they be protected by normal sprinkler systems, or must they have special storage facilities?

Explosives. Types and volumes of explosives. Must they have electrostatic protection, special bunkers, etc?

Toxic substances. Are materials toxic, do special clothing or masks have to be worn when handling?

Security Minimum. Items that can be left in open storage for routine use. Usually consists of parts being manufactured, bulk materials, bar stock and plate, and small-expensed items stored in free bins. Protection is normally provided by plant guards at gate entrances.

Normal. Items that are pilfered due to in-plant use during off hours or personal use. Normally protected by locking of storerooms during off hours and prohibiting of entry by unauthorized persons. Many items in this category are protected for control of inventory records.

Maximum. Valuable articles, usually small with a high resalable value or attractive for home use, usually protected by locked doors or cabinets within the storage area with only authorized persons permitted to open. Additional maximum security can be provided by safes or bank vault storage.

Storage Space Requirements

A storage space data sheet is used for organizing the data and figuring the volume and type of storage space necessary. Figure 1 is an example of a typical tabulation that may be used. The columns are identified as follows:

    1. *Stock number* is the inventory number of the item being considered, usually consisting of a six- to nine-digit number with certain digits identifying the family or class the item is identified with. If the family is not identified, then another column may be necessary.

    2. *Order point* is that level of stock inventory at which time an order must be placed to replenish the stock.

    3. *Order quantity* is the number of stock items that must be placed to replenish the inventory.

    4. *Activity* is the quantity of stock items issued in a given period of time.

    5. *Mean storage* is the number of items stored determined by adding half the order point to the order quantity for fast-moving items and by adding the order point to the order quantity for slow-moving items such as spare parts.

    6. *Unit of storage* is the quantity involved for packaging and issuing, i.e., each foot, pound, gross, 100 pounds, gallon, etc.

    7. *Height* occupied by the stock item or unit of storage.

    8. *Width* occupied by the stock item or unit of storage.

    9. *Length* occupied by the stock item or unit of storage.

    10. *Weight* of the stock item or unit of storage.

    11. Type of storage is designated by:

Bins	Racks
Shelves	Pallets

STORAGE SPACE DATA SHEET

Stock number (1)	Order point (2)	Order quanitity (3)	Activity (4)	Mean storage (5)	Unit of storage (6)	Height, in. (7)	Width, in. (8)	Depth, in. (9)	Weight, lb (10)	Type of storage (11)	Size (12)	Enviroment (15)	Hazard (14)	Security (15)

Fig. 1 Storage space data sheet.

Drawers   Skids
Boxes   Open

12. *Size and or type* of bin, shelf, drawers, racks, pallets, or skids required. Usually specified by some system of coding designating the space required for the type of storage designated (Fig. 2). Storage types and sizes come in numerous shapes and designs. Some one or two manufacturers of equipment should be decided upon and their equipment coded accordingly.

13. *Environment* designates the type of storage necessary for protection against the elements.

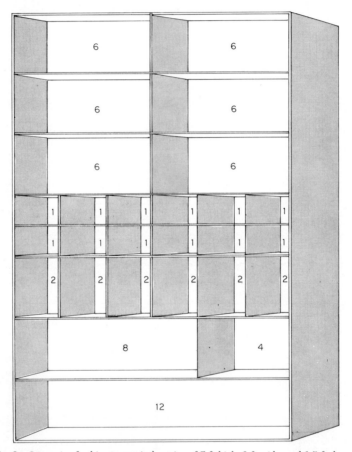

Fig. 2.   Space size for bin storage in bay size of 7 ft high, 3 ft wide, and 1.5 ft deep.

14. *Hazard* designates special precautionary matters of handling and storage necessary.

15. *Security* designates the type of security necessary for protection of the item.

At this time, two important factors must be considered. First, the cost of tabulating the data is high. It can be figured that an average of 15 minutes is necessary for determining the data for one item in stock. If 8,000 items are in inventory, then a man-year of work is required, and in many plants manpower is too scarce for such work of a temporary nature.

In lieu of analyzing every item, a statistical analysis can be made of the inventory. Table 1* can be used to determine the size of sample to be made, assuming that the

* From Heiland and Richardson, *Work Sampling*, New York, 1957.

probable error is tolerated. If the probable error cannot be tolerated, then a greater sample or total sample must be made. Column p of Table 1 represents the proportion of the sample of any one type of storage-space size to the total sample taken. Estimating that the maximum for any one storage-space size will be p = 20% or 0.20, then, for a 95 percent confidence limit with not more than ±0.02 error, a sample of 1,600 items must be made. The sample can be taken by sampling every fifth item in the inventory—sys-

Table 1   Sample Sizes Required for Various Limits of Error—95 Percent Confidence Limits

	Sample size required for confidence limits at 95%					
p	± 0.01	± 0.02	± 0.03	± 0.04	± 0.05	p
0.01	396*	100*	44*	25*	16*	0.99
0.02	784	196*	88*	49*	32*	0.98
0.03	1,163	292	130*	73*	47*	0.97
0.04	1,535	384	171	96*	62*	0.96
0.05	1,900	475	212	119	76*	0.95
0.06	2,200	565	252	142	92*	0.94
0.07	2,604	654	200	163	102	0.93
0.08	2,945	738	328	184	118	0.92
0.09	3,278	820	364	205	131	0.91
0.10	3,600	900	400	225	144	0.90
0.11	3,918	980	435	245	157	0.89
0.12	4,224	1,055	470	264	109	0.88
0.13	4,520	1,130	504	282	181	0.87
0.14	4,820	1,210	535	302	103	0.86
0.15	5,100	1,275	568	318	205	0.85
0.16	5,380	1,350	600	337	216	0.84
0.17	5,650	1,415	628	353	226	0.83
0.18	5,900	1,475	656	369	236	0.82
0.19	6,160	1,545	685	385	246	0.81
0.20	6,410	1,605	715	400	256	0.80
0.21	6,640	1,660	740	415	266	0.79
0.22	6,870	1,720	765	430	275	0.78
0.23	7,100	1,780	790	444	284	0.77
0.24	7,300	1,830	815	456	292	0.76
0.25	7,500	1,880	835	470	300	0.75
0.26	7,690	1,925	855	481	308	0.74
0.27	7,885	1,970	875	493	316	0.73
0.28	8,065	2,015	895	504	323	0.72
0.29	8,240	2,060	915	515	330	0.71
0.30	8,400	2,100	935	526	337	0.70
0.31	8,555	2,140	950	535	343	0.69
0.32	8,705	2,175	965	545	349	0.68
0.33	8,840	2,210	985	553	354	0.67
0.34	8,975	2,245	1,000	561	360	0.66
0.35	9,100	2,275	1,010	569	365	0.65
0.36	9,220	2,305	1,025	576	369	0.64
0.37	9,325	2,330	1,035	583	373	0.63
0.38	9,425	2,355	1,045	589	377	0.62
0.39	9,515	2,380	1,055	595	381	0.61
0.40	9,600	2,400	1,065	600	384	0.60
0.41	9,675	2,420	1,075	605	387	0.59
0.42	9,745	2,435	1,085	609	390	0.58
0.43	9,805	2,450	1,090	613	392	0.57
0.44	9,855	2,465	1,095	616	395	0.56
0.45	9,900	2,475	1,100	619	397	0.55
0.46	9,935	2,485	1,105	621	398	0.54
0.47	9,965	2,490	1,110	623	399	0.53
0.48	9,985	2,495	1,110	624	400	0.52
0.49	9,995	2,500	1,115	625	400	0.51
0.50	10,000	2,500	1,115	625	400	0.50

* Since, as a rule of thumb, np should equal 5 or more, the numbers followed by * should be increased to meet this criterion. For example, for p-0.03, n should be increased from 130 to 167, so that 0.03 (167) = 5.

tematic sampling—or by numbering the inventory from 1 to 8,000 and then using a table of random numbers—random sampling. Say that after the 1,600 items are identified, 336 of them, or 21 percent, are of the maximum samples of any one storage-space size. Then, from Table 1, the limit of error is a little greater than ±0.02. For our purposes, we can use ±0.02, without making a linear interpolation.

Since our sample is taken from a small population, 8,000 items, we must make an adjustment factor to the limits of our error. This correction is made by multiplying the error limits by the factor†

$$\sqrt{\frac{n-x}{N-1}}$$

$$\pm 0.02 \sqrt{\frac{8{,}000-1{,}600}{8{,}000-1}} = \pm 0.018$$

The error in the analysis could range from 330 to 342 for items of the maximum sample for any one storage-space size. Depending upon the cost of the number of bins required

		BAY STORAGE	
Bins, plain		Shelf, 36″ X 18″ X 12″	Bay, 86″ X 36 X 18″
1	2,400	÷ 12 = 200	÷7 = 29
2		÷ 6 =	7 =
4		÷ 3 =	7 =
6		÷ 2 =	7 =
8		÷1.5 =	7 =
12		=	7 =
3-in bin fronts			
1		÷ 12 =	÷7 =
2		÷ 6 =	7 =
4		÷ 3 =	7 =
6		÷ 2 =	7 =
8		÷1.5 =	7 =
12		=	7 =

TOTAL   =

Bay floor space occupied = total no. of bays X 3 X 1.5

=

Square feet required for storage
Bay space + aisle space
4.5 + 6 = 10.5
X number of bays

=   sq. ft.

Fig. 3 Bay storage.

for the particular storage-space size, the risk of error in a statistical analysis must be weighed against the cost of tabulating every item. Assuming a 5 percent or 10 percent increase for future expansion, then the risk of error in making a statistical analysis is nil.

Second, there are a number of storage hardware manufacturers and consultants who have either manual or computerized systems for determining the types of storage necessary for the inventory being analyzed, based upon the hardware that they manufacture or represent. Management should determine if outside help is to be used and to what degree.

When the storage-space data sheets are completed, the data must be summarized in order to determine the number and space for the types of storage required. Figure 3 is a summary sheet showing a typical calculation for bay storage. Example: Assume 2400 type-1 bins required, as shown in Fig. 2. The calculation 2,400 ÷ 12 gives 200 shelves required, 36 inches wide, 18 inches deep, and 12 inches high. Figuring 200 ÷ 7 gives 29 bays required, 86 inches high, 36 inches wide, and 18 inches deep.

† From John E. Freund and Frank J. Williams, *Modern Business Statistics*, Prentice-Hall, Inc. Englewood Cliffs, N.J., 1958.

Functional space Within the storage area, additional space must be considered for:

Railroad rights of way	Disbursements
Truck turning radius	Shipping
Unloading ramps	Offices
Receiving	Restrooms
Inspections	Janitor's closet

In many warehouses, it is found that the functional space exceeds the storage space requirements.

LOCATION

The Storeroom

Work sampling surveys reveal that traveling for materials can vary from 5 percent to 20 percent, depending upon a number of factors. One of the most important of these is the location of the storeroom. The closer the storeroom is to the center of activity of the workmen using materials and parts, the less time is spent in traveling.

If the parameters are variable, that is, if one is free to locate the storeroom where practical, then the location is usually adjacent to or within the maintenance shop. In turn, the plant shop is located within the center of the manufacturing facilities in order to keep traveling distances to a minimum.

One of the best practices is to have a centralized storeroom adjacent to the maintenance shop, with a telephone order service for delivery of parts and materials beyond the limits of the shop. This allows the workmen to remain at the jobsite for work continuation while additional tools and materials are being delivered to them.

The location of storage facilities in relation to the maintenance shop layout is shown in Fig. 4. The storage facilities are located within the maintenance shop. Rack storage for bar stock and pipe is located adjacent to the machine and pipe shops respectively. The toolroom is located within the machine shop area for tool disbursement within the shop area and, for convenience, adjacent to the storage area. Both toolroom and storage have accessibility for disbursement external to the shop to eliminate traffic within the shops building and for truck deliveries. Internal and external delivery windows and the truck pickup area are located in the same vicinity so that they may be manned by the same people. Material is received at one end of the storage area and disbursed at the other.

There are many parameters that determine the location of storage facilities, and all fixed parameters should be determined before a storage-room layout is made. In a "grass roots" plant, the parameters are variable except those that may be determined by policy or cost. In an existing plant, fixed parameters may be:

1. Storeroom locations
2. Storage space
3. Building designs
4. Material handling facilities
5. Storeroom accessibility

Parts and Materials

A survey is made of the storage-space data sheets; those items that are not to be kept within the regular warehouse space are isolated and their storage space and location determined.

Free bins materials are fast-moving, low-cost items stocked in open bins near their point of usage. The bins are stocked from the storeroom at regular intervals and expensed to an overhead account. Free bins are normally located in maintenance workshop areas and accessible only to maintenance personnel during normal working hours.

Machine tools and regular tools are normally stored within the toolroom area, and tools and tool parts are bought directly to the toolroom for storage and use.

Insurance items consist of large, bulky, capitalized items or spares with long delivery dates for replacements. The items normally involve special approval for stocking and are relatively expensive.

Environmental and hazardous materials are isolated and stored according to their particular requirements. Where possible, their location is within or near the warehouse proper.

After isolating all storage items that are not to be stored within the storeroom proper, storage space is distributed for the remainder of the items.

Aisle space must be provided for the mechanical equipment which will handle the material. The type and size of handling equipment is determined and the proper aisle space provided for width and turning radius. Central aisles run the length of the storage area, with direct access from the unloading dock to the disbursement areas. To provide room for fork-lift trucks to pass requires a width of about 10 feet. Narrower aisles of about 4 feet are provided for stacker cranes and other one-way traffic. Turning room should be provided at each end of one-way aisles. For hand trucks and carts, a space of 3 feet may be provided between rows.

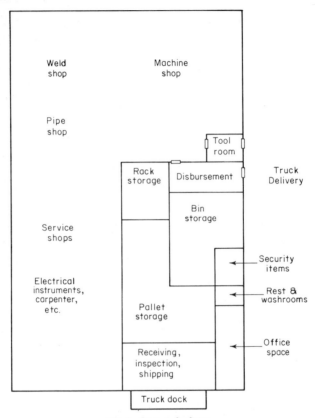

Fig. 4 Storage facilities.

Once the space necessary for storage within the storeroom is determined, the next concern is where to locate the particular item. Three factors remaining determine where an item is located. These factors are:

1. *Family storage*—storage of items of a particular classification. These items may be classed according to stock catalog number, parts for a major item of equipment, names of parts for a particular type of equipment (such as all spare pump impellers be stored together), or functions (such as all safety equipment or clothing, storage by department or foreman, etc.).

2. *Activity storage*—locating items within the storeroom according to usage. The faster the turnover of an item, the closer it is located to the area of disbursement. Slow-moving items are located away from the disbursement areas.

3. *Size storage*—includes the total volume required for the mean number to be stored as well as the individual item. If weight is a critical factor, then it should be considered.

A combination of these three factors should prove the best solution for most plant engineering storerooms. Where family storage is specified—as for safety items, light bulbs, clothing, etc.—the family storage should still be located according to activity and size. Light, bulky items should be stored in the tops of bays or overhead. Heavy items should be located near the floor, and easily handled items in the middle of the bays.

All items handled by a storeroom should have a stores location code, identifying where the item may be found. The stores location code gives every single storage space, big

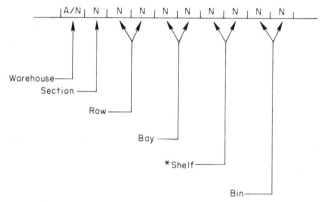

Fig. 5 Stores location code; A/N = alphanumeric, N = numeric. (*For shelving units having two work levels or floors, the ground floor shelves are numbered upward "11, 12, 13 . . . 1N" and the first floor shelves similarly "21, 22, 23 . . . 2N".)

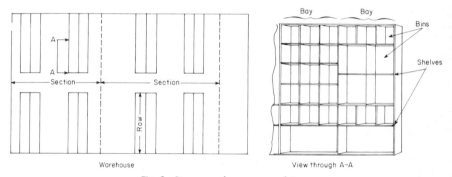

Fig. 6 Stores warehouse nomenclature.

or small, a unique designation. Each item within the storage system, usually identified by a stores catalog number, is also assigned a stores location code.

Figures 5 is a stores location code with each field defined. "Warehouse" could be a storeroom shed, yard, or any other place where material is stored. "Section" is the first subdivision and is an area of the floor space. This space can be left blank if not used. "Row," "bay," "shelf," and "bin" further divide the storage space to one specific location, as shown in Fig. 6. Any combination of these may be used in developing a stores location code.

With this code or a similar one, each bin has its own address in a logical sequence throughout the storeroom, allowing the individual or a computer to produce "pick lists" that will enable the storeclerk to fill an order without wasted movement. The code also helps those who are unfamiliar with the storeroom to find items in it in an emergency.

DISTRIBUTION

On any job where material is required, the material must be requisitioned from the storeroom, held for the job, and distributed to the jobsites for usage. Various techniques used to provide these services are described in the following paragraphs.

Requisitioning of material is handled by some form of written order known by numerous names that vary according the company and the purpose the order serves. The most common names are "material requisition," "stores requisition," and "bill of material." All material disbursing requires a written order for control purposes. Figure 7 is a typical requisition form.

Information may be added or deleted by the particular requirements of a company.

Requisitions may be received manually from the requisitioner at the disbursing counter, by mail, by telephone, or through any type of transmitting device (such as

STORES REQUISITION	Date _____		
Requisitioner _____ Phone _____ Charge No. _____			
Badge _____ Date needed _____		Delivery station _____	
Quanitity	Catalog No.	Description	Location

Fig. 7 Stores requisition.

computer printout, cathode ray tube, or written transmission). Where verbal or visual requisitions are received, the storeroom clerks must convert the orders into written requisitions.

Disbursing of materials Upon receipt of the requisition, some action must be taken depending upon the nature of the requisition. The requisition form is usually used as the "pick list" and the order is filled and handled as follows:

Counter requisitions are filled and delivered to the worker who has waited at the counter for the requisition to be filled.

Phone requisitions can be filled and held for the requisitioner to pick them up, or they can be delivered by a route truck for routine deliveries or by a "hot shot" truck for emergency delivery.

Requisitions for material with a future delivery date can have the material in the bin held by a "hold tag," or special "hold bins" can be designated for a particular order within the storeroom near the disbursing area. This provides a means of making sure the material will be available for the job the day it is scheduled. A release order is necessary to have the material delivered to the jobsite.

On larger jobs, special areas near the work site may be designated as hold areas for accumulation of material.

Routine delivery of material is normally handled by route trucks, which deliver material to designated stations throughout a plant. Emergency delivery items are handled by "hot shot" trucks, which deliver only those items called for. Special delivery items of a bulky or heavy nature usually require additional handling facilities, and the material is delivered directly to the jobsite.

One copy of the requisition is normally a hardback and is attached to the material or its container for delivery to the field.

Route trucks are used to deliver material from station to station throughout the plant. Figure 8 is a tag used for transfer of material between route truck stations and as a shop work order for material going to and from the shop for repairs.

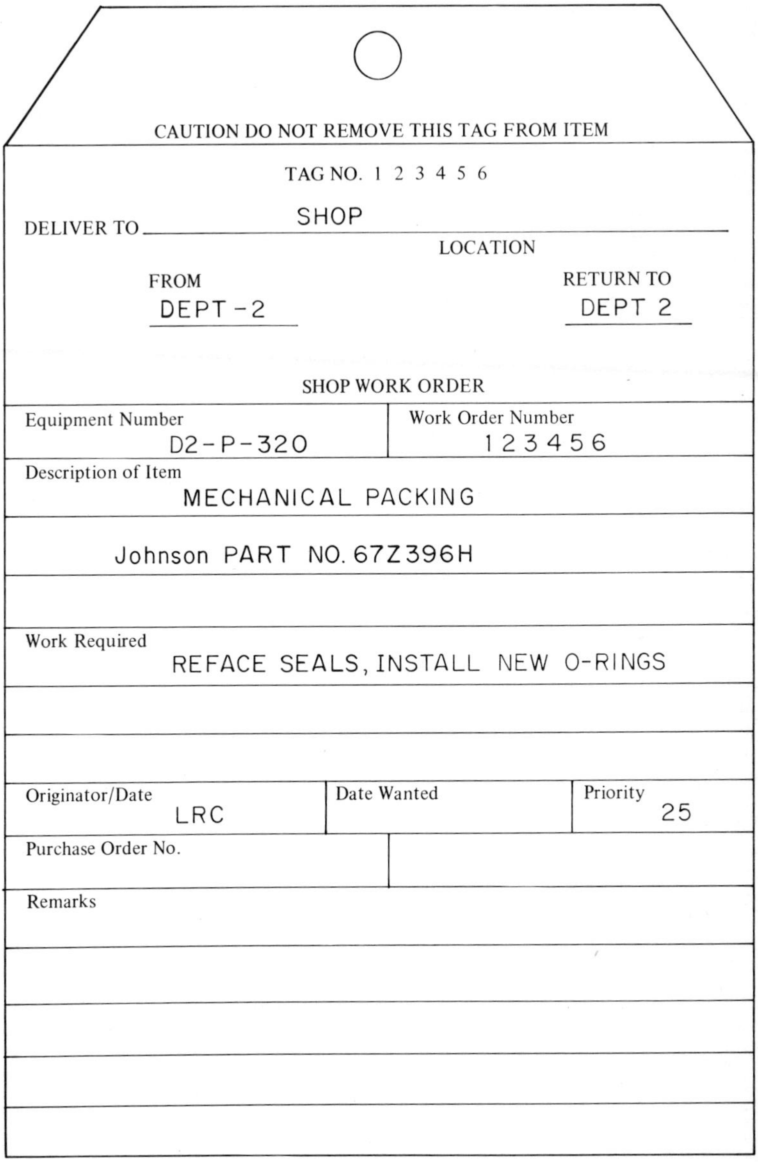

CAUTION DO NOT REMOVE THIS TAG FROM ITEM

TAG NO. 1 2 3 4 5 6

DELIVER TO _____ SHOP _____

LOCATION

FROM   DEPT-2

RETURN TO   DEPT 2

SHOP WORK ORDER

Equipment Number	Work Order Number
D2-P-320	1 2 3 4 5 6

Description of Item

MECHANICAL PACKING

Johnson PART NO. 67Z396H

Work Required   REFACE SEALS, INSTALL NEW O-RINGS

Originator/Date	Date Wanted	Priority
LRC		25

Purchase Order No.

Remarks

SHOP WORK ORDER

Fig. 8 Shop work order.

Locked boxes can be provided at delivery stations for reduction of pilferage. Only the foreman and the truck driver should have keys for opening the boxes.

Where "free bins" are designated within a work area, a storeroom clerk should be responsible for keeping the bins stocked with inventory. Where material catalogs are provided in the work area, they also should be the responsibility of the storeroom. This guarantees that all catalogs in a plant are properly updated and are alike. Such work should not be the responsibility of a skilled workman or a foreman. The same philosophy should apply to obtaining materials from the storeroom. Counter requisitions should be discouraged. A telephone requisition and "hot shot" delivery keeps the worker near the jobsite and provides greater working utilization of the worker.

Relationship with Purchasing

SYLVESTER H. O'GRINCE

Director of School Buildings and Grounds, Baltimore City Public Schools

INTRODUCTION

Since providing service is a prime function of plant engineers, it is their responsibility to be in position to offer such services as quickly as possible and at the lowest cost possible. All such services should be accomplished within policies and procedures established by the firm, agency, or institution by which they are employed. To meet those requirements, they will have to be in position to take advantage of all resources available within the firm, one of which is centralized purchasing. If this holds true, one should then determine what purchasing is, or better still, what purchasing's function is. The National Association of Purchasing Agents' *Guide to Purchasing* states that the "purchasing function is an economic function, assisting in creating additional profit for the company, and the purchasing manager, who is an integral part of this management team, is the authorized person delegated to procure materials, capital, equipment, supplies, tools and services." It must be recognized that the authorization mentioned above refers to the delegation which grants the powers of officially executing this function under the laws of agency. The purchasing manager is the legal agent for procurement in a given company. The purchasing manager also provides assistance in the specialized field of purchasing to management and to other departments, being mainly concerned with receiving the best values to the company for money expended. It also has been proved that those companies that have recognized purchasing as being an integral part of management learn they have benefited immensely. It follows, then, that the plant engineer, who is charged with keeping the plant facilities operating at minimum cost, relates to purchasing at the highest level possible, since it is apparent that both are working for the same company objectives.

Ally in purchasing   Unfortunately this is not always the case. The plant engineer in some organizations is not aware of the benefits that can be derived through a good relationship with procurement. In many instances the plant engineer treats purchasing as a necessary evil or as a group of obstructionists. This engineer is usually deeply engrossed in problems as they relate to plant maintenance and operations and fails to appreciate the fact that purchasing can be an ally. On the other hand, the plant engineer's relationship with the purchasing agent should be one of mutual trust and understanding, with respect for each other's skills and a desire to work together voluntarily in the best interests of the company. One has to recognize the fact that engineers, by nature, are individuals who are strong of character, who consciously or unconsciously demonstrate that they usually expect to be the deciding factor in any transaction involving them. Instead of downgrading purchasing, the engineer, as a professional, should strive to establish a friendly and cordial association with the purchasing agent as another professional, with mutual respect for each other's responsibility.

Small plant engineer   Small plant engineers accustomed to doing their own buying may find it initially difficult to work with centralized purchasing. They are usually in good control of their buying procedures, probably have excellent sources of supply, and in general feel that they need no large bureaucratic operation informing them of their needs. They maintain their own stockrooms, approve for payment all invoices, and essentially manage good operations for their companies. Then why break this combination up? One good reason could be that the company may wish to expand. Maintenance and operations will have to grow, and as it grows, it becomes more unwieldy to operate. Keeping the complete operation "under one hat" begins to be a problem. The plant engineer then has to depend on other staff members to take over some of the responsibility. When the plant engineer begins to lose close control over all functions of buying, problems start to develop, not only in the procurement of materials and supplies but in other areas as well. A quick solution would be simply to unload all buying responsibility. The plant engineer should meet with purchasing and go over the requirements, give them a chance to plan volume buying, let them help with the inventory, let them research the new items on the market, allow them to clear invoices, and in general do the job in which they are specialists. The plant engineer can advantageously use the time once spent in those areas to develop and improve upon other operations. Time is of the essence. It is a valuable commodity which should be conserved whenever possible. The responsibility of buying should be that of the buyers in purchasing, not in maintenance, as it was formerly. Management is observing the plant engineer's operation. Therefore the plant engineer should be willing to grow with the company and adjust to new procedures rather than simply remaining a member of the "old school"—resisting new approaches, concepts, and ideas. The latter course can lead to difficulty. So if the word is "go with central purchasing," the plant engineer should go with purchasing, get to know the organization, and use it to maximum advantage. The plant engineer will then find that this department exists to provide assistance, not to encroach upon other functions. The engineer should therefore be willing to help purchasing by offering them ideas and the fruits of experience. A good relationship with the procurement section, in the long run, will pay off many times over.

The medium-sized plant operation   The plant engineer in a medium-sized operation should also strive constantly to improve relations with purchasing. Here both begin to function as an integral part of the firm, with the same objective in mind. Remember, the plant engineer is only a small part of the total plant operation, and combining all requirements puts purchasing in position to buy at a substantially lower cost than would be possible if the plant engineer "went it alone." Because the company is larger, the purchasing staff is often more competent and is usually directed by a purchasing agent or purchasing manager. This individual should be kept informed of annual requirements so deliveries can be properly scheduled. In turn, the plant engineer should explore "open end" contracts with the purchasing agent or the agent's staff. The plant engineer should also standardize specifications and stay alert to scarcity of materials, as well as market conditions in general, throughout the nation. The plant engineer should be able to assist with purchasing procedures during emergencies and in some instances give technical assistance. In general, keeping a high level of respect for purchasing would seem to be a requirement. Granted, the plant engineer is a specialist, but so are they. The plant engineer should let them perform their functions to the best of their ability in their area of responsibility while doing the same in the engineering department. Again, mutual trust and understanding will help both divisions grow. As they grow, so does the firm's business.

Large plant operation   It is in this area that a plant engineer and purchasing should develop the highest type of relationship possible. The work crossing a plant engineer's desk is so complex and of such nature and volume that accomplishing procurement without the assistance of the purchasing department is almost unthinkable. Company policy will usually spell out procedures in this area as it is. To work within this framework, one will have to do all buying through purchasing in any case. In this situation the plant engineer will be under so much pressure that any assistance in the specialized area of purchasing will be welcome. Not only that, but the purchasing division is usually made up of a competent purchasing agent and a well-rounded and experienced staff of buyers, many whom are specialists in their own rights. Therefore the plant engineer should take advantage of them, letting them, for example, find a source of supply for a special item, or contact a particular testing lab to assist with a complex problem, or work out a legal problem as related to buying. The plant engineer should let purchasing assist in taking full advantage of the computerized system available or come up with a standardized specification to cover a repeated type of problem. Purchasing can also be of help with stock inventory, or they can assist with a revolving account. All the facets of purchasing mentioned above and several others, which will be discussed later in this chapter, can be of valuable assistance to the plant engineer. All purchasing needs is a little cooperation from the plant engineer. They will thus be able to perform far above what the plant engineer expected and thus free the engineer to perform other duties.

COMPARISON OF BASIC OBJECTIVES OF PLANT ENGINEERS AND COMMON PURCHASING OBJECTIVES

Earlier in this chapter it was stated that both divisions, maintenance and operations and purchasing, were service organizations. In general, the goal of the plant engineer is to give proper quality service at the lowest cost possible, while that of purchasing is to obtain maximum value for the company's dollar. It then is apparent that both are striving for the same objectives. In the area of service and support, both again have a common objective, i.e., to improve upon this goal. As for materials to be procured, both divisions strive to obtain a quality of material that will be suitable for the intended use and be delivered on time. Both apparently need an effective planning system with good controls—a system that will further relationships with other company divisions through proper communications.

Some other objectives shared by both divisions are to avoid waste and duplication, to optimize systems procedures, to use to advantage private enterprise to fulfill the company's needs for goods and services, and—finally—to require the full cooperation of all divisions to the end that the company may obtain maximum advantage of the service offered by both maintenance and operations and purchasing.

IMPROVING UPON THE BUYING FOR MAINTENANCE, REPAIR, AND OPERATIONS IN PROCUREMENT

Maintenance, repair, and operations (MRO) supplies are usually neglected in many purchasing organizations. Because they are so-called nuisance items and do not fall in the category of production items, the buyer is usually the least regarded person or the novice in the purchasing division. Buyers, as soon as they reach some competence, are immediately moved into more responsible positions in the procurement hierarchy. The plant engineer should guard against this type of action by informing the purchasing agent that some continuity in staff has to be maintained in the area of MRO procurement. First, though, let us define maintenance, operations, and repair supplies.

Defining Maintenance, Operations, and Repair Supplies

What are MRO supplies? Basically speaking, the maintenance and operating supplies of a manufacturing concern consist of products that are used in the manufacturing process but that do not become a part of the end product itself.

Maintenance supplies To clarify further, most plant engineers consider maintenance items those that are needed to keep the physical plant and grounds in good condition, well lighted, easy to clean, attractive, and pleasant to its employees. Such supplies would include paint, lumber, hardware, electrical supplies, and plumbing, heating, and custodial supplies.

Operating supplies Operating supplies are those supplies used in processing or making an end product that do not become part of the product. Included herein are items such as lubricating oils; cutting oils; processing materials for painting, plastering, and heat treating; perishable tooling; and abrasives. Office equipment, stationary supplies, printing, forms, etc., also fall in this category.

Repair parts Repair parts are replacements needed to repair lubricating equipment, machine tools, test equipment, heating plants, motors, and other capital equipment in the course of normal wear or a breakdown. Hence sources for major repair parts are obviously more limited than are either maintenance or operating supplies, and the original manufacturer is usually the only dependable source. However, not infrequently some replacements may need to be duplicated by a supplier for lack of original equipment manufacturer (OEM) availability.

From the above one can immediately see the great variety of stock carried under MRO. These items differ not only as to what they are but also as to where they come from, how they are priced, and—most importantly—how much lead time is necessary. A repair part for a vital piece of machinery can cause costly downtime. The MRO buyer's task is a complicated one to be sure and should justify the employment of a well-experienced buyer.

MAJOR AREAS OF REAL ASSISTANCE TO THE PLANT MANAGER BY PROCUREMENT

In what areas can purchasing give real assistance to a plant engineer? Why is it that the plant engineer's staff cannot make this service available? Will involving purchasing upset the plant engineer's usual close control of materials buying such as quality, quantity, cost, and delivery? What about storage and inventory? Computerization? What about the third-party effect on a contractual service? How does the plant engineer's relation with purchasing affect the answers to these questions and hundreds of others of similar nature? The following will be an attempt to answer such questions of concern on a variety of subjects involving the plant engineer's relations with purchasing

Standardization Too many plant engineers wish to "go it alone"—in lieu of working with purchasing on the problem—when it comes to standardization of parts and supplies. They feel that they may lose control of quality and availability, particularly if they have a good source of supply. What they do not realize is that procurement can, after reviewing usage, combine or consolidate the plant engineer's needs with similar requirements from other divisions, incorporate them into a single specification, and place an order of considerable quantity which, because of its volume, will show a savings in cost. This factor of cost alone should make the plant engineer consider parts standardization. Along with a savings in cost, there will also be the advantages of better delivery and reduced inventory needs.

What are some of the objections the plant engineer has toward standardization other than losing a good source of supply or giving up a supply item with a name brand? Is it that the quality of an item may be reduced? If so, a specification that is good enough will eliminate the poorer product. Purchasing will support quality/cost optimization and welcome a change in the specification to make certain that the plant engineer receives the product that is needed. Usually quality drops if the specifications are poorly written or kept in a general form. If there is a question of quality of a specific item, the plant engineer should feel free to ask for a report from an independent testing lab covering the material. Furthermore, the plant engineer has the option of turning down through a field test what seems to be a poor material, such as paint, for example. Does it cover adequately? Does it apply smoothly? Other questions of this nature can be answered when making a field analysis of such a product.

Even so, generally speaking, a good, well-written specification will bring the product that is wanted; and if the specification is used as a standard, there are the added benefits —in cost savings, better delivery, and fewer items to be carried in stock—that accrue when purchasing buys the product.

Reducing paper costs The plant engineer should work together with purchasing to reduce paper work. Many of the items purchased are small by volume and inexpensive. Processing their order and finally their payment through established procedures costs more in some instances than the material itself. The plant engineer should work with purchasing toward a simplified system for low-valued items. The plant engineer's objective should be to reduce to as few steps as possible the purchase of an item, from its request through to its delivery. It is useful, in this regard, to develop special small-order techniques, i.e., use of petty cash, direct purchases, consignment buying, stockless buying, costless buying, and other methods that will be described later. Also, the plant engineer should remember that every time a formal purchase order is bypassed, other paper work such as receiving requests, invoices, and checks are also eliminated. The result is a net savings to the company. Possibly a change in forms could assist in making "rush" or emergency pickups. Even so, the plant engineer should work everything through purchasing so that they have an overview of what is needed. This will give them an opportunity to devise the best system possible and to satisfy the requirements at the lowest possible cost.

SOME BUYING TECHNIQUES

Blanket order Since buying for maintenance and operations (M&O) differs from buying for the normal production techniques, the plant engineer should explore with procurement general approaches to buying. One such approach is use of a blanket order. This method of buying is probably the most widely used and usually involves an agreed-to price for special items which are repetitive. Or it may be an agreement to supply all a buyer's needs for certain items at agreed-upon prices. The plant engineer should review problem areas, list all items that relate to such a piece of equipment with reference to a supplier's catalog or some other form of description, give quantity needed, list the usual source of supply, and forward the data to purchasing. The plant engineer should then let them analyze and review M&O needs, and, once they feel all data are in order, let them find a source of supply and place an order. Immediate savings can be shown in the elimination of paper work alone and on the time saved in locating an item when needed. The supplier may deliver many of these items.

Direct purchases An arrangement can be made with purchasing to allow the plant engineer to procure an item up to a prearranged figure such as $50 or $100 whenever necessary. Advantage can also be taken of this approach when emergencies arise. A direct purchase order is written covering each item. When costs of an item exceed the prearranged figure, the plant engineer should arrange with purchasing to be able to call a buyer over the phone. A purchase order number is then usually given, and this clears the transaction. Many emergency purchases of sizable amounts can be made through this controlled process. Why use this approach? Company policy usually does not permit the processing of items directly from a source without purchasing becoming involved. Usually, if the plant engineer takes on the responsibility, letters of explanation have to be written covering such action. Auditing frowns on this approach and disbursement may not process the invoices covering such a purchase without formal approval by procurement. Clearing the payment of an item sometimes causes the plant engineer more frustration and conern than clearing the emergency.

In general, then, the plant engineer should use purchasing to assist with an emergency. Once they are made aware of the problem, they usually give the plant engineer all the freedom required to complete the job. And remember, when the invoices start coming in, lengthy letters of explanation will not have to be written. An axiom worth repeating is "resolving an emergency is fine, but resolving it through established procedures is finer." That is the mark of a good plant engineer.

Revolving account for inventory   Another technique the plant engineer may wish to explore is the use of a revolving inventory account for purchased stock items. A special account is set up by purchasing which permits the procurement of sizable quantities of material against this account for stocking. This material is charged against your account only when it is withdrawn by authorized employees of your organization.

Consignment buying   This method of buying is popular with plant engineers because it maintains a high level of stock whose items are paid for only after they are put to use. Only special materials fall into this class, such as electric motor belts, which come in hundreds of sizes and types. The vendor maintains a preestablished level of the item, which is distributed by the customer's stockroom personnel. The same personnel reorder the items and are held responsible for furnishing the vendor with accurate usage reports. Billing to the cutomer then follows.

The advantage of this approach to buying is simply that the plant engineer has a ready stock of material available, a tremendous reduction in paper work, and a reasonably priced item on the shelf, with further reductions in order if the system works to the vendor's satisfaction.

Stockless buying   Same as above except that the vendor does all the work and makes the material available from vendor's stockroom inventory.

Catalogs   In some of the larger purchasing organizations, catalogs showing supplies available are published by procurement. Once your staff become aware of this source of supply, it is simply a matter of writing out a requisition, using a catalog number to cover the item. Delivery is usually prompt, since the majority of the items are available through a central warehouse. This approach prevents long delays in delivery and again reduces paper work, which is to your advantage.

Petty cash   Most plant engineers are made aware of this approach to buying low-cost, hard-to-procure items. Some parts are just difficult to locate and are not covered by an of the above methods. Using petty cash then seems most appropriate. Normally the office of the plant engineer is held responsible for the fund and its periodic audit, but this is a minor inconvenience for all the advantages derived from the use of such a fund.

Cashless buying   This involves use of a purchase order by buyer with check attached for completion by supplier on delivery of order.

Using data processing as a control device or buying aid   Most larger companies have an integrated data processing system (discussed in a later chapter) that is already in operation and is probably used by the purchasing department for the purchase of production material primarily. It does not, however, include maintenance and repair supplies. The plant engineer should be alert to the advantages of such a system and should, through discussions with the purchasing director, make an effort to become a "user" in the system. The plant engineer should review with the purchasing agent just exactly what data M & O would like to have made available, what the requirements would be to become a user in the system, and finally what reports the plant engineer—as a user—would like to have available for review and study. These requirements may be of such an exacting nature and procedures so severely disciplined that it may not be practical for the typical plant engineer, with a limited staff, to become a part of the automated system. Just cataloging and coding all standard parts needed by maintenance and operations is a gigantic task. Is staff available? Is the level of competence such that the data are accurate? Remember, the information received from such a system is only "as accurate as that put into the system." Many such operations have failed miserably just because of this one fact.

Even so, every plant engineer who has the opportunity should work with purchasing on the overall applications of processing supplies and materials for M&O. If this system is closely controlled and the results are accurate, it will relieve the plant engineer of such responsibilities as inventory control, reorder point, purchase orders, and—most important—lead time. This will then allow the plant engineer to concentrate on other duties and responsibilities that more than likely could use some attention.

Further, much of the record keeping and paper work as related to buying supplies then becomes unnecessary. Also, reports received will be of assistance in the development and control of the M&O operation.

Contractual services   An area that should not be overlooked by the plant engineer, after a satisfactory relationship with purchasing in the area of procurement of materials and supplies has been developed, is the larger, more complex area of contracting for services through purchasing. Repetitious heating plant repairs—such as boiler tube replacements or circulatory pump installations—are an example. The contracts referred to are those that cannot be completed because of a lack of staff or in-house help. Roofing installations, exterior painting, plant exterior maintenance, and waterproofing also fall into this category. Your chief responsibility would be making up a satisfactory specification covering the work to be contracted, while purchasing would follow through on all other procedures such as covering your specification with instructions to bidders, general conditions, and so on. More importantly, they would also make certain your contract was legally sufficient. They, of course, then would advertise for bids, accept the bids, review same with the user do any necessary negotiations, and award the contract. Purchasing is organized to pursue this type of activity. Let them be responsible for it.

One area in contractual services the plant engineer may wish purchasing to explore is that of janitorial services. Many plant engineers, particularly those associated with institutional-type organizations such as city and state agencies, depend on in-house staffs to take care of their building and office cleaning responsibilities. Develop a specification covering the cleaning requirements of your firm of agency and let purchasing research the market for firms with such capability. After the bids are in, compare their results with your costs. Experience has shown that contractual cleaning normally costs less than in-house building care and eliminates many of the problems associated with such work. The point is, review some of your problem areas, discuss them with the purchasing agent, and see whether it is not possible to develop an alternate approach that could possibly not only save you money but eliminate a number of problems now beyond your control.

LIABILITIES

As mentioned above, once purchasing does take over your contractual services, they then are held responsible for all legal sufficiency of the contract. If, for example, a contractor defaults due to lack of performance, purchasing—not the plant engineer—is responsible for settling the matter in the courts. This usually is a lengthy and time-consuming affair. It is true that such defaults are generally settled out of court, but nevertheless purchasing is the responsible party acting for the company they represent. If, on the other hand, the plant engineer puts out the contract, the plant engineer would then be held responsible for its final settlement. Days are consumed on the legal aspects of such a case with your firm's legal representative before settlement is reached. Nothing can frustrate a plant engineer more than participating in a legal battle with a contractor who apparently never could complete a given contract even if every opportunity to do so were provided. So why should the plant engineer take on this job? Let your purchasing agent take this responsibility. Purchasing is prepared to pursue such a conflict and accustomed to working with legal counsel. Purchasing agents are trained to perform such duties, while the engineer is obviously not. This does not mean that the plant engineer is completely free of all responsibility. Not so. It is still your project. It would behoove the plant engineer to work closely with the purchasing agent by providing all the facts available and giving all possible help toward a satisfactory solution to the breach of contract. This may even lead to being a witness in court. But the point is that the purchasing agent is responsible for the contract if it was let through purchasing, and it is the purchasing agent's responsibility to pursue the issue to a satisfactory conclusion. The plant engineer is only obliged to provide all possible assistance.

FORECASTING MARKET CONDITIONS

A good purchasing agent will keep the plant engineer abreast of all market conditions. There are periods when economic conditions are such that certain materials become scarce. The most recent such instance has been the fuel oil crisis, with its many side effects. The plant engineer should be kept abreast of what materials may be in short supply. Purchasing can help with such forecasting, since they are continuously kept abreast of fluctuating conditions in the open market. The plant engineer is in no position to watch market conditions on a regular basis. Even so, with the information obtained from the purchasing agent on such shortages, the plant engineer may be able to adjust project schedules according to the lead time given for ordering material or the purchase of large quantities of a specific item as a "hedge" against a coming shortage—all this valuable information just for keeping up an excellent relationship with the purchasing agent. By trying to "go it alone," the plant engineer will eventually be fighting a losing battle. No matter how good a plant engineer may be, there just is not enough time in a day to cover such areas of responsibility.

DISPOSAL OF SURPLUS PROPERTY

Plant engineers from time to time have to dispose of surplus property. This may be a large piece of production machinery or just plain junk. Nevertheless, if correct procedures are not followed, serious problems can arise. Discuss surplus property disposal with purchasing. They usually have a procedure developed whereby they dispose of such property or scrap material for other divisions, and they can easily integrate the sale of your surplus with that of the others. Disposing of such property in a junkyard is not the answer. Each firm has a procedure that is available for such disposal. Chances are that purchasing is the authorizing agent responsible for such a transaction. Consider the process as buying in reverse.

SOME DISADVANTAGES FOUND IN WORKING THROUGH PURCHASING

Feedback   From the above, it is obvious that a plant engineer should develop a high level of respect for the purchasing agent. The purchasing agent, in turn, should respect the knowledge and judgment of the plant engineer concerning plant maintenance. Even so, one should be warned that there are certain pitfalls that become apparent once procurement is totally responsible for the purchase of M&O supplies and materials and for contractual services. One of the most frustrating of the lot is the complete lack of feedback. Every plant engineer wants to know the status of each order. Why the lengthy delay? Why is there no information about the delays? What is the source of supply? Even that is difficult to find out at times. In any discussion of the takeover of procurement by purchasing, the need for feedback must be emphasized. The plant engineer must insist on being kept abreast of all items on order, their exact status as to delivery, and what firm has the order. If your firm is computerized, this information may be given to you automatically, but the majority of firms are not. The important thing is to insist on the need for feedback at all times.

Areas of responsibility clarified   Another area of concern when purchasing is responsible for service contracts is that there be a clear understanding of where the plant engineer's responsibility begins and ends in a contract. Is the plant engineer responsible for the inspection? Who will authorize the contractor's invoices for payment? Not the buyer, certainly. The buyer is not aware of the progress in the field. Who is the contractor to deal with? The purchasing agent or plant engineer? Remember, the contract is with purchasing. Will the contractor deal with the plant engineer, the latter's designated agent, or the purchasing agent? How do you propose to reach the standard you set in the specifications? Just the simple matter of knowing when a contractor will begin to work can be a problem. These details all have to be worked out ahead of time to prevent later problems and embarrassment. The plant engineer always has to be aware of being the third party in the contract. Just what does this imply?

Inexperienced buyers used   Maintenance and operations materials and supplies are usually not given top priority in the typical purchasing department. The items purchased are usually in the small-order, small-value category and are almost considered a nuisance by a buyer who spends thousands of dollars on production items. The effort made by purchasing when buying M&O supplies is just not the same as it is when other divisions in the firm are being served. Inexperienced buyers are usually given the M&O assignment. Nothing is more upsetting than having to explain to a new buyer the plant engineer's requirements. The plant engineer should be on the lookout at all times for a lowering in standards of buying for M&O. The purchasing agent has to be made aware that some materials and supplies are vital to keeping downtime to a minimum. Work together to perfect a system. Failures develop rapidly if there is no communication between the two divisions.

Understaffing of the purchasing department   Understaffing of the purchasing agent's department is another disadvantage the plant engineer has to be made aware of. Like all sections in any organization, purchasing could usually use more help. Delays in processing orders develop when this occurs. Requisitions lie on desks for days and weeks, with no action taken because of the large volume of work to be performed as related to staff. When this occurs, make the purchasing agent aware of the problem. If the latter is the manager of such an organization, this problem should be readily correctable. But the purchasing agent will not be in position to make a change without having been convinced of the need to do so. Document your problems. One cannot overemphasize this one point. Document everything that even approaches being a problem when purchasing is concerned. Let the purchasing agent be made aware of your concern. A telephone call works on occasion, but a letter to that effect is much more effective. Give the purchasing agent a chance to make the necessary changes. Once the purchasing agent is aware of the problems, corrective action will doubtless follow.

CONCLUSION

In conclusion, what can one state concerning the plant engineer's relationship with purchasing? In today's business world, it would be proper to state that the plant engineer should recognize the purchasing department as another tool that can be used to do a complex and difficult job. Therefore the plant engineer should make every effort to develop this relationship in that direction. The day when a plant engineer ran everything from "under one hat" is long gone. Today's plant engineer is a professional who has become an important cog in a larger machine, part of which is purchasing. It takes foresight to use this resource, like all others within the organization, to full advantage. Unfortunately the plant engineer is an engineer by training, with strong individualized ideas. At times, these tend to conflict with the views of other division heads in the firm. The plant engineer must try to recognize and correct this fault for the sake of personal advancement as well as the good of the company as a whole. To work with purchasing, the plant engineer will have to give up some preconceived ideas of buying. This will be ego-deflating at times, but in the long run it will prove beneficial. The modern plant engineer no longer lives in a small individual world but must learn to associate and communicate with all other departments. Becoming closely associated with purchasing is a proper start in that direction.

Section 7

Systems and Reports

Chapter **1**

Systems

W. H. WEISS
Manager of Engineering and Maintenance, Chemigum Plant,
Goodyear Tire & Rubber Company

SYSTEMS

Systems and Their Use

Plant engineering management's job is the setting of goals and objectives, followed by providing and supervising the means of achieving them. The task is formidable when organizations are complex, competition is stiff, and the profit margin is narrow. A high degree of efficiency is required.

Operations are carried out most effectively through a system, a system being a planned and orderly procedure of attaining goals. The system may be simple or complex in its scope, depending on the magnitude of the task and the difficulty of achieving it.

Systems are developed with a purpose, the most common being maximization of profit or minimization of cost. Some systems also have aims of organizational growth and stability. While a specific objective is desirable with all systems, it is also advisable that the extent of their application be determinable. Systems need to be measurable in order to ascertain their effectiveness and to enable them to be changed and improved.

Every significant system also has subsystems, which should have similar requirements. Maximizing a profit in a subsystem might not result in maximizing it for another subsystem or for the whole system. For example, an engineering department might keep its costs low through minimizing preventive or corrective maintenance but yet be the cause of low production due to machine failures because of this policy.

Characteristics of Systems

To justify its creation and serve its purpose, a system must have certain characteristics. It must be:

1. *Acceptable.* Users of a system must have faith and confidence in it. They must believe that it can do the job expected of it. Without this, the system may be modified, bypassed, or misused, thus diminishing its value.

2. *Simple.* Simplicity promotes understanding and acceptance. Errors are less likely to occur if a system is easy to learn and use.

3. *Effective.* It must do the job for which it was designed. Users must be able to depend on it to produce results.

4. *Efficient.* A minimum of difficulty coupled with low cost are the signs of efficiency. Completeness and adequacy must be realized.

5. *Adaptable.* Broadness and flexibility are features required to enable a system to handle a wide range and scope of situations. Ease of adaptability contributes to usefulness and acceptability.

Requirements of Systems

A system is devised to accomplish an objective. It needs to be explicit in how it will do this. Although a system may be quite detailed in scope, the more specific it is, the more likely it will be to be understood and followed. A system that encompasses all possible functions of an organization may thus spell out numerous procedures relating to each.

Clearly, the system must leave no doubt as to its scope and coverage. The range and type of information which it handles should be presented, along with the forms which contain this information; how the forms are used should be explained. Equipment that the system employs must be listed. What the people do, along with their responsibilities, must be understood.

Thus, in its entirety, the system consists of three basic components: people, equipment, and procedures. All three are involved with data and information.

A system is concerned with the processing of information—in how it is collected, recorded, analyzed, and summarized, followed by how it is used, stored, and discarded. Information is needed by the users of the system for planning, decision making, and execution. The system should also provide the means of analyzing results so that accomplishment may be assessed.

How Systems Are Created

Since a system is originated to do a job, how it is created is determined by the type, magnitude, and complexity of the task to be performed. In the case of information systems, decisions must be made on the types of data or reports wanted, their number and frequency, and their detail or completeness.

The first step in the creation of any system is to do a system analysis. In engineering, this would define the problem and prescribe the course or steps to be followed in solving it. Aside from problem solving, engineering management is interested also in business procedures that aid decision making and control. Thus managers want data related to their operations, such as inventory, cost, capacity, and personnel. The systems analyst therefore tries to provide integrated data processing in which the computer's capabilities provide timely and widely encompassing information.

STANDARDS

What Is a Standard?

An engineering standard is a technological condition described in a document, adoption of which results in compatibility, interchangeability, and acceptability because of its uniformity. The most common definition of a standard is something set up as an approved example.

Standardization is the act of establishing standards, having them agreed to and accepted, and then putting them into practice. Standardization is also the procedure for developing an orderly approach to scientific undertakings in order to achieve optimum economy, safety, and benefit to those employing the standards.

In management language, setting a standard means establishing a level of accomplishment. Generally, standardizing is synonymous with achieving uniformity. Product standardization is very important to the engineering field, where many items such as nuts, bolts, and screws need to be uniform or untold difficulties would be encountered. Forms, shapes, and materials of construction that are standardized result in numerous benefits to manufacturers, distributors, and consumers.

Types of Standards

Plant engineers are concerned with two basic types of standards:

1. The technical and material type, which apply to the practices and methods, tools, supplies, and parts relating to the engineering function
2. The policy and management type, which apply to the purposes, accounting, controls, and people involved in conducting engineering procedures

Purpose and Worth of Standards

Standards are set and employed to achieve the advantages of uniformity and consistency. The principles permit simplification, clarity, economy, and ease of implementation of plant engineering functions.

Many benefits arise from the use of standards. Some of the most important to the engineer and their characteristics are as follows:

1. Material specifications
    a. Simplify study and evaluation of substitutes
    b. Reveal unique characteristics
    c. Minimize decisions in development and research work
    d. Make known performance data
2. Engineering practices
    a. Permit use of standard drafting procedures
    b. Promote comparability through uniform test methods
    c. Support designs that are practical and efficient
    d. Restrict practices that delay progress
    e. Further investigation of new techniques
    f. Promote economy and cost savings of methods

The use of standards results in a great number of benefits to management of organizations in all phases of the business. The most apparent of these are:

1. Policy and objectives
    a. Promote coordination and cooperation among departments
    b. Define goals, suggest direction
    c. Support managerial decisions
    d. Aid community and customer relations
    e. Simplify review and evaluation

2. Managerial technique
   a. Improves confidence and morale
   b. Simplifies routine decisions
   c. Permits comparison of departments with each other
   d. Bolsters use of the "exception principle"

How Are Standards Established?

Standards are not created without considerable planning and effort. Usually a five-step course of action is necessary:
1. Recognition of the need
2. Assignment to study and recommend
3. Presentation of recommendations
4. Acceptance and approval
5. Publication and distribution

Many of the over 3,000 associations and technical groups in the United States are involved in the establishment of standards, and nearly every company uses standards to some degree. While some standards are unique to a particular organization, many are the result of cooperative efforts of a company with its suppliers and its customers. Thus, over a period of time, standards of all types become established, grow, and expand.

Safety Standards

The Occupational Safety and Health Act of 1970 brought attention to the need for standards to protect the health and safety of workers exposed to potential hazards at their places of work. Criteria and recommended safety standards based on them were developed and prepared by the National Institute of Occupational Safety and Health.

Standardization of Computer Equipment

Computer manufacturers have recognized the necessity of standardization and are working with users on such programs. In addition, two sectional committees of the U.S.A. Standards Institute (USASI) have developed standards pertaining to computers and information processing. Many standards have been approved and issued by USASI covering magnetic ink coding for bank checks, digital transmission speeds, flowchart symbols, tape for numerically controlled machine tools, perforated paper tape, and magnetic tape.

Review of Standards

Standards should be periodically reviewed and brought up to date so that they are kept in line with engineering changes. Systems and procedures are continually undergoing revision—standards must follow suit.

A standard should be reviewed every 6 months to a year to see that it is technically correct and covers current procedures. Proof that this has been done should be shown by dating and noting on the document words to this effect. If a procedure for maintenance of standards is not established, they will lose their value to users.

When a standard needs to be revised, the change should be initiated and implemented as if a new standard were being adopted. After approval, it should be published and distributed with a note that the new standard supersedes the old.

DATA COLLECTION

The Purpose of Data Collection

Collecting data involves planning what information is wanted, obtaining it, and then converting it into a form which can be used by automated processing equipment. *Data* are the raw material out of which *information* is made. Information is data which have been sorted, analyzed, interpreted, and arranged in a form useful for problem solving and decision making.

Plant engineering management must look to the needs of the company in planning what type of information it needs to perform its functions. It should be selective in order to limit it to that, for example, which is needed to satisfy management by objectives.

The value of the collection system depends on the choice of data to be collected. Will some data really be needed? How will they be used? Not to be overlooked is the purpose behind the collection.   The ability of management to solve problems and make good decisions depends on how accurate, complete, and up to date the information is that it has to work with.

Data collection is the obtaining of facts in a machine-sensible form, which allows the data to be read directly into a machine or computer.   The accuracy of the management reports produced by the computer depends on the accuracy of the collected data.   Thus, data must be entered into the computer in proper form by trained personnel.   Several types of machines can collect data in a form that the computer will accept.

Computer Input Media

Modern bookkeeping systems operate under the unit record principle.   Any paper record from which raw, basic data can be taken is called a source document.   Data are taken from a source document and recorded on a machine-processable medium, which can be used for many purposes.   The most common machine-processable media are punched cards, paper tape, and magnetic tape.

A punched card can contain considerable information and is a lasting record that can be used in data accumulation and transmission.   The IBM punched card shown in Fig. 1 is typical.

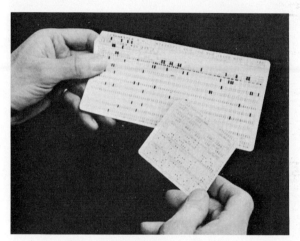

Fig. 1   IBM punched card (V20–9923).

Punched paper tape is another popular medium for the collection of data.   Its one drawback is its slow input speed to the computer.   This is sometimes surmounted by transferring the data from the punched tape to magnetic tape, which can be fed much faster.   Punched paper tape is economical, efficient, and relatively free of errors.

Paper tape was originated for the transmitting of telegraph messages.   An advantage of paper tape over cards is that tape is a continuous recording medium and hence data of any length can be recorded.   Paper tape is not as durable or flexible as cards, therefore it usually serves as an intermediate step to some other medium.

Magnetic tape is a newer development and very useful in large computer systems. The tape is coated on one side with a metallic oxide.   Data are retained through point magnetization and are permanent until erased or written over with new data.   While just as permanent as cards or paper tape, magnetic tape is much more compact.   The data in a stack of punched cards over 100 feet high can all be stored on a single reel (about 2,400 feet) of magnetic tape.   Such a reel can be read or written in less than 5 minutes.

A useful device that collects data is the optical character recognition machine.   This equipment reads ordinary printing or handwritten numbers and transfers the information onto magnetic tape or directly into the computer.

Data collection is also accomplished by magnetic ink character recognition.   A machine of this type senses the amount of iron oxide in the printed characters and either sorts documents or transfers data into the computer.   Magnetic ink characters can be read by people as well as machines. This method of handling data has been used mainly by the banking industry in the processing of checks.

Computer Output Media

Most of the media used for input can also be used for output. Printed reports, however, are the most common means of dispensing data or information from computers. Reports are printed by a typewriter or a printer connected to the computer, some machines being capable of printing more than 2,000 lines a minute.

Another output medium is the cathode ray tube, which is similar to the tube in a television set. The visible output is called *soft copy*, in contrast to the other types of

Fig. 2 IBM 3270 information display system (GV20–9440).

media output which are called *hard copy*. A camera can be attached to the tube to provide a permanent hard-copy record if desired. The cathode ray tube is used in scientific work where the data is presented graphically. This equipment is also useful in the plant, where a system may create and maintain sources of information such as a machine assignment list or a work sequence program. At any time, an individual can review the status of orders, jobs, machine assignments, and similar operational information at any work center by requesting the display on a terminal. A typical display unit which operates from a cathode ray tube is shown in Fig. 2.

AUTOMATIC DATA PROCESSING

Scope of Data Processing

Every business organization is different in its problems and needs for information. Thus data processing systems will differ from company to company. The individual responsible for introducing a system needs to understand the business—how it operates and what it is trying to accomplish. With this knowledge, that person will know what information management will want and need in conducting its operations. The systems planner can then set up a system that will furnish the forms, records, and reports useful to the executive and decision maker.

Data processing is concerned with systems and subsystems that are interrelated, their purpose being to collect, accumulate, and produce records accurately and quickly. Through the use of data processing, management is able to plan and make decisions. Technology has progressed to the extent where machines now make decisions formerly made by executives.

Integrated Data Processing

While all systems are made up of subsystems, when a system is viewed as a whole, the word "integrated" describes it and its goals. Integrating a system involves analyzing a wide range of its data and processes. Integrated data processing requires two types of machines: electric accounting machines and electronic data processing machines; the latter are commonly referred to as computers.

The Role of the Computer

The computer is the mainspring of an electronic data processing system. It receives data and instructions, stores them in memory cells, and puts out the data when asked for them. It also does arithmetic operations; it adds, subtracts, multiplies, and divides; it makes comparisons in taking action called for by a result. The computer does all these things at electronic speed, but only when directed by human instructions called a *program*. Table 1 shows the capabilities of various types of computers in multiplication operations.

TABLE 1   The Decreasing Cost of Computations

Means	Time to do one multiplication	Cost of 125 million multiplications
Man	1 minute	$12,500,000
Desk calculator	10 seconds	2,150,000
Harvard Mark I	1 second	850,000
ENIAC	10 milliseconds	12,800
Univac I	2 milliseconds	4,300
Univac 1103	5,000 microseconds	1,420
IBM 7094	25 microseconds	132
Stretch, IBM	2.5 microseconds	29
CDC 6600	0.3 microsecond	4

SOURCE: *Computer Needs in Universities and Colleges,* National Academy of Sciences, National Research Council, Publication 1233, Washington, D.C., and Business Equipment Manufacturers Association.

The heart of the computer is known as the processing unit. It consists of a control unit, a storage device, and an arithmetic unit. Input devices "read" data into the computer and output devices "write" (print out) data from it.

Data processing generally begins with a source document that provides the data for input to the computer. The storage unit in the computer receives the data, stores them, performs arithmetic or comparison operations, and releases them as instructed by the program through the control unit.

In the field of data processing, programs are referred to as *software* and the machines as *hardware*. Software is important because regardless of how versatile the machines are, they are not effective and will not perform satisfactorily without good programming.

Data entry units collect data at any origin point—the factory, the storeroom, or the office—and prepare them in a form suitable for entry into a data processing system. Such machines may produce their own output in the form of cards or tape, or they may transmit the data directly to a central unit that collects them from many points and prepares them for processing. Figure 3 is an IBM data entry unit. In-plant computers (or minicomputers), such as the IBM System 7 pictured in Fig. 4, can be used to gather data directly from machines or processes.

All data processed by a computer must be stored. Two methods of storage are commonly used, primary and auxiliary. Primary storage is employed when data and instructions are to be processed almost immediately, while auxiliary storage handles data that are not needed quickly. Core, magnetic drum, and thin film are three means of primary storage; while cards, paper, and magnetic tape handle auxiliary storage.

The time needed to locate and transfer data to and from storage is called *access* time. Usually the faster the access time, the more expensive the computer equipment. A slow

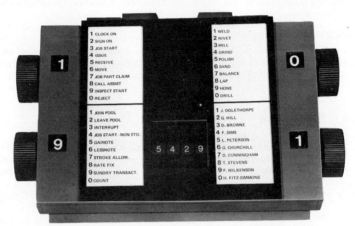

Fig. 3 IBM 2796 data entry unit (GV20–9416).

Fig. 4 IBM System 7 (GV20–9376).

access time would be half a second, whereas a fast access time would be less than a millionth of a second.

Fast access time is usually not needed for business data processing. More important here is speed in putting data and instructions into storage and getting them out again. However, when engineering or scientific calculations totaling in the thousands are involved, fast access time would be desirable.

Real time can be defined in two ways. It is the time in which the occurrence of an event and the reporting or recording of it are almost simultaneous. In real time applications, the actual time used by a computer in solving a problem is measured in seconds and is immediately available to control effectively a process that is going on at the same time. Many real time systems employ time sharing, which means that several users can have almost simultaneous access to the same computer.

How a Data Processing System Works

In a typical automatic data processing system created for a maintenance department in an industrial plant, each piece of equipment in the plant has its own separate punched card. A service schedule for the equipment based on 48 weeks for a year is ideal, because all frequencies (weekly, monthly, quarterly, semiannually, and annually) are evenly divided into 48, simplifying the balancing of the workload from week to week.

Each week the punched cards are sorted to separate out those keyed for that week. These cards are reproduced to provide a work order and a file set. The work order set is arranged by department and the craft that will do the work. A scheduler then passes them to supervision for distribution to the proper craftsmen who will do the work.

As jobs are completed, the work orders are returned to the scheduler, where they are matched against the file set. File cards left over represent work scheduled but not completed. Management can review these by having them automatically printed in an uncompleted work report. Such a report enables priorities to be arranged for future weeks to ensure that the most important work gets attention first. The report also enables management to make adjustments, if necessary, in labor assigned, so that an optimum backlog of jobs is maintained.

All phases of this typical system are handled on just three unit-record automatic data processing (ADP) machines: a keypunch, a card sorter, and a print-out calculator.

AUTOMATIC DATA PROCESSING APPLICATIONS

Inventory Control

Engineering management depends on inventory control to assure availability of material under the category of MRO (maintenance, repair, and operating supplies). Automatic data processing can provide the data and information regarding availability, lead time, and costs. The purchasing department is deeply involved with the stores department in this management of materials. ADP, by providing up-to-date information, enables both departments to work closely together on decisions concerning minimum levels of inventory, annual consumption of machine tools and parts, maintenance material reorder quantity, analysis of obsolescence based on usage, and emergency order procedure.

Data processing computations can be made much more quickly than manual ones. Thus control limits can be updated with changing demand. The advantages are apparent in working with economic order quantities. Inventory levels may also be reduced safely, since control reports provide the time and knowledge needed to make immediate corrections should unforeseen circumstances arise.

Engineering and Preventive Maintenance

Data processing aids management in engineering functions such as determination of work priority of the craftsmen based on cost of downtime of various production equipment; machine utilization and cost of processing as determined by machine hours; planning and scheduling operations to increase manpower efficiency; and analysis of job backlog man-hours to determine labor need.

Data processing systems have been of great help to engineering management in automatically scheduling preventive maintenance, making realistic performance comparisons for cost analysis, and gathering maintenance data in easily accessible form.

Scheduling by computer assures complete coverage and frees supervision from the need to manually schedule maintenance at optimum intervals. As a result, such operations are performed better and with lower labor and material cost.

Operations Research

Operations research is defined as the application of mathematical methods to the study and analysis of complex overall problems. The techniques for solving problems using operations research methods include linear programming, the critical path method (CPM) of scheduling, queueing, simulation, and others. Typical problems that can be solved are determining the optimum time for performing preventive maintenance, the optimum number of people that should be employed in a toolroom for minimum cost, and the lowest level of machine parts inventory that should be maintained consistent with management policy. Other problems are handled by the computer by constructing models simulating actual conditions in the plant and then studying the effect of altering variables.

Oiling and Lubrication

Automatic weekly work orders can be provided for oiling and lubricating operations. The system is built around standard frequencies for servicing equipment and provides detailed instructions as to specific machines, type of service, and frequency of attention.

Many systems, in addition to directing the servicing function, also provide feedback to management on labor time, oil consumption, repairs performed, and lost operating time.

Benefits from data processing of these functions include increased productivity of lubrication personnel, reduced unscheduled or emergency calls for service, reduced loss of lubricants by leakage, and reduced number of lubricants needed.

MANAGEMENT INFORMATION SYSTEMS

Reports to Management

Through automatic data processing, engineering management can have daily reports of operations that once took weeks to compile. Moreover, information can be presented in a form that facilitates control and decision making. Reports that used to be lengthy can now be condensed, brief, and to the point. Thus the manager is able to assimilate the pertinent data he needs without being burdened by voluminous, incidental information. Furthermore, reports can now show percentage changes and indicate trends.

When providing a management information system, only the information that is needed should be directed to a manager's attention, and the cost of it should not exceed its value. Management is responsible for profit of the organization. It is just as important to achieve a maximum return on the investment of installing a data processing system as it is to achieve a return on investment on a new production line.

Information Retrieval

With data processing machines, management can store its data and records in a computer, update this information daily, and get all or any part of it, including totals, at any time. Thus, through such information retrieval systems, an executive can use computer terminals to inquire into (or "read out") machine data, parts inventory, order size, maintenance costs—for that matter, almost any information that is required to solve problems or make decisions. Equipment that can provide such information to the person in the shop is shown in Fig. 5.

One of the problems being encountered with retrieval systems is that they are too thorough—they produce too much material for the researcher to absorb. This results from a very broad range of index caused by a desire to assure that no relevant information will be overlooked. A problem is that the researcher must spend much time in studying each article published to determine its usefulness. Some of the newer retrieval systems attempt to overcome this through key-word matching and with frequency-of-word indexing. Microfilm storage and retrieval is another approach to the handling of large amounts of information.

Control Reports

The control report is an extremely important document for management in that it compares results with objectives. Control reports provide information that enables the decision maker to take corrective or preventive action in business trends, to initiate new action, or to confirm and maintain current procedures. A typical report, for example, might compare current costs with those budgeted.

For maximum usefulness, the control report needs to be designed along certain lines. The following characteristics are desirable:

Familiar format A standard form facilitates and speeds comprehension. Consistent arrangement of information and the method of presentation from one report to the next minimizes the possibility of overlooking or misunderstanding.

Up to date Management control depends on the latest information available. Along the same line, the report needs to be timely and to be issued at regular intervals. The value of a control report declines with age.

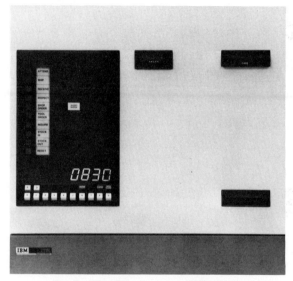

Fig. 5 IBM 2791 area station (GV20-9413).

Accurate and reliable Facts arranged in standard form and obtained from confirmed sources provide the "meat" which the decision maker looks for and uses to provide the basis for decisions.

Cost Reports Cost reports of various types are common to all management information systems. Budgets provide management the means of controlling costs, since they restrict the expenditures of the organization. Reports on costs reflect the success of the cost policies on pricing and levels of profit to be realized.

To be most useful, cost reports should contain certain elements. They should:
1. Present data in summary form, be easy to read and understand
2. Refer to standards or norms, thus facilitating budget comparisons
3. Be structured to call attention to unusual charges and expenses

Annual Reports

An annual report provides the summary of a department's activities and is made to apprise management of accomplishments and efficiency. It should be a concise and factual document.

An engineering annual report would list department costs of labor and material. It would give maintenance and repair costs appropriately broken down to facilities and equipment. The cost of capital investments would be shown, as well as an analysis of the work performed.

Information relating to personnel is also found in annual reports. Numbers and classes of individuals, turnover, and absentee records provide such data.

Special Reports

Engineering management needs special reports to assist it in problem solving, planning and scheduling, and unusual engineering operations. Under this category come work schedules, inspection reports, and capital project status reports, to mention only a few.

A job backlog report is an example of such a special report. The maintenance departments of industrial plants should be sized in number of workers, or available man-hours, so that a backlog of jobs of at least 1 or 2 weeks duration exists. If the backlog begins to show a trend to become larger or smaller, management may make adjustments to alter the trend to the desired level.

Trends in Management Information Systems

As management information systems continue to grow and change to meet the needs of their users, trends that suggest what may be expected in the future have become apparent. While there is no end in sight to innovations and the capabilities of machines, limits to their availability and competence may be posed by people problems.

Emphasis is shifting from clerical automation—such as payroll, accounts payable, customer billing, and other office operations—to managerial applications involving economics. More system analysis on servomechanism engineering and on mathematical economics are examples of what may be expected.

Large companies with multiple, worldwide facilities will likely expand their use of a central, time-sharing system of computer use to do most of the data processing work for the entire organization.

Maintenance Management Reports

N. B. POST, P.E.
Manager
and

JAMES VanKERKHOVE
Facilities Planner, Plant Engineering and Maintenance, Xerox Corporation

SCOPE

The maintenance department can have a variety of faces in the organizational setting. To the production plants, it becomes a staff service function whose sole purpose is to support operating demands. To top management, on the other hand, maintenance may be viewed as a fact-of-life component of overhead, where costs must be minimized to achieve operating efficiency. In any case, the maintenance function must respond to both line and staff goals as well as to its own internal objectives.

Expectations regarding movement toward this set of goals are often expressed to the maintenance manager through the routine questions that surface both formally and informally from any sector, questions such as "Are we receiving the most for our maintenance dollar?" from top management; or "How are we progressing as a well-tuned maintenance team?" from maintenance submanagement; or "What have you done for me lately?" from production management.

The concept central to the useful design and application of maintenance management reports is that integrated communication-information flow is a requisite for effective planning, control, and feedback—and thus for successful decision making.

As both technology and size of operations increase, maintenance management becomes more a job of management than maintenance and the associated principles of administration must be adapted to fully organize the maverick and multifaceted resources involved. Furthermore, the expanding scope of modern maintenance has come to include dimensions beyond the factory walls, such as environmental protection, energy conservation, personal development, community participation, etc. In this mode, the maintenance manager must rely on more than simple exposition of dollars and percentages to put a point across. It now becomes necessary to deal with priorities, issues, and impacts that relate to the outside world and the worker as well as to organizational goals.

OBJECTIVES

The overall objectives of the battery of management reports utilized relate to the whole maintenance system.

1. Operating units are to be served by keeping productive equipment operable, efficient, and safe.

2. Materials, manpower, and equipment will be coordinated to provide timely availability of resources at the work site.

3. An optimum level of maintenance will be established and provided in the most practical, low-cost manner, in compliance with corporate policy regarding economics, appearance, safety, and environmental standards.

4. As a guide for directing improvement, management will be provided with information on status, effectiveness, and cost of maintenance activity and programs.

The usefulness of the management report lies in its objectivity and value as both a working tool and a meaningful "report card." In this respect, the report facilitates management by *fact* rather than *opinion* and by *exception* rather than by *rule*. Each report in itself is also intended to address specific management action on a time continuum; that is, a report may serve as raw input, as a call for immediate action, as a justification for short-term strategies, or as a long-range planning indicator. The classification of reports by "time utility" provides a framework for both identifying information needs and clarifying interrelationships.

To satisfy the above requirements for report *usefulness,* specifications for information *flow* and *content* should be outlined. Information is gathered from the bottom up, starting with primary feeder reports from maintenance line units. (At Xerox, the maintenance subdivisions are assigned to designate their own responsibility center for project work, coverage, planning and engineering, vehicle repair, custodial activity, etc.) Unit reports are then aggregated and reformulated through a central control point, from which individualized reports flow out to each area where information is required. Since the volume of this flow can become overwhelming, it is imperative to design a reporting system that is not an end in itself but rather adaptable to machine processing and continuous change.

Content of maintenance reports is dictated by the intended use. However, some commonsense guidelines can ensure the basic intent of objectivity and meaningfulness. The form and format for effective reporting should embrace the following points:

Simplicity and readability
Brevity and clarity
Minimum paperwork and hard copy
After-the-fact summarization (results-oriented)
Prioritized wherever meaningful
Bottom-line accumulation (total cost, time, etc.)
Related to stated objectives
Exception principle (significant deviation from target, norm)
Necessary action highlighted
Timely distribution (as "real-time" as possible)
EDP-adaptable (for keypunching, etc.)

Comparative with own past (vs. others)
Consistently applied parameters
Appeal to reader's interest

The effort to communicate maintenance goals in a clear and meaningful manner is an essential one to make any subsequent reporting system successful (Exhibit A). The statement of organizational objectives serves as both the start and the finish line in the

EXHIBIT A   Sample Statement of Objectives

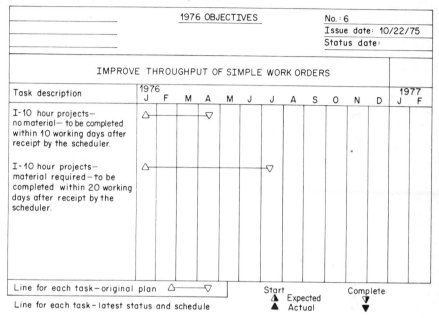

effective management system, wherein today's performance is evaluated to determine tomorrow's goals.

WORK ORDER SYSTEM

The first-order mechanism for maintenance planning, control, and reporting is the work order system. Its purpose is to accumulate, process, and sort all relevant data input via customer request. The result is a series of reports that reflect basic cost, labor, material, and scheduling *activity* flowing through maintenance and referenced according to the specific needs of information users (such as listings by project number, by customer budget center, by job crew or craft, by priority, etc.).

In conjunction with a maintenance planning and standards system, cost and labor *performance* reports are also generated, based on timely, accountable sources (labor cards, etc.) in a clear, systematic format. These reports, in turn, are used as both "hands-on" decision documents and *primary input* to short-run operating and control reports.

The work order itself is the key document in the system and should facilitate the communication of adequate, relevant job information for each step in the system (Exhibit B). The work order flows through stages of maintenance planning and is scheduled for initiation dependent upon availability of workers, materials, and equipment. As execution of the job progresses, all actual associated labor and material (including contracted) charges are recorded against the work order number by the responsible foreman from data on daily labor cards, material receipts, etc. These data are summarized and periodically fed into a central control system, where they are sorted into prescribed formats by both a *cost-collection subsystem* and a *status-tracking subsystem*. The former sort is primarily for financial-accounting control use, while the latter is intended for customer and management use. At each report readout cycle, all activity in the system is referenced, whether a work order is closed out, still in process, or standing open.

Input

Maintenance work order (Exhibit C)   As the source document required to initiate maintenance activity, the work order form should include the what, when, where, who,

EXHIBIT B   Maintenance Work Order Service Request Flow

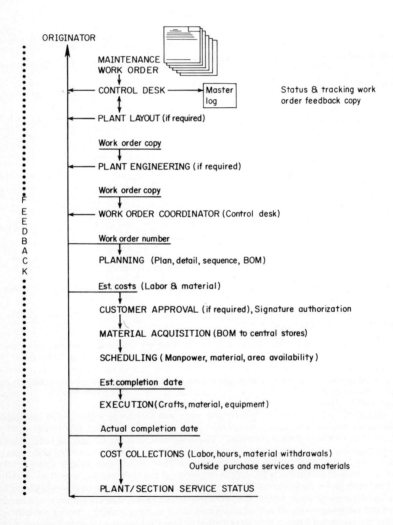

MAINTENANCE WORK ORDER SYSTEM

SERVICE REQUEST FLOW

ORIGINATOR

MAINTENANCE
WORK ORDER

CONTROL DESK ────► Master log   Status & tracking work order feedback copy

PLANT LAYOUT (if required)

Work order copy

PLANT ENGINEERING (if required)

Work order copy

WORK ORDER COORDINATOR (Control desk)

Work order number

PLANNING (Plan, detail, sequence, BOM)

Est. costs (Labor & material)

CUSTOMER APPROVAL (if required), Signature authorization

MATERIAL ACQUISITION (BOM to central stores)

SCHEDULING (Manpower, material, area availability)

Est. completion date

EXECUTION (Crafts, material, equipment)

Actual completion date

COST COLLECTIONS (Labor, hours, material withdrawals)
            Outside purchase services and materials

PLANT/SECTION SERVICE STATUS

FEEDBACK

•••••••••••TRANSFER ACCOUNTING

EXHIBIT C   Sample Maintenance Work Order Document

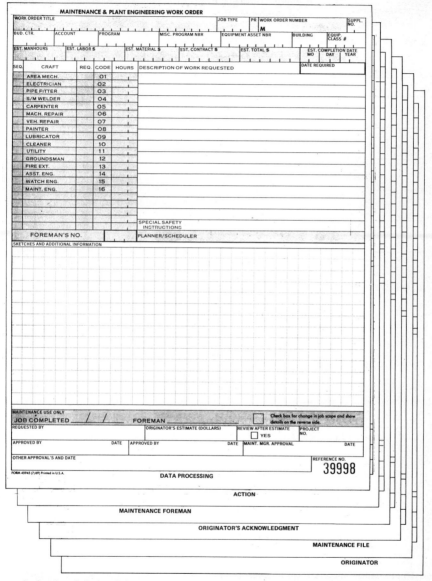

and why details behind the request as well as authorization and budget coverage. Upon completion of work, a "closeout" document is fed into the control system.

Maintenance planning standards   Where practical, maintenance work measurement or sampling standards should be developed and applied to work orders that involve skilled crafts. Standards are essential in developing reasonable estimates and schedules and in improving maintenance productivity (potential 50 percent or better increase in initial years).

Labor cards and reports (Exhibit D) To record actual hours against work order numbers, daily time cards are completed and fed into the system via the foreman's summary report. Special standing orders for delay, sickness, administration, etc., should be established to account for nonproductive time.

EXHIBIT D Sample Labor Card and Summary Report

FACILITIES LABOR REPORT

EXHIBIT E Sample Material Withdrawal Slip

Maintenance material withdrawal (Exhibit E) Inventory materials for internally executed jobs are charged against the proper work order and fed into the system when the materials are signed out.

Accounts payable feed On a weekly basis, accounting data on purchased labor and material invoices, as approved by both maintenance and the customer, are cross fed into the work order record system.

Output

Activity report (Exhibit F) The current week's charges on work orders against the appropriate budget center are reflected in this report. It is used to enable continuous review of actual vs. estimated costs, so that overruns will be visible as early as possible. The creation of an "exception report" of excessive overruns on current, major, in-process

EXHIBIT F Sample Weekly Activity Report

MWO WEEKLY ACTIVITY REPORT

Maint. group K   K fork truck PM & repair   Page   Date / /
Bgt. ctr.

W.O. No.	Description	Cat Prt	Current week hours Div.RG Div.OT TR.RG TR.OT Total	Weekly charge	Tot.div hours	Tot. TR hours	Tot.est cost	Totact cost	% of est expended— lab. mat. pur. tot.

Bgt. ctr.   Expense charges
Bgt. ctr.   total charges

EXHIBIT G Sample Performance and Coverage Reports

MAINTENANCE PLANNING SYSTEM   Page
COVERAGE REPORT

Div	Foreman	Name	Craft name	Actual hrs.	Hrs. against stds.	Coverage, %

MAINTENANCE PLANNING SYSTEM
COMPLETED WORK ORDERS
PERFORMANCE REPORT

Div	Foreman	Name	Work order	Description	Hours Actual App Craft	Adjusted App Total	Std. hours	Perf., %

projects will enhance management's ability to pinpoint areas requiring immediate attention.

Performance and coverage reports (Exhibit G) These reports depict manpower coverage and performance by maintenance crew on hours worked against applied standards. This information is reviewed by maintenance staff and operations management to measure productivity of functional areas (actual hours worked against total standard hours planned) on a timely basis for responsive action.

Performance by craft report (Exhibit H)   Craft standard hours, actual total hours, nonproductive time, and percent efficiency are depicted by work order for each functional maintenance area (e.g., projects, preventive maintenance, coverage).   This report enables maintenance management to monitor individual craft performance in specific work categories and thus identify potential for better distribution of manpower resources among functions.

EXHIBIT H   Sample Performance by Craft Report

Report MW
Date

MWO PERFORMANCE BY CRAFT
MAINT. GROUP CAPITAL WORK ORDERS   Page

W.O. No.	Description	Craft	Std. hrs.	Act. hrs.	Eff, %

EXHIBIT I   Sample Monthly Closed Report

Maint. group B   B project maintenance   MWO MONTHLY CLOSED REPORT   Page   Date
Bgt. ctr.   LIFE TO DATE

| W.O. No. | Prog. No. | Estimated costs | | | | | Actual costs | | | | | % of est- | | | Comp |
		Man hrs	Labor $	Matrl $	Purch $	Totals $	Man hrs	Labor $	Matrl $	Purch $	Totals $	M hrs	Lab	Total	Date

Bgt. ctr.   Expense charges
Bgt. ctr.   Total charges

Closed report (Exhibit I)   The closed report provides a summary of actual labor and costs vs. planned estimates on completed work; this provides a final tally for reviewing estimating performance and total project spending against budget.

Accounting-financial reports   In the cost collecting subsystem, costs for maintenance services are transferred out to the "customer" and ultimately to the company's general ledger, which reflects the financial performance of each budget center.

Customer status report (Exhibit J)   This set of reports will provide a periodic status of maintenance costs incurred by budget center for each customer organization, thus aiding both service and user to monitor spending.

Priority and preventive maintenance reports   For each functional area, the total cost and time spent on completed work orders is listed by priority (breakdown, safety, pollution, routine, etc.).   Cumulative data for preventive vs. corrective work are also carried for major capital equipment.   This information provides management with a profile of work composition, the maintenance dollar distribution, and equipment replacement and overhaul criteria.

Although different reports are valuable to certain areas more than others, it is paramount that paper work be minimized and unessential reports eliminated at the foundation level.   Even with a sophisticated EDP work order system in place, the cost of report generation must be weighed against utility for management decision making. The hard copy reports generated by the work order system are intended as *primary feeds* into broader operating and staff reports, and only exception reports on areas of critical concern should be directed to *functional* maintenance management.

EXHIBIT J   Sample Monthly Status Report

| Maint. group 9 | 9 Coverage- | Plt. | | | MWO MONTHLY STATUS REPORT | | | | Page | | | Date | / / |

W.O. No.	Description	Capital Prog. No.	Div. hr.	Tr. hr.	Labor $	Matrl $	Purch $	Total $	Tot. hrs.	Labor $	Matrl $	Purch $	Totals

Column groups: "Current month charges" spans Div. hr. through Total $; "Cumulative charges" spans Tot. hrs. through Totals.

Bgt. ctr.   Expense charges
Bgt. ctr.   Total charges

OPERATING MANAGEMENT REPORTS

Along with overseeing throughput progress, it is also imperative to maintenance operating managers that productive resources be available and utilized optimally.   This task can be approached through development of the following *"immediate action"* reports.

Project tracking reports (Exhibit K)   As a corollary to the cost monitoring function of the status report, a further step toward responsive maintenance involves a single-point project control service to the customer via up-to-date tracking of work orders in the flow cycle and their scheduled completion.   This report identifies scheduled vs. actual throughput dates for each step in the system and gives an early warning of possible slippages, their magnitude, and the causal factors involved.

A recent aid to project tracking is the Mark III Management System developed by the Program Control Corporation.   Its basic purpose is to provide a symbolic format that is flexible enough to handle a wide variety of information and also to serve other purposes.

Mark III application to maintenance project monitoring can include concurrent chart display of schedule, interfaces, estimate vs. actual for cost and labor, and responsibility. This single report thus provides the operating managers with all relevant status data and permits the manager to evaluate the impact of changes on other projects scheduled in the same time frame.   Mark III also provides an option for cumulative graphical tracking of any desired parameter.[2]*

Backlog report (Exhibit L)   The backlog report shows scheduled work awaiting execution by priority and craft in addition to indicating the required manning to sustain the prescribed service "readiness" level.   This provides an interactive mechanism by which

* Superior numbers refer to the list of references at the end of this chapter.

EXHIBIT K Sample Project Tracking System

PE&M PROJECT TRACKING SYSTEM

①	②	③	④	⑤	⑥	⑦	⑧	⑨	⑩	⑪	⑫	⑬	⑭
BCTR#	PROJ	SU	EP	STRT	FACPL	ENGRG	PLAN	SIGN	MATL	IMPL.	EST	REQ	SLACK
M532	40372	00	B	S08/28	N-A	N-A	09/12	N-A	10/31	11/07	11/07	11/08	9*
				A08/28		09/04					⑮ P-OUT = 10/30		

⑯ MWO:SFTY
⑰ DCR:ERECT CRIBBING

---

1. BCTR# =   Budget center number   M532
2. PROJ =   Project (work order) number   40372
3. SU =   Supplement number (in case work order   00 (has not been supplemented)
   has been supplemented)
4. EP =   Entry point (where work order went after   B (complex B—plng. supr. 311)
   receipt in 304)
5. STRT =   Start date   S (scheduled 8/28/74)
       A (actual 8/28/74)
6. FACPL =   Facilities planning   N-A (work order does not have to go to Personnel
   space plng.)
7. ENGRG =   Plant engineering   N-A (work order does not have to go to Plant Engineering)

NOTE: IF WORK ORDER HAD TO GO TO EITHER PERSONNEL SPACE PLANNING OR PLANT ENGI-
NEERING, A SCHEDULED *OUT* DATE WOULD APPEAR; AND WHEN IT *LEFT* THE AREA, AN ACTUAL
OUT DATE WOULD BE RECORDED.

8. PLAN=   Maintenance planning   9/12/74 (*scheduled* out date)
                                           9/04/74 (*actual* out date)

9. SIGN=   Signature cycle outside PE&M (if required)   N–A

10. MATL=   Material due to arrive at warehouse and be staged for work   10/31/74 (scheduled) (no actual yet, indicates work is awaiting mat'l)

11. IMPL=   Scheduling and implementation   11/07/74 (scheduled job completion)

12. EST=   Estimated completion date (when all crafts & contractors are scheduled to be completed)   11/07/74

13. REQ=   Required date—completion date customer originally requested on work order   11/08/74

14. SLACK=   Slack time—a calculation reflecting the difference between the latest P-OUT date and the customer's requested date minus behind schedule time.   9 (days ahead of schedule)

15. P-OUT=   Probable out date—a calculation reflecting the latest forecast (based on most recent actual date) of when the project will *probably* be done.   10/30/74

16. MWO:SFTY=   A special note, in this case signifying that this work order was safety. (Could be "on hold, contract, cancel, etc.)

17. DCR:=   Description or title   Erect cribbing

operational areas can track, forecast, and feed back to management in order to keep the maintenance system balanced and responsive.

Workload summary analysis (Exhibit M)   Planned workload against standard craft hours available for scheduling are compared, in addition to the current "hands-on" (previously scheduled and ready but not started) load and contracted activity.   By com-

EXHIBIT L   Sample Weekly Backlog Report

WEEKLY CURRENT MAINTENANCE
BACKLOG (MAN-HOURS) AND
FORCE REPORT

Area _____   Zone _____   Date _____

Priority	Area mechanics	Electricians	Pipefitters	Welders/SM	Carpenter	Machine repairmen	Vehicle repairmen	Painters	Lubricators
Urgent									
Essential									
Subtotal									
Routine									
Shutdown									
Subtotal									
Grand total current backlog									
Net forces available (permanently assigned)									
Additional forces required									

Shutdown priorities should not be carried in current backlog unless it is known that the shutdown is planned for the following week.

EXHIBIT M   Sample Weekly Workload Summary Analysis

PE&M WEEKLY WORKLOAD SUMMARY ANALYSIS PROJECT

Date	Craft	(1) Stand. hrs. avail.	(2) Avg. st. hr. plan	(2÷1) Plan ratio	(3) 13 wk st. hr. wkld.	(3÷1) 13 wk manpr. cyc.	(4) Hands on work	(5) Contr ind. No.	Comments/action	(6) Total std. hr workld.	(6÷1) Total manpwr. cycle
	Area mech. Electricians Pipefitters Welders Carpenter Mach. repair Painters										

puting a standard planned workload and comparing it to an average work order turn-around cycle (e.g., 13 weeks), the report user is given a projected workload picture for each craft and the estimated minimum number of weeks wait before a newly input work order could be scheduled to start, with the current manpower constraint. Recommended management action is again noted by exception.

MAINTENANCE CONTROL REPORTS

Control reports are a step removed from the planning-operating phases of maintenance management. The content involves statistical data manipulation, trend analysis, and performance tracking rather than absolute values; the intent is to facilitate broader decision making related to *short-term strategies* and maintenance objectives (e.g., for an annual operating budget cycle). Although accounting and financial control reports are integral to good management, their purpose and procedures are more appropriately defined in the comptroller's policy manual. This chapter will outline only maintenance functional control reports.

Schedule compliance report (Exhibit N) Usually prepared weekly, this report provides a summary of input/output characteristics for the maintenance planning and scheduling function. Variances from schedule are noted by exception and specific causal factors identified, thus ensuring clear accountability and management follow-up.

Planning and scheduling performance (Exhibit O) This report tracks weekly activity performance data against established targets or desired goals. Graphical plotting of successive data over the year lends itself to trend and time-series analysis, useful in forecasting expected performance. The data themselves are collected from special MWO feeder reports (such as craft performance, distribution of craft hours, etc.) and weekly compliance reports.

Contracting report (Exhibit P) Information similar to the compliance report is collected by a central contract administrator for all newly negotiated and ongoing services purchased from outside the company. This provides a review of work off-loaded against a target "percent in house" and a check on contractor performance against planned hours.

Preventive maintenance report The preventive maintenance report should show a comparison of preplanned maintenance costs and costs of repair and parts replacement for prior month, year to date, and life to date for each major equipment number (usually corresponding to a standing work order number). This information then provides the base upon which an equipment replacement policy can be implemented, with an exception report generated to identify equipment accumulating excessive repair costs.

MANAGEMENT EFFECTIVENESS REPORTS

Higher-order reporting requires filtering out detail to arrive at a synopsis of performance, useful to top management, customer, and maintenance management alike in evaluating service and formulating *long-range plans.* Report presentation is a subject in itself, including use of audiovisual techniques, art work, etc. Although the medium employed to convey the subject has obvious impact on reception, an emphasis on *meaningful* content is most critical. The study of maintenance productivity measurement occupies a major portion of staff effort and is enlisted to justify or "sell" associated programs, proposals, and budgets. Unless, however, worthwhile ideas can be spelled out on paper and communicated both up and down the management structure, programs may be doomed to be ineffective, the victims of organizational inertia. Thus, the effective maintenance management report becomes a tool of dynamic organizational impetus.

Apart from the notion of a "report card," expertly prepared reports can be ready references for making maintenance objectives operational. Such reports must be clear enough to facilitate uniform interpretation yet broad enough to enhance creative and feasible implementation at the functional levels. The presentation should get right to the focal point of the audience's interest, like a newspaper headline, then expand into rationale, and finally present action proposals for management decision. Again, though technique is important, the information must reveal fact, not opinion or surmise.

Major issues Major maintenance achievements and plans should be "scoped" or overviewed in a narrative format including these major points:

1. Executive summary of issue
2. Objectives to be achieved
3. Impact statement on:
    a. Manpower and organization
    b. Facilities and equipment
    c. Capital and expense exposure
    d. Opportunities and risks
4. Action plan

This document serves as the crystallization of previously defined objectives and a

EXHIBIT N   Sample Schedule Compliance Report

COMPLEX A, B, C SCHEDULING PERFORMANCE

Week starting _____

	A	B	C
Work orders scheduled to start			
Work orders scheduled & started			

Reasons for work orders not scheduled
(List Work Order No. on the back with code.)

	A	B	C
1. Material not available			
2. Manpower not available			
3. Area not available			
4. Other – list _____			

_____

_____

_____

_____

	A	B	C
Work orders sched. for comp.			
Work orders actually completed			
Work orders comp./not sched.			

Reasons for work orders not completed
(List Work Order No. on the back with code.)

	A	B	C
1. Material not available			
2. Materials received wrong			
3. Materials not on BOM			
4. Materials not in area			
5. Manpower not available			
6. Area not available			
7. Other – list			
Change in job scope			
Originator change			
Originator material			
Vendor/wrong material			
Planning error			
Scheduler error			
Weather			

Reasons for work orders completed that were not scheduled
(List Work Order No. on the back with code.)

	A	B	C
1. Scheduled on overtime			
2. W.O. dropped from schedule			
3. Emergency (safety)			
4. Production critical			
5. Other			

Past due work orders – _____ Hours – _____ % – _____

EXHIBIT O   Sample Scheduling Performance Report

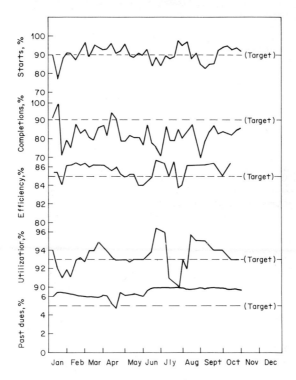

1974 PE&M SCHEDULING PERFORMANCE
--OPERATIONS--

EXHIBIT P   Sample Contracting Report

CONTRACTING STATISTICS—Organization PE&M/Scheduling

	WEEK ENDING	YEAR TO DATE			
Number of work orders contracted	_____	_____			
Number of work orders closed	_____	_____			
Total number of work orders open	_____	_____			
Estimated dollars contracted	_____	_____			
Number of work orders contracted by reason:					
Pool manpower not available	_____	_____			
Special tools/equipment	_____	_____			
Craft specialty	_____	_____			
Other	_____	_____			PERCENT
Estimated hours by craft:	ESTIMATED	PLAN	TOTAL	CONTRACTED	
Area mechanic	_____				
Electrical	_____				
Pipefitting	_____				
Welding	_____				
Carpentry	_____				
Machine repair	_____				
Painting	_____				
GRAND TOTAL	_____				

preliminary statement of resource requirements. Such "headlines" as energy conservation, safety and environmental compliance, recycling efforts, conversion to sophisticated systems control, etc., are ripe topics to focus management awareness on maintenance.

Product cost input An important overall indicator of maintenance stature and degree of control necessary is reflected in a summary of contribution to direct product cost relative to the company's profit-and-loss picture. In conjunction with product cost, an objective evaluation of maintenance service level should be developed, such as decreased downtime due to preventive maintenance or fraction of maintenance dollar spent on production facilities and equipment. The chief point here is not one of too little or too much but rather matching cost with appropriate service level. Action implications of such a report characteristically lead to directives aimed at cutting "frivolous spending" and forcing customers to decide which work is really mandatory.

Effectiveness indicators Efforts to quantify maintenance performance at a glance have yielded a bevy of indicators, ratios, formulas, and checklists. The use of an indicator to evaluate an entire system varies with the objective in mind but nevertheless must, by definition, exclude much *absolute* information for the sake of *relativism*. In any case, indicators, when used, should be consistently applied to avoid bias, be based on a refer-

EXHIBIT Q Sample Effectiveness Indicators

PE&M PERFORMANCE EVALUATION—DATA REQUIREMENTS

MAJOR INDICATORS	DATA
A. Productivity	
1. Labor (%)	O Std. Hrs.
	O Act. Hrs.
	O By Division
2. Labor/Material (%)	O Actual Labor $
	O Actual Matl. $
	O By Division
3. Maintenance Force (%)	O Total PE&M Indirects
	O Total MD Directs
B. Throughput	
1. Current Backlog (Wks.)	O For Maintenance & Plant Engineering
	O Avg. Backlog in Man-Wks.
2. % In-House (%)	O Purchased Cost
	O Total W.O. Cost
	O % Hrs. Contracted
3. Composition ($/order)	O $ Actual on closed W.O.
	O Total # Closed W.O.
4. Preventive/Repair (%)	O Act. Hrs. on PM
	O Total Act. Hrs.
C. Planning	
1. Jobs on Schedule (%)	O # Jobs Scheduled
	O # Jobs Completed
2. Estimating (%)	O Actual $
	O Estimate $
	O Actual Hrs.
	O Estimate Hrs.
D. Spending	
1. Maintenance/Product Cost (%)	O Planned Direct PE&M Spending
	O Planned MD Production Spending
2. Budget Performance (%)	O $ Budgeted
	O $ Actual
3. Maintenance Cost "Per"	O $ Actual
	O Elec. Usage
	O Total Sq.Ft.

ence point to ensure comparative value, and be tracked to identify trends. A brief listing of indicators relevant to maintenance is shown in Exhibit Q; value or meaningfulness will depend upon where and how the parameter is used and whether appropriate data are available. A variety of techniques for measuring effectiveness have been developed, adaptable to the degree of comprehensiveness required.[3]

At this point, we come full circle back to the statement of maintenance *objectives.* How have we done? What has changed? And where are we headed? By flexing the original statement, an updated profile of performance can be provided along with a new set of objectives determined from the preceding reports. This then becomes the starting framework for the system through the next period.

REFERENCES

1. B. Lewis: *Maintenance Management,* Rider, New York, 1963.
2. *Mark III Management System,* Basic Training Manual, Program Control Corporation, Van Nuys, Calif., 1971.
3. W. Armitage: "Maintenance Effectiveness," in A. K. Jardine (ed.), *Operational Research in Maintenance,* Manchester University Press, Manchester, England, 1970.
4. B. Lewis and J. Marron: *Facilities and Plant Engineering Handbook,* McGraw-Hill, New York, 1973.
5. E. J. Miller and J. W. Blood: *Modern Maintenance Management,* American Management Association, New York, 1963.
6. L. Morrow: *Maintenance Engineering Handbook,* McGraw-Hill, New York, 1966.
7. E. T. Newbrough: *Effective Maintenance Management,* McGraw-Hill, New York, 1967.

Chapter 3

Utilities Management Reports

ROBERT C. COLLINS, P.E.
Manager, Plant Engineering and Maintenance, Xerox Corporation

INTRODUCTION

Classification

Electricity, telephone, gas (natural or manufactured), oil, coal, and water are the utilities basic to the operation of a modern industrial plant. There are other utilities that are what might be termed plant-generated utilities, since they are derived from the basic utilities. Compressed air, steam, steam condensate, heating and cooling, and even sewerage and antipollution devices can be categorized in this class.

Need for Utility Reports

In this day of energy crisis, the need for good substantial utility reporting is more than ever evident. The savings that result from energy conservation are becoming less important than the savings in energy accomplished for the benefit of the nation. The energy crisis has crystallized our thinking and led to the realization that the foreign view of the American as wasteful may be close to the truth.

In order to derive the greatest economic benefit from utilities and ensure that proper use of them is made, it is important that members of management receive detailed and comprehensive information on the operations involving the utilities existing in their facilities. Appropriate utilization of energy and economic considerations dictate the requirement for utility reports to upper management. From such reports it should be possible for management to make intelligent decisions concerning energy utilization, cost reductions, and other determinations, such as selection of equipment for process work, etc.

Responsibility

The responsibility for providing utilities reports rests with the organizations within the corporate structure that are involved with plant operations on a day-to-day basis. The expertise to prepare collected raw data for analysis is usually available within the organization.

The responsibility for collecting and analyzing the utility report can be centered at the corporate staff level, centralized plant engineering, or divisional plant engineering, or it may be done by someone in a facilities small plant operations. In a large, multiplant organization, the reports will generally be handled by the corporate staff, drawing on information from either central or divisional plant engineering personnel.

TYPES OF REPORTS

General

The simplest type of utility report is an inventory of how much gas, oil, etc., was expended, usually on a monthly basis. This could include the use of plant-generated utilities as well. A report of this nature merely provides a history of usage that can be utilized in preparing the budget for the following year's expenditure on the main sources of utility supply.

Simple utility reports can be correlated to degree-days for heating purposes to accent the cash flow of utility costs and provide a basis for future budgeting purposes. Process work will usually show as a constant unless sales are on an upswing.

In the case of multiple divisional use of utilities, metering of individual buildings and recorded results can determine proportionate shares of utility costs.

The simple report will not provide management with any kind of tool that can be used to spotlight areas for energy conservation or means of economizing. In order to control the outlay for utilities, management must have adequate reporting. This is necessary to determine the cause of variations from the norm so that corrective action can be taken. Measurement and evaluation are part of the decision-making process that will lead to and make possible the achievement of objectives. Management has a need to compare performance from period to period.

More sophisticated reports are required when emphasis is to be placed on energy conservation and attendant economic benefits. We can examine this type of report in more detail when we see it applied to the various utilities outlined previously.

No plant can operate efficiently unless an up-to-date inventory of utility facilities is maintained. Knowledge of operations and utility applications provides an insight into growth pattern. Unless adequate information is maintained, reserve capacity originally built into utility operations may be consumed without warning, with an attendant breakdown in ability to supply. Emergency plans for alternate sources cannot be prepared properly unless vigilance is maintained.

In examining utilities, management must have certain basic requisites in mind. Industrial strength rests in economizing energy in all forms and in many ways. Questions arise that can be answered only by examination of utilities as they present themselves for economic considerations.

Electric

Utility costs can show the way to extend the life of equipment by highlighting areas such as oversized equipment handling light loads, underloaded electric motors, or heat loss from buildings inadequately insulated. Maintenance costs could be lowered by programs instigated by reports of this nature.

It is possible, through the judicious use of plant operations, to schedule work so as to take advantage of utility rate structures by reducing or spacing demand loads.

Electricity used in nonessential areas, lighting left on after employees have vacated work stations, thermostats not reset for lower weekend temperatures, equipment left idling too long, etc.—all these waste energy that can never be recovered. Utility reports can bring some of these areas into focus so that programs can be established for the conservation of energy.

Compressed air Excessive pressure results in wasted energy. Factors such as clogged intake filters and incorrect usage of cooling water cause unnecessary power use and should be monitored. The aftercooler water coils need attention to prevent buildup of lime deposits, which will cut down heat transfer surface and require more water than necessary.

A certain amount of water in the compressed air itself may be acceptable, depending on the application. The use of such compressed air will reduce the requirement for drier application and result in savings.

Compressor loads should be monitored to provide only the amount of compressor operation necessary to take care of current loading.

Without proper maintenance, the distribution system may be sustaining power-robbing leaks.

In order to monitor for the economic operation of compressed air systems, data should be collected and reported periodically. This report should include the total amount of compressed air produced, power consumption, man-hours worked on operation and routine maintenance, the number and type of stations using compressed air, and the operation pressures involved. Fluctuations in these factors will point the way to properly directed investigation for the reduction of costs.

Lighting Lights left on unnecessarily burn costly energy. Too high a lighting level wastes energy. Lack of relamping preventive maintenance uses energy disproportionate to the lighting effect, as do improperly working ballasts.

Any worthwhile utility report should give indications of excessive uses of power. This will become more apparent as historical statistics show patterns of increase.

Although it is somewhat costly, separate metering of electricity for lighting purposes can be beneficial in providing selective data for investigative auditing. If it is not convenient or practical to meter separately, periodic measurements of voltage and amperage should be made in order provide data for analysis.

The electric power bill and periodic readings can be very significant tools for the plant engineer to work with, since they provide data to establish and analyze trends in demand loads, kilowatthour consumption, and power factor.

Induction Loads Motors operating unnecessarily when equipment is no longer functioning, aging motors accruing changing power factor, and air-handling-system motors unchecked for excessive operation are among the items that can be monitored through a utility report with periodically measured current readings. Again, historical data are the key to analysis of load variations and performance of inductive electrical loads.

Power factor is a measure of efficiency, and since lighting (except ballasts) and other resistive loads—such as electric heat—operate at or near 100 percent, attention must be paid to inductive loads. Many motors may have been selected to provide service for future loads that never materialized and may thus be running at less than full capacity. This inefficiency in usage can be corrected by reduction of motor size. Application of capacitors will bring the power factor up to provide full use of power.

The power company's rate structure should be studied to make sure advantage is being taken of power factor and demand rates.

Heating and Cooling

Factors in this area that can be monitored by utility reports are many and varied. Steam for heating and hot water, condensate return systems, electric heating elements, heat exchangers, ovens, furnaces, hot water boilers, refrigerant compressors, and cooling towers can be monitored and reported on to provide the information necessary for investigative activities. The point cannot be stressed too often that detailed historical data are the way to economy and full utilization of energy available. Trends can be observed as they develop, and the effects of various programs can be monitored.

Records should be maintained of boiler operation and thermal efficiencies, water chiller operation and flow rates, cooling towers, and condenser water, etc., with periodic checks on all measurable parameters.

Degree-day records kept by the local weather bureau office are available to provide concurrent information for anticipation of excessive load requirements for heating.

Gas

Gas used to heat domestic and process water, produce steam, and operate absorption air conditioning as well as in the course of integral product manufacture is usually supplied by gas companies who bring the gas to a metering point from which local distribution is made. Three types of services are available for which differing rates are charged:

1. Uninterruptable service, which guarantees continuous service despite commercial use restrictions at a premium rate.

2. Interruptable service, which may be cut off when restrictions on gas usage are effected, usually with a minimum warning period.

3. Combined service, which is based on a fixed amount of uninterruptable service with an additional amount supplied on an interruptable basis. The latter is usually the greater proportion of the contract.

In addition to metered gas supplied by a public utility, manufactured gas can be obtained in pressurized form. Records are easily kept concerning usage for either method of supply.

Oil and Coal

Oil delivered in bulk to storage tank demands little in the way of record keeping other than logging the number of gallons replaced. The amount of steam or hot water produced can be associated with quantities of oil or coal consumed to give an approximation of usage, thus enabling forecasts to be made based on demand.

Water

Water as a plant utility is used for domestic purposes in toilet rooms, kitchens, locker rooms; for industrial purposes in process work, cooling, boiler makeup, rinsing; for fire protection in metered water from a public utility and in company-owned backup systems with tank, fire pump, and sprinkler system. The excessive use of water, which is in reality a limited natural resource, is a factor to be controlled, and proper reports can be of benefit to management in this respect.

Control of water through utility reports can be very productive in energy saving programs. Regulation of water flow through heat exchangers by temperature-rise control will be of benefit. Recirculating water systems can be installed where practical, with ultrafiltration or reverse osmosis providing the means for recovery. Storage tanks should be maintained. Preventive maintenance on valves and distribution lines should be done. The utility report, if properly prepared, can provide the insight for investigation into causes of fluctuations in usage.

Collection of Information

In large plants, the data collected and information made available from current utility programs can reach monumental proportions. Assessment of this information will be accelerated if the data are computerized. Programming of the information and the preparation of plotted data will enable management to have the most up-to-date information available for decision making.

General Data Required

In examining utility reports, it should be kept in mind that any savings accomplished through the proper interpretation of the reports should be keyed to production. There are many processes, products, and company operations in which this may not be possible. Whichever way we look at these reports, the cost of obtaining the data, metering the utility, and the analysis of production impact should be included.

Evaluation of operations requires that costs be measured to enable the manager to compare relative performance from one period to another. This demands that the utility be reported on a unit basis, such as kilowatthours of electricity, gallons of oil, pounds of air, or cubic feet of gas. Consistency of measurement is imperative. Without this, the data can become meaningless.

By eliminating inaccuracy as much as possible at the point of data taking, the reliability of the data is increased. Variables such as weather and production changes should be carefully noted to minimize erroneous interpretation. The important point to keep in mind is that with accurate data at the source and notation of variables in the report, management can then recognize trends more clearly. A single report has no value without analyzable historical data. Control by exception is to be desired.

Selection of data required for the proper preparation of utility reports can be critical. If certain necessary data are not available, then the means must be found to obtain them. This could result in a major program of instrumentation, logging of equipment operations, calculations to determine actual heating and cooling loads, etc.

It will be necessary to conduct a survey of the utilities in the plant to determine the equipment involved. This survey should include such items as number and types of lighting fixtures, light intensity levels, number of electric motors of significant horsepower, and electric heating elements (such as reheat coils), transformers, battery chargers, air conditioning compressors, air compressors, ovens, furnaces, boilers, deaerators, water meters, electric meters, gas meters, etc.

With this information it will be possible to determine just how much data will be available and where to apply instrumentation to obtain data presently not known. Economy of operations will sometimes restrict the installation of equipment, and this requires judicious use of funds and selection of parameters to enable the most applicable data to be obtained.

Contributing conditions should be cataloged. Parameters of outside influences can be useful, such as the following, using monthly averages:

Maximum dry-bulb and wet-bulb temperatures
Minimum dry-bulb and wet-bulb temperatures
Precipitation
Approximate sunlight during working hours
Degree days—heating and cooling if available
Other unusual occurrences

These can all be helpful when analyzing data for trends.

General data on the facility and equipment are mandatory for examination. It is important that the following information be recorded:

Building
    Facility identity
    Location
    Floor space in square feet (for each type of use such as offices, manufacturing assembly, process areas, vacancies, etc.)
Compressed air
    Number and types of compressors
    Compressor rating—delivered pressure and cubic feet per minute
    Electric motor horsepower
    Other types
Electrical
    Primary voltage
    Substation voltage
    Number and types of transformers
        Power
        Lighting
        Other resistive loads
    Kilovoltampere capacity for each
    Voltage conversion for each
Heating and cooling
    Steam or water boilers
        Number of boilers (heaters or process)
        Type of fuel

    Operating pressures
    Rated input
    Continuous output in pounds per hour
  Boiler feed water systems
    Number and type ratings
    Ratings
  Water chillers
    Number and type
    Rated input
    Continuous output in gallons per minute at operating temperature (with rated temperature difference)
Gas
  Type of gas
  Specific gravity
  Heat value
  Yard pressure
  Number of meters and capacity
Oil
  Types of oil by number
  Specific gravity
  Heat value
  Number of storage tanks
  Storage capacity in gallons
Coal
  Type
  Proximate analysis
  Heat value
  Storage capacity in tons
Water
  Main size and pressure
  Number of meters, types, and capacity

Specific Data Required

Data obtained from individual operations, motors, and systems should be collected and combined in one comprehensive report totaling these individual items for an overall operations picture. Once the survey is made and the numbers and types of equipment are known, the data to be obtained from each source can be selected and the specific information that is deemed useful can be reported and collected.

Some of the specific data required are outlined in the following paragraphs. Other data may also be required, depending on the operation of individual plants; it should be an easy matter to have the plant engineer delineate the differences and make proper preparations.

Degree-days The best indicator of heating load (and cooling load—though not as well-cataloged as heating) is the degree-day. This is a unit established as the difference per degree between 65°F and the mean temperature below 65°F that exists for any one day. (The cooling degree-day is above 65°F.) If the mean temperature for a 24-hour day is, say, 45°F, then 20 degree-days of heating exist.

The system is used for estimating fuel consumption and is extremely reliable per year compared from year to year, although monthly variations do occur from year to year.

The information is available from the local U.S. Weather Bureau station on a daily basis, although it is not necessary to keep daily records, utility bills usually being prepared on a monthly basis.

Electrical

COMPRESSED AIR. Periodic checks should be made to determine the voltamperes and watt current draw of the electric motors driving the compressors. It is important to determine this when the compressor is operating at full load in order to form the basis of any resizing determination.

From the information obtained, it may be possible to plan on utilizing the compressor for additional loading.

The amount of air compressed can be determined by formulas available in most handbooks on compressed air provided that the following information is known:

Ambient air (intake)
  Temperature
  Pressure
Cooling water
  Intake temperature
  Discharge temperature
  Flow rate in gallons per minute
Compressed air
  Intercooler temperature
  Discharge temperature
Compressor
  Amperes
  Volts
  Watts
  Revolutions per minute

The cubic feet per minute of compressed air is of no use without knowledge of operating time. This can be determined by observing the operation over a period of time or by installing a running time meter. The latter will have an additional benefit in that it will be useful in preventive maintenance programming.

LIGHTING. Metering the electrical energy used for lighting separately may be detrimental to the budget, since examination of the rate structure usually will indicate a penalty upon smaller users of electricity. It would seem that this system is designed to encourage wasteful use of electricity rather than to reward the conservation of energy.

The possibility of accurate record keeping without separate meters is remote. However, an approximation of lighting loads can be obtained if the following information is known:

Area illuminated, in square feet
Type of illumination
Number of various types and watt ratings
Number and rating of ballasts
Record of hours of operation based on regular work hours, shift work, etc.

This information can be used in conjunction with the electric bill to assess the power used in lighting the facility.

INDUCTION LOADS. Again, if separate metering is possible or practicable, the data obtained will be valuable in determining the effect of the power-factor-prone portion of the electrical load.

In large plants, it may well be impossible to catalog and test every motor; but the significantly large motors can be singled out for examination. This examination can be set up for periodic review of the motor to check on operational efficiency, to determine if it is adequately sized, and to aid in preventive maintenance on motors in general use.

Measurements and data taken of motors in operation should include the following:

Amperes
Voltage
Watts
Type of motor (direct-current, single-phase, three-phase)
Horsepower rating
Full-load ampere rating (FLA)

Comparison with the measured amperes and the rated FLA will indicate how well loaded the motor is and may indicate a reason for reducing the size or increasing the load to take advantage of this.

The measured amperes multiplied by the voltage and compared with a wattmeter reading will indicate the power factor and may reveal the need for a capacitor to increase the useful consumption of energy.

The electric utility charges for demand plus normal energy charges. "Demand" can be defined as the highest average load in a given period, usually 15 minutes. Because of this high load factor, utilities charge a premium to underwrite the additional cost for larger equipment that they are obliged to install to handle this load. Reducing this demand is a desirable objective.

TYPICAL ELECTRIC RATE.   A typical public utility electric rate for commercial and industrial service is comprised of the following charges:

Monthly rate (subject to fossil fuel adjustment)

Kilowatt demand charge . . .
  First 50 kilowatts of demand or less, $158
  All in excess of 50 kilowatts of demand, $0.0202 per kilowatt
Reactive demand charge . . .
  All reactive kilovoltamperes in excess of 50% of kilowatt
    demand, $0.24 per kilovoltampere
Energy charge . . .
  Any part of first 50,000 kWh, $0.01804 per kilowatthour
  All in excess of 50,000 kWh, $0.01381 per kilowatthour

It is easy to see that the demand charge can be 50 percent of the total power bill. This leads to the decisive conclusion that large economies can be realized in control of demand in plant consumption of electricity.

The application of a demand recording meter to the power lines provides a chart which indicates the time and size of demands. The power company will usually provide such a meter upon request.

If a demand recorder or other measuring device is not available, a recording ammeter can be used with nearly equal results if applied over several 24-hour periods. However, this requires considerable effort.

The log of total amperes and time will give signal indications when peak loads are incurred and, with individual checking of suspected loads, can provide the means of spreading out the load, reducing demand and, consequently, lowering the rate charged.

New developments in the electronics industry have made available a device which can automatically monitor the demand load in a plant and, by a staging sequence, turn off preselected loads in a priority mode to reduce demand pulses and concurrently turn these loads back on service as the demand reaches preset minimums. The loads have to be carefully selected from equipment that can be cut back without detriment to plant operations. Such loads as electric furnaces, water heaters, air-conditioning fans, large motors, and compressors are the types of loads for which this system is applicable.

Heating and cooling   Information obtained from any individual piece of equipment is useful for a variety of reasons. Data taken can be used to determine efficiency of the machine for possible performance improvement, for preventive maintenance programs, and for utility consumption.

The equipment to be examined for utility measurement should be that used to generate hot water or steam for heating or process purposes; cooling water or brine for air conditioning, freezing, or other process work; cooling towers; large compressors; RO (Reverse Osmosis) units; etc.—in other words, anything that may be considered significant in the overall operation of the plant.

Following is an example of the type of periodic data needed from equipment to provide data for calculation:

Water chiller
  Chilled water
    Flow rate
    Inlet temperature
    Outlet temperature
  Condenser water
    Flow rate
    Inlet temperature
    Outlet temperature
  Amperes (assuming electric drive)
    Compressor
    Pump motor
    Fan motor
  Voltage
  Watts
    Compressor
    Pump motor
    Fan motor

Nameplate data

Operating time

Gas, oil, and coal quantities are obtained from utility meters or measurement by gallons or pounds delivered, the data being obtained from actual power plant operations reports.

A typical report should contain the information in tabular form, with data as shown below:

	Previous month	Current month	Year to date
Personnel costs			
Watch engineers			
Power plant maintenance			
Operating engineers			
Supervision			
Allowances			
Indirect costs			
Material costs			
Chemicals			
Coal (in tons at dollars per ton)			
Ash removal			
Gas (in cubic feet at dollars per cubic foot)			
Oil (in gallons at dollars per gallon)			
Consumables			
Maintenance costs			
Facilities			
Motors			
Equipment			
Pumps			
Sewage treatment			
Antipollution devices			
Other utilities			
Water, including sewage assessment			
Electricity, including fossel fuel assessment			
Compressed air			
Steam			
Chilled water			
Heating hot water			
Fixed charges			
Insurance			
Depreciation			
Taxes			

This information can be obtained by competent operating engineers familiar with the equipment and costs of operation.

The value of the specific data obtained is in its use in determining local corrections to deviations found by examining the overall utilities in context with each other and measured by productivity, man-hours of labor, or costs.

The main components of a plant's utilities are ultimately manifested in the utility bill, and this is where attention should be initially directed.

APPLICATION

Planning

The basic purpose in preparing and examining utilities reports is to apply the information in planning and economic determinations. These reports are of value in themselves, but comparison of trends can aid tremendously by providing a useful picture of the utilities operation. One such method, which is considered by many to be the best indicator, is the composite graph. This is the clearest way to present historical data, and it provides an invaluable tool to assess the plants utilization of energy. It can also be used to evaluate overall efficiencies and provide the basis for forecasting the utility budget.

A typical composite graph (Exhibit A) shows the realtionship of the degree-day curve to the consumption of gas as the heating utility. Electricity and chilled water indicate a relationship with degree-days opposite to the heating utility, which is indicative of the air-conditioning load.

If possible, depending upon the type of manufacturing, the composite graph should indicate production units or dollar profits as related to the utilities.

The graph and a report on the existing utilities capabilities should make possible intelligent interpretation in order to forecast short- and long-range planning needs. Empirical data can be obtained using the relationship indicated between curves on the graph and is useful in prognosis of utility requirements.

This type of utility analysis will help management to determine such things as need for new facilities, expansion of existing facilities, whether second or third shifts may be an acceptable means of increasing production, etc.

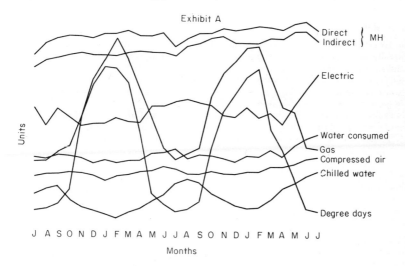

Exhibit A

Economic and Energy Conservation Consideration

The utility report can be used to provide information for effective cost reduction programs, waste control, and energy savings directed toward economic expenditure of our natural resources.

The report can highlight waste areas, and plant engineering management should develop means of examining this area.

For example, if the report indicates an excessive use of electricity that can be traced to lighting, steps should be taken to determine how the excess is being expended and corrective action should be taken. Are the excesses being expended during working hours, at lunchtime, or in unoccupied areas? Are they being expended after the normal workday is over?

Many areas of plant operations can be examined to determine excessive lighting levels originally designed for, but unnecessary for, actual use. The simple expedient of removing bulbs from selected fixtures can provide the means to reduce illumination to acceptable levels.

The suspected areas can be inspected quickly and at random, the responsibility being assigned to a supervisor. Instructions may be given to security to turn off all lights that are not necessary. Plant engineers should ascertain if more than adequate lighting levels exist and recommend means to reduce the levels.

Measures should be taken to ensure that cleaning personnel do not use unnecessary lights and that they do not leave on the lights that are not safety oriented.

The consumption of compressed air can be monitored to determine effective pressures to be used for various operations. Perhaps the pressure of air in blowoff stations is excessive and should be reduced. Air may be used in bootleg drying operations. Vacuum cleaning may be substituted in many cases for compressed air blowoff; hot-air blowers are effective replacements for compressed air used for drying purposes, etc.

The consumption of water for a multitude of plant purposes can be monitored to check on excessive water use. Water used as a cooling medium for heat exchangers should be regulated automatically with temperature-differential controllers. An inspection should be made to determine where the application of controls would be effective in reducing waste during shutdown periods for dip-tank cooling or heating coils, process air conditioning, or water-quenching systems.

No program of this nature is effective unless the unnecessary operation of motors for all purposes is monitored. Equipment left running when the operator is gone, during lunch periods, after working hours, or on weekends consumes electricity that can reach considerable portions. Motors for equipment that requires warmup time for expeditious operation should be exempt.

Conclusion

The trend in plant operations is toward the plant of the future, where utilities will be centrally monitored and controlled from banks of computers and consoles designed to maintain their economic use.

Utility conservation programs will be rapidly assessed as to value of results commensurate with capital outlay. Directions for determining concentration of energies in utility management can be quickly ascertained.

No program will be effective without the dedication of all personnel involved. Data plugged into computers are only as good as the programmer's input, and that input is only as effective as the people who provide it and the instrumentation from which it is obtained.

Chapter **4**

Engineering Management Reports

RICHARD RYAN, P.E.
Plant Engineer, Hamilton Standard Division of United Technologies Corporation

INTRODUCTION

Plant engineering activities cover a wide spectrum. In many plants, this encompasses not only the design of buildings, roadways, and similar brick-and-mortar-type structures but also includes design of utilities, maintenance of machines, machine modifications, design of equipment and test rigs, etc. In general, the techniques used to control the design phase of any particular project can be managed in a format similar to that described in this chapter. Most major projects run into difficulties in initial stages of studying, designating, and setting up the general area of project management. This area has received far less attention than perhaps the actual construction phases, in which PERT and other processes are widely used. However, the planning stage is most important to the success or failure of any job. The planning process must have the same management techniques of planning, coordinating, and measuring results applied.

GENERAL DESCRIPTION OF DUTIES

Engineering activities can largely be related to three areas:

Study Programs These initial steps could be subcategorized into main area activities. The main study phase would include planning of new projects, conceptual design, and selecting of alternative actions. Many of these activities should be reviewed not only by plant engineering supervision but also by operating personnel for adequacy to perform the intended functions. The second study phase should seek solutions to existing problems. This is probably highlighted more today due to the energy crisis than has been apparent in past years. The requirements for change could come about because of obsolescence or a change of one of the previous criteria—as, in the case of the energy crisis, that of fuel no longer being a relatively cheap and plentiful commodity. A third area of study deals with forecasting facilities requirements (facilities include utilities, floor space utilization, and utilization of equipment). Forecasting is a risky business since long-range forecasting is not an exact science. Many firms have experienced an overcrowding due to not building soon enough. Even worse, but rare, are the cases where a just completed building lies idle. Obtain *top management's thinking and policy when preparing forecasts to improve outputs.*

Design   Design activity includes concept identification in general layouts, final estimates, and detailed design of both new facilities and modifications. Details of construction drawings, specification writing, and bid instructions are included in this phase.

Project control   Project engineering activity includes cost determinations, schedule control, and control over the quality of the material and workmanship.

DESIGN CRITERIA

In all engineering activities, the following design criteria should be used as management guidelines and evaluated by the design team. The main criteria are:

1. *Customers' needs.* A design effort for a customer's needs must be provided; e.g., when the maintenance department needs to replace obsolete equipment or a building is required for a new project.

2. *Costs.* Both initial and long-range costs must be evaluated in light of inflation. Knowledge of annual unit maintenance and operating costs and management return-on-investment objectives is essential for design cost estimates.

3. *Legal requirements.* These include pollution control regulations, zoning requirements, and any requirements of the specific product under test or construction such as requirement for a license from a state agency for the installation of a still. Obviously, conformance to OSHA, fire code, and other regulations is mandatory.

4. *Esthetic value.* This is an intangible quantity that must be considered in obtaining acceptance by operating personnel.

Perhaps the best way to evaluate and set design criteria guidelines is to follow a checklist indicating the anticipated lead times required to obtain approval for each of the various functions. The time span required to obtain a zone change is an example, or your particular state might have a requirement that 90 days be permitted to the air pollution enforcement agency to evaluate any new stack discharges. The checklist serves best as a communication link between management and the designer. It shows that these factors have been taken into account and that acceptance or approval has been gained along the way.

TEN STEPS FOR DESIGN AND CONSTRUCTION PROGRAM ACCOMPLISHMENT

A majority of all design and construction programs can be accomplished in ten specific steps. The path and forms used in the steps related to this chapter are discussed below.

1. Project scheduling and assignment
2. Investigation
3. Conceptual review
4. Design and specifications
5. Design and specification review
6. Bidding
7. Construction award/estimate review
8. Construction supervision
9. Project review
10. Project closure

FLOW PATH FOR WORK AUTHORIZATION AND REPORTING

The method by which work inputs are received, processed through the design system, and brought to ultimate completion will vary from company to company. In general, the best approach is to have a designer or team of designers work from initial concepts determination through completion. In many instances the preliminary work, gathering of source data inputs, and working out of alternative actions for future study are best handled by senior engineering personnel qualified to screen inputs and provide direction for final design team efforts.

THE INPUT DOCUMENT

Figure 1 describes a typical flow path. The most important part of any project is ensuring that the customer knows what the needs and alternative courses of action are and is capable of justifying those needs. The best method, in this regard is a written communication between senior operating personnel and senior plant engineering personnel, followed by discussion of alternative courses of action and a redefinition of original inputs.

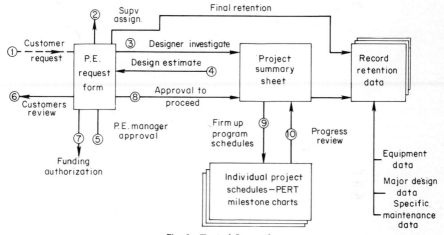

Fig. 1 Typical flow path.

Generally, most operating personnel have little or no concept of design elements and costs involved or the range of alternative possibilities that exists. Thus the final results and final inputs may be considerably different than the original written communication. The document for work input is the plant engineering request form (Fig. 2). The job number is assigned by the plant engineering department recipient. The sender completes the block indicating the request type, reason for the program, initial justification, and approval by a department head. The lower portion of the form is intended for plant engineering department use as a communication both internally and for final communication to the operating department. Purposes for plant engineering request forms are:

1. To provide an initial communication. This is, perhaps, the most important function in that it forces requesters to do several things, the first of which is to organize their thoughts and put them on a piece of paper to communicate to someone who may not share their knowledge of what they are requesting.

2. It arranges type of units and description in some logical degree of request priority, as well as providing a description of what may be the final form of completion.

3. The requirement for operating management approval indicates that the requester has obtained approval from his or her department for requesting expenditure of funds necessary to perform preliminary design or study work. That, together with the justification, assists in determining the relative priority of this request or compared

to requests of other department heads for purposes of plant engineering units assigned. Classification of the request also provides estimate as to priority. For example, a safety item would normally take precedence over rearrangement or other activity. The lower part of the form for plant engineering use provides an internal communication:

To the design group authorizing initial effort, transmitting basic information policy, and, perhaps, giving additional guidelines as to design criteria or background information.

The designer having made the initial investigation can communicate a summary of the findings and recommended course of action. This would normally include a

PLANT ENGINEERING PROJECT REQUEST	JOB NUMBER	

REQUEST TYPE

PLANNING

REARRANGEMENT □ NEW FACILITIES □ COST ESTIMATE □ SAFETY □

DESCRIPTION

DATE _____

REQUESTED
BY _____

PHONE X_____

REQUESTED COMPLETION
DATE _____

DEPT. GROUP
TO BE CHARGED
_____
(SEE NOTE 1)

REASON   EXPLAIN _____
NEW   COST   MANAGEMENT   CONTRACTUAL
PROGRAM □ SAVING □ DIRECTIVE   □ REQUIREMENT □ OTHER □_____

JUSTIFICATION

APPROVED BY
DEPT HEAD _____
TITLE _____ DATE _____

FOR P.E. DEPT USE ONLY	ASSIGNED TIME	ACTUAL TIME
ASSIGNMENTS _____ DATE_____		

INITIAL INVESTIGATION

RECOMMENDED ACTION

		APPROVAL	
EST. - COST ±20% DESIGN TIME	HRS.	P.E.	DEPT. HEAD

NOTE 1 – ALL REARRANGEMENTS AT COST OF REQUESTING DEPARTMENTS.
         ASSIGN WT ACCOUNT NO. WHEN LAYOUT COMPLETED.
         INSTALLATION OF NEW EQUIPMENT CHARGED TO DEPARTMENT HAVING APPROPRIATION
         FUNDS.

Fig. 2   Plant engineering project request.

sketch of the concepts, the alternatives, the results of any additional information gleaned from going back to the operating departments and, finally, the estimate of the cost involved in a particular project and any other important comments.

This estimate and concept must be approved by the plant engineering department and returned to the operating department to aid in their evaluation of the alternative courses of action and the impact the various alternatives might have on their particular operations. At this time, the cost estimate should be a preliminary estimate of plus or minus 20 percent accuracy. This recognizes that initial concepts and estimates have a high fatality rate; therefore an enormous amount of time should not be spent in engineering design activities for obtaining a precise estimate on a request doomed to failure. ("I had no idea it would cost $51,493.35!")

The plant engineering project request form therefore serves as a two-way communications link between the operating department to plant engineering and for plant engineering's response. The job number applied by plant engineering allows for recording the document in its assignment to an individual for initial design review; the document can thus form the beginning of what may ultimately be an approved project. Thus one document remains in the file for future reference, together with summary of background information necessary to continue the program.

PRELIMINARY WORK REVIEW AND APPROVAL

The project summary form (Fig. 3) aids in following the project through the request phase until ultimate completion. This highlights further work, including completion of a specific step—initial design concepts. It indicates planned design man-hours, construction time, and overall schedule. This form, however, contains only those projects actively being worked on. Once a project request has been completed, but no immediate action is pending (for whatever reason), it would be removed from the project summary. The project summary contains a description of the activity and a project number. Further detail, of course, is available on the project request form. The initial work and review stage would involve making the final estimates, preparing approvals for funds, and sched-

PROJECT SUMMARY

Project No.	Description/title	Eng.	Schedule			Cost				Remarks
			Time Expended	Est. % compl.	Target compl.	$ Authorized	$ Expended	% Complete	Target compl.	

Fig. 3 Project summary form.

uling the design activity. The project summary is intended to provide an overview to management of projects being worked, location status, and when they are to be completed. Details of actual construction would be found in other reports.

From the initial review and approval through the completion stage, the project summary serves as a weekly or biweekly report from the design group to the plant engineer, indicating the status of the particular planned activity. The designer's weekly report should involve no more than the designer indicating "on time" for each of the various projects. However, in the event that does not occur, the specific projects in trouble could be explained either verbally or with an attached report. Before the final management approval of a project, a detailed master plan for each project should be prepared, showing the planned design, construction, and administrative target dates. This detailed master plan should contain sufficient information to plot each design team member's activities in terms of the number of hours for each phase.

DESIGN ACTIVITY

The design phase actually begins when all approvals have been received and a detailed master plan is prepared and approved. At this point, the individual designer—or team—is given a specific assignment, general design criteria, and firm targets on cost, quality, and timeliness. The master plan then becomes the short interval scheduling plan. The team leader can follow and report design activity, forecasted work, and backlog work on the project summary sheet and the weekly operating plan. These individual projects can be highlighted for exception on the project summary. The project summary could be either a constantly updated report sheet, wall chart, or computer runoff.

PREPARATION OF PROJECT MANAGEMENT

The work accomplishment and cost expenditures reported in the project are the start of project management. If a PERT chart was not made at the time the job was initiated, this is the appropriate time to prepare such a chart.

The first step in the construction phase is to obtain bids and estimates to ensure that data are available on costs of various elements, better ways of doing that type of work, etc. Therefore, on the initial construction bid package, bids should indicate that the contractor will provide a work breakdown in accordance with the work breakdown structure as outlined in the master schedule. Thus, when a project is completed, or at the time when a bid is received, it can be compared with the original milestone target to ensure that the total program cost can be met at completion. Project management reports on construction, therefore, consist of reports on time—by means of the work accomplishment chart—and costs compared to each of the specific milestones to indicate specific problems foreseen in the future (e.g., sheet metal contractors' strike possibilities, etc.).

RETENTION OF RECORDS/FEEDBACK

A most important part of project management deals with records retention. Documents of prime importance include the original plant engineering request form that outlines the basic goals to be achieved and an actual description of what happened, together with other pertinent information. To evaluate performance of the project for future corrective action, detailed cost breakdowns related to factors that could be used in current construction estimates should be included. For example, the cost of dry wall construction could be computed on the basis of cost per running foot installed, or something similar, to update current projects that are estimating similar types of construction. Other records that are important to retain are specifics on equipment installed in a plant. At the time equipment is purchased, sufficient sets of maintenance and installation instructions should be obtained. These should be turned over to the maintenance department to aid that department in keeping the equipment in good condition. The plant engineering department should use a system whereby each piece of equipment is identified by a category number. Information on the particular equipment, so numbered, should be kept both in the engineering department and in the maintenance department. Drawings referencing the equipment numbers are assigned by the project manager and should appropriately cross-reference equipment installations.

Chapter **5**

Construction Management Reports

ERIC M. BERGTRAUN
Manager, Plant Engineering and Maintenance, National Semiconductor Corporation

INTRODUCTION

This chapter is devoted to the management reports placed in the hands of the plant engineer, representing the owner, in that engineer's duties of supervising facility construction. The plant engineer may be known by many different titles, such as project manager, project administrator, project engineer, construction plant engineer, clerk of the work, or resident engineer. For the purpose of this chapter, the plant engineer will be referred to as the project manager.

The project manager in a modern firm, when placed in charge of a construction project, has responsibility for maintaining complete records and documentation during accomplishment of the construction project.

Construction management reports—together with detailed records, correspondence, and various submitted reports—provide complete documentation of the project and afford means for effectively controlling the progress and quality of work, the budget, and any contractual obligations.

At project completion, these reports and other pertinent information provide complete historical construction project documentation. Pertinent information in most projects will include meetings and conference reports, site plans and surveys, design criteria and scope of work, preliminary estimates and budget, plans and specifications, general condition, contracts and subcontractor agreements, letters of intent and purchase orders, shop/working drawings and submittals, change orders and budget adjustments, as-built drawings and instruction folders, layout information, schedule and PERT charts, project-cost buildup, construction progress reports, insurance and safety reports, certification and inspection reports, and the final acceptance of the project.

CONSTRUCTION MANAGEMENT REPORT OBJECTIVES

The construction management team in plant engineering is that group which deals with the transition from idea, plan, concept, and design to a physical plant and facility. Reports from this organization, along the tedious road from developing a plan to the final occupancy of the facility, will include the following:

1. Prior to the start of actual construction, the concept of the project is defined in detail and a budget estimate is developed to provide a completely documented project proposal.

2. When the budget has been approved and work is started, the project cost is controlled by daily records and buildup of actual expenditures.

3. Daily, weekly, and monthly progress reports provide good job communication information for all personnel interested and concerned with the construction project.

4. A visual record of the availability and scheduled arrival at the jobsite of capital equipment and critical construction material, with the ordering, shipping, and arrival dates.

5. Complete diary that will provide pertinent job data and also historical documentation for the management of future construction projects.

6. Documentation for legal purposes of any important event in connection with the project.

7. Recordkeeping requirements under the William-Steiger Occupational Safety and Health Act of 1970. This OSHA requirement includes accident reports, safety instruction and regulations, minutes and attendance sign-up sheet of safety meetings.

It is the project manager's responsibility to administer all these and many other reports.

TYPES OF MANAGEMENT REPORTS

General Reports

In general, most management reports will be handwritten or typed on letterheads or regular paper, on readily available or specially designed forms. Two other ways of implementing a good reporting system, described below, have become increasingly popular.

Tape-recorded Reports

Modern project engineers, superintendents, engineers, and inspectors make good use of solid-state tape-recorders. They carry these miniature machines in their pockets on the job, ready to record a project meeting or dictate into the recorder important findings during inspections or when they find special problems and safety infractions.

Reporting by Photos, Slides, and Movies

Old sayings tell us that "A picture is worth a thousand words" and "Every picture can tell a story." Modern project managers keep photographic records of the progress on their jobs. This has become such a valuable tool that just about every plant engineering, design engineering, or construction office keeps Polaroid cameras ready and available at all times. This is the handiest way of having a picture available right away. It provides immediate records that can be used for legal purposes and also as a proof that certain things were done or have been neglected. A series of Polaroid shots can provide a continuous construction photo record. Of course, any camera can be used. There can be a mix of black-and-white and color pictures. On larger jobs, besides these amateur pictures, it is the practice to have a professional photographer take official photos at regular intervals. It is important to mark on the back of these prints such important information as:

Project name and number
Project title
Firm's name
Description of picture
Date and time
Special notes

It is best to mount pictures in either a photo album or on special pages of a three-ring binder, complete with the above information. This can become a very important and valuable progress record of a construction project. Some companies also keep complete 35-mm slide files and even moving-picture records of their projects. This is very effective when a presentation has to be made to the board of directors, at annual meetings, or for a group of customers. This is also most valuable for training purposes or when it is necessary to recreate or look at certain phases of performed work.

OUTLINE OF CONSTRUCTION MANAGEMENT REPORTS IN THIS CHAPTER

The aim of this chapter is to provide the reader with an insight into the techniques used by contracting organizations and plant engineering offices in preparing different management reports for various construction projects. Examples of available reports will be described and illustrated. Contractors are used to working with such reports and have them available for their clients when required. Such reports are also frequently used by architects, engineers, and consultants. Unless plant engineers request these reports, they might never be provided. Reports and records will vary to some extent with the size of the project, but essentially they will be very similiar in nature. These reports and records are important enough that organizations like AIA (American Institute of Architects), AGCA (Associated General Contractors of America), NECA (National Electrical Contractors Association), and others provide ready forms to aid their members. Large contracting associations, engineering offices, and plant engineering departments have developed their own forms.

The majority of all reports, estimates, and records have as their main objective that of keeping the construction project running smoothly and on time. Above all, they help to assure that the owner receives the proper return and value for funds expended and that the project is within budget. The reports also provide the information needed by architects, engineers, consultants, and concerned managers to provide administrative control of the project. This control concerns itself mainly with the time that certain events took place, the cost of labor and material, the type of material and equipment used, the way certain jobs are done, and the legal aspect of the circumstances arising at any construction project. Depending on the size of the project, the manager will be able to keep records and make reports with a minimum of clerical help. Good managers are those who develop their own reporting and recording systems. Such a system should be simple and streamlined enough that the paper work will help control the project but does not overburden the manager's administrative ability. Reports are the tools by which the project manager informs management and coordinates the contractors on the job.

CONSTRUCTION PROGRESS REPORTING

The project manager, alone or with the help of staff, should maintain complete records and reports during the history of the construction project. As a supervisor, the project manager will demand and collect various construction reports from different contractors and support people performing the work. One of the manager's prime jobs will be to keep company management completely informed by providing weekly detailed reports that will record job progress. These reports—together with various records, correspondence, and other documentation—will provide the administrative control, assuring the owner that the project is on time, meets all specifications, and remains financially within the approved budget. This will show the owner that a proper return on investment is being received. Following is a brief rundown of the more important reports that will provide good construction progress reporting.

Site Progress Meetings

These weekly meetings provide job communications, motivate the different contractors, and keep up the momentum. Their main purpose is to coordinate efforts of all superintendents, foremen, and management personnel. When special problems arise, the project manager requests attendance of the architect, engineers, and special consultants. The project manager should hold these meetings at the same time each week and should ensure that an agenda is always used. The project manager can maintain good control by being well organized, firm, explicit, and brief. Minutes of the meetings should be taken and their distribution expedited. Action items should be clearly shown, indicating expected date of start and completion.

Correspondence

All communications between the project manager, contractors, architect, engineers, building inspectors, suppliers, etc., should be carefully recorded. This is usually done by speedy memos or transmittals. The correspondence file will have sections for incoming mail, copies of letters sent, copies of speedy letters, submittals, inspection reports, etc.

Construction reports

Various operations will require special reports that will be made on regular forms recording time, volume, quality, and special results. Such reports will be for concrete pours, concrete tests, soil tests, pile driving, steel erection, weld tests, material inspection, high-voltage tests, and others.

Field Reports

Surveys and inspections are usually kept in field notebooks that supplement the job diary. The surveyor's notebook, concrete mix control, tilt-up layout, etc., fall under this heading.

Job Diary

This is the most important construction report and job record. In it the superintendent records everything that occurs on the project. These diaries should be maintained by each individual contractor on a large construction project and will include important information like weather, general progress, number of workers, report on subcontractors, equipment and material deliveries, unusual events, accidents, visitors, inspections, conferences, telephone conversations, special instructions, safety items, etc. A job diary sample is shown in Fig. 1.

Design Details

Design engineers will keep special notes of their specific designs. These notes will include design criteria, specifications, and the final design calculations.

Weekly Project Manager Progress Report

Based on the various daily reports received, the project manager will be able to give his management a formal weekly and monthly progress report. These reports will summarize the daily reports and occurrences and will include pertinent information contained in diaries and daily job files. Progress photographs and charts will often accompany the monthly report.

Equipment and Tool Records

A major factor of construction costs is the use, rental, and purchase of equipment and tools. The project manager must insist on proper management of this important cost item and must decide whether to purchase or lease certain tools and equipment. Sometimes it pays to purchase some tools and equipment that would be used by the contractors over a long period of time. These items, at the completion of the job, can be turned over to the maintenance department. In any case, the project manager must insist that contractors be responsible for equipment and tools and that idle leased equipment is speedily removed from the lease list. The project manager must also insist on

JOB DIARY
RUDOLPH & SLETTEN, INC.

Weather ______ Report No. ______

Number of working/calendar days left to complete job ______ Co. Job No. ______ Date ______

Job ______

WORK BY GENERAL CONTRACTOR

WORK BY SUBCONTRACTORS

VISITORS

COMMENTS

SUBS No. of Men	TRADE	O.H.R. No. of Men
	Carpenter Foremen	
	Carpenters	
	Carpenters' Apprentices	
	Labor Foremen	
	Laborers	
	Concrete Finishers	
	Bricklayers	
	Iron Workers	
	Plasterers	
	Electricians	
	Roofers	
	Rein. Steel Workers	
	Marble	
	Tile	
	Terrazzo	
	Plumbers	
	Heating	
	Sheet Metal	
	Painters	
	Glass Setters	
	Equipment Operators	
	Superintendent	
	Asst. Superintendent	
	Timekeeper	
	TOTAL	
	Equipment:	

DIRECTIONS:

Note work behind schedule and reasons for same; also when it can be brought up on time

Note any important events; also names of representatives of the Architects, Owners or Company who visited job.

Send two copies to office. Keep one on job.

SUPERINTENDENT ______

(Diary must be signed by Superintendent)

FORM # 300

Fig. 1 Job diary.

a good maintenance program for equipment and tools, seeing to it that equipment is covered by insurance for loss and liability for injury to people and damage to property.

The following are forms and reports used for equipment and tool records:

Tool and Equipment Inventory Rental Schedule
Tool and Equipment Requisition
Tool and Equipment Return Record
Tool and Equipment Preventive Maintenance Record
Tool and Equipment Insurance Record

Material Control

The control of construction material is probably one of the most important factors contributing to the success of a construction project. The best superintendent is helpless without a good flow of material and capital equipment for the particular project. Consequently, on larger jobs, contractors provide purchasing agents and expediters in the field. Usually the contractor's office provides the bill of material and bidding of subcontracts, material, and equipment. Once this has been done, it will become the responsibility of the field office to place the purchase order, negotiate delivery, and provide follow-up expediting. The field-office telephones will be kept busy checking on orders and expediting deliveries all the way to the factories and production lines. It is the purchaser's responsibility to see that all equipment and material is ordered in time for delivery to the jobsite when required for construction. The efficiency of good construction management starts with a well-designed, properly filled out purchase order.

Expediting procedures have to be established. Most of this can be achieved by a well-designed master form that includes important information like the following:

1. Date order received by vendor, name of contact
2. Date order received in manufacturer's engineering department
3. Date when shop drawings and submittals were received on the job
4. Date when shop drawings and submittals were approved and sent back to factory
5. Date when order was entered in factory production schedule (depends on receipt of approvals)
6. Periodical dates when factory schedule has to be checked for progress reporting
7. Factory schedule date of completion
8. Factory shipping date
9. Transportation routing schedule
10. Arrival date on jobsite
11. Inspection and acceptance on jobsite, storage location
12. Date when actually needed for construction

This master form is very often displayed on the wall of the construction trailer, side by side with construction bar and CPM charts.

Expediting never stops, since the construction schedule is built around delivery needs and promises by suppliers to perform at a specific time. Even when a factory reports that the material has been shipped, it is very important to get transportation routing information and to follow up on the delivery. Some very critical items might get shipped on time, but if there is no follow-up they can get lost or hung up in some transportation terminal. The project manager must insist on complete expediting and very detailed material status reports. The manager must also have a very good handle on expediting the approval of submittals and shop drawings. It is not uncommon for valuable days and weeks to be lost in the approval process. Another important point is efficient material handling on the jobsite, including inspection and acceptance by the contractor and project manager. This is critical when a damaged shipment is received, resulting in insurance claims and on-site repairs.

The next important step is to store material and equipment on the site. The project manager and construction supervisors must know were all items are stored. They must also make sure that everything is protected from weather, fire, theft, and parts removal. This requires a good inventory and location system, periodic safety and fire protection inspections, and an around-the-clock security system that can never relax.

Labor Control

Of all costs incurred on a construction project, the payroll cost is of greatest concern to plant engineering management. Since so many contracts are negotiated on a time and material basis, the control of the construction manpower must be a major item for the project manager to look after. The manager's main concern will be to choose contractors who:

1. Control manpower well. By carefully providing good manpower planning to staff jobs, over- or understaffing can be avoided. Special attention must be given during the periods of setting up the field operation and demobilizing the job.
2. Have the best available personnel. This holds true for the project management as well as skilled and unskilled labor required for construction.
3. Provide good orientation, training, and personnel development for their employees. This is achieved by a good industrial relations effort on the contractor's part. A well-motivated employee group is essential for the success of any construction job.
4. Use an efficient and simple payroll system that provides accounting by man-hours and their costs by categories. This will help in evaluating the initial cost estimate. This is usually provided by an electronic data processing (EDP) system. This system requires good timekeeping support and job reporting.
5. Keep a running account of actual labor hours vs. estimated labor hours. This will alert the construction management when the project starts slipping.

To maintain good labor control, the project manager has to monitor economical staffing, a good timekeeping and payroll control system, weekly labor reports, and comparison report of actual vs. estimated labor hours. This can be accomplished by obtaining the following data:

Attendance records
Payroll change notices
Weekly time cards
Labor man-hours reports (Fig. 2)
Estimate comparison report
Certified payroll

LABOR MAN HOURS REPORT DATA

ADD MAN HOUR CODE ☐   CHANGE MAN HOUR CODE ☐ (INSTRUCTIONS ON REVERSE SIDE)
(or new job)
OFFICE CODE_____ JOB NO _____   JOB NAME _____

ENGINEER_____ JOB LOCATION_____

CHANGE NUMBER _____ DATE_____

MAN HOUR CODE	DESCRIPTION (Limit to 30 Spaces)	MAN HOURS ESTIMATED				MAN HOURS TO DATE				% EST COMP
		ADD	10ns	DEDUCT	10ns	ADD	10ns	DEDUCT	10ns	

D-027 REVISED 6-73   TOTAL HOURS ⟶

APPROVED_____

☐ CHECK IF OPTIONAL CRAFT TITLES CODED ON REVERSE SIDE.

Fig. 2a Labor man-hours report.

Change Orders

It would be ideal if a construction project could be completed without any changes. Since almost any project is subject to changes before it is completed, the project manager has to be prepared to handle these changes and include them in management reports.

Even if these changes reflect no cost change, they must be well documented and approved if they alter the plans and specifications of the project and have to be picked up in the as-built drawings. Whenever a change alters the contract price, a formal change-order request must be initiated with all necessary support documents (e.g., drawings, sketches, submittals, and specifications). The contractor will price the change order and note important factors like time of completion extension, coordination with other crafts, etc. If the project manager agrees with this, a formal authorization to proceed

```
OPTIONAL CRAFT TITLES:
                                            ENGR-SUPV
    1.  CRAFT TITLE _____    NAME _____

            CRAFT 100 ☐   200 ☐   600 ☐   700 ☐

                                            ENGR-SUPV
    2.  CRAFT TITLE _____    NAME _____

            CRAFT 100 ☐   200 ☐   600 ☐   700 ☐
```

LABOR MAN HOURS REPORT DATA

FORM D-027 INSTRUCTIONS

1. To add a new job, or a new man hour code on an existing job, it must be checked in "ADD MAN HOUR CODE" and must include Man Hours Estimated. Any report changing the status of a previously added Man Hour Code, should be checked "Change Man Hour Code".

2. The name of the Engineer (front page) is printed on every craft and every page of the report for the job specified.

3. Change Number is optional.

4. Man Hours Estimated and Man Hours to Date should be to the nearest tenth of an hour.

5. Percent Estimated Complete is optional. It may be reported on the duplicate copies of the reports which are sent to District Manager once each month.

6. One or two additional sub titles and names may be specified for each craft in a job. Data should be entered in the space provided above, or on additional D-027 sheets, to be printed for the craft specified. Some examples of craft titles which might be specified are Estimator, Foreman, or Superintendent. If two are specified for one craft, they will be printed in the order they are entered.

Fig. 2b   Labor man-hours report.

will be issued. The project manager can use the following forms and management reports:

Change Order Request for Quotation
Change Proposal Estimate (Fig. 3)
Extra Work Order (Fig. 4)
AIA Change Order
Monthly Report of Change Orders

Monthly Financial Reporting and Progress Billing

The project manager should provide management with a monthly financial report covering the project. This report will give the monthly progress billings and other expenses accrued against the project. It will usually list change orders, retentions, and a forecast of monthly billing amounts to the completion of the project. Figure 5 shows a contract billing record form that can be used to keep track of billings.

Sizable projects usually involve monthly progress billings of contractors. The project manager should discuss the format of these billings at the start of the job and establish guidelines with each contractor. Monthly applications for payments are usually used as the invoice. They must be checked and approved speedily, in accordance with contract terms. In some cases these progress bills have to be approved by the architect before they are submitted to the project manager. Another important formality is the certification by the contractor that the work listed has been completed in accordance with the

---

RUDOLPH & SLETTEN, INC.

P.O. BOX 1089 • MOUNTAIN VIEW, CALIF. 94040

CHANGE PROPOSAL ESTIMATE

NO.

TO: Date:
                                                            Proj:
                                                            Job No.

Gentlemen:

We submit for your approval the following cost estimate of changes in work as follows:

This change was requested by:

I T E M	ENCL. NO.	LABOR	MTL./EQUIPMENT	SUBS	T O T A L
T O T A L S					

Labor Taxes & Insurance @ ____ % . . . .

Subtotal

Overhead @ ____ % . . . .

Subtotal

Contractor's Fee @ ____ % . . . .

Subtotal

Additional Bond Premium @ ____ % . . . .

Total Amount of Change Proposal A—
Extension of time necessary for this change-(calendar days) . . . .

☐ We have proceeded with this change, and work orders have been sent to the subcontractors, pursuant with: _____

☐ We will not proceed with this change until receipt of a signed copy of this proposal. This proposal must be accepted by _____ in order to avoid additional time extension and/or expense.

APPROVED   RUDOLPH & SLETTEN, INC.

Title   BY:

Date

Fig. 3 Change proposal estimate.

contract documents and that all charges for labor and material covered by previous certificates for payment have been paid by the contractor.

To avoid unnecessary corrections and delays in payment, it is advisable that the contractor's representative review the rough billing draft with the project manager prior to submittal of the billing. In this way the project manager can point out errors, and corrections can be made easily. A good billing format will include itemized charges together with the agreed-upon contract amount, contractor's fee, percent of work completed, previous payments, billing payments not yet received, retentions, and the present month's invoice amount.

A good monthly billing should also include a package of backup documentation such as the following:

Labor billing, including certified payroll (Fig. 6)
Signed time cards
Material billing record (Fig. 7)
Subcontractor billings (Fig. 8)

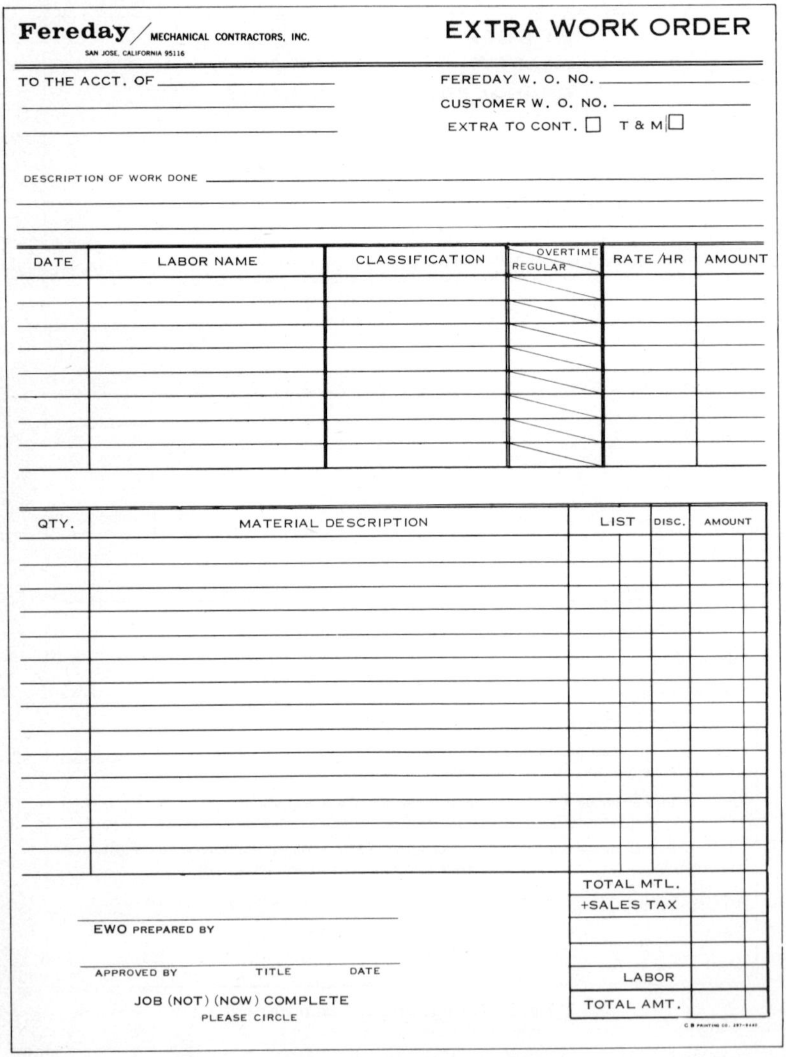
Fereday / MECHANICAL CONTRACTORS, INC.
SAN JOSE, CALIFORNIA 95116

EXTRA WORK ORDER

TO THE ACCT. OF ____________

FEREDAY W. O. NO. ____________
CUSTOMER W. O. NO. ____________
EXTRA TO CONT. ☐ T & M ☐

DESCRIPTION OF WORK DONE ____________

DATE	LABOR NAME	CLASSIFICATION	OVERTIME / REGULAR	RATE /HR	AMOUNT

QTY.	MATERIAL DESCRIPTION	LIST	DISC.	AMOUNT
		TOTAL MTL.		
		+SALES TAX		
		LABOR		
		TOTAL AMT.		

EWO PREPARED BY

APPROVED BY TITLE DATE

JOB (NOT) (NOW) COMPLETE
PLEASE CIRCLE

Fig. 4 Extra work order.

Equipment rental schedule
Detail of personal job expenses

The project manager should file these monthly progress billings and backup documentation as part of the project historical record.

Final Inspection and Acceptance

At the completion of the construction project, the project manager will request from contractors and suppliers the following before acceptance and payment of final bills:

CONTRACT BILLING RECORD

Name of Project _____

Job Number _____

Date of Contract _____

Date Work Started in Field _____

Billing Number	Date Submitted	Amt. of Request	Date Paid	Amt. Paid	*Month-End IBM Cost	Over-Under Billings

*List all IBM totals from date costs are first reported.

N-174

Fig. 5 Contract billing record.

Progress Billing No. _____

Invoice No. _____
Our Job No. _____
Month: _____

Labor

Accumulated Labor

_____
_____
_____
_____
_____
_____
_____
_____
_____

Amount of Previous Billings _____
Add: _____ labor _____

Certified Payrolls Submitted With This Billing

Week Ending _____ _____
_____ _____
_____ _____
_____ _____
_____ _____

TOTAL AMOUNT OF THIS BILLING _____

SUMMARY

Labor _____   Labor Ins. @ _____%

Total Labor To Date _____   _____
Less: Amount of
Previous Billings _____   _____

TOTAL DUE THIS INVOICE _____   _____

Fig. 6 Contractor labor billing.

1. Written notice that the work has been completed as defined in the conditions of the contract.

2. Transmittal of required guarantees, affidavits, releases, bonds, and waivers.

3. Final inspection and acceptance by the architect/engineer, code enforcing agencies, and insurance company.

4. Turnover of all keys, manuals, as-built drawings, acceptance test certificates, de-

Fig. 7a   NECA contractor material billing record.

sign calculations, revised specifications, list of suppliers, maintenance instructions, spare part lists, and maintenance stocks and tools.

5. Turnover of the facilities to the plant maintenance department. This will include explaining all systems and installations and providing factory training where applicable. When all this has been done, the project manager will sign off the final acceptance and billing and then prepare a final report to management that will include the final budget review.

CONCLUSION

Professionalism is essential for the plant engineer who is responsible for any construction project. It is the project manager's responsibility to provide construction decisions, supervise and approve the construction design, and deliver the project as required by the owner, on time and within the approved budget. The project manager—as manager of decision, design, and delivery—must rely heavily on the types of management reports and records described in this chapter. Some of these the manager will design, set up,

Form JM-28

TOOL AND EQUIPMENT REQUISITION

REQ. NO._____
JOB NO._____
JOB NAME_____ DATE_____
JOB ADDRESS_____
DELIVERY INSTRUCTIONS_____

SIZE	DESCRIPTION	ORDERED QUANT.	DELIVERED				RETURNED			
			QUANT.	SER. NO.	COND.	DATE	QUANT.	SER. NO.	COND.	DATE

DELIVERED BY_____ RECEIVED BY_____ DATE_____

COPYRIGHT 1954 NATIONAL ELECTRICAL CONTRACTORS ASSOCIATION, INC.

and maintain. Others will be demanded and received from the architect/engineer, consultants, contractors, and suppliers.

There can be no effective construction management without clear and concise construction management reporting. Some of the administrative services can be provided or backed up by computerized reports. Reports will provide summaries of developments as they occur on the project and will point out both progress and problems. They will also provide cash flow information. The other very important aspect of management reports is that they will provide historical data of the construction project that will

To our Subcontractors:

_____

_____

_____

Attention: BILLING DEPARTMENT
Reference: BILLING PROCEDURE

Gentlemen:

Following is the form which must be used in all progress billing to this firm in order for us to pay you promptly.

Contract Amount	$1,000.00
Adjustments to contract C.O. A–1	100.00
C.O. A–2	100.00
Extra (covered by signed work order before commencing extra work)*	20.00
Adjusted contract amount	$1,220.00
Complete to date 50%	610.00
Less 10% retention	61.00
Net bill to date	$ 549.00
Less previous payments	90.00
AMOUNT THIS INVOICE:	$ 459.00

Thank you for your cooperation in this matter.

Very truly yours,

RUDOLPH & SLETTEN, INC.

NOTE: All invoices to our office must show our job number and an A-number covering each change to the base contract before payment of the invoice will be authorized.

_____

Extras will not be paid unless a signed work order has been obtained prior to commencing work.

Fig. 8 Billing instructions to subcontractors.

support future continuous maintenance of the facilities.   They will also provide historical data for the next construction project.

REFERENCES

1. Robert W. Abbett: "Engineering Contracts and Specifications," 4th ed., Wiley, New York, 1963.
2. *Accident Prevention Manual for Industrial Operations*, 5th ed., National Safety Council, Chicago, 1967.
3. *Architects Handbook of Professional Practices*, American Institute of Architects, Washington, D.C., 1973.
4. John B. Bonny and Joseph P. Frein: *Handbook of Construction Management and Organization*, Van Nostrand Reinhold, New York, 1973.
5. George E. Deatherage: *Construction Company Organization and Management*, McGraw-Hill, New York, 1964.
6. George E. Deatherage: *Construction Office Management*, McGraw-Hill, New York, 1964.
7. William B. Foxhall: *Professional Construction Management and Project Administration*, published jointly by *Architectural Record* and The American Institute of Architects, 1972.
8. John A. Havers and Frank W. Stubbs, Jr.: *Handbook of Heavy Construction*, 2d ed., McGraw-Hill, New York, 1971.
9. Bernard T. Lewis and J. P. Marron: *Facilities and Plant Engineering Handbook*, McGraw-Hill, New York, 1973.
10. Frederick S. Merritt: *Building Construction Handbook*, 2d ed., McGraw-Hill, New York, 1965.
11. Joseph J. Moder: *Project Management with CPM and PERT*, 2d ed., Van Nostrand Reinhold, New York, 1972.
12. Roy Pilcher: *Principles of Construction Management*, McGraw-Hill, New York, 1966.
13. *Recommended Guide for Bidding Procedures and Awards*, published jointly by The American Institute of Architects and The Associated General Contractors of America, 1972.
14. David R. Showalter: *How to Make the OSHA 1970 Work for You*, Ann Arbor Science Publishers, Inc., Ann Arbor, Mich., 1972.

Section 8

Budget and Costs

Chapter 1

Identification, Preparation, and Administration of the Maintenance Budget

DONALD E. TOONE
Engineering Editor, Maintenance Engineering Magazine

INTRODUCTION

It is important, when discussing the terms "maintenance cost" or "maintenance budget," to define exactly what one means by them. Many times, individuals discussing and comparing maintenance cost in their respective plants find, after lengthy discussion, that they are talking about a term that needs further definition. What is sometimes termed maintenance cost and included in the maintenance budget is not necessarily the same in all plants. Therefore this chapter addresses itself to the definition of the terms "maintenance budget" and "maintenance cost" in the industrial plant today. The differences between different maintenance cost accounting methods used by many industrial plants are discussed in detail.

Maintenance costs, in the typical industrial plant today, are defined as costs incurred to keep the plant running. In other words, the cost of maintenance manpower, supporting machinery and equipment, repair and replacement parts, building material, and daily operating supplies required to operate and maintain the plant on a daily basis—all these, totaled, make up maintenance cost. These are the costs which must be taken into consideration when discussing the term.

Plant administrative costs are often included in the overall cost under *supervision*. Sometimes utility production cost as well as usage of same is included in the originally stated budget. Some plants include housekeeping, safety, and security, while others include none of the above. So when discussing the term "maintenance cost" or preparing the maintenance budget, be specific and define the term first.

Most accounting departments in industry today use six major categories to define maintenance cost in their respective plants. These six categories are (1) equipment, (2) supplies, (3) labor (direct and indirect), (4) outside services, (5) department overhead, and (6) plant overhead. There are many variations to this, as there are with most anything. Some plants may combine department and plant overhead, while others choose to break them down further with a series of number identifications. Every plant usually has several individual maintenance cost accounting methods peculiar to its individual operation, but these are the basics.

Equipment

Items purchased as units from a manufacturer or distributor or items manufactured in the plant maintenance shop as complete assemblies for support of the maintenance function within the plant are usually defined as *equipment cost*. Cost of the equipment may range from a $45 amperage meter to a $5,500 roof moisture detector or a $10,000 computer used by maintenance in troubleshooting and diagnosing operating problems on numerically controlled machine tools.

Maintenance performed in the plant depends upon two major factors: (1) qualifications and expertise of the skilled tradesmen and (2) the equipment and tools the tradesmen have with which to perform their assigned work. Maintenance tradesmen cannot be expected to perform quality work in support of modern production machine tools and sophisticated production processes unless they have the equipment and tools to diagnose and troubleshoot the problems. Once they have defined a problem, they also need, in many cases, special tools to assist them in performing their jobs efficiently and at minimum cost. These special tools include equipment needed to do the job. Costs of such items are termed *equipment cost*.

New equipment such as portable tools, pumps, hoist lifts, and other related items (such as pullers required by maintenance tradesmen to support continuous and efficient daily plant operations) are also termed equipment cost.

Supplies

Items carried on the shelf either in the maintenance shop or in maintenance stores to support continuous, efficient, and reliable daily operations of production machinery and facilities equipment are defined for cost accounting purposes as *Supplies*. This cost area includes such material as mechanical packing and seals, pipe, fittings, valves, electrical wiring devices, V-belts, lubricants, filter media, paint and coatings, water-conditioning chemicals, insulation, and many other items used daily in support of production and plant operations.

Special machine repair parts are maintained in maintenance stores and are controlled on a minimum-maximum basis based on usage. Items such as bearings, power transmission equipment, motors, and special individual machine components (such as a machine spindle head or a special shaft or gear head) are all part of maintenance supplies as defined by cost accounting. Maintenance supplies are items determined by maintenance supervision (foreman, planner) as being essential to continuous and efficient operation of production machinery and equipment and plant facilities.

Maintenance supervisors determine what items are to be maintained in maintenance stores. They also determine the specification by brand name or approved equal, along with minimum quantity as well as maximum quantity to be maintained in stores. On certain items which have heavy usage, the control level is based on the amount withdrawn from stores within a given period of time. Purchasing may set up an annual contract and have a specified quantity of items delivered to maintenance stores each month based on the anticipated usage. The original request is set up and determined by maintenance.

Individual items maintained in maintenance stores are usually assigned a material code number by inventory control planners for cost control and ease of identification.

An important point to consider when discussing maintenance budgets and maintenance cost is how much of the dollar figure cost is tied up in supplies. Another important consideration, and an area each maintenance manager should keep tabs on, is overstocking of supplies and provisions as well as removing obsolete material and supplies from inventory control. A check of items in maintenance stores should be made on an annual basis. Items that do not show usage for a 12-month period should be removed from inventory and the material codes canceled.

When machine tools are removed from service, all supporting spares should also be removed. This does two things: it reduces dollars in inventory cost and keeps maintenance stores clear of obsolete stock. This, a common oversight in many plants, results in excess dollars tied up in inventory and may lead to a space and material handling problem.

Not all items that do not show usage for a year can be included in this category and automatically removed from inventory. Some of the items in maintenance stores are termed *insurance items*. These items are available at the plant site for immediate use should a failure occur that would shut the plant down or shut down a critical piece of machinery or equipment. Often, transformers, power cables, or starter motors are included in the category. At any rate, a close scrutiny should be made of the items to be removed, so that none of the insurance supplies are included.

Labor

Craft time charged against a specific job is defined by accounting as *labor cost.* Labor costs are normally considered to be the wage rate plus fringe benefit cost times hours spent by a tradesman in performance of the work assignment. Today—with the increased emphasis on more efficient utilization of manpower, facilities, and equipment —labor costs are being more accurately defined. In many plants, especially where time standards are employed, the breakdown distinguishes between direct and indirect labor cost.

Many factors make up the total labor cost on a job. Factors such as scheduling and planning, reviewing prints, preparation of tools and equipment, travel to and from the jobsite, and work execution all go to make up the labor cost.

When discussing maintenance labor cost, one cannot talk only about maintenance labor, lumping all the other facets that support actual work performance under the heading of labor cost, and be completely accurate. What you are really talking about is direct and indirect labor cost. Direct labor costs are those costs incurred in actually performing the work. Indirect labor costs are those costs incurred in preparation for the work to be performed. Travel to and from the jobsite, requisitioning parts from maintenance stores, and reviewing job plans are but a few of the functions that make up indirect labor cost.

Labor costs incurred by maintenance are usually charged to a predetermined factory order number which denotes a particular production operation. The charge is then billed against production departmental operating cost. Labor charges that cannot be charged to a production-supporting factory order are charged to the maintenance department overhead.

Outside Services

Costs incurred under the heading of *outside services* are in the form of labor and know-how purchased through a contractor, consultant, or supplier. Many maintenance managers supplement their in-plant work force with outside services for various reasons. One main reason for the use of outside services is to assist the existing staff in peak workload periods, enabling management to maintain a more stable in-house work force.

Another reason management will use outside services is to employ special talent or services to meet an infrequent need. Sometimes, special skills or tools and equipment are needed for a special job that does not warrant an in-house investment in talent or equipment. Engineering consultant services and fees are included in this cost area.

Many times, especially in modern industrial plants today, temporary employment of outside labor is needed to supplement the in-house work force. Use of outside labor is often necessary in the performance of highly technical work, such as compressor rebuilding or performance analysis or efficiency checks of compressors or boilers (steam analysis.)

Outside services are also often employed to perform large-scale facility repair such as roof overlay, painting, new floor coverings, and other large-scale jobs that are infrequent and upsetting to the existing work schedule. Other areas where outside services are often employed is in the performance of specialty work such as cleaning air-handling systems and removal of waste material, both solid and liquid. All these costs are often lumped together and termed maintenance cost.

In most plants, maintenance has the responsibility to maintain and operate the plant efficiently. Their training, skills, and expertise as well as the tools and equipment they have to work with are geared toward daily routine maintenance and plant operation. When infrequent needs arise for special skill or work performance, as mentioned above, management often turns to outside sources for performance of the work.

Often it is more economical to contract special work to outside services (for reasons previously discussed) than to try to do it in house with the existing labor force.

There are no cut-and-dried guidelines for determining when work should be contracted to outside services. However, there are a couple of areas that are usually good indicators. One of them is backlog of work. When backlog hours reach a certain level, this means certain work needs to be done. The other is criticalness of need for work to be completed. When either of these conditions prevails, it is time to consider the use of contracted services.

Department Overhead

All expenses of the maintenance department operations that cannot be charged directly to a specific work assignment (factory order) are charged to *department overhead.* Usually the expense of supervision above the foreman level and engineering assistance are recorded as department overhead. In every maintenance budget there is a certain amount of cost incurred that stems from the mere existence of the department. These costs are usually budgeted for as department overhead operating cost.

Maintenance and depreciation of machine tools used by the department and also cost of supplies such as hand tools, drills, files, gloves, and nut-and-bolt items used in daily support of the maintenance work force—all these are budgeted as department overhead. In addition to materials and supplies, other items including vacations, absenteeism, and labor discussions are also considered part of department overhead operating expense. Heating, steam, the production of compressed air, water service, and other utility costs incurred for plant operations are termed department overhead. These costs are usually totaled at year's end and distributed proportionally to production operations based on square foot of occupancy. In other plants, department costs are tallied totally as a maintenance cost and are not proportionally charged against production.

The difference in accounting methods—that is, the various ways in which departmental costs may be carried on the books—reemphasizes the importance of defining the term "maintenance cost."

Plant Overhead

Plant administrative expenses that must be shared by all departments, including maintenance, are termed *plant overhead.* Top-management salaries as well as the cost of the personnel department, purchasing, and other similar service organizations—and also other expenses necessary for plant operation that cannot be conveniently allocated to a specific department or activity—all these are put in the plant overhead cost. These costs are divided among the plant operating departments.

Costs charged to maintenance are termed plant overhead cost and are all part of the total maintenance cost which goes to make up the total maintenance budget.

PREPARING THE BUDGET

Every plant has individual maintenance budget preparation exercises peculiar to itself that are gone through to prepare budget estimates. There are no cut-and-dried methods of preparing the maintenance budget, mainly because of the various levels at which maintenance is carried out in individual plants.

Preparation of the proposed maintenance budget should start at the foreman level in the plant. After all, the foreman is the one whose "head is on the block" to ensure continued and efficient operation of production equipment and facilities equipment, not the purchasing or plant engineering department.

If failure of a critical piece of production equipment occurs, management does not call engineering to get the equipment returned to service; they call the maintenance foreman either directly or indirectly. The foreman is the one responsible, through direction of the assigned work force, to repair and return the equipment or facility to service. It is also the maintenance foreman's responsibility to make sure that repair and replacement parts are available for immediate use in maintenance stores. The maintenance foreman should be recognized as an important cog in the industrial management wheel when the forecast of anticipated future expenditure is being prepared.

All maintenance foremen should be required to submit to higher maintenance management a proposed expenditure for their areas of responsibility. This input should be only one of many required by management in preparing the maintenance budget. Only people directly responsible for continued efficient operation of plant facilities and the equipment thereof are cognizant of individual equipment or facility needs. They have the cost records, through planned maintenance and also firsthand information, of current conditions that might warrant heavy expenditures at any given time.

Other inputs required, in addition to the estimated manpower (labor cost), to prepare budget figures include cost of inventory material, daily supplies, utilities, and supporting services. Certainly fringe benefits, vacations, holidays, absenteeism, and even long-term manpower demands should be part of the total figure.

Once all preliminary estimates of maintenance cost are put together, they are submitted to higher management for review and consideration. The proposed budget expenditure is either approved as submitted or returned with specific instructions for budget reduction. Often, large expenditures such as resurfacing a large roof area or resurfacing a manufacturing floor area, etc., can be spread out over a period of years and the job done in phases to prevent large expenditures in a short period of time. In most budget control structures, any large maintenance or repair expenditures for building or facilities equipment can be handled this way. Usually, production machinery and equipment is not included except in extremely large process facilities where a particular modernization or renovation may take place.

Other methods of identifying and handling maintenance costs that are often used in preparing the maintenance budget might include those described below.

MAINTENANCE OF PLANT SERVICES

This cost accounting area includes all costs, both labor and material, incurred in the *maintenance of plant services*. Plant services are defined as those services required to maintain and operate the plant on a daily basis. Maintenance of utility services (once they leave the generating area), waste handling and disposal, etc., and housekeeping may or may not be included under plant services.

MAINTENANCE OF PRODUCTION MACHINERY AND SUPPORT EQUIPMENT

Material and labor cost incurred by maintenance in support of daily production operations of machinery and support equipment are charged to *maintenance of production and support equipment.* Daily operating supplies such as lubricants, coolants, repair parts, preventive maintenance, and all other costs incurred in support of production machinery and supporting equipment are included in this cost area.

OPERATION OF PLANT SERVICES AND UTILITIES

Labor, material, and operating supplies costs incurred in the production and control of compressed air, steam, and other utility services such as electricity and water, sewage and waste control are termed *plant services and utility cost.*

Usually, only charges incurred at the point of generation or control are included in this account. Once the distribution service lines leave the four walls of the power plant (room), the charges then become part of maintenance of plant services. Again, this distinction between operation of plant services and utilities and maintenance of plant services is an individual plant definition. However, a distinction is usually made through use of a series of factory order numbers.

VACATIONS, HOLIDAYS, SICK DAYS, ETC.

Days of missed work and holiday pay and overtime are also part of the maintenance budget and must be considered when preparing the estimated cost of plant operations. Because of the character of maintenance work, often the only time a piece of critical production equipment is available for necessary maintenance and service is on a holiday or weekend. This premium time of work performance costs extra dollars and must be taken into consideration in planning the maintenance budget. If these expenditures are not planned for and they do occur, they usually upset preplanned budget figures at the year's end. Then adjustments are hard to make, especially when an overexpenditure is involved.

BUILDINGS AND GROUNDS MAINTENANCE

Cost incurred for labor, material, and equipment to perform necessary repair and maintenance work on the building structure inside and out—such as roof repair, painting, floor repair, air distribution and handling systems, etc., or on the plant grounds, such as parking lot repair, fence work, grass mowing, etc.—are termed *building and grounds maintenance cost.* Labor, material, and/or equipment costs are distinguished by separate predetermined factory order numbers.

OTHER MAINTENANCE COSTS

Other individually distinguished maintenance cost areas may include transportation, portable tool repair, furniture and office equipment repair, rearrangement, safety, security, etc. As previously mentioned, these costs are not always deemed maintenance costs. However, if they are included in maintenance, they play an important role in putting together the maintenance budget. No two plants are the same. Plants differ in their budget preparation methods and cost accounting procedures. However, most plants use one of the two formats previously discussed as a base, incorporating their own needs and detail into the methods of preparation and control to achieve individual goals and objectives.

USE OF FACTORY ORDER NUMBERS

When the factory order numbering system is used, usually a basic factory order number is established. In a number such as F.O. 088–195–6000, for example, the first three digits show that it is a maintenance factory order number. The second three digits usually represent the specific department within maintenance, such as 195 for electricians, 192 for welders, 191 for carpenters, etc. The third group, consisting of four digits, is used for specific work areas. For example, all 2000-series numbers could be for a specific area or building within a plant. Individual jobs are assigned specific F.O. numbers, and work is then charged to these. The use of factory order numbers can be as creative as the plant chooses to make it. The more specific the breakdown in numbering, the more specific the cost detail. Sometimes the last group of numerals is required to be a five- or six-digit number because of the size of the plant and the complexity of its activity.

As previously stated, for various reasons, no two plant maintenance budgets are the same. However, listed below is what a typical maintenance budget would look like in an industrial plant that is average to large in size. These percentages include both labor and material cost.

Budget item	Percent of budget
Maintenance of plant services	8.7%
Maintenance of production machinery and equipment	23.7%
Lab equipment maintenance	4.0%
Operation of plant services and utilities	22.3%
Vacations, holidays, etc.	4.1%
Buildings and grounds maintenance	19.5%
Other maintenance	17.7%

CONTROL OF MAINTENANCE COST AND THE BUDGET

Today, increased emphasis is being placed on maintenance management to ensure efficient plant maintenance and operations. The managers of modern industrial plants require maximum return on dollars invested in maintaining plant facilities, production machinery, and equipment. For this very reason, improved work methods, procedures, standards, work sampling, and quality control—along with automation—have become a way of life for industrial plant maintenance.

Production control experts study methods of improving process and production procedures, looking for ways to improve effectiveness and utilization of manpower, facilities, and equipment. Their ultimate objective is to increase productivity and minimize cost.

In the industrial plant today, many of these same production techniques and controls have been carried over into the maintenance function. Plant managers are no longer concerned only that a large piece of production or support equipment is producing an end product. They are concerned about unscheduled machine and equipment downtime, repetitive repairs, improved quality control, and more effective utilization of maintenance manpower, facilities, and equipment.

Many of the same principles of work measurement techniques previously applied to production by industrial consultants are now being applied to maintenance. The objective of applying work analysis and performance data is to improve the effectiveness and utilization of assigned manpower.

Labor costs are further defined through work analysis. Schedulers/planners have been added in many plants to more effectively execute the function of maintenance at minimum cost. All this has the final objective of getting maximum return on the dollar invested.

Sophisticated work measurement programs, material standards, and improved work methods and procedures have given maintenance in industry today a new engineering profile and, in many plants, a new organizational structure.

To help maintenance management implement its changing role, a new title and job function has been added in many plants—that of the maintenance engineer.

In maintenance today, there is an increased demand for:

Profitability

Maximum return on dollars invested

Engineering reliability in facility and equipment operations

Buying proved and performance-tested supplies, equipment, and materials

Improved procurement standards and inventory control

Efficient utilization of manpower and facilities

Improved overall plant performance

How has maintenance changed and what effect does this have on preparation of the maintenance budget? What made this change take place? Here are but a few of the reasons:

1. New operating guidelines by federal, state, and local authorities. (Government regulations as dictated by OSHA.)

2. New and improved machinery and equipment operating at higher speeds and temperatures—more specifically, the numerically controlled machine operating on as many as 12 different axes and controlled by tapes and computers.

3. Greater need for higher-caliber tradesmen to troubleshoot, inspect, and maintain new high rolling production machine tools with their electromechanical control valves and solid state and integrated circuit control.

4. Greater emphasis on cost reduction, improved operation, and more efficient utilization of existing manpower, facilities, and equipment.

5. Shortage of trained and skilled manpower for both production and maintenance because of the changing profile.

6. More sophisticated production methods and procedures.

Maintenance in the industrial plant today is certainly no longer the "broom and mop" operation thought of for so many years. Such an operation may do for an office complex—a commercial and institutional building, but it will not suffice in the industrial plant, where maintenance has the distinct responsibility of maintaining several thousand square feet of building facilities under roof and the complex and sophisticated machine tools and systems that produce the company's end product.

Maintenance today in the industrial plant is more than the function of housekeeping. When you hear maintenance managers talk about budgets of 10 to 15 million dollars to operate and maintain the plant, you know they are talking big business. Maintenance in industry today represents a total expenditure of approximately 40 billion dollars.

Control of maintenance cost in the industrial plant today starts with the plant management. Efficient operation of production equipment and plant facilities is only as good as the programs implemented by management.

Direction given by those responsible for maintenance plays a big part in determining the maintenance budget. Often a particular plant may be planned to be maintenance-oriented, another may have a run-till-breakdown operating philosophy. Certainly, planning of the maintenance budget would be more realistic in the first plant than the second.

There are no cut-and-dried rules for budget preparation or budget control. Each plant, however, must determine goals and objectives for its maintenance department and then plan from there to estimate the proposed maintenance cost and to provide the controls to ensure these goals.

Chapter **2**

Capital Investment Analysis

HERBERT L. ANTZES
Chief, Engineering Instruction Division
Postal Service Training and Development Institute

INTRODUCTION

In the field of plant engineering management, certain fundamental tools and definitions are required to provide the plant engineer with an understanding of basic economics, accounting, and finance. This chapter contains an overview of economics, accounting, and financial analysis as they apply to capital budgeting, and, in particular, an approach to analyzing the costs of improving plant working conditions. Each plant engineer should understand this approach before attempting to make simple economic comparisons of alternative investments. Improved or newly acquired facilities may be justified solely on the basis of economic benefits to be gained.

DEPRECIATION

Deterioration of equipment and facilities takes place over time. This should be reflected in an economic study for capital investment. The deterioration or lessening in value is called depreciation. Factors influencing depreciation are:

1. Life of enterprise
2. Life of equipment
3. Inadequacy of equipment
4. Obsolescence of equipment
5. Requirements of law

Depreciation may not be equal to the actual physical lessening of value, since it is merely an accounting for this lessening in value and does not necessarily represent a fixed sum of money set aside. The objective of depreciation accounting is to amortize the invested capital funds. In the perfect situation, the value of the equipment plus the accumulation in a depreciation fund would be equal to the original investment.

Normally, depreciation is taken into account yearly, in accordance with a predetermined function. The service life, salvage value, and mathematical function serve to determine the yearly depreciation cost. The usual depreciation methods are listed below:

1. Straight line
2. Declining balance
3. Sum of the digits
4. Sinking fund
5. Appraisal or book value
6. Unit method

COMPARISON OF ALTERNATIVES

A rational decision concerning investment of capital usually requires a comparison of several courses of action. The difference between possible alternatives are expressed in monetary terms. Company policy should stipulate that new or improved facilities may be justified solely on the basis of economic (monetary) benefits, requiring an economic study of various alternatives for all projects over an assigned total cost.

It is important that the alternatives be clearly defined and that all appropriate alternatives be evaluated. In many situations, decisions are made by default; that is, not all the alternatives are recognized and a decision is based upon a poor alternative. In other situations, no consideration is given to improving existing conditions. For example, a work simplification study might show reduced costs as an alternative to procuring new mechanization.

Comparisons are made by considering the alternatives in pairs. That is, a base alternative (alternative A) is a make-do alternative. Each of the other alternatives is compared to alternative A. It is necessary to make calculations that will produce comparable figures for the alternatives. The common methods of calculation are as follows:

1. Equivalent annual cost
2. Present worth
3. Rate of return

When it is possible to determine only one of the alternatives, each method of comparison will give the same result. However, other matters (minimum rate of return, for example) may add advantages or disadvantages to each method.

Equivalent Annual Cost

In this method, a nonuniform series of expenditures is converted to an equivalent uniform annual cost over the life of the alternative. This term is sometimes shortened to "annual cost."

Generally, operating costs are stated as annual figures or can be estimated as average costs. The only nonuniform costs are investment costs. It is necessary, then, to convert the investment cost to an annual cost of capital recovery. Convention dictates that expenses or savings that occur during the year are treated as if they occurred at the year's end. This convention is almost universally used in economy studies. The use of capital recovery factors accounts for the "time value" of money. Sometimes it is useful to merely tabulate the annual cash flows of one alternative as compared with another. However, a comparison of this type is not useful for choosing between alternatives, since it does not take into account the time value of money.

Once the rate of interest is decided upon, the equivalent annual cost provides a satisfactory and simple method of comparing alternatives.

Present Worth

The present worth method converts cash flows to an equivalent single figure at the start of the project life. It also depends upon deciding upon a standard interest rate. In one sense, present worth is the opposite of annual cost, since it converts annual figures to an equivalent single amount at zero date. In fact, present worth can be converted to equivalent annual cost by multiplying by the capital recovery factor. Calculations are based upon either differential cash flows or annual expenditures.

Rate of Return

Discounted cash flow rate of return is used when it is desired to determine the prospective interest rate of return for an investment. This is a trial-and-error method and is the primary method used in large industry.

Salvage Value

Salvage value is the net amount of money that is expected to be realized from a piece of equipment when it is sold at the end of its life. If the economic study is for a shorter period than the expected life, residual values at the end of the economic study are used instead of salvage values.

In equivalent annual cost studies, salvage value is subtracted from investment cost; but an annual simple interest charge is added to pay interest on the salvage value since the principle will be repaid by the salvage value.

In the present worth method, salvage value is converted to an amount which will yield the desired salvage value at the end of the investment life.

In cash flows, salvage value occurs as a positive value (receipt) at the end of the investment life.

Fig. 1 Profit or loss as a result of investment income.

ECONOMIC STUDIES

The purpose of an economic study is to decide on a selection between quantified alternatives based on money and time.

The economic analysis involves an input of some type of investment over a period of time. This investment results in an output of an income over the same time frame. In order for the investment to be a measured success, the ratio of output to input must be equal to or in excess of unity.

In comparing alternatives in an economic study, the goal is to produce the greatest output for a given input. Profit is a resultant of two components in the investment mode; investment and income. Investment involves the outlay for performance of an activity. Income is the return derived from the investment. The difference between income and investment is profit or—in the case where the outlay exceeds income—a loss results.

Consider the following alternatives, A and B.

Alternative	Investment	Income	Profit (Loss)
A	$ 500	$ 600	$100
B	$1,000	$1,100	$100
C	$2,500	$2,400	($100)

In terms of profit alternatives, A and B are equal, with C having a 100-dollar loss. Another measure of profitability is the ratio of income and investment.

Alternatives A and B have a ratio greater than one which is favorable when compared to alternative C, in which investment exceeds income, resulting in a ratio of less than one.

Alternative	Investment	Income	Income investment ratio
A	$ 500	$ 600	1.2
B	$1,000	$1,100	1.1
C	$2,500	$2,400	0.9

Income after deduction of investment is called net income. Income as a return on investment before deduction of operating expenses is gross income. Operating expenses deducted from gross income are operating cost, depreciation, interest, and taxes.

The following is a mathematic model for income and investment:

N—Net income
G—Gross income
O—Operating cost
D—Depreciation
I —Interest
T—Taxes

Where

$$\underbrace{N}_{\text{Profit}} = \underbrace{G}_{\text{output}}^{\text{Income}} - \underbrace{(O+D+I+T)}_{\text{input}}^{\text{Investment}}$$

Investment

Input investment includes the following under the four general categories of costs:

1. Operating costs
    Direct labor
    Direct material and services
    Indirect labor
    Indirect material and services
2. Depreciation
    Equipment
    Building
    Land
3. Interest
    Investment in depreciable items
    Funds borrowed from operation
4. Taxes
    Inventory
    Sales
    Net earning

Income

Income output includes such items as products, monetary return, physical plant, concepts, plans, and any act or object quantifiable in terms of output productivity in monetary terms.

PLAN FOR ECONOMIC ANALYSIS

In an economic analysis, engineering and economic consideration are joined. In order to have a sound analysis, a logical sequence must be followed. As a guide to this sound analysis, a four-step plan can be followed.

1. Creative step
2. Definitive step
3. Conversion step
4. Decision step

Each of these steps will be reviewed in detail in the following paragraphs.

1. Creative step   The creative step involves searching for facts or new combinations of facts. Some facts may be gathered through combination of previously known data or, in other cases, facts may be gathered through new research into a problem.

The creative step results in finding an opening through a barrier of economic and physical limitations.

Facts and economics combined with innovation are the prime ingredients needed to create a feasible solution for a problem. The creativity step can and usually does involve more than one solution to choose from.

2. Definitive step   The creative step of analysis revolves around general concepts. For the purpose of evaluating alternatives, the broad concepts must be converted into detailed alternatives that can be quantified for future evaluation. Some alternatives can be eliminated on the basis of being beyond the scope of the current area of activity. Constraints and limitations narrow down and eliminate some alternative in this step of analysis.

3. Conversion step   Alternatives can be compared only if they have the same common denominator. This common denominator is normally expressed in some sort of monetary terms for economic analysis. The alternatives must, first, be converted into receipts and disbursements with a time base and, second, be reduced to a common monetary base with a time frame. Items not definable in quantitative terms must be qualitatively described for evaluation. Common facts required in the conversion step are present cash outlay, capital recovery period, flexibility of proposal to future changes, finance, and effect on employees.

4. Decision step   In order to arrive at a decision, the previously developed alternatives must be reviewed along with the alternative of making no decision or maintaining the status quo. Quantitative and qualitative data are reviewed and a quantitative profit is arrived at with regard to a decision on an alternative. If facts are missing or unavailable, judgment must be used. The ultimate decision on an alternative is measured in quantitative and qualitative terms and judgment is added where facts are missing. In the case of an economic decision, the ultimate decision reduces to what is the most economic or cost-effective alternative.

ESTIMATES IN ECONOMIC ANALYSIS

Income or a return on an investment is the normal measure used in economic analysis. From the model presented in Fig. 1, income is defined as:

$$N = G - (O + D + I + T)$$

The outcome can, with judgment, be estimated.

Estimates of income should be based on objective information as much as possible. If income must be estimated, casual factors having a bearing on results should be estimated separately rather than as a whole.

Operating expense should be estimated in the same manner as income, using related parts to make up the total expense.

Depreciation is estimated by using four separate estimates—installed cost, service life, salvage value, and depreciation schedule.

Interest is measured as an expense using the current rate. The rate is determined in case of borrowing money at the current lending rate or, in the case of investment, the rate that would be obtained if the money were invested rather than used as capital money.

Tax rates vary but are normally considered on the basis of percentage of the investment.

CAPITAL INVESTMENT

Every business has limited monies to fulfill its mission. Every business must generate funds necessary to expand or improve its services or products. This must be accomplished with the realization that unlimited resources are not available to do everything that management might desire. This chapter has as its objectives the general criteria for facility investment analysis. Many current economic analysis textbooks are available to provide the theory and mathematics for implementing detailed cost analysis.

From a budgeting viewpoint, a capital investment is one in which company monies are committed for expenditure that will, in a future planned period of time, return the invested monies and profits.

Many industry groups and various trade associations will make data available for comparison purposes. Other sources of ratio information as well as definition of the accounting terminology and capital management concepts are provided by such organizations as Robert Morris Associates and Dun & Bradstreet for specific industries.

Criteria and Strategy for Capital Investment

Once policy for resource allocation has been established in terms of budget level and the accompanying procedures have been developed, then—within constraints of capital amiability—several basic types of projects must be developed. These may then qualify for budgeting and, ultimately, commitment of capital funds. Such projects would be:

1. Facilities and equipment which will improve service and return at least a 10 percent or an assigned rate of return over 10 years or less on a discounted cash flow basis

2. Facilities and equipment essential for security

3. Facilities and equipment essential to provide adequate capacity to operate even if an acceptable rate of return is not achieved.

4. Facilities that will provide an adequate and appropriate safety and working environment for all employees

In other words, the project must pay back the original investment plus an addition equal to the amount which could be earned by investing it at 10 percent interest or other assigned factor for the life of the project in 10 years, whichever is shorter. This is considered a very reasonable expectation in today's security market, especially when the *risk* of new projects is considered. A general basis of justifying capital expenditures can be established with three general criteria.

1. Working environment

2. Capacity of facility to perform its mission

3. Economic opportunity

Capital expenditures that are a result of any of the three listed criteria require justification. The type of justification required will differ in each case.

Working Environment   A basic general objective derived from policy and procedures as a strategy is to invest funds as may be necessary to provide an adequate and appropriate working environment. Each facility manager has the prime responsibility to provide and maintain at a fully functional quality level the physical conditions surrounding all employees within that manager's jurisdiction. A priority and starting point to improve working conditions in the case of multiplant facilities is to direct resources to those facilities containing the greatest number of employees, since the available resources should be used accordingly. Benefits should be provided for all employees, as the resources permit. In general, upgrading facilities factors should include but not be limited to the following:

Fire safety and environmental standards

Building use life

Employee benefits per dollar of investment

Mission of facility

Interim repair costs prior to replacement

Four alternatives to be considered are these:

1. Make do (meet all standards)

2. Upgrade within policy and authority

3. Upgrade beyond control limits

4. Replacement

Selection of Alternatives

A standard practice should be developed to implement an economic analysis if facility improvements are justified due to environmental factors. Policy should support the view that under normal conditions the most cost-effective correction should be selected. Other alternatives, if selected, must be fully justified.

Capacity of Installation to Perform Its Mission

The capacity of a facility to perform its mission must be considered in decisions to improve, modify, extend, or replace these facilities.

Always consider economic analysis in seeking realistic alternatives for meeting capacity requirements. The most cost-effective alternative will normally derive from sound management principles; where other alternatives are chosen, they must be fully justified.

Economic Opportunity

Improved or newly acquired facilities may be justified solely on the basis of economic benefits to be gained.

Economic analysis of capital expenditures   The purpose of economic analysis is to determine which alternative is most economical when considering capital investments that are justified on the basis of working environment or facility capacity.

If the case is one of pure economic opportunity, the economic analysis serves to determine whether the investment is economically justified.

Methods and criteria of economic analysis

1. A primary method of economic analysis is the discounted cash flow rate of return.

2. The company's capital investment policies and procedures should stipulate that improved or newly acquired facilities may be justified solely on the basis of the economic benefits to be gained. In addition, this policy requires an economic analysis to determine the most cost-effective of the alternative means of correcting an environmental or capacity deficiency. These specifications are intended to apply to all analyses of proposed requirements over a management-designated total cost. An individual project or procurement over assigned limitation of total cost may be considered for approval based upon economic factors exclusively; it is estimated to produce a benefit/cost ratio in excess of one (1.0) when benefits and costs are discounted at 10 percent to determine their present value. Individual projects or procurement under the assigned limits of total cost require no formal economic analysis. Any investment over the maximum assigned may be considered for approval based upon economic factors exclusively only if it is estimated to produce a discounted cash flow rate of return of at least 10 percent.

3. Studies normally shall commence with the date of decision and shall cover a 10-year operating span or the useful life of the investment, whichever is shorter. If an exception is warranted, it must be fully explained in the project analysis. A typical exception would be a lease agreement with option to purchase other than in the tenth year. Studies shall consider a time span appropriately selected to fit the significant factors pertinent to the project, such as life of investment, period of occupancy, or purchase option dates.

4. The base study shall be presented based upon actual anticipated dollar amounts of cash flow. For each year under consideration, the best available projection should be used for the values of such elements as land, buildings, equipment, taxes, wages, rents, and contracts services. A constant dollar study based upon current costs may also be presented if desired, but recommendations shall be based upon the base study described above.

5. The basis for each decision and assumption must be included in the analysis. The economic and decision analysis, as well as the assumptions, will be validated by the organization comptroller or the comptroller's equivalent prior to submission to the approval authority.

Sources of information and assistance   Data for justification of economic analyses can be categorized as internal and external.

Internal sources include:

1. Previous economic studies
2. Current manning levels
3. Current space
4. Volume projections
5. Current financial reports
6. Organization and staffing matrix
7. Projected pay grades

External sources of data are:

1. Contractors
2. Sales representatives
3. City and regional planning boards (useful for obtaining growth figures)

JUSTIFICATION AND REQUIREMENTS

The study report must contain the following:

1. Problem definition and either the reasons for an economic analysis, or, conversely, the reasons for not presenting an economic analysis.

2. Qualification and quantification of the need to be satisfied by the recommended course.

3. An analysis showing that present conditions must be corrected in order to meet present or projected requirements. (Not necessary when investment is based strictly on economic (opportunity.)

4. Economic analysis including, whenever applicable, the following:

     a. Projected work level on future use to which the proposed alternative will be subjected

     b. Description of alternatives presented in order of increasing initial investment

     c. For constant dollar analysis, land and building valuation

     d. For anticipated dollar analysis, land value may be escalated at a compound rate of 6 percent and future building value may be increased at a compound annual rate of 3.5 percent while simultaneously declining elliptically at 50 percent.

     e. Cash-flow analysis for each alternative and cash-flow comparisons between pairs of alternatives

Economic Evaluation and Intangibles

The discounted cash-flow analysis of investment alternatives gives a basis for comparing alternatives on an economic scale. However, alternatives may differ on more than just an economic basis. For example, two alternative methods of air conditioning may be under consideration. Alternative A involves individual units placed in windows, while alternative B involves one large, centralized air-conditioning unit. Although the economic analysis may show that A is slightly more attractive than B, consideration should be given to intangible benefits of having one single unit with less chance of failure than several small units. In addition, the single large unit may be quieter and less unsightly than the small window units. Notice that the economic analysis should take into consideration the cost of maintenance of the units in each alternative, but it cannot consider the inconvenience of failure and repair.

Economic analysis does provide us with a means of evaluating intangible benefits. If alternative A is superior, both economically and intangibly, then the decision is clear. However, if the intangibles of alternative B are more attractive than the intangibles of alternative A, the decision is more complex. An economic approach can be taken, however, by asking whether we would pay the difference between alternative A and alternative B in order to pick up the intangible advantages of B.

Again, if alternative A on a present worth basis is valued at $5,000 less than alternative B, we must ask ourselves whether the intangible benefits of B are worth $5,000 over the life of the alternatives. If the answer is yes, then we may well prefer B to A, although on a pure economic basis the decision would be reversed.

There is an inherent danger in this type of analysis, however, as it always permits noneconomic elements to suddenly take on economic status. It is essential that *all* intangible benefits of each alternative be enumerated before such analysis is undertaken.

Validation

1. The purpose of the validation study is:

     a. To assure full compliance with company policy and procedure

     b. To assure the integrity of all economic and arithmetic calculations and the integrity of all facts and figures

     c. To assure the validity of all reasoning, rationale, logic, and resulting conclusions

     d. To assure accuracy of all statements of historical fact and future prognosis

     e. To assure that no pertinent information is omitted

     f. To assure that all reasonable alternatives have been given adequate consideration

     g. To assure all alternatives presented fulfill the operational and environmental requirements of the company

2. The responsibility for validation rests with the comptroller, or the comptroller's equivalent, at each designated level of authority.

3. The validation process is initiated during the development of the economic analysis and continues through final approval. The validation of an analysis should take place after the analyst developing the analysis has compiled all the justifications, assumptions, and economic data but prior to completion of the economic analysis.

4. The validation report will be composed of at least:

   a. The name of the manager who developed the study

   b. The findings and validation of the findings on each of the points mentioned in the specifications for validation

   c. A statement of omissions, reasons for the omissions, and impact of omissions on the analysis (i.e., missing alternatives).

Chapter **3**

Facilities Value Engineering Techniques

NICHOLAS B. POST
Manager
and
MAHENDRA JAIN
Facilities Planner, Plant Engineering and Maintenance, Xerox Corporation

FACILITIES ENGINEERING

The term "facilities engineering and maintenance" or "plant engineering and maintenance" seems to mean something different in almost every manufacturing concern. In
an industrial corporation of the size of Xerox Corporation, it may cover the following
facilities support activities:

   Long-Range Planning Future space and manpower resources are determined for a
series of products by long-range planning, where manpower is broken down by personnel
type and space is categorized by production, warehouse, office, laboratory, and service.

Short-term planning An activity plan is prepared in conjunction with short-term planning, which identifies new building requirements, the use of temporary leaseholds, and the necessary budget estimates. This document is used by the architect for initial planning and development of design concepts for the facility.

Plant layout When the planning reaches the stage of preproduction, the plant layout personnel prepare final ¼-inch plan-print layouts which may show equipment location, utility drops, conveyors, benches, work in process, etc. Acceptance of the layout and approval of the necessary funds mark the beginning of the implementation procedure.

Plant engineering Designs and specifications are prepared for the complete installation of the facility. These are then followed by work order and requisition issue.

Project scheduling This group determines—through industrial engineering measurement techniques—the craft manpower mix needed to perform specific work orders for installation.

Project maintenance This group implements planned rearrangements and new equipment installation. They also provide an emergency service to support ongoing production and monitor utilities to minimize downtime.

VALUE ENGINEERING

Value engineering is a methodology for obtaining the best value for the lowest cost throughout the life cycle of the facility. It is more properly called value analysis. The cost of value engineering is usually 0.25 to 1.0 percent of the expected project costs. Expected savings are usually ten times the cost of value engineering in project costs or in operational costs. Value engineering has been used as a construction incentive provision where the owner shares 50:50 or 90:10 with the contractor.

The use of value engineering is not as effective during construction as during design, as shown in Fig. 1. Value engineering should begin at the conceptual stage of design where it has a greater impact and there is no cost to make design changes. The latter stages of design require money to make changes. Note that only approximately 5 percent of total costs of a typical facility goes for engineering, yet the decisions made in engineering will either cause or prevent large expenditures made later in the construction work (expenditures much greater than the total 5 percent fee).

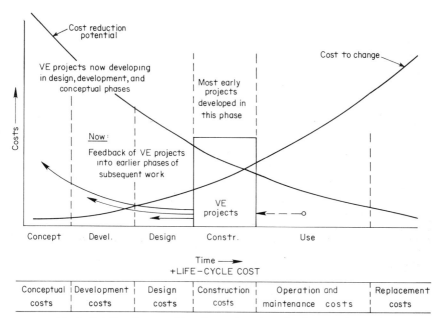

Fig. 1 Relation of costs and benefits to phases in cycle of construction work.

VALUE ENGINEERING TECHNIQUES

Value engineering is the systematic application of recognized techniques which identify the functions of a product or service and endeavor to provide those functions at the lowest total cost. At Xerox Corporation, value engineering has four phases: (1) information, (2) innovation, (3) evaluation, and (4) implementation.

During the *information phase*, four primary tasks are performed. First, an appropriate project is selected. Information needed to gain a thorough understanding of the problem is then gathered and analyzed. Functions are identified, classified, and evaluated. The project scope is then established. During phase 2, the *innovation phase*, methods for performing functions identified in phase 1 are generated. During the *evaluation phase*, the concepts generated during the innovation phase are analyzed and outstanding concepts are selected for implementation. During phase 4, *implementation*, a report is prepared to summarize the study, present conclusions, and specify proposals for the decision maker. In addition, follow-up is made to ensure implementation.

Information Phase

After a project has been selected (which is usually done by the management of the company or its various departments), all the information pertaining to performance, schedule, and cost data of the project is gathered and analyzed. The functions of each component of the project are then identified, classified, and evaluated, and the project scope is established.

Identification of functions   In value engineering, functions are identified through the use of two words—a *verb* and a *noun*. The verb chosen should be demonstrative and clearly express the action to be performed. The *noun* chosen should be the object of the action performed by the verb. Preferably, the noun should be a physical parameter that can be measured or counted. For example, the function "support weight" clearly specifies that a supporting action is needed and the thing being supported is weight. "Weight" is a measurable noun enabling the number of ounces or pounds involved to be easily specified and related to the function.

Classification of functions   After functions are properly and specifically identified, they must be classified to establish their specific relation to each other and to the total system function. A function is either basic or secondary. Basic function is the specific purpose for which an item is intended. A secondary function is an action that supports the basic function and usually results from the design approach chosen to accomplish the basic function. Essentially, a secondary function is either a *necessary* function required to support the design method chosen, an *esteem* function needed to make the system acceptable, a function requested by a customer regardless of need, or an *unwanted* function which is not needed. In any case, a secondary function is performed by some item in the course of performing another function, as, for example, a light bulb gives off heat as a function secondary to providing illumination.

The above is very useful in focusing attention on the primary purpose of the project and gives visibility to the reasons for the existence of different functions of various components of the system under consideration.

To determine and/or verify the basic function of the system being studied as well as to determine the ascending order of importance of the secondary functions, either of the following two methods can be used:

1. Numerical evaluation of functional relationships, which is based on Thurston's Case V method of paired comparisons. (See Fig. 2.)

2. Function Analysis System Technique (FAST).

In the first method, the function that has the greatest total weight factor determines the basic function; all other functions listed are secondary unless they have the same weight factor. In our example, shown in Fig. 2, the function "Prevent Breakdowns" is basic.

This method may be further expanded to develop value indexes of the functions. This is accomplished by comparing the percentages of importance, which can be easily calculated in the above case, to the percentage cost for that function. An index below 1 indicates poor value in that the percentage of cost used to perform that function is greater than the percentage of importance of that function.

In the second method, a better understanding of the interaction of functions and costs

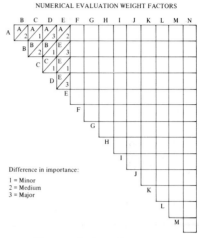

VALUE ENGINEERING   Date _____ Sheet _____ of _____

Project name _____ Project No. _____

Building No. _____ Drawing No. _____

Subject _____ Maintenance product _____ Reference _____

EVALUATION SUMMARY

Key letter	Functions	Weight
A	Prevent breakdowns	8
B	Give service	3
C	Make repairs	1
D	Do construction	0
E	Make savings	7
F		
G		
H		
I		
J		
K		
L		
M		
N		

NUMERICAL EVALUATION WEIGHT FACTORS

Difference in importance:

1 = Minor
2 = Medium
3 = Major

Fig. 2 Work sheet for numerical evaluation of functional relationships.

is obtained. This is useful in value engineering an entire system or a major portion of a system. FAST consists of function determination logic, critical path determination, supporting function determination, and determination of scope.

FUNCTION DETERMINATION LOGIC. The use of this system requires the construction of a FAST diagram utilizing the determination logic questions "How?" "Why?" and "When?" The steps necessary to construct the FAST diagram are as follows:

1. Prepare a list of all functions by an entire system or a major portion of a system, using the verb and noun technique of identification of functions.

2. Write each function on a small card. Select a card with the function that you consider to be the basic function. Determine the position of the next higher and lower function cards by specifically answering the following logic questions: "How is this function accomplished?" "Why is this function performed?" "When is this function performed?" Using one of the functions selected, apply the logic questions to determine the functions to the right and left of it, as shown in Fig. 3.

<pre>
                           | FUNCTION |
        ASK WHY? ←| SELECTED |→ ASK HOW?
</pre>

Fig. 3 The "why" and "how" logic.

Let us look at the example of a room air conditioner with a remote thermostat controlling the operation of the air conditioner. The function selected was to "cool room." By asking the logic question "Why do we cool room?" we answer, "Provide comfort." The next question is "How do we cool room?" It is answered "By cooling air," as shown in Fig. 4.

At the same time, the question "Why?" must be answered. Why do we "cool air?" "To cool room." Why "cool room"? To "provide comfort," etc. By this method we can check the proper order of the functions in the diagram and also determine the completeness of the diagram by assuring that all functions are accounted for.

In the next step, we ask "How is the cool-air function performed?" The reply is, "By

<pre>
| PROVIDE | | COOL | | COOL |
| COMFORT | | ROOM | | AIR |
</pre>

Fig. 4 "Why" and "how" function diagram.

creating refrigeration" and "By discharging air." The next question, "How do we create refrigeration?" gives three answers: (1) by pushing refrigerant, (2) by cooling refrigerant, and (3) by expanding the refrigerant. Therefore all the three answers—"push refrigerant," "cool refrigerant," and "expand refrigerant"—are required to complete the answer to the question "How?" What about the question "Why?" The answer to all the three questions—"Why do we push refrigerant?" "Why do we cool refrigerant?" and "Why do we expand refrigerant?" is "to create refrigeration." The answer to the question "How do we cool refrigerant?" is "by cooling condenser." How do we "cool condenser"? "by pushing air." The logic questions are satisfied, and we have the blocks on the FAST diagram shown in Fig. 5. The determination logic questions are then applied to each function, and the FAST diagram is continued until we arrive at a function that is an accepted interface function for the scope of the problem (see Fig. 6). Many times, asking the question "Can we do without it?" helps to eliminate an unnecessary function.

CRITICAL PATH DETERMINATION. When all the determination logic questions "How?" and "Why?" are answered for each function, we have established the relation between the functions at higher and lower levels that are required to perform the

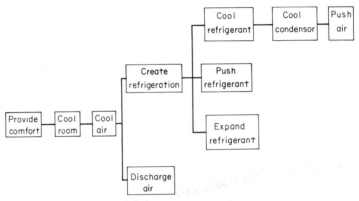

Fig. 5   Basic FAST diagram.

highest-level basic function. The arrangement of these functions, as shown by the FAST diagram (Fig. 6), establishes the critical path. The critical path identifies the functions that are the result of other functions to be performed.

SUPPORTING FUNCTION DETERMINATION. After the critical path functions have been selected and positioned on the FAST diagram, the remaining functions from the list in step 1 are placed on the diagram by applying the question "When?"

On the accompanying complete FAST diagram for the room air conditioner, if there were a function that was being performed at the same time as the function "discharge air," then it would be placed in the same vertical line and there would be a dotted line connecting the function being considered to the "cool air" function. The dotted line would indicate a secondary or supporting path. The secondary function paths are usually the result of specific methods chosen to implement the function.

If the hardware details have been or are being designed, the parts that perform a function can also be added to the FAST diagram and are placed directly below the function that they perform.

DETERMINATION OF SCOPE. In order to limit the FAST diagram to a specifically determined problem, the scope of the problem is defined and outlined on the FAST diagram by the scope lines (vertical broken lines). The left scope line is placed between the basic function under consideration and the highest-order basic function. In other words, the function on the left of the scope line is the next higher-order function, which will not be completely satisfied by the solution of this problem. The function on the right is the basic function, which must be satisfied by this product or service. In the example considered here, the room air conditioner must satisfactorily "cool room," but it will only partially perform the "provide comfort" function. The right scope line is drawn to the left of a function that is an acceptable interface to the product or service under consideration—a suitable input to the system.

In our example, the "provide power" interface function is the lowest-level function we wish to consider in discussing the room air conditioner. The manufacturer of the room air conditioner will expect the user to provide an AC power source. The choice of the scope if arbitrary, and it is often necessary to reevaluate the scope at the completion of the FAST diagram.

This completes the mechanics of constructing the FAST diagram. A careful analysis of the details of the diagram will reveal interesting and useful relations. The function to the right of a selected function tells how the function is performed. The function to the left indicates why the function is performed. The functions above and below show which functions are happening at the same time. Finally, if parts are available, the diagram shows what functions are performed by which parts. (See Fig. 6.)

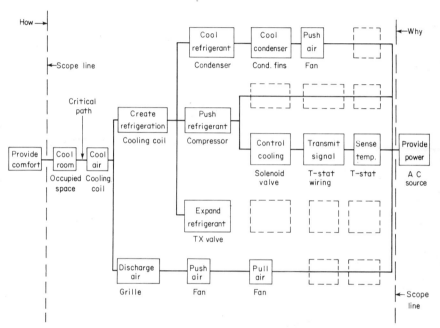

Fig. 6 FAST diagram of a room air conditioner.

Evaluation of functions   Once all the functions have been classified, they are evaluated by placing a value on each function and establishing a cost/value ratio for that function. The cost/value ratio is a measure of the worth of the present approach. It is also a measure of the ultimate amount of unnecessary cost or the value improvement potential. Depending on the method of evaluation of function, these indexes may run from two to one up to several hundred to one. If consistent methods are used for the evaluation of functions, it is possible to establish standards of value that indicate when an index is higher than "Normal." There are four basic methods of evaluation of functions:

1. Record the cost of material content only.

2. Use the technique of evaluation by comparison to establish the value of the elemental basic function only.

3. On a system, use evaluation by comparison to establish the value of each of the functions that are identical to the basic function of the system, then add together.

4. On a system, add the actual cost of the functions that are identical to the basic function of the system.

To assure valid comparisons, only indexes generated by the same method should be compared. Using this technique, cost/value relations can be determined for functions, products, customers, etc. A plot or chart which indicates these ratios can be analyzed to identify out-of-line areas. With each block of this chart identifying the function, cost, value, and ratio, an analysis of this chart would indicate poor and good value areas. The chart can be done on a generation breakdown basis and the part name put in each block (see Fig. 7), or it can be done purely on a function basis, without part names.

If the function classification has been performed by the construction of the FAST diagram, the evaluation may be performed utilizing the diagram.

To perform this cost allocation, the function blocks on the FAST diagram are num-

Fig. 7 Cost/value ratio record form.

VALUE ENGINEERING

FUNCTION/COST ANALYSIS
WORKSHEET

Project Name _____ Reference _____ Date _____ Sheet _____ of _____

Project number_____

Subject _____

Item No.	Item	No. req'd	Cost/ item	Ext. cost	Functions (verb/noun)					
1										
2										
3										
4										
5										
6										
7										
8										
9										
10										
11										
12										
13										
14										
15										
16										
17										
18										
19										
Parts count		XXXXX	XXX	Function classification B (basic), S (secondary)						
Total cost/item										
Total extended cost										
Total cost per function (C_f)										
Function cost target (C_t)										
Differential ($C_f - C_t$)										

Fig. 8 Work sheet for function/cost analysis.

bered. These functions are used as column headings under a related number on the function/cost analysis sheet (Fig. 8) or function/time analysis sheet (Fig. 9). Items or part names, number required, cost per item, and extended costs are added in the case of function/cost analysis or sequential actions, and the time required to complete each action is added to the sheet in the case of function/time analysis. The functions of the part or sequential actions are analyzed and the cost is allocated actually or proportionately to each of the functions performed. The totals at the bottom of the page provide the visibility of cost for each function as well as the total costs for basic and secondary functions. It is sometimes desirable to transfer these totals to the blocks on the FAST diagram to give added visibility to the lateral buildup of cost that provides the basic function. This method makes immediately apparent where the costs are distributed and shows the total costs involved in performing the functions on the critical path.

VALUE ENGINEERING

FUNCTION/TIME ANALYSIS
WORKSHEET

Project name_____ Reference_____ Date_____ Sheet____ of____

Project number_____

Subject_____

Action No.	Actions (sequential)	Time	Functions (verb/noun)							
1										
2										
3										
4										
5										
6										
7										
8										
9										
10										
11										
12										
13										
14										
15										
16										
17										
18										
19										
20										
	Total time		Function classification B (basic), S (secondary)							
	Total time per function (T_f)									
	Function time target (T_t)									
	Differential ($T_f - T_t$)									

Fig. 9 Work sheet for function/time analysis.

Innovation Phase

In the innovation phase, we generate ways to perform functions. By examining those functions on the FAST diagram that are adjacent to each other or are performed at the same time, many ways to combine, modify, or otherwise perform these functions can be developed. One of the many techniques that can be used to generate problem-solving ideas is brainstorming, which is often used in conjunction with the synectics technique. After a quantity of ideas have been produced, they can be separated into categories. By manipulating this material, a stepping stone for developing definitive potential solutions or feasible concepts can be achieved. When an appropriate number of concepts have been developed, evaluation can take place, as described in the next phase.

Evaluation Phase

The concepts obtained in the innovation phase are evaluated using a systematic approach consisting of the following seven steps:

1. *Select criteria* upon which decisions will be based. Such criteria are actually expressions of specifications (requirements) to be met and may involve cost, weight, delivery, reliability, human factors, and so on. Criteria should reflect not only the specifications and requirements but also the preferences of the decision makers; they should be chosen by those who can make the decision to implement the proposals. Since the decision maker sometimes sees proposals after selections have been made, the probability that they will win acceptance depends to a large degree on how well the criteria upon which the decisions were based agree with the decision maker's viewpoints. It is extremely important to know the environmental conditions, to understand the ramifications involved, and to place oneself as closely as possible in the decision maker's position when selecting criteria for evaluation. This is also important when determining the relative importance between criteria.

2. *Assign relative weights* to the criteria. Although you may be interested in several

CRITERIA WEIGHTING
WORKSHEET

VALUE ENGINEERING _____ Date_____ Sheet _____ of _____

Project Name_____ Project No. _____

Building No. _____ Drawing No. _____

Subject _____ Reference_____

A. Paired comparisons. Pair each criterion with each of the others. Decide which one of each pair is more important.

Decision number	Paired comparison (Which is more important?)		Decision
1	A-	or B-	
2	A-	or C-	
3	A-	or D-	
4	A-	or E-	
5	A-	or F-	
6	B-	or C-	
7	B-	or D-	
8	B-	or E-	
9	B-	or F-	
10	C-	or D-	
11	C-	or E-	
12	C-	or F-	
13	D-	or E-	
14	D-	or F-	
15	E-	or F-	

B. Relative importance. (1) List criteria. (2) Place an X under each decision number which corresponds with the decision made above. (3) Indicate totals under n. (4) Divide n by the total number of decisions. This is the weight factor.

Criteria	1	2	3	4	5	6	7	8	9	10	11	12	13	14	15	n	Weight factor $(\frac{n}{t})$
A-																	
B-																	
C-																	
D-																	
E-																	
F-																	
													Total			t	1.000

Fig. 10 Work sheet for criteria weighting.

criteria, it is probable that you ascribe varying degrees of importance to each. There are a multitude of techniques available to aid in determining the magnitude of weighting to be assigned each criterion. One of the methods of weighting, the paired-comparison method, was developed by L. L. Thurston, the father of psychophysics. Criteria are paired in all possible combinations. Each pair is considered separately, and the criterion that is of more importance is selected. Important criteria are repeated frequently. See Fig. 10 for the work sheet that can be used for such comparisons.

3. *Develop measurable ranges.* Criteria should be expressed in measurable terms so the degree to which a particular approach meets requirements can be ascertained. A range is established to reflect the following limits: (*a*) the best condition we can hope for and (*b*) the worst condition we will tolerate.

4. *Select a standard scale.* A standard scale must be selected so that various criteria can be compared on a common basis. For example, lead and feathers may not be compared per se, but if correlated to weight, a relationship between these dissimilar items can be made. Any numbers can be used for the scale. The important point is that the same scale must be used for all criteria.

5. *Develop a utility curve.* A curve must be developed for each criterion so that all points along the range can be translated into points along the scale. Scale points are now related only to the upper and lower ends of the range.

6. *Compare alternatives to criteria and assign points.* The information we have developed thus far is summarized in matrix form. See Fig. 11.

7. *Apply criteria weighting and sum-weighted points for each choice.* Weights must

VALUE ENGINEERING   EVALUATION MATRIX
                                        WORKSHEET

Date _____ Sheet _____ of _____

Project name_____   Project No. _____

Building No. _____   Drawing No._____

Subject _____   Reference _____

Criteria / Alternate solutions	WT.	A	B	C	D	E	F	G	H	I	J	Total (figure of merit)
1												
2												
3												
4												
5												
6												
7												
8												

Fig. 11 Work sheet for evaluation matrix.

now be incorporated, with each point assignment so that the relative importance of each criterion can be taken into proper consideration. This is done by multiplying each point assignment by each weight. The total score is determined by summing weighted points for each criterion.

Implementation Phase

The implementation phase of the value engineering plan is very important, because without implemented solutions, the remainder of the plan becames academic. To promote implementation, the decision maker should be involved from the very beginning of the task. If the decision maker(s) is part of the study, the probability of implementation is high. Since value engineering will most often by applied during the design stage, the

VALUE ENGINEERING PROPOSAL
WORKSHEET

VALUE ENGINEERING

Date_____ Sheet_____ of _____

Project Name_____ Project No. _____

Building No. _____ Drawing No. _____

Subject_____ Reference_____

Present (show sketches)	Proposed (show sketches)

Nonrecurring costs (est.)				Direct Mat'l	Direct labor	Variable portions of burden	Total variable cost
	Hrs.	$					
Design			Present cost				
Drftng.			Proposed cost (est.)				
Evaul.							
			Net savings:				Proposed by:
Admin.			1. Difference var. cost,				
Maint.			proposed vs. present _____				
Permits			2. Less nonrecur.				
Contract Admin.			costs _____				
Misc.							
Total			3. Net savings _____				

Fig. 12   Work sheet for value engineering proposal.

design engineers should be the key members of the team. The personal contribution from them will greatly enhance implementation and study success. However, the elements of change, risk, embarrassment, and opportunity should be carefully considered as they relate to the design engineers. Many ideas are implemented informally. Oral and written reports should be short but well documented. See Fig. 12.

VALUE ENGINEERING USING COST ANALYSIS TECHNIQUES

Cost analysis techniques are used to identify high-cost areas to assist in directing value engineering efforts to work on those elements that offer the greatest opportunity for value improvement and pinpointing areas of unnecessary costs. It is these areas which offer the maximum return on investment for value engineering effort.

Getting familiar with the costs is the most basic of all cost-analysis techniques. Just knowing the cost can often be enough to motivate an engineer to take that early second look at the work that has been done and to improve the cost at a point in the design cycle where changes are easier to make. The simple act of finding out the cost of an item will frequently be the signal for prompt action. The signal may be simply intuitive, or perhaps an actual mental comparison is made, consciously or unconsciously, with the known cost of something else.

While the techniques discussed below do not represent all analysis methods, they do highlight those that have been found most useful in value engineering work.

1. *Cost arrangement analysis.* This involves preparing a generation breakdown of all the components of a system in a natural descending order, starting with the most important component of the system and descending by natural breakdown to the accessories that perform secondary functions in the system. See Fig. 13.

The generation breakdown of costs (Fig. 14) provides data that are in good form for further analysis. It permits quick identification of high-cost items.

From the generation breakdown, a relisting of high-cost items can be made which will help in separating the "significant few" from the "inconsequential many." It is clear that maximum return from value engineering effort will result from concentration on the significant few.

2. *Cost visibility displays.* It often helps in cost analysis to be able to get a picture of the cost situation. Pie charts, tree charts, and graphs or bar charts are often used for such purposes.

a. Pie charts. If a circle or pie is representative of the total cost of an item under study, it can be divided into sections which represent the various cost elements, cost increments, or other cost factors. Such a chart may dramatically show that certain elements are out of line. Comparison with pie charts by overlay or section comparisons of similar parts, units, or functions will identify the amounts of unnecessary costs (Fig.

Level	Description	Drawing no.
0	Chiller	J1975 M-3
1	Chiller pump	J1975 M-4
1	Chiller piping	J1975 M-2
1	Cooling tower	J1975 M-3
2	Valves and accessories	J1975 M-4
2	Expansion tank	J1975 M-4
2	Cooling tower pump	J1975 M-4
2	Cooling tower sump	J1975 M-4

Fig. 13 Generation breakdown of the components of a chiller system.

Part	Quantity	Labor	Overhead	Material	Total
Chiller (100-ton)	1	$2,500	$ 775	$13,000	$16,275
Chiller piping	500 ft	$7,500	$1,000	$ 3,000	$11,500
Cooling tower	1	$ 500	$ 300	$ 6,000	$ 6,800

Fig. 14 Generation breakdown of the costs of the elements of a chiller system.

15).   In Unit I, we might question the high material and overhead factors; in unit II, the high inspection factor.

  b. Tree charts. It is helpful for management and value engineering to be able to visualize cost arrangements.   Thus the generation breakdown obtained earlier in this chapter could be displayed in a tree chart, with costs assigned in each block (Fig. 16).

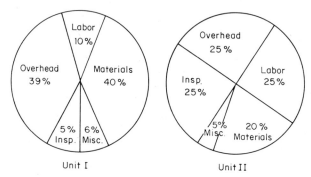

Fig. 15   Pie charts.

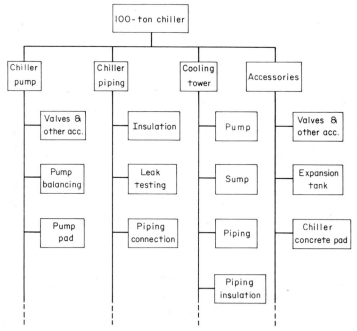

Fig. 16   Tree chart of a chiller system.

  c. Graphs or bar charts. The cost allocation techniques using the graphs or bar charts are often used for cost visibility displays.

  The plotting of cost per weight or property—for instance, on rectangular, log, or log-log graph paper—can document relative cost data in readily visible ways.   This is very useful for comparison purposes and helpful for value decisions.   Graphs are also useful for plotting of costs of different approaches, determination of breakeven points, estimating savings, and learning curve data analysis.

In cost-per-pound analysis, if log-log paper is used and the cost per pound is plotted for several different parts that have something in common—such as function, size, shape, method, etc.—a 45-degree line drawn through the lowest cost per pound will reveal items with higher ratios which should be further analyzed.

The above cost analysis techniques are an essential part of value engineering. They are first used in the *information phase*, but they are also essential in the *evaluation phase* to compare, analyze, and present the cost and function picture. Not all these tools (techniques) need to be used on each value analysis effort. With experience, the analyst will determine which method is best suited to the decision-making process involved and which will best meet the needs of the problem or of finding a better way, procedure, design, or product.

VALUE ENGINEERING STUDY APPROACH

Value engineering studies may be performed by one of the three approaches: (1) by a team, (2) by an individual, or (3) by a modified team.

Most studies are performed by teams, although it has been shown that an experienced individual can do competent value engineering studies when provided with adequate support. In the modified team approach, the individual conducts the value engineering study and uses the team members more in the capacity of a sounding board for ideas, approaches, etc. For training purposes and for most complex items, the team approach is the most desirable means for the performance of a value engineering study. In all cases—individual, modified team, or team study—the same value engineering procedure is followed.

A value engineering team usually consists of from four to eight persons. A team size above six persons should be avoided because the group becomes unwieldly and inefficient. The team is formally organized and appointed by competent authority for the purpose of conducting a value engineering study of a particular system, item, or project. An experienced value engineer is assigned as one member of the team. The reason for appointing him as a team member is to assure that the value engineering method is implicitly followed. This is desirable so that project time is used to best advantage and so that team members follow value engineering principles properly. A team chairman and secretary are normally selected by the team members.

Selection of team members is based upon individual work experience or background and upon the technology involved in the particular project under study. Team members should have had value engineering training, if at all possible, prior to appointment. A typical value engineering study team might consist of one or more persons from each of the following areas:

1. Engineering (electrical, mechanical, civil, etc.)
2. Procurement
3. Maintenance

VALUE ENGINEERING INVOLVEMENT

Since 1947, value engineering has come a long way. It was first used by Mr. Lawrence D. Miles in General Electric Compnay (GE). It was in 1954 when the first Department of Defense organization, the U.S. Navy Bureau of Ships, began setting up a value engineering program to reduce costs. Many defense contracts now contain incentives for contractor sharing in all approved value engineering change proposals. As a result of these contract incentives, value engineering savings have increased consistently and rapidly to the point where they now account for an increasing portion of the value engineering savings reported in the Department of Defense Cost Reduction Program.

The General Services Administration (GSA) is deeply committed to value engineering. Starting in April 1974, on all jobs under 3 million dollars, the GSA required one certified value engineer. On larger jobs, everyone on the design team has to be trained in the 40-hour workshop. This new requirement caps an intensive analysis of value engineering over a four-year test period. Don Parker, director of value engineering, says that the GSA has spent $480,000 on value engineering administration and fees which has saved 4 dollars on every 1 dollar spent. Out of a number of contractor proposals for cost savings, some of the proposals were approved for a total savings of 6 million dollars, with

3 million dollars going to the GSA and the contractor earning 50 percent of the savings. Under GSA regulations, if a subcontractor comes up with a cost-saving idea, the GSA gets only 40 percent of the savings and the rest is split between the prime and subcontractor.

At Xerox Corporation, the Information Technology Group has a formal 40-hour training program under which the employees from all disciplines—including plant engineering and maintenance, procurement, manufacturing, and research and development—are taught value engineering techniques.

VALUE ENGINEERING APPLICATION

Now to the guts of the proposal. How do you use the people trained in value analysis in plant engineering? There are several basic options. If you believe the best place to obtain maximum cost effectiveness is before work is done—and this is a valid conclusion—you can assign value analysis people to the areas of developing design criteria and standards.

Function

   1. Reduces dust (cleanliness)
   2. Screens operations (hazardous)
   3. Provides privacy (for people)
   4. Provides security (for things)
   5. Stores materials (dangerous items)

Need

   1. Temporary   30–180 days
   2. Temporary   6 months–1 year
   3. Semipermanent   1–2 years
   4. Semipermanent   2–3 years
   5. Permanent   More than 3 years

Construction

   A. Drape
   B. Pipe and canvas
   C. Purchased prefab partition
   D. Stud wall—covered two sides
   E. Masonry

Function	1	2	3	4	5
Need 1	A	A	C	C	B
2	B	B	C	C	C
3	C	C	D	D	C
4	C	D	D	D	D
5	D	E	D	D	E
			Construction		

Fig. 17 An example of partition standards matrix.

The person who sends you a plant work request usually asks you to do something and tells you how to do it or mentions an end product that will be satisfactory. If it is a good plant work request, both the criteria and solution are furnished. Since the requestor is likely to be an amateur in plant engineering solutions, the value analyst can review the need, using techniques we have talked about, and develop a value-analyzed solution to the problem for use as a design criterion. A partition, for example, can be a brick wall, a concrete block wall, a stud wall with sheet rock on both sides, a prefabricated metal panel, a screwed pipe and laced canvas construction, or a drape of cloth or plastic. The determination as to which partition satisfies the function ensures lowest cost and makes the plant engineering job easier.

To establish plant standards using value analysis, you can take the same set of partitions, from brick to drapes, and analyze the detailed construction of each for the better way to build each. These analyses, when converted into standards, can then be matched with criteria to give the plant engineering staff a preengineered, quick design capability. A simple approach to the application of criteria is shown in Fig. 17. This sample matrix lists functions; need, stated in terms of time; and preengineered, prevalue-analyzed methods or designs.

Identification of the requirement in terms of function and need establishes criteria leading to selection of the appropriate design. High-volume, repetitive work is extremely susceptible to this method of handling. Equipment evaluation, made using value analysis techniques, may well give you standards which enhance your ability to satisfy management and purchasing questions.

Another area for value analysis application in plant engineering is in the design of unique installations. A value analyst can work with the design engineer, or the design engineer can become a value analyst. Use of a value analysis checklist that includes considered alternatives to a given design may be required. If you use this technique and hear the scream that a value checklist on a design is an onerous, unnecessary chore, you are probably hearing the reaction of a design engineer who does not want to think.

A final application of value analysis can often be found in evolution of the methods used to communicate the plant engineering product or solution to the doer. Some different methods may be devised that yield excellent results. Alternatives varying from a marked up layout, a sketch rather than a drawing, marked up standard drawings, or marked up standard specifications may be satisfactory as far as getting the job done is concerned— just as much so as fresh drawings and specifications might be. Here again the matrix approach may be used to establish standards to do the job more easily and quickly.

In conclusion, do not be satisfied with what has been suggested in this chapter or with the way you are doing things. Blast the image, think a bit, use the value analysis approach to develop your own program and applications. You and your company are sure to benefit.

REFERENCES

1. American Cyanamid Company: *Value Engineering & Analysis,* Basic Training Manual, 1967.
2. E. O. Clark: "Application of Value Analysis to Plant Engineering Efforts," paper delivered at the 20th Plant Engineering and Maintenance Conference, held concurrently with the 20th Plant Engineering and Maintenance Show, Cleveland, March 24–27, 1969.
3. B. T. Lewis and J. P. Marron: *Facilities and Plant Engineering Handbook,* McGraw-Hill, New York, 1973.
4. D. W. Lindsay: "What Is I.T.G. All About?" Xerox Corporation, April 10, 1974 (interoffice memorandum).
5. L. D. Miles: *Techniques of Value Analysis and Engineering,* McGraw-Hill, New York, 1972.
6. U.S. Department of Defense: *Principles and Applications of Value Engineering,* vol. 1, 1968 (a course book).
7. Xerox Corporation: *Value Engineering,* Basic Training Manual, 1973.

Chapter 4

Computer Impact on Plant Engineering

EFRAIM TURBAN
Professor of Management, Florida International University
and
ALAN J. PARKER
Associate Professor of Business Administration, School of Business and Organizational Sciences, Florida International University

INTRODUCTION

Computers* were originally developed for scientific calculations; however, as certain technical problems in the design of computers were solved, other application areas were

---

* The word "computer" as used here is synonymous with the terms "electronic data processor," "data processor," and "electronic digital computer."

developed. Most large companies have computerized their formerly manual accounting systems; budgeting is usually performed with computer analysis; and, finally, the computer has been making itself felt on the plant floor.

A computer is an information processing machine; it is capable of performing thousands (and in some cases millions) of calculations or manipulations of information in a second. Two types of information enter a computer—*programs* and *data.* *Programs* are instructions to the computer that tell it how to manipulate the data. As plant engineers, and "users" of the computer, the information that will be input is *data.*

Computer Personnel

Within most large firms, computer centers are common due to the need for highly technical personnel. The centers have the following hierarchy and functions:

1. The manager (vice-president) of data processing
2. Systems analyst: Talks with users, helps determine computer needs of users, designs the programming system for the user
3. Programmer: Receives the programming specifications from the systems analyst and actually writes the program in a language that the computer can understand
4. Machine operator: Monitors the computer, places information into input units, removes information from output units

All these individuals are responsible for seeing that user requirements are met.

THE COMPUTER

A computer consists of five functional units: input, output, arithmetic-logic, control, and storage. The input unit accepts information in some form—punched cards, magnetic tape, etc.—and transforms the information to electronic impulses. Within the system boundaries, information is moving around as electronic impulses. The output unit transforms the electronic impulses into a form that is readable: printed pages, graphs, charts, etc. The arithmetic-logic unit is the place where all arithmetic and logical processing takes place. The storage unit (memory) acts as a retainer of information. The control unit controls the operation of the system by following the instructions (program). The components of the computer are called *hardware;* programs are called *software.*

ALTERNATIVES TO IN-HOUSE COMPUTERS

There are alternatives to the use of in-house computers. One of these is *timesharing.* With timesharing, many users buy time on a large computer system that may be located nearby or thousands of miles away. The user has a terminal (usually a teletype) in the plant and uses software available through the time-sharing service. The terminal acts as both an input and output unit. Users may also develop and use their own programs on the time-sharing system.

Minicomputers have had a large impact on plant engineering. The application of minis in process and production applications is the greatest use of these inexpensive computers (they usually cost under 2,000 dollars). By 1975, the United States market for minis is expected to reach a quarter of a billion dollars.

APPLICATIONS IN PLANT ENGINEERING

The computer can be used in plant engineering (as well as in other areas) for routine data processing operations such as issuing work orders and keeping and updating cost records. It can also be used in the analysis of information for decision making purposes by executing the required computations more rapidly and accurately than a person could.

The purpose of this section is to evaluate the use of computers in plant engineering. The discussion consists of two major parts. In the first part a computerized system is described; the second part outlines computer uses for nonroutine decisions.

The Components of the System

The system described here is a hypothetical one. Most organizations have only segments of it. As a matter of fact, very few (if any) organizations have such a progressive system, and many companies will never require such. However, this is a complete system, and

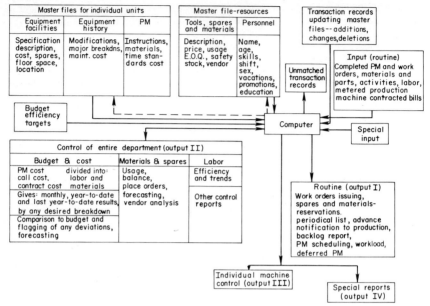

Fig. 1   Computerized plant engineering.

as such it can point out to the user the potential and paths of expanding the use of computers in plant engineering.

The system consists of three major parts: (1) master files, (2) preventive maintenance routines, and (3) plant engineering control routines. Such a system is schematically described in Fig. 1. The major features of each part and relevant references are discussed below.

Master Files for Individual Units

The master files contain the following:

1. *Facilities file.* Relevant information is kept for all (or major) facilities such as buildings, machines, groups of machines, utility systems and roads. (Included are such data as descriptions, cost, economic age, setup costs, floor space, locations, and specification.)

2. *Facilities history.* The routine task of keeping individual facility history cards that note all repairs, modifications, and their associated costs usually involves large amounts of paper work.* This is the major reason why most companies do not have this valuable information.† The computer can maintain up-to-date records of all major repairs, parts replacements, and breakdown diagnoses. The information is recorded directly from field reports and returned work orders. Examples may be found in the references at the end of this chapter.[19,24] ‡

3. *Preventive maintenance.* In this file all Preventive maintenance instructions and frequencies are kept. Also, time standards for repairs, instructions, and materials required can be kept here.

Master Files for Resources

The master files for resources contain all desired information about the resources available to serve the facilities. Such files may include:

---

* Keeping records by machine components is reported by IBM to be impractical since it generates reports too voluminous for realistic analysis.[20] Instead, major machines or systems are now used as control units.

† In a national survey conducted in 1965,[28] it was found that only 42 percent of the large companies in the United States keep history cards for individual facilities.

‡ Superior numbers refer to the end-of-chapter references.

1. *Personnel.* A detailed file is kept on each employee in the plant engineering area; such file includes personal data such as age, education, skills, and positions.

2. *Spare parts.* Spare parts that are interchangeable for different machines are usually recorded here. The information includes such data as usage, price, economic order quantity (E.O.Q.), safety stock, and recommended vendor.

3. *Maintenance materials and tools.* All major maintenance materials (such as lubricants) and tools (such as power tools) can be listed in this file, with their price, usage, capacity, and recommended vendor.

4. *Other resources.* Desired maintenance resources, such as a list of subcontractors, can be listed here.

5. *Budget and targets.* Plant engineering budgets classified in desired forms (e.g., by department or by machine) are listed here. Also, efficiency targets such as work standards or waste rates are recorded here.

These master files should be kept constantly up to date. This is done through the *transaction records,* which are fed into the computer at any desired interval (daily, weekly, etc.). These records include addition or deletion of workers or machines and any changes in the stored information. If transactions cannot be matched against the master files, they are reported in the *unmatched transaction records* for further investigation.

Input

The data fed into the computer can be classified into two groups, routine and special.

Routine input   The routine input includes the *completed (returned) work orders* for any type of work, (including preventive maintenance). It usually includes the labor, spares, and materials used as well as the description of the work executed. Other routine inputs may include the running time of production machines (especially if metered) and the subcontractors' bills. Routine data are generally submitted at regular intervals.

Special input   Special reports may be fed into the computer according to their special use. For example, if a maintenance cost comparison is done with other plants belonging to the same company (or with another plant in the same industry), the relevant data take the form of special input reports. Such an input report is the basis for a special output report.

Output—Routine (Output Type I)

Work order issuing   Work order* issuing is probably the plant engineering area in which computers are used most today. The computer prints out work orders and especially preventive maintenance work orders according to area, craft, or any other desired classification. It can also prepare material and parts reservations for the preventive maintenance work orders as well as an estimate of the time necessary to complete the job. The interested reader is referred to the references at the end of this chapter for detailed descriptions.[1,2,4–6,8,9,21,24]

Periodic list of outstanding work orders   Such periodic lists can be prepared at desired intervals. They are then sent to the *maintenance manager* (or other foreman) for *control* purposes and to the production managers as an *advance notification.*

Preventive maintenance scheduling   In some progressive cases, the computer uses the preventive maintenance orders and time standards for the daily or weekly scheduling of specific workers.[5] The total maintenance workload can be computed, compared, and matched with available resources. If there is an excess workload, the computer can assign overtime, call for subcontracting, or defer second-priority jobs to the next period (in an attempt to provide a constant workload throughout the year). Similar scheduling can be performed for any plant engineering job.

Backlog monitoring   A complementary step to preventive maintenance is backlog monitoring. Since returned work orders (preventive maintenance and call maintenance) signal completion, it is easy to list the overdue ones as a backlog. The computer can also check the "required completion dates" and classify the backlog into "overdue" (which can be automatically rescheduled by the computer for the next period), and to "work

---

* A work order may include all preventive maintenance instructions in the form of a checklist, or the work orders may call for activities which are posted on the machine or filed as standing instructions in the maintenance department.

in progress" (which means that the jobs are not yet overdue). An example of a backlog report is shown in Fig. 2. Other examples appear in the references.[4,8,21,24]

Output—Control (Output Type II)

General The most important part of the computerized system (from the managerial point of view) is the control area. We distinguish between plant engineering departmental control (to be discussed in this paragraph) and individual facility or machine control (to be discussed next). The departmental control system is divided into three major parts: labor efficiency, material and spares control, and overall cost control.

LABOR EFFICIENCY CONTROL. The computer can produce any desired labor efficiency indexes and comparisons (e.g., comparison with last year, with other plants of the

WORK BACKLOG LIST									
Cost actg. No.		Work ord. No. & craft code	Pri-or-ity	Trou-ble code	Work or trouble description	Date sub-mitted	Due date	Std. job No.	Action taken
Unit	Equip.								
06	025717	005732 I	1	03	Mal-funtg Cont. V.	9-14-6	now	856	Started
06	180323	005875 P	1	76	Leaking pump	9-14-6	now	1275	Started
06	751882	005720 M	1	25	Loose str. tread	9-15-6	now		Started
06	092308	005751 P	2	12	Repair insulat'n	9-01-6	S.A.P.	101	
06	051210	004709 D	2	17	Inspect reflux dr.	3-15-6	Next T	1572	
06	041989	005923 E	3	80	Replace lights	9-12-6	S.A.P		Started
06	082095	004712 T	3		Paint oper room	8-30-6	DurTur	288	
06	023315	004890 M	3	09	Overh'l sp. motor	9-02-6	2 mos	1029	Started
06	026092	004910 P	3	71	Install water fount.	9-10-6	S.A.P		
06	073499	005004 L	3		Clean-up grounds	9-09-6	1 mo.		Started

Fig. 2 Work backlog list.

industry, with the time standards, with the targets, or with other plants of the same corporation), showing deviations and the general trend. Such information can be displayed in the form of graphs or images on a cathode ray tube.

MATERIALS AND SPARES CONTROL. Computers are used by many companies, especially in the process industries, to control spare-parts inventories. The computers are used to keep track of the inventories, to issue orders when inventories go below the reorder point, and sometimes to calculate the reorder point, the safety stock, and the economic order quantity to be purchased.[5,8,19] Other applications are for tracing inactive materials and spares and for A.B.C. classification (value-volume analysis). Figure 3 shows examples of inventory control reports.

COST CONTROL. Computerized facilities and plant engineering cost control, almost unknown 10 years ago, is gaining considerable acceptance by many companies today. The major feature of the cost control system is a periodic report (see example in Fig. 4), usually issued once a month. This report gives a complete breakdown of costs by labor and materials and, if desired, into any other category (such as machine component,* maintenance craft, preventive maintenance, contract maintenance, manufacturing department, or group of similar machines). The report usually lists costs during last month, year to date, and last year to date. Such computerized cost control is illustrated in the references.[2,11,19,24] In a more progressive report, a comparison with the budget (or target) is given and any deviation larger than a certain preassigned percentage is marked with an asterisk, using the "management by exception principle".† Trend lines can be

---

* As mentioned above, it is usually undesirable to use machine components as a control unit. However, in special cases where excessive costs are suspected, a detailed recording and analysis by components is advisable.

† Here, an "exception" type of reporting may be used where only "out of control" activities are reported.

presented in a way similar to what has been mentioned in the labor control discussion.

OTHER CONTROL REPORTS. Additional reports may be used at any desired intervals as a control device for measuring the overall effectiveness of the plant engineering department. Some such measures of effectiveness are maintenance downtime as a percentage of scheduled machine hours, average size of backlog, maintenance cost per standard machine hour, maintenance costs per standard production hour, maintenance

a.

EQUIPMENT PARTS USAGE SUMMARY								
Equipment Ident. No.	Equipment description	Work order No.	Invent- tory No.	Parts description	Qty.	Unit of M.	Total parts cost
93045101	Equipment No. on crude unit		53916G 39512M	Gasket $1\frac{1}{2}$ in. ut.	2 1	EA BX	3.10 .70

b.

INVENTORY ACTIVITY REPORT												
Invent. No.	Part description	Max	Min	Bal	Prev bal	Allo	Re-or Qty.	On ord	Lead Time	Rec'd	Iss'd	Fore cast
14032M	3/4/20 in SS Bolts	180	120	120	170	60		40		20	70	25

c.

VENDOR ANALYSIS					
Invent. No.	Description of part	Vendor name	Rating of vendor		
			Cost	Reli'le del'y	Del'y cond.
13547P	2 in. gasket on J. J. Pump No. 12763	John Jones, Inc.	Good	Good	Poor

Fig. 3. Material and spares control reports.

cost per ton of product, or maintenance cost as a percentage of total cost. In all such cases a target comparison to last year or to other departments can be executed.

Individual Facility Control (Output Type III)

Most of the control methods presented in the previous paragraph for the control of the entire plant engineering department can be used for the control of other organizational levels, e.g., processing unit, a group of machines, or even an individual unit. It is usually desired to break down the total plant engineering cost and to point out the "most cost consuming" facilities. Then, a special analysis can be performed for each such facility. The computer can be programmed to check the ratio of preventive maintenance cost to total maintenance cost and take one of several possible actions, including a change in preventive maintenance frequencies.

Special Reports (Output Type IV)

The routine system can generate several *special reports* when desired. Examples are manpower requirement prediction, periodical availability of machines for maintenance, ratio of preventive maintenance cost to total maintenance cost, ratio of total maintenance cost to total manufacturing cost, equipment failure rate, and analysis of sources of trouble. The quantity (and quality) of the special reports is, of course, limited by the cost involved, but it is restricted more than that by the user's lack of imagination.

MONTHLY   MAINTENANCE COST REPORT PERIOD ENDING SHIP DATE 660

SYSTEM	DESCRIPTION	BLD/DPT	MO/PM	MO/CALL	MO/SCHO	MO/CONT	MO/TOT	YTD/PM	YR/CALL	YR/SCHO	YR/CONT	PM/EST	ACT
160003	STEAM GENERATOR 3	030770	21				21	21		46		9	7
160004	STEAM GENERATOR 4	030770	264				264	264				171	91
160005	STEAM GENERATOR 5	030770	301				301	301				162	104
160006	STEAM GENERATOR 6	730776	19				19	22				6	7
160007	STEAM GENERATOR 7	730776	13		23		36	15		23		5	4
160008	STEAM GENERATOR 8	730776	134	23			158	136	23			141	46
163001	STEAM LINES INSIDE	030770	130				130	132				68	45
163002	STEAM LINE LAB	730776	22				22	22				12	8
167001	STEAM LINE OUTSIDE	770		9			9		9				
169001	STORM SEWER LINES 1	772											
169002	STORM SEWER LINES 2	730776	1	6			7	1	6			1	1
170001	TRUCK LEVELER FL-1	004698	13				13	28				10	5
182001	WATER SOFTENER 1	020770	5				5	5				6	2
182002	WATER SOFTENER 2	730776	32				32	32				16	11

(a)

SEMI-ANNUAL MAINTENANCE COST REPORT PERIOD ENDING SHOP DATE 660

MACHINE NO	DESCRIPTION	BLD/DPT	PUR/GY	SYS/COST	YTD/PM	YR/CALL	YR/SCHO	YR/CONT	YR/TOT	PREV/PM	PREV/TOT
160001003734	VALVE SAFETY	030770									
160001003858	VALVE STEAM	030770									
160001004734	VALVE SAFETY	030770									
160001	SYSTEM TOTAL										
160002000000	STEAM GENERATOR 2	030770		62000							
160002001231	STACK EXHAUST	030770									
160002001304	CONTROL	030770			12				12		
160002001306	CONTROL SWITCH	030770									
160002001307	VALVE CONTROL	030770			6				6		
160002001330	COUPLING	030770			6				6		
160002001407	EXHAUST FAN	030770			35				35		
160002001467	HEATER AIR	030770			17				17		
160002001543	METER STEAM	030770			6				6		
160002001734	VALVE SAFETY										

(b)

KEY

MO/PM = Monthly P.M. cost	YR/SCHO = Year-to-date scheduled maintenance cost
MO/CALL = Monthly call Maintenance cost	YR/CONT = Year-to-date contract cost
MO/SCHO = Monthly scheduled maintenance cost	PM/EST = Total estimatal P.M. Labor hours
MO/CONT = Monthly contract maintenance cost	ACT = Total Actual P.M. Labor hours
MO/TO = Monthly total maintenance cost	YR/TOT = Year-to-date total maintenance cost
YTD/PM = Year-to-date P.M. cost	PREV/PM = Previous year's total PM cost
YR/CALL = Year-to-date Call maintenance cost	PREV/TOT = Previous year's total maintenance cost.

Fig. 4 Cost control reports.

The Routine System—Evaluation

The routine system just described deals mainly with clerical functions (such as issuing work orders) and with repetitive decisions (such as computing E.O.Q.), where data are readily available and where substantial savings are more likely to be realized. However, there are several more complicated decisions, such as determining preventive maintenance frequencies, which can be computerized and added to the system. The routine system can be expanded to include even more sophisticated decisions. Evidence of increasing interest in the use of computers for such maintenance decisions will be discussed next.

More Sophisticated Computerized Decision Making

In addition to the use of computers in the routine areas described in the previous paragraph, there is some evidence of pioneering work in which operations research (O.R.) models have been developed for solving more complicated plant engineering problems. Practical use of these O.R. models requires computers. Some interesting examples are listed below:

Project control with computerized PERT and CPM Many companies are using computerized PERT and CPM techniques for the control of large plant engineering projects such as equipment installation or relocation and major plant overhauls. Almost all major airlines and refineries use it in their annual (or periodical) shutdowns. Steel companies repair and reline their furnaces with computerized PERT. The same tool is reported to be used by an instrumentation company in its plant rearrangement[12] and by a pharmaceutical company for major overhaul.[15] The computer can produce a complete critical path network,[25] arranged in any desired form (for example, activities which can be processed first can be printed in the first column). Also, any constraints can be automatically positioned. Paths of activities can be logically grouped and coded across the chart.

Optimizing the plant engineering crew size Several theoretical models (e.g., queuing, simulation) were developed to solve this important problem.* The problem here is to balance the idle time of the repair crew vs. the idle time of facilities waiting for repair. However, there is very little evidence of practical use.[19,21]

Facilities replacement decisions In this area, too, considerable theoretical work and very little practical application have been performed.[7] For example, computer simulation has been used in group replacement.[32] Also, component replacement schedules for vehicles were developed with the aid of computers.[6]

Maintenance diagnosis and self-control Computers can process and analyze information recorded by diagnostic instruments and make the appropriate decision; e.g., "stop machine," "adjust machine," "call attention," etc. This is one of the most sophisticated uses in which both maintenance decisions and resultant actions are completely automated. A computer is used in this manner in the International Monetary Fund building in Washington, D.C. Here the computer operates and controls all air conditioning, ventilating, and heating equipment. It gives warning when maintenance is required for mechanical equipment and shuts equipment down automatically before there is any damage. A related problem that the computer solves is to decide when to use computers for diagnosis.[22]

Equipment-breakdown analysis Equipment breakdown analysis, by part type or by any desired classification, can be performed by a computer.[19] Here the computer can fit theoretical distributions and identify and classify causes of breakdown.

Assignment problems Matching the work to workers may be one of the most complicated plant engineering problems. Simplified models can be used in certain cases. An example is cited in the references.[21]

Revise preventive maintenance frequencies The computer can be used to analyze the effect of a change in preventive maintenance frequencies on the breakdown rate and to revise these frequencies accordingly. Detailed discussions appear in the references.[2,21]

Inventory decisions Various sophisticated plant engineering inventory decision models have been developed. Most of them require computers for implementation. For example, a refinery decides whether spare parts should be item-controlled or bulk-controlled. Another interesting example is to find how many spare parts to stock at various locations[11] (i.e., echelon stocking). As with the replacement and crew-size cases, there is considerable gap between the theoretical work and the practical application.

All these special applications are in various stages, but considering the expected developments in computer technology, it is believed that their use will spread into many plant engineering departments in the near future.

REFERENCES

1. K. L. Alvey and W. F. Parker: "Computer Schedules Instrument Inspection," *Plant Engineering*, July 1964, pp. 146–148.

* Maintenance labor amounts, on the average, to about 50 percent of the total maintenance bill.

2. Lorin Andrews: "Maintenance Program Computer Controlled," *Plant Engineering*, September 1965, pp. 133–135.
3. R. A. Bernstein: "How Computers Work," *Factory*, April 1965.
4. J. H. Carl: "Computer System Puts Squeeze on High Maintenance Cost," *Iron Age*, October 24, 1963, pp. 71–73.
5. B. Carson: "EDP Memory Schedules Maintenance Operations," *Plant Engineering*, February 1966, pp. 115–117.
6. R. L. Cash: "Computerized Control of Maintenance" in *Techniques of Plant Engineering and Maintenance*, vol. XVI, Clapp and Poliak, Inc., 1965.
7. L. S. Dryden: "Computer Keeps Careful Check on Vehicle Maintenance Costs," *Plant Engineering*, August 1967, pp. 123–125.
8. "Would You Believe . . . This Computer Printout Upgrades PM in Three Minutes a Month?" *Factory*, December, 1966, pp. 70–71 (editorial).
9. "Is a Computer the Best Maintenance Management Tool?" *Factory*, January 1968, pp. 12–13 (editorial).
10. W. C. Field: "Plant Engineering Projects Computer Controlled," *Plant Engineering*, April 1965, pp. 122–124.
11. S. Fielden et al.: *Maintenance Parts Logistics—A Simulation Approach*, IBM Corporation Field Engineering Division, Poughkeepsie, N.Y., 1965.
12. A. S. Goldman and T. B. Slattery: *Maintainability: A Major Element of System Effectiveness*, Wiley, New York, 1964.
13. P. Green et al.: "Solving Your Plant Problems by Simulation," *Factory*, February 1959, pp. 80–85.
14. D. Gross and L. L. Ray: "Choosing Spare Parts Inventory Operating Procedure—Balk Control Versus Item Control," *Journal of Industrial Engineering*, November–December 1964, pp. 310–315.
15. L. M. Hansen and D. M. Wright: "Application of Critical Path Scheduling to Maintenance," *Modern Maintenance Management*, American Management Association Publication, New York, 1963.
16. R. F. Hespos: "Simulation as an Aid to Staffing Customer Service Function," *Management Technology*, December 1963, pp. 160–166.
17. IBM, *Plant Maintenance Management System*, IBM Publication, No. E20–0124–0, D. P. Division, White Plains, N.Y.
18. IBM, *General Information Manual—Preventive Maintenance and Cost Control*, IBM Publication, Poughkeepsie, N.Y.
19. G. H. Jorgensen: "What the Computer Can Mean to Maintenance," *Mill and Factory*, March 1966, pp. 65–66.
20. G. H. Jorgensen: "Avoid These Pitfalls When Setting Up Computerized Maintenance," *Plant Engineering*, May 2, 1968, pp. 101–103.
21. G. G. Kellerman et al.: "Maintenance Control through Processing," *Control Engineering*, vol. 10, no. 4, April 1963, pp. 105–106.
22. J. A. Lifsey: "Optimization of Maintenance Resources," *Operations Research*, November–December 1965, pp. 1007–1019.
23. J. Mill: "Time-Sharing vs. Mini-Computers: Pick the One for the Right Job," *Modern Manufacturing*, October 1970, pp. 84–85.
24. R. C. Monson: "Computer Schedules Preventive Maintenance Work," *Plant Engineering*, January 1967, pp. 129–131.
25. L. Newton and J. Bley: "Computer Printout Monitors Critical Path Network," *Plant Engineering*, May 2, 1968, pp. 111–114.
26. G. C. Quinn and G. V. Schultz: "Dial a Computer—Get Fast Action on Plant Problems," *Modern Manufacturing*, August 1970, pp. 37–41.
27. Simon Ramo: "The Computer Spawns a New Breed of Management", *Plant Management and Engineering*, vol. 33, May 1974, pp. 38–39.
28. John Sarjeant: "Unlocking the Computer's Profit Potential", *PAIE*, vol. 3, January 1972, pp. 30–31.
29. John A. Silva: "Computer Assisted NIC Programming," *Industrial Engineering*, vol. 5, no. 4, April 1973, pp. 16–18.
30. Efraim Turban: "Some Determinants of the Use of Mathematical Models in Plant Maintenance," unpublished Ph.D. dissertation, University of California, Berkeley. See *Factory*, June 1966, pp. 98–110, *Management Science*, February 1967, pp. 342–358.
31. D. Van Utt: "Computers Work for Small Plants, Too!" *Factory*, March 1965.
32. Thomas C. Votaggia: "Is Time-Sharing Feasible in the Small Chemical Plant?" *Plant Operating Management*, July 1971, pp. 44–45.
33. W. H. Weiss: "Forecast Equipment Breakdown by the Monte Carlo Method," *Plant Engineering*, December 1964, pp. 122–125.
34. W. H. Weiss: "Computerized Maintenance Decision Making," *Plant Engineering*, October 1968.
35. W. H. Weiss: "The Complete Computerized Maintenance System," *Industrial Engineering*, March 1969.

36. W. H. Weiss: "Tackling the Manufacturing Problem," *Data Processing*, January–February 1973, pp. 13–15.
37. W. H. Weiss: "Computers on the Plant Floor," *Plant Management and Engineering*, October 1972, pp. 41–42.
38. W. H. Weiss: "Computer Controls Nuclear Processing," *Plant Management and Engineering*, vol. 33, February 1971.

General Interest

39. David McDonald: "Report: Computers in Industry," *Plant Administration/Engineering*, vol. 29, March 1970, pp. 51–62.

Chapter **5**

Management by Objectives

ROBERT H. PRINTUP
Director of General Services
University of Chicago Hospitals and Clinics

INTRODUCTION

In previous sections, budgeting, costs, and related items were discussed. Presented in this chapter are step-by-step methods for applying industrial engineering principles to a service department.

DEFINITION OF MANAGEMENT BY OBJECTIVES

Almost every plant engineer today has had academic experience in the art of management. To be a good manager one must be able to *plan, organize, direct,* and *control,* and one must be able to deal with *people.*

Buildings, machinery, and equipment need little or no direction or control, but people do. People want and need help in obtaining objectives. Thus the term "management by objectives" refers to people and dollars.

Planning involves formulation. It answers the questions What is to be done? How? When and who? Planning is a preliminary activity where one can formulate ideas, goals, objectives. It is the first step a good manager must always take. Without good planning most objectives are lost.

Here we pause, and because we are in the planning stage, we ask ourselves a question. Who is involved in planning? Before the person involved, usually, was the "boss," the person in each company or corporation who set goals for the group. Today planning is a team effort, accomplished not just by one person but by the whole management team, each adding expertise to the overall picture. What is the purpose, the objective? How is this accomplished? Planning involves "brainstorming" by the team. Written objectives are the results of good planning.

Organizing is step two: Organizing involves utilization of workers, activities, and skills. It also involves finding the right tools or equipment. An excellent tool for the application of step two is the organizational chart. An organizational chart should show the direct and indirect lines of responsibility and communications. Each job involved should have its place on the organization chart.

Definite lines of communications and responsibility are established. Who reports to whom? Who is responsible for what? The organizational chart should include every job within the activity, project, or department, from the highest to the lowest. Laborers, semiskilled and skilled, workers, supervisors, and managers should each have their place.

Each position designated on the organization chart requires a job description. (See Section 9.) Another good step is preparation of actual job assignment sheets. These are detailed, step-by-step descriptions of the daily duties for each job. You may also want to include approximate allowed times for each function. Standard time data can be used in formulating a job assignment sheet with readjustments as necessary to include delays, breaks, lunch, etc. This is a useful tool for good organization. You may want to include this as the first implementing step. *Implementing* includes action tasks. Instruction, telling, ordering, and assigning are all included under implementation. A continuous training program for supervisors and workers alike, keeping everyone current on changes and project updating is important (see chapter 8–6). A good manager must be a good teacher. A new employee must be able to perform his or her job properly and as quickly as possible to save time and money. New people must be properly indoctrinated as to the aims and goals of the company, the department, and each specific project. They must feel "in on things," members of the team. They must see how their skills and talents fit into the overall objectives. A good indoctrination program shows immediate results by helping employees reduce errors, accidents, frictions, tensions, frustrations, absences, and dissatisfactions.

Supervisors and older employees need periodical retraining. Each individual plays a key and unique role in the implementation program. Time needs to be spent in the classroom as well as in on-the-job training. All employees need constant stimulus.

Evaluation is step four. Evaluation is the method for complete overall control. "Evaluation" means comparing and analyzing—comparing actual performance with standard performance. Performance and quality can and should be methods of measuring people and the work they accomplish.

To measure an individual's performance one must have incorporated, in the original planning, predetermined standards. Time standards required to complete a given task, or a group of tasks, are called for in your goals and objectives. Time standards are now available for almost any procedure. If someone is assigned the task of overhauling an engine, this person should be able to complete the job within a certain number of allowed hours, according to established time standards. If the job is not completed within the standard time, management needs to know why. This is a very important part of the overall objective.

Quality is another part of evaluation. Good quality control will eliminate rework, redoing what has already been done, and the expenditure of more time and money. Here again quality standards, established by past performance and engineering determination, are evidence of good quality or poor quality of work.

PRACTICAL APPLICATION

It must be understood that applications of the management by objectives theory is a step-by-step procedure. But like all realistic endeavors, it must be flexible enough to be practical. People change, things change, aims and goals change; so too management programs are subject to change. When you change the objectives, it will change the end result; but the step-by-step method of attaining a result stays the same.

LONG- AND SHORT-RANGE OBJECTIVES

Keep in mind, though, that management by objective theory can be applied to almost any given objective or group of objectives. However, every member of the team must be included.

Overall goals are established by coordinators. This group should always include the prime company executive. This is the individual who establishes the overall objectives, along with the team. A good group of overall objectives could be these:

1. To provide better care and services to our customers through
   a. Better quality control
   b. Better performance
2. To execute a 5 percent overall cost reduction
3. To reduce employment turnover by 10 percent

These are goals, or objectives established by the management team. The goals must be realistic and attainable. Never set goals that are impossible to accomplish. You will be defeated before you start. Each member of the management team must keep the overall goals in mind at all times, during each step. Achievement of the goals, using the system, is the target. A time limit must be established. It could be a month, 6 months, 1 year, 5 years, or whatever is felt is a realistic time limit. The time limit is another step in overall planning that is most important. Things need to start and they need to stop, and there must be pauses to allow the team to evaluate the results. Most projects or objectives are best accomplished within a 1-year period, from January 1 to December 31 or July 1 to June 30. Anything less than a year should be classified as short-term objectives. Long-range objectives are those involving 1- to 5-year plans.

TEST CASE 1

The following is an example of a 1-year plan for implementing a preventive maintenance program for all plant physical assets so as to maximize plant efficiency and minimize overall maintenance costs. Here our overall objective is to comply with the administrative goals of:

1. Providing better care and services
2. Executing an overall cost reduction

THE PROGRAM PLANNING

The goal is to develop and apply a preventive maintenance program to the entire plant. The total task will be divided into smaller, more easily handled elements. In this way, more immediate results will be obtained and can be evaluated. Here is a brief description of the projects in priority order:

1. *Project:* Develop and implement a program to assure proper lubrication of machinery and equipment.
2. *Project:* Develop a program for the adequate maintenance of clean rooms and dustfree areas.
3. *Project:* Develop a program for the routine calibration of plant equipment and instrumentation.
4. *Project:* Develop a program for the routine maintenance of process equipment.
5. *Project:* Develop a program for the routine maintenance of machinery and equipment.
6. *Project:* Develop a program for the routine maintenance of inspection equipment, that is, Rockwell Hardness Testers, Comparators, etc.
7. *Project:* Develop a program for the routine maintenance of factory power systems.
8. *Project:* Develop a program for the routine maintenance of buildings and building installations.

Timing

Complete within one year. It is recognized that all projects cannot be delayed to coincide with a schedule, so stopgap measures can be used until a total program is developed.

Organizing

Each project should be broken down into organization steps. For example, the first item might be broken down as follows:

1. *Project:* Develop and implement a program to assure the proper lubrication of machinery and equipment.

   a. Determine lubrication requirements based on analysis of manufacturers' recommendations and local experience.

   b. Investigate and evaluate lubrication methods and equipment for possible job improvement.

   c. Evaluate lubrication control systems such as Texaco Stoploss, Mobil Spectrol, and other systems in use in the industry. Develop a control system.

   d. Evaluate methods for scheduling machine lubrication such as calendar period, machine run time, oil sampling, etc. Develop a system for scheduling.

   e. Prepare a machine lubrication program including controls, methods, routings, and procedures or manuals as required.

   f. Estimated man-hours to complete: 172. Time span: 14.5 weeks.

Implementing

Each project will need to be implemented separately. Each step should stand on its own merit. At this point actual performance can be measured and results indicated.

1. *Project:* Lubrications of machinery and equipment. Periodic reports of progress.

   a. Lubrication standards within the division are to be compatible with the corporate system.

   b. Evaluation of lubrication requirements and permanent lubrication inspection of recommendation checkpoints itemizing lubrication requirements for approximately 400 machines has been completed. These machines are located in various buildings.

      (1) Permanent lubrication/inspection recommendation checkpoints and maintenance lubrication record cards (approximately 400) will be installed on the machines in the production building during the next month.

      (2) Permanent maintenance lubrication record cards for machine tools in the R&D building are being developed at the present time.

      (3) Balance of lubrication requirements for miscellaneous machine tools and equipment throughout the plant will follow.

   c. Daily routing for oiling and equipment checks for machines in the production building within column A is completed. Oiling routes have been established, but due to various rearrangements need to be updated.

   d. Development of decals to be placed at all lubrication points on machines denoting daily, weekly, type of lubricant, etc., has been completed and a request for quotes has been issued to purchasing.

Evaluation

Again, each project should be required to have periodic evaluation reports after a number of months have elapsed.

Estimated completion of development and implementation of the entire preventive maintenance program detailed above is January 31.

Estimated total additional manpower required to completely implement this program is:

1. Five (5) additional maintenance mechanics
2. Two (2) additional electricians
3. One (1) additional oiler
4. One (1) additional plumber

Two additional mechanics could be utilized now in area 8 to allow completion of preventive maintenance work on equipment in the production building, column area A, as scheduled. One of these mechanics could be made available from area B after machine tool rebuilder trainee is received. The other mechanic could be picked up as a replacement for the mechanic being terminated out of area B. The charts showing progress in the various project areas listed above will be completed and ready for use by August.

As can be seen by the above information, things are not looking too good. Instead of saving money, the project is costing time and money. Again, we must be able to project completion. Common sense and experience tells us that in the end, with proper preventive maintenance, we can shorten downtime for our machinery; and this will save time and money.

A Final Evaluation

By the end of a 14-month period all 8 projects in this case had been completed. A detailed analysis of the results was then undertaken. We will not go into all of the detailed analysis, but this part should show a good example of what was accomplished.

Ten machines were selected for this study. A two year study of downtime for 10 machines was made. It includes breakdown repair time and preventive maintenance time. Total downtime was 25.5 percent. These results were recorded before the new preventive maintenance plan was put into effect.

Two years after the preventive maintenance plan was placed in effect, four more machines were added. Total downtime was now 10.8 percent.

Also, the maintenance staff was reduced from 17 to 12 men. Total annual cost savings amounted to approximately one hundred thousand dollars.

SUMMARY

This chapter presents general information on management by objectives. We should like to repeat that this is an overall team effort, from top management down to individual workers who perform assigned tasks.

Planning begins at the administrative level. The establishment of objectives at this level must be broad and realistic. They must encompass the entire organization. Each member of the management team is then required to establish specific ways of accomplishing the overall goals or objectives. A good communication system up and down the chain of command is an absolute must. Each department and each division must be a part of the overall plan. Regular conferences need to be held and exact methods of reporting progress should be established on a daily, weekly, and monthly basis. Constant evaluation of quality and performance will tell us if we are progressing toward the objective. Department heads and supervisory levels must be free to change direction when needed, yet always keeping objectives in mind.

REFERENCES

1. P. F. Drucker: *Managing for Results*, Harper & Row, New York, 1964.
2. _____: *Management, Tasks, Responsibilities, Practices*, Harper & Row, New York, 1973.

Chapter **6**

Training

CLIFFORD R. SAYRE
Sayre Technical Service Company

WHY A TRAINING BUDGET IS NEEDED

Because technology is rapidly becoming more complex, the importance of training cannot be overemphasized; everyone in industry is affected by technological advances.

During the last 15 years, production in the United States has doubled while the number of production workers remained almost the same. During the same period, the number of maintenance employees increased by nearly 50 percent. (This information was obtained from the Bureau of Labor Statistics of the U.S. Department of Labor.) These statistics reflect the fact that highly productive automated equipment requires fewer production people but *more maintenance* people. Because the end result of this trend is higher production and lower costs, it is certain to continue.

Often, semiskilled and unskilled people must be hired. To be effectively trained, they should be tested and placed in a program that will waste no time in preparing them for the highest level of skill they are able to achieve.

Because of the shortage of skilled tradesmen, a suitable training program is needed to fulfill present as well as future manpower requirements.

Training too frequently takes a back seat to other functions such as production or marketing. Such an attitude can hurt manpower effectiveness as well as company profits.

Training is necessary to keep craft personnel and first-line supervisors abreast of the technical advances continually made in plant equipment and processes and to constantly update the knowledge of the older, more experienced workers.

The spending of time, effort, and money on maintenance training is justifiable for the following reasons:

Employees are unable to perform certain jobs

They are unable to do the jobs well enough

They are doing a job wrong

With proper training, these conditions can be corrected and the company will make more money.

Training can be a cure as well as a preventive to a job performance problem. Used as a preventive—before an employee starts to do a job wrong—training can save time and costly errors. Used as a cure—after mistakes become obvious—training can only get the job back to normal, not make up for the lost profits and time.

If mistakes are being made on the job or if the work is not being done fast enough, training can become a cure—provided that the deficiency was a lack of training—*but not* a cure-all. First determine what the problem really is. Then take a comprehensive look at the task to find the weak spots and determine exactly what the job requires. Some interesting things may appear when you approach the problem realistically. For example, a job may have been set up inefficiently. In this case, an analysis may show that it is impossible to perform the specified operations properly. Methods improvement is needed here rather than training.

Looking closely at a job may also reveal that work operations are inefficiently laid out. If the employees have been properly trained and the task still is not being performed acceptably, the problem could be caused by fatigue, poor attitudes, or some other seemingly unrelated reason which had not been recognized. In this case, job training is *not* the answer, although other training may be.

RESPONSIBILITY FOR TRAINING

Some plant engineers or maintenance managers may not think of training as an essential part of their jobs Some may insist that the training department should handle all training. However, training is the responsibility of all managerial and supervisory personnel. It is essential that employees be trained in all aspects of their craft. Training should be an integral part of job enrichment within the department and company.

Training requires management, including the supervisor, to take a close look at the job and the employee. It is necessary to define what it is the employee should be doing and to determine whether he or she is doing it properly. It is equally important to find out why a particular employee is not performing as well as he or she can, so that the employee can be made aware of any deficiencies or problems.

The development and promotion of an effective plan for training is especially dependent on a managerial climate that encourages the employee to seek training. This climate can be created through sound managerial techniques. Management support must be effectively continued and not relegated to just lip service with no real support or follow-up.

In all situations, especially training, let your employees know they are important members of your team and that their jobs are vital to the successful operation of the department. Make them aware that training not only gives them a chance to learn about new equipment and techniques but also can qualify them for more responsible positions. Training can also help you show your employees that you are interested in them personally. People need to feel important and wanted, individually as well as collectively. Nothing will do more for a worker's morale than your recognition of him or her as a person.

DETERMINING TRAINING NEEDS

Questions that may arise about your training needs and training programs are as follows:

- What are the results of your present maintenance training or retraining programs?
- Do they accomplish their objectives?
- Is the employee able to perform a specific job requirement after training has been completed?
- Are the trainers able to relate textbook knowledge to the skills and know-how of practical "nuts and bolts" jobs?

A training needs analysis, similar to that in Fig. 1, can be made and used as an appraisal technique by which a training supervisor can determine the present scope of individual skills and knowledge requirements. This will help answer the questions relating to what training is needed. Training needs may be determined by finding out what is going on now and matching this against what should go on, now or in the future. The gap, if any, gives clues to the kind as well as the amount of training needed.

When analyzing a problem for training purposes, the thinking and suggestions of others can be helpful and can increase the value of the eventual solution. However, weigh all ideas carefully, for training may not be the best solution in a given situation, even though some of the people involved may feel it is.

Clues to training needs can also come from an analysis of the behavior of individuals or groups. Chronic absence, spoilage of work, carelessness, accidents, irritability, resistance, or resentment toward instruction are symptoms of conditions that may call for corrective action involving training. For example, a manager may need to be a better

TRAINING NEED ANALYSIS

Item Importance
Very high - VH
High - H
Meduim - M
Low - L

Pipe-fitter's trade

Interpreting drawings and laying out the job

TRAINING LEVEL
Qualified -3
Trained -2
Semi-trained -1
No training -0

	Understand piping symbols	Understand isometric drawings	Understand flow charts	Understand notes and legends	Be able to visualize completed job	Know how to plan for future maintenance	Know how to plan for operator convenience	Understand drawing scale	Know how to interpret detailed drawings	Know how to interpret sectional drawing	Know how to sketch pipe layouts	Know how to compare blueprints with area	Know how to layout dimensions in area	Know how to spot job with use of strings	Know where to locate hangars	Know how to requisition materials
Item importance	VH	VH	M	M	H	L	L	L	VH	VH	M	VH	VH	M	M	VH
Inst. emph's's Skill-S, Know.-K	K	K	K	K	K	K	K	K	K	K	SK	K	S	S	S	K
Approx. time req'd.																
Bill Elbow	3	3	3	3	2	2	2	3	3	3	1	1	1	0	0	1
Geo. Coupling	1	1	0	1	0	0	0	0	0	1	1	1	1	0	0	1
Harold Tee	3	3	3	3	2	2	2	3	3	3	3	2	2	2	2	2
Jim Stillson	0	0	0	0	1	0	0	0	0	0	0	0	1	1	1	0

Fig. 1   Training need analysis.

planner or communicator, or a group may need to know more about a policy. The department policies or job standards may not be clearly understood. In many cases, the standards for job performance can be written in clear terms, lending themselves to discreet measurement. The standards for management jobs are often expressed as the goals or objectives of the organizational unit for which a manager has responsibility.

The training needs of new workers and the benefits present craftsmen can get from additional training should be determined before a training program is developed. A training needs analysis can be of great value in making this determination.

The scope and level of knowledge a training program should have will be determined by the difficulty of the tasks to be learned.

Training is most valid when the knowledge and skills being taught are required and will be practiced on the job. The equipment and facilities to be maintained will help you determine the needs of your training program. Some basic steps for instituting a good training program are as follows:

- Accurately determine job requirements.
- Accurately determine skills requirements.
- Ensure that training materials are at the trainees' level of comprehension.
- Use training materials that can be easily adapted to the needs of the company.
- Maintain good supervision, personal contact, and follow-up with trainees.
- Institute good environmental conditions that encourage learning.

A successful training program depends on the trainer's and the employees' knowledge of the job. Usually, the supervisor has the background to recognize the need for training and its value to the company while also understanding the capabilities and limitations of the workers. Often, only the supervisor can determine whether the workers will understand a subject that is taught a certain way.

The qualities of a good trainer are difficult to define; they may include such characteristics as the ability to like people, to be enthusiastic, and to speak distinctly. However, each of us need only think back to our schooldays to remember someone who violated all the rules and was still a good trainer.

A trainer is expected to produce to be acceptable, and the trainer must be held accountable. Too often, employees are entrusted to an unqualified trainer, and then their performance on the job is evaluated as though they had had professional training.

Once the responsibility of training is accepted, the trainer should consider the best way to instruct the trainees. This involves learning about visual aids and communications and knowing how to generate involvement, motivation, interest, and enthusiasm.

DETERMINING TRAINING OBJECTIVES

When training is needed, a *job analysis* can be quite valuable. A job analysis can help you determine exactly what constitutes a good job, what an employee should be able to do, what parts of the job are not being done properly, and where the training emphasis should be placed. A job analysis will also justify training because it reflects directly on any job deficiency. It can be used to help set realistic objectives for an employee's performance after training has been completed. You can then tell what that employee will be able to repair (specific equipment) within a certain time (repair certain equipment or locate defective components). An analysis will also reveal what the employee knows and can do before the training. This is essential, because the training should start where the trainees are, not where they may think they are or where they should be.

If the training starts beyond an employee's level, that individual has little chance of progressing to the goal you have set. The purpose of training is to change behavior or work habits. This means that the supervisor must know what behavior now exists and what behavior or change is desired. Training should not begin until this is determined. Training should be designed to fill the gap between where an employee is and that employee's predetermined goal after training. Every employee will not be at the same level and should not be expected to end up at the same place. This is why some training can be formal and other training informal or on the job.

Studies have shown that while they are demonstrating what they have learned, people remember about 90 percent of what they say. But they will remember only 10 percent of what they have learned if they do not apply the information (by repeating it or using it). This means that the trainee must participate by saying and doing whatever he or she should be learning.

The objectives of an in-plant maintenance training program should provide for:

1. Training of selected personnel in the knowledge and performance of tasks required for them to progress from trainee to craftsman
2. A means by which they can refresh or update present knowledge
3. Steps for continued development of all craftsmen
4. A climate that encourages individual effort so that knowledge can be most effectively gained
5. Sufficient flexibility so training will not interfere with plant work needs
6. Planned work assignments that meet experience capabilities (on-the-job training)
7. Scheduled participation and study time in the training program
8. Help and support for overall trainee achievement

Factors important to trainee achievement are given in Fig. 2.

A skills outline and a knowledge reference list should be developed and used to help trainees direct their efforts to becoming competent craftsmen. A skills outline can also serve as a guide for the trainee to determine the knowledge and skills he or she must improve. This can also help motivate a trainee to have a stronger desire for improvement.

Specialized training conducted by factory representatives or suppliers can be used very effectively to complement your training program. Supplemental reference texts and manuals may be made available to provide information on specific equipment operation and repair instructions. Manufacturers' instruction manuals on special equipment should be available and kept updated. Training films or other visual aids are helpful and can be shown during supervised study sessions as needs and availability warrant. Information sheets or pamphlets should be written and distributed to strengthen knowledge and give specific instruction about the maintenance or repair of plant equipment and systems most applicable to the trainees' job responsibilities.

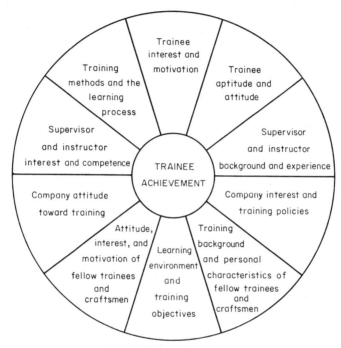

Fig. 2   Trainee achievement.

SCHEDULING TRAINING

Training in the maintenance department should be scheduled at the same time a new machine, new employee, or new job assignment is planned. Any new person working on an existing machine or assignment will need some training. An experienced employee on a new machine or new job will require training in his or her new responsibilities and environment. Training is simply insurance against making errors at the start and can save costly downtime and repairs.

When new equipment is installed, employees need to know its maintenance requirements. The complexity of the equipment and the number of people to be trained will obviously determine the extent of preparation, cost, and mode of training. The quality of a training program should never suffer because of relatively simple operations or too few trainees. The machine, the company, and the technicians deserve adequate training if they are to perform effectively. "Telling" and "training" are, unfortunately, often considered synonymous. This can cause a hit-or-miss training approach, which is costly and will result in inferior results. Assess the problem situation and, at the same time, seek out ideas for solutions that can be achieved through training.

You may find three levels of employees involved in the problem, and interviews should be conducted with the more knowledgeable and experienced individuals from all three levels.

1. Those who supervise the people for whom the training is being scheduled
2. The people for whom the training is being scheduled

3. The people supervised by the people for whom the training is being programmed

The amount of training necessary depends on the present level of skills in the shop. Sophisticated equipment requires updated repair and maintenance techniques. This means educating existing personnel in advanced methods of maintenance and mechanical repairs.

Specific items that need to be determined before a schedule can be established are:

1. The training group size
2. The frequency of the training sessions
3. The length of the sessions
4. The time of day
5. The place for training

Group size   How many trainees will be enrolled in the total program? How many separate sessions will be required to train all the trainees enrolled? Usually twelve to eighteen trainees is considered ideal for each training session.

Frequency   How often are the instruction sessions to be held? Experience has shown that too much training in too short a time is not effective. Additional time is often required of the trainee outside working hours to complete homework assignments. With this in mind, it is a good idea to schedule at least one but probably no more than two sessions per week.

Length of sessions   The exact schedule depends on local conditions and requirements for getting the job done. When training periods are too short, there tends to be a lack of continuity and too much time is lost in starting and stopping the session. On the other hand, the interest span of adults who have been out of school for some time is quite short. If the sessions run for too long a time, trainees become bored and much of the training effectiveness is lost.

For most industrial maintenance training situations, the schedule should probably fall within the range of one to two sessions per week for 1 to 2 hours each session. Work not completed during the allotted time period should be assigned as homework to be turned in at the next training session.

The time training is conducted   As near as possible, the sessions should always be conducted during the same time of day except when emergencies disrupt the schedule. The actual time of day is not too critical, except that the hour before lunch or the first hour in the morning are probably best from the standpoint of the trainee's alertness. The period immediately after lunch is probably the worst. Sometimes, training sessions are scheduled during shift changes. Their employees from the first shift stay extra time and employees from the second shift come in early. With this system, both the company and the employees contribute some time to the training program.

The trainees should know the *place* for knowledge training, where and exactly when the program is intended to take place, what is expected to be accomplished, and when that particular segment of training should have a specific start and stop date.

When developing a training program for new equipment, each plant will determine the details of its own program. However, these basic rules should be followed:

1. *Plans* for training should be developed when plans for the new equipment are made.

2. *Money* for training should be included in the cost of installing and converting to new equipment.

3. *Time* for training should be allocated when personnel requirements for the new machinery are determined.

4. *Responsibility* for training should be specified when other responsibilities pertaining to the equipment are handled.

5. *Accountability* for training should be just as strict as the accountability for equipment operation.

When these rules are followed, the training for the operation and maintenance of any new equipment will not present any serious problem. If the rules are not followed, the training will be mediocre.

COSTS AND THE TRAINING BUDGET

When company funds are expended for training, you must know why it is needed. Just as expenditures for mechanical equipment must be justified, so must expenditures for training the maintenance force be justified.

The use of properly administered pretraining tests can reduce training costs and the time needed to complete training. Trainees can be given pretests to determine the subject areas they know best as well as the extent of their present knowledge.

The training budget must provide sufficient flexibility to allow you to carry out your responsibilities for training. Training is not a science, and the approach to budgeting should allow for both known and unknown factors in the daily activities of your department. Thus, you will be able to predict with accuracy the number of trainees for any given training program and the resulting costs for each trainee. However, if you decide to change from one type training to another—one heavily supported by visual aids, for example—there should be sufficient room in the budget to provide for the expense of preparing the visual aids without causing a financial crisis.

An accurate forecast of training expense can be made only if there are records from previous years or programs to support decisions made for the coming period. If there are no such records or if the entire budgeting procedure is new, there never will be a better opportunity to fashion a system for your training budget. Such typical questions as these should be examined slowly and carefully:

1. *Why* is training needed?
2. *What* are the objectives?
3. *Who* will be trained?
4. *When* should training take place?
5. *Where* should training be done?
6. *How* will training be conducted (media)?

Standard budget periods are usually established by the company. Conformance with the company's financial structure is essential, whether it follows a quarterly, semiannual, annual, or special pattern. Determining this framework before analyzing training budget requirements will place the training program in proper perspective. Budgeting for training is sound financial practice for the department manager and should include funding for special training such as seminars and vendor schools or other off-site training projects.

Sometimes a functional budget rather than a project budget will meet your needs to operate your training program more effectively. A functional budget is most applicable when the department is organized on a functional basis. Thus there might be sections devoted to education, training aids, and special training. Each of the functional sections would have budgets for all activities. A budget of this type has some advantages in that it helps decentralize control and audit. By division of the budget into small units, it also helps localize any problem areas.

Wherever possible, however, it is to the manager's credit if every training dollar is followed to its destination. Training is a business now, and as such it takes on the responsibility of supporting itself. Salaries and other costs—administrative, supervisory, training, and clerical—must not be economically out of line with the results of training. Trainees trained in productive assignments must justify the costs. Training films produced or purchased must be evaluated for definite results in terms of better service and increased skills. Training must provide the instruction and knowledge necessary to help the employee do the job.

Granted, these are intangible areas, but their relation to a company's profit picture or fiscal soundness is obvious.

DETERMINING TRAINING EFFECTIVENESS

To check overall effectiveness, periodically make spot checks of the program to assure yourself that satisfactory progress is being made. Spot-check the work of the trainees out in the plant to make sure that knowledge gained in the training program is being applied to the job. It is a good idea occasionally to survey the shop supervisors, the trainers, and the trainees themselves to determine whether the training is producing satisfactory results and to spot any trouble areas that may be developing.

It is more difficult to measure learning than it is to measure reaction to a training program. A great deal of work is required in planning the evaluation procedure, in analyzing the data obtained, and in interpreting the results. Wherever possible, it is suggested that training supervisors devise their own methods and techniques. It is relatively easy to plan classroom demonstrations and presentations to measure learning where the program is aimed at the teaching of skills. Where principles and facts are the objectives of the training program, it is advisable to use a written test. Where suitable standardized tests can be found, it is easier to use them. In many programs, however, it is not possible to find a standardized test. Then the trainer must resort to skill and ingenuity in devising a measuring instrument.

A *performance rating sheet* can be used as an appraisal tool to evaluate individual performance with respect to the quantity and quality of work. This management tool can also be used to determine growth. As workers become more skilled and knowledgeable, any change in performance can be recognized and evaluated.

From an evaluation standpoint, it is best to evaluate training programs directly in terms of results desired. There are, however, so many complicating factors that it is extremely difficult, if not impossible, to evaluate certain kinds of programs in terms of results. Therefore it is recommended that training be evaluated in terms of reaction, learning, and behavior.

This can be accompanied by a job analysis or writeup to help determine the degree of skill needed for a particular job. Progress reports on the effectiveness of classroom training and plant exposure can be used to evaluate training techniques.

A training course can be tailored to specific requirements by using special training materials. This would apply to such courses as blueprint reading, machine repair, and electricity. If a vocational school is near your plant, try to arrange a training program in cooperation with the school. Upon completion of the training program, each trainee should receive recognition in the form of a certificate. This will encourage the trainees to continue their training.

Customer service schools, although somewhat restricted to special crafts or skills, are also helpful for specialized equipment training.

The trainees should be given jobs that have the greatest learning potential. Be sure they are assigned a variety of plantwide work. Nothing can hurt an employee's initiative more quickly than to be stalled on one type of job in one department because he or she does this job best or the department has a heavy workload.

Workers who are not interested in advancing will usually not apply themselves very effectively in a training program. Occasionally however, a demonstrated lack of interest may be a sign of poor motivation. The employee may not see any advantage in giving up time for study. There are also some employees who prefer to pass up the opportunity to advance to higher jobs because they would rather be "one of the gang" or do not want the added responsibility.

SUMMARY

When an employee does not perform properly but knows how, then skills training is not likely to help. A communications problem as to exactly what is to be done could exist between the employee and the supervisor.

Always keep in mind that skill is developed through concentrated training. Training means telling, showing, and supervising. The trainer must have the desire to teach and supervise a trainee. You may want to start the trainee's on-the-job training by assigning him or her to work with the most skilled people in the crew.

All classroom practice, programmed instruction, text, and equipment manual instructions should be supplemented as much as possible with actual hands-on demonstrations for the most effective results.

Equipment models should be used to allow trainees to practice, under the supervision of an experienced trainer, what has been learned.

For example, a model could be used to illustrate a coupling alignment problem. A motor coupled to a pump mounted on an adjustable base will permit the trainee to actually align the drive and use such tools as feeler gauges, a dial indicator, and a micrometer. This situation covers text study concerned not only with coupling alignment but with mechanical drives and measuring tools as well.

With a proper balance of study and in-plant rotated work experience, trainees should soon become proficient in their particular craft fields. Equally important, the chances are good that they will develop morale and a sense of responsibility. The achievement of such a combination of skill and proper attitude can soon repay your training investment. Improved performance on the job should be the prime objective of any training program.

REFERENCES

1. J. W. Rantala: *Organizing and Using a Maintenance Training Program,* Maintenance Library, Technical Publishing Company, 1962.
2. M. M. Broadwell: "Developing a Training Philosophy," *Plant Engineering,* March 1968.
3. M. M. Broadwell: "Planning—Key to Successful Maintenance Training," *Plant Engineering,* April 1968.
4. R. F. Jansen: "Our Answer to Your Most Critical Problem," *Plant Engineering,* March 1969.
5. J. J. Siedel: "Where Should Your Maintenance Training Begin?" *Plant Engineering,* September 1967.
6. J. J. Seidel: "Maintenance Training Essentials: Documented Materials and Qualified Instructors," *Plant Engineering,* October 1967.
7. R. L. Oliverson: "Effective Maintenance Training Is an All-Out Effort," *Plant Engineering,* October 1971.
8. Craig-Bittel: *Training and Development Handbook,* New York: McGraw-Hill Book Company, Inc., 1967.

Chapter **7**

Staff Development

LESTER F. ZERFOSS
Professor of Management and Chairman of the Management Department, University of North Carolina

This chapter will attempt to do four things: (1) assess the "state of the art" in management development as it applies to engineering management; (2) identify some of the critical elements in the management climate that must be generated in a company to make possible the development of its technical people; (3) describe the major barriers or blocks that prevent the development of employees and managers in the organization; and (4) present an administrative blueprint or model for an experiential approach to staff development within the engineering organization.

THE STATE OF THE ART

Confusions and Inconsistencies in the Literature

Plant engineering executives who look to the current literature on management development for answers to questions on the development of people are apt to become both disillusioned and confused. They will be disillusioned because they will find little theoretical support for evaluating programs of selection, placement, training, progression, career utilization, termination, or retirement. They may be confused because there is so little consistency in theory or practice among the writers on the subject.

In a previous publication* the author has made the following observation:

> There is accumulating evidence that the greatest waste of human resources lies in the unused potential of scientific and other professional employees. Performance of these people is, of course, quite satisfactory when compared with worker efficiency levels of the traditional manufacturing organization. However, when we realize what could be their contribution to the enterprise when highly motivated and given stimulating intellectual leadership which their special abilities and professional backgrounds make possible, the opportunities are exciting! This wasteful underutilization may be critical to any company depending on its engineering or/R&D input to stay alive.
>
> These scientific professionals hold tremendous potential for desperately needed creativity and resourcefulness in the *idea generation* needs of the company. However, the price tag on the creative utilization of these people is a challenging developmental climate far more sensitive to the requirements of the individual than industry has had any experience within the traditional manufacturing organization. It would be difficult to overemphasize the highly strategic value of this select group. The industrial world has a vital equity in their contribution. Yet, from the point of view of on-the-job development, they have been the most neglected people in business, industry, and government.

Weisbord,† in an article in *Think*, observes that most companies, even though research in the behavioral sciences has gone on for years, stress the management of their financial and physical resources and pay only sporadic attention to the human side. A survey of the voluminous literature describing industry's struggle to learn how to manage the development of its people reveals very little that plant engineering managers can put to work in their own situations. They will find hypotheses and theories still frozen in the jargon of the behavioral sciences; they will find case studies of companies who have rushed into print to tell the stories of their bright and shining programs before they have been evaluated or tested. (The writer has followed up on many of these touted programs, only to learn that they had been discontinued—often the first casualties of company cost reduction programs.)

Need to Separate the Wheat from the Chaff

However, if we will take care to separate the wheat from the chaff, we will be able to find some useful information that will give us some guidance in designing a development program good enough to do the job intended. With considerable agreement, the literature records the belief that the development of personnel can only take place in a management climate that is strongly supportive of such development.

Before we can understand the nature of a climate which makes possible the development of people, we need a workable knowledge of what we mean by "development." We will need to discriminate between "development" and "growth," "education," "training," and "experience"—all key terms that come into the picture when a development program is being explained. All these terms have a place in the developmental processes. All too often, they are used interchangeably in describing phases of the learning processes that take place in development. This is misleading. It encourages limited approaches to so-called development programs that fall short of the comprehensive thinking needed to achieve real developmental goals.

Need for a Common Understanding of Major Concepts

Though there are any number of activities that have a place in a development program, such as *appraisals of performance, human relations seminars, sensitivity training, con-*

---

* Lester F. Zerfoss, *The Major Resources of an Organization for Developing Its Professional Personnel,* 1968 (lecture series).

† Marvin R. Weisbord, "What, Not Again! Manage People Better?" *Think,* January–February 1970.

ference leadership training, simulation, coaching, rotation, etc., they are at best only a small part of a comprehensive development program.   One of the most costly mistakes a company can make is to set up an educational or training program and then depend on it to take care of the development of its people.   Let us reexamine some of the major terms we find in the language of development and see if we can define them more usefully for the purposes of this chapter.

Development   This is the overall term that should be used to describe the ongoing processes throughout the employee's lifetime.   It includes living a life as well as making a living.   It includes the growing-up stages from infancy to adulthood.   It includes the maturity goals of the adult—from where the person is right now to where he or she will be in the future.   It has to do with ongoing experience; what is does to and for the individual.   More specifically, from the manager's point of view, it has to do with a person's career in the company.   This includes one's capability, competence, job progress, values and ambitions, potential for grasping new opportunities and taking responsibilities.   It concerns one's long-term ability to adjust to the needs of the organization and continue to make the contribution the company requires.   And also it concerns the employee's ability to realize his or her own career expectations as a member of the company staff.

Thus we see that development is the comprehensive concept.   All the other terms we use are more limited, having to do with specific aspects of development as a learning process.

Growth   In this chapter we will use the term "growth" as a step in development at any point in time.   We will apply the concept of physical growth, so relevant to childhood, to mental growth in the areas of personality, maturity, intellectuality, decision making, perspective.   In general this might be summarized as the translation of the individual's potential into improved performance—the development of a specific ability from a person's general bank of capability.

Education   We will use this term in the traditional sense of schooling.   In the minds of most people education is equated to the acquisition of knowledge.   It has become the major avenue of learning.   For better or worse, our society has institutionalized education and has depended on it to be the primary change agent in equipping children to move into the world of adults.   In actual practice, education is mostly thought of as the presentation or discussion of subject matter in formal classroom situations.   Educational activities are generally conducted at the verbal level of theory, principles, subject matter, or knowledge.   Too often the result is weak, vicarious experience—experience ahead of the gut experience it substitutes for.   In most schools the students get knowledge long before they will have occasion to use it.   In the meantime they may forget much of it or it may become obsolete.   The same thing is true of management seminars, plus the added factor that the language of the seminar is seldom the language of the job situation where it is supposed to be applied.

A classroom with an instructor and a textbook is a good place to *start* a learning process that may lead to development, but it is a poor place to *end* it.   To put the matter more bluntly, a company that expects to have its people develop by sending them away to schools and seminars must inevitably be disappointed.   Such educational digressions are not likely to turn poor employees into good ones or to turn even the most promising recruits into good managers.   It is not that education has failed us—just that we have blindly expected education to take over the whole developmental process of which it is only a small part.   This mistake has taken place because we know a lot more about education than we do about development.

Training   In its relation to education, most people think of training as a more "plebeian" process than education.   Universities have high status, while training institutions have much less.   Education has to do with theory; training has to do with practice.   Falsely perceived, education has to do with the "head" while training has to do merely with the "hands."   Training concerns itself with improving skills, habits, and routines.   Industry uses it as the mechanism to improve performance.   In fact, training—with its wide variety of sophisticated techniques (role-playing, case study, audiovisuals, simulation, to mention a few of the common ones)—has been so useful in doing the job of improving performance that companies are expecting it to do more than it is capable of doing.   Like education, training can do only a part of the development job.   Calling a training program a development program does not make it one.   At present, successful

ers in a given period of time. The same study also supported these conclusions: (1) the kind of supervisory leadership a person works under will importantly affect his or her training techniques are at their best when jobs are relatively stable, know-how is constant, and the status quo can be maintained. However, a word of caution is in order. In a rapidly changing technology, training as we now conduct it may bring undesirable results, such as resistance to change.

Experience   The role of experience in the developmental sequence has usually been misunderstood in industry. Consequently it has been greatly misused. In the narrow sense, experience is simply doing a job. An old German adage had it that "you can steal a trade with your eyes." Literally, the job being done is what an observer can see the worker doing. Industrial engineering has tended to measure experience by the amount of work being done accurately in a given length of time. The most frequently heard statement an individual makes about his or her experience is: "I have had x years of experience on this job." For our purpose in this chapter, we will need to redefine "experience" in terms of its role in the learning processes that contribute to development. In this broader sense, real experience is what the individual learns from doing a job.

Really, what do people learn? Do they learn to just get by, to ignore or get away with mistakes, to hate their jobs, to resent their bosses, dislike their companies, and perhaps a host of other negative reactions? Or, do they learn to improve their knowledge and skills, to use their jobs as stepping stones to better ones, to feel the importance of what they are doing, to appreciate their own contributions to the company's success? In short, are these people learning the things that make them outstanding employees and also qualify them for the advancement of their careers?

This perception of experience places it as the last link in a learning chain that finally results in development. We might not be far wrong if we thought of education as *eating;* training as *digestion;* and experience as *assimilating.* At the point of assimilation, food becomes new protoplasm. In this chain, what began as new knowledge and information ends as new understandings, skills, attitudes, and abilities. The individual has grown in competence and has taken another step in his or her ongoing development.

All too often, companies have had good educational programs, good training programs, and good systems for administering experience without ever seeing their relation to each other or to the development of their personnel. Through a lack of management of these programs as interrelated parts of a whole, a company may well be spending the money and the time needed for development and get no development!

The behavioral scientists have a new term to describe the results of this developmental process. It is "behavior modification." The company's management climate must be good enough to produce favorable behavior modification in individual employees sufficient to motivate them to achieve their realistic life goals and to make their work contributions productive and profitable throughout their working careers.

THE MANAGEMENT CLIMATE

The top management team in a company must realize that the development of brainpower in the technical and managerial levels of the company is a *must.* There can be no compromise with complacency. Development cannot, at this late date, be thought of by the top team as a luxury, a fringe activity, an on-again–off-again proposition. Nor can it be thought of as a program that can be initiated at the top and then turned over to lower groups in the chain of command to implement. The responsibility for creating and maintaining a management climate strongly supportive of employee development is the top team's continuing and never-to-be-relinquished *first* order of business. The future competitiveness and profitability of the company depend on it.

Responsibility of Top Management

A top-management climate study* made by the author in the middle-sized company showed strong evidence that when a company's top-management group consciously organizes its developmental resources into a systematic plan for the development and training of its personnel, it can measurably increase the number of its promotable manag-

* Lester F. Zerfoss, "Some Effects of Executive Climate on Job Performance, Training Activities, and Promotability of Intermediate Levels of Management," A Pennsylvania State University study, University Microfilms, Ann Arbor, Mich., 1959.

developmental progress; (2) an employee-centered executive climate will be more conducive to growth and development of managers at lower levels than a work-centered executive climate will be; (3) a climate that provides opportunities to utilize newly developed skills is more conducive to continuing growth than a static climate not providing such utilization; (4) managers whose subordinates are developing will themselves be more apt to develop; and (5) the perception of a subordinate as a high performer on his or her present job will increase that subordinate's likelihood of receiving a promotion.

The study further indicated that more acceleration in the development of managers could be obtained (1) as the company obtained greater integration of its staff support and line training activities; (2) educated both the individual manager and the chain of leadership above that manager to realize that development is a team effort with reciprocal relationships; and (3) brought more clearly into focus throughout the management structure an awareness that the goals of the individual for his or her own development and progress are mutually supporting and compatible with the goals of the company.

In an address before the International Plant Engineering conference at Anaheim,* California, the author pointed out that the most significant change top management can make in its understanding of employees is the realization that they must be managed in terms of their *potential* as well as their achievement. For most executives, this calls for new insights into the wellsprings of human behavior. It calls for a deeper understanding of human nature than management has previously felt to be necessary in order to get the work out.

Even a brief review of some of the characteristics of a development climate will show the central role of potential in the growth processes. The following list highlights some of the characteristics of the growth climate as perceived by supervisors from middle-sized companies (the list was an outgrowth of a supervisory training program):

The most important characteristics of the growth climate

1. The company is a profitable company—consistently earning a high rate of return on investment.

2. The company is an expanding company—constantly increasing its share of the business in the industry.

3. There is a systematic planned approach to the development of people (not hit or miss).

4. People who do outstanding work are identified, are religiously looked over, and are considered for appropriate promotional vacancies.

5. There is a fundamental faith that the potential of people exceeds their achievement by enough margin to make their training and development a profitable undertaking.

6. The subordinate is being supervised by a boss who is also growing in maturity and considers a supervisor's major responsibility to be that of getting the job done through people who can grow.

7. The accountability of managers is such that they will not be promoted themselves unless they are successfully training the personnel under them to meet the demands of group maintenance, including the demand for their own replacement.

8. The basic learning experiences are provided through the work experience by means of good delegation, guided experience, and interpreted experience.

9. High demands are placed on people, and much is expected of them.

10. Supervision capitalizes on the mistakes of subordinates and uses them as growth points.

11. Security is earned through competence rather than seniority.

12. Leadership puts a very high premium on behavior that shows originality, resourcefulness, creativity, innovation, suggestions, and uninhibited comment.

13. Training is primarily beamed on job improvement *and* preparation for advancement.

14. The subordinate is given a maximum opportunity to share in decision making, planning, and problem solving.

15. Individuals know where they stand—how they are doing—and what else is required of them to progress.

* Lester F. Zerfoss, *Proceedings of the 1971 International Plant Engineering Conference,* Anaheim, Calif.

16. The individual is not exploited or deprived of the rewards and recognition of increased productivity.

It should be noted that in the foregoing list of characteristics of the growth climate, items 1 and 2 deal with the profitability of the company; items 5,6,7,8,9,11,12, and 16 reflect the supervisor's concern for the company's philosophy as to people values; and items 3,4,10,13,14, and 15 are primarily concerned with training policy and its implementation. The list taken as a whole reveals a strong supervisory faith that employees grow and mature through their work experience.

Need for Organizational Flexibility

Organizational psychology is just beginning to probe the effect of organizational structure on the performance and contribution of employees. As the work of the world becomes more sophisticated—more mental and less physical in nature—older, rigid patterns of structure have become a brake on employee development. An age-old question reasserts itself: Was humanity made for the Sabbath or was the Sabbath made for humanity? Should a company set up a logical or "ideal" organization and then seek ready-made people to fill its blocks? Or should a company find good workers and build an organization around them, a structure flexible enough to support their growing abilities? For any number of compelling reasons, the answer must be the latter. The traditional manufacturing organization is bogged down with an inherited line-staff organization heavily practiced in downward communication, pressure, and control. It has paid scant attention to upward communication except during crises, and then only until things got back to normal. New ideas have usually come from the outside. The feeling seems to be that it is better not to have any ideas coming from the ranks than to have to cope with an embarrassing one once in a while! This traditional pattern of organization was good enough to get the work out when that work was engineered to be routine, repetitive, and geared to the mass production of interchangeable parts. With automation taking over more of the jobs of this dimension, management must find more flexible ways to organize people into specialized work teams.

The development of technical people can best take place within an organizational structure that will fully support and stimulate competence, opportunity, innovation, experiment—in short, a rich learning environment. People who are growing will always break out of organization blocks and stretch the limits of job descriptions. A flexible organization will help them do it.

Key Role of the Supervisor for Staff Development

The role of the supervisor takes on new dimensions when his or her company begins to take on the responsibility for the development of its technical and professional personnel. (Most of the thinking in this section is taken from the author's publication* dealing with the role of the supervisor.) In general, growing professional employees place higher demands on their company and expect more from their leadership than do nonprofessional employees. This is especially true of engineers. They also expect more specialized services and support for their endeavors. These increased demands and higher expectations may take shape in ways such as the following:

1. Much more of the communication between the supervisor and professional employee must be at the intellectual level rather than at the administrative level.

2. The level of motivation needs to be much higher to achieve creativity and *intrinsic* job satisfaction than would be necessary for productivity in more routine types of work.

3. Activities must be perceived at meaningful and reasonable levels in terms of goals and purposes. Professionals expect competence in leadership, competence well above the level of condusion and drift. They will not accept with docility improvisation as a substitute for planning.

4. The supervisor must take the initative in meeting the needs of professional employees. For example, a competent employee with a salary raise long overdue would be more apt to quit on a pretext and get another job than he or she would be to ask for a salary increase.

* Lester F. Zerfoss, *The Role of the Supervisor in Developing His People,* 1968 (lecture series).

5. Professional employees expect to have their own views and insights fully considered in any evaluation or review of their work performance.

6. The administration of the professional work group must be service-oriented. The supervisor is expected to provide the resources and tools needed for competence at the expert level. Conversely, the supervisor is expected to remove any administrative or red-tape barriers that get in the way of top-notch performance.

7. The professional employee expects that the standards and ground rules that bind the work group members together and control the intergroup relationships in the organization will be compatible with professional ethics and moral values.

8. The professional employee is much more highly sensitive to concepts of fairness, mutual sacrifice, objectivity, respect for personal privacy, status, authority of knowledge and expertise, etc.

9. Professional employees tend to find their security in their competence and contribution rather than in loyalty or seniority. This is especially true in their earlier years of service. (*Note:* This author has a growing concern that unless engineering managements move much more rapidly to set up comprehensive development programs in their organizations, engineers will reverse their field and resort to group pressure and collective bargaining to maintain the basic security they need.)

Professional employees are really not different from less educated employees in the kinds of qualities they possess. The difference lies rather, in the degree to which these qualities are disciplined or sensitized in a person's behavior. Long years of academic, professional schooling have emphasized objectivity, the scientific approach to problem solving, and the importance of logic and reasoning. Such training tends to make people distrust their feelings somewhat and to repress any expression of emotionality. All too often, the professional comes to his first job with little training in self-understanding or in the skills of interpersonal communications. Nor is such a person apt to be highly experienced in the working relationships needed to produce teamwork and cooperation in sophisticated group endeavors.

In the light of these observations, it is evident that the supervisor of technical and professional employees will need to develop some special abilities and skills. May I propose for a start, that such a supervisor must:

1. Learn to understand the nature of motivation, appreciate its influence on behavior of the individual, and become skillful in its applications on the job.

2. Learn an acceptable way to evaluate and feed back performance results as a basis for stimulating the development of the employee.

3. Learn how to use on-the-job training to ensure competence, confidence, and acceptance throughout the work team.

4. Be able to get employees to place high demands upon themselves.

5. Learn the career expectations of employees and know how to supervise them both for present competence and for preparation for the next jobs in their career progression.

6. Know how to accelerate the experience of the employees of high potential.

7. Find new and better ways to secure teamwork and cooperation through mutual-support relationships.

8. Be able to lead employees to work out developmental work programs for themselves.

9. Be able to build and maintain a flexible, dynamic work group organization able to cope with the changing demands of the company.

While these nine supervisory growth areas are by no means the whole story, they do provide a place to start development.

Goals of Staff Development

There is clearly much greater definitiveness in management's ability to manage its physical and financial resources than in its ability to manage its human resources. In the management of plant, machinery, materials, and money, management has learned how to set minimum standards, establish break-even points of costs and profits, and measure quantitatively the results obtained. The movement in management toward "management by objectives" and "results management" are evidence of rapidly growing skills in these fairly concrete management responsibilities.

When it comes to the management of human resources, these newly designed systems are less applicable. Setting standards for *professional services* is much more difficult than setting standards for *making products*. Whenever management has been unable to determine and measure results, it does the next best thing: it evaluates methods, procedures, or techniques. In this retreat, management is really saying, "If I can't measure the results of your work, I'll make sure you are kept doing it the way I want you to do it." When an engineer leaves the drawing board and looks out the window, is he or she woolgathering, reliving last night's party, or putting new ideas into perspective? Management will never know for sure! Since the development of people is so complex and abstract, it is without doubt the least managed of all managerial responsibilities.

The following table attempts to bring into focus the significant development concepts in such a way as to put them into perspective for the use of top management in (1) designing a development program, (2) evaluating what it is already doing in the name of development, (3) identifying the goals or results to be achieved, and (4) managing the development program in terms of its objectives.

In Table 1, the first vertical column shows the sequence of stages of learning activities that lead to development of personnel. Column II notes the kind of organizational

Tables 1   Goal-directed Development

Stages of development I	Organizational support needed II	Learning goals to be achieved III
1. Education	Instructional program	Knowledge of program understood and accepted at verbal level
2. Training	Simulation program	"Know-how" translated into job competence at approved performance level
3. Growth experience	Developmental supervisory leadership	Individual's developmental work program; accelerated mastery of new skills and abilities; outstanding performance
4. Increased utilization	Top-management administrative action: transfer, rotation, progression, promotion, recognition	Take next steps in career progress development of identified potential for advancement; valuable job contribution

support that must be provided by top management to implement each stage in the sequence. Column III identifies the learning goals that must be accomplished at each stage. This table, taken as whole, illustrates the central principle of staff development: *the end goals of a development program are greater utilization of people at their highest skills and abilities.*

BARRIERS TO DEVELOPMENT

Few people question the importance of development for individuals in all their life roles. The individual perceives this as *self-development*. Personal development is each person's own responsibility, and anyone would rightly resent the attempts of others to take over that responsibility. The individual senses that such manipulative practices, engaged in under the guise of "personnel management," are a threat to his or her self-respect.

Few managers question the need of the organization to have in its employ a staff of developing people able to fill the jobs vital to the continuing profitability of the enterprise. However, in their eagerness to have key people ready for use right now, managers have allowed themselves to become manipulative—moving people around like checkers on a checkerboard, arbitrarily assigning them to jobs, ignoring the wishes or needs of those most immediately affected by these administrative moves. Essentially, the employee is expected to believe that "father knows best," and that what is best for the company is best for the employee. This may be, in part, the reason why companies have produced so few examples of successful development programs and why they have produced so many technical and professional people who turn into "deadwood" long before their normal retirement years.

Much of the answer to lack of development lies in the negative elements in the management climate that act as blocks or barriers to development. This section will identify six major blocks that prevent the individual from realizing his or her potential. The author has found these blocks to be present to an unhealthy degree in most organizations. They are caused both by growth problems in the individual and by restrictive forces in the organization. All six can be significantly reduced by a comprehensive development program.

Underutilization

This barrier takes on many forms. It may be a by-product of overselection. Incompetent supervisors may be holding people back. Management may be limiting its vision of employees to their achievement, ignoring their potential. An underutilized employee soon learns to cover up with busy work, routine activities, work at the lowest level.

Chronic Frustration

Unrelieved tensions, low threshold of capability, meaningless work activities, state of confusion or disorganization—all these take a heavy toll in lowered motivation and eventually result in chronic frustration. Unhappily from the point of view of management, a good employee who is frustrated behaves like a poor employee. For all practical purposes, while such a person is in a state of frustration he or she is not likely to make progress in development.

Low Standards of Performance

Where performance standards are set by the manager without the participation and acceptance of the employee, they are usually minimum standards—much lower than the employees would set for themselves were they motivated to do so. Low standards take the challenge out of work. They make it difficult for the employees to test their strengths or become aware of their potential.

Obsolescence

Technical change is an ever-present challenge to the employee to keep updated. The older employees feel the pressure to keep their skills and abilities competitive with those of the young grads entering the department. A decade ago, 7 or 8 years of experience on the same job was thought of as evidence of superior know-how; today, it is apt to be thought of as evidence of obsolescence. Sophisticated know-how is forcing more employees to become highly specialized in areas that can make them victims of technological change. Under these conditions, our older and more experienced employees are increasingly likely to "become obsolete." The threat is not only one of technical obsolescence but of mental obsolescence as well. The problem has become so acute in some companies that retirement plans, originally designed to hold people to age 65, are more and more being used to cope with middle-age obsolescence through early retirement.

Professional Myopia

With the trend toward more intensive specialization, the specialist or expert is often confined to a narrow work niche. Such a person is always working with small parts of tasks and rarely gets to see the task as a whole, suffering from a narrow time frame and myopic vision. Without prompt recognition, this predicament can lead a person to lose the broad perspective that a generalist (and almost by definition, a manager) must have to further a career. We are all familiar with the specialist who has become imprisoned by the wrong kind of experience or too much of the same kind.

Career Drift

It is painlessly easy for some employees to slip comfortably into the status quo and become passive or procrastinating about their career aspirations. Under the guise of cooperation, they can let their company place them or move them around in terms of company expediency, only to wake up too late and discover that they have drifted through the best years of their lives in terms of career development and qualifying themselves for greater opportunities. They slide through their twenties, their thirties, and their early forties still waiting for something good to happen to them.

These six barriers are fatal to development. In the good old days when manpower was cheap and expendable, an organization could muddle through with fairly high levels of block in its people. In the future, a company's survival may depend on its batting average in learning how to reduce these important causes of poor work performance and costly waste of employee potential.

ADMINISTRATIVE ACTION NEEDED TO MOTIVATE DEVELOPMENT

The goal of development is the more efficient utilization of people to make them more productive and more likely to realize their own growth potential. Both employees and the company gain when development takes place. *Sterile* management development programs seem to forget this goal; they are sterile because they make *activities*—brought into the company in the name of development—*ends in themselves.* They ignore a most basic principle of human nature—the intrinsic motivation for development is more rewarding utilization. The following administrative action pattern is a psychological approach designed to "build in" organizational *readiness* for development. The administrative action taken by top management puts high demands on the staff to move up to the competence needed for developmental implementation. Thus the organization is quickly motivated to learn.

Model of Administrative Action Needed to Set the Goals for Optimum Utilization of Personnel

Step 1 Adopt and begin administering a policy of *promotion from within* that will provide maximum opportunity for employees to take increased responsiblity and qualify for advancement within the organization.

Step 2 Set up internal selection procedures (*A, B,* and *C*) that will make sure all employees who are qualified and available for advancement get looked over and are not overlooked. This calls for the development and maintenance of:

A. Organizational replacement charts to forecast present and future manpower needs

B. Inventory of personnel in terms of developmental status—readiness and availability for filling organizational vacancies and new positions

C. Accelerated *individual development programs* for high-potential candidates in critical replacement areas

Step 3 Review supervisory evaluations of employee performance; identify outstanding performance and evidence of growth potential.

Step 4 Require periodic supervisory appraisal and evaluation of employee's work performance and developmental progress.

Step 5 Require, at the work-group level, a developmental work program for employees, designed and carried out jointly by the supervisor and the employee, to achieve present job competence with supportive job training *plus* developmental experiences prerequisite to furthering career values and opportunities.

Step 6 Provide the on-the-job training resources needed for implementing the individual employees' developmental work programs.

Step 7 Provide employee orientation to get people off to a good start on their new jobs, help them become aware of their own potential for growth and development, and acquaint them with the opportunities available to qualified employees. In short, equip them to be *active participants* in their own education, training, growth experiences, and development.

The reader will note that each step in this sequence becomes an objective for the preceding step and puts pressure on the prerequisite function to achieve that objective. The developmental learning that the individual engages in to support each administrative action step becomes *immediately* useful and meaningful to him or her.

SUMMARY

This chapter has attempted to explain the nature of development—what it should be and what it should not be. Table 1 and the model for administrative action bring the thinking of the chapter into focus and, taken together, provide an overall blueprint of what has to happen in order for a company to have a comprehensive management development program. Obviously, it is not possible within the scope of this chapter to present the "how-to" side of the picture. However, most companies have within their own staffs the resources to implement the blueprint.

Chapter **8**

Cost Engineering in Construction

ROBERT G. ZILLY

Construction Management Department, College of Engineering and Technology,
University of Nebraska

INTRODUCTION

To the plant engineer faced with a demand for increased production, production at lower cost levels, or changes in production dictated by new or improved products, there are only three alternatives involving construction:

1. Remodel existing plant
2. Add additional space to existing plant
3. Abandon existing plant in favor of new production facilities

Choices 1 and 2 are, of course, not mutually exclusive. Management production objectives may be achieved by one or the other or a combination of both. Choice 3 is a unique solution, but there are situations in which it might be feasible to provide new facilities for a portion of the required production, with the balance coming from a remodeled existing plant. Figure 1 illustrates a warehouse cost study showing how a new facility may increase fixed costs but result in overall cost reduction by greatly lowering variable costs.

Assuming that use of the applicable tools of engineering economy leaves one of the construction options as a potential solution to the production problem, the plant engineer must then develop a construction cost estimate. In an era of rapidly escalating labor and materials costs complicated by on-again–off-again government regulation of the economy, this is no small task. Even with a complete set of working drawings and specifica-

RICHMOND FOOD STORES/NEW WAREHOUSE

DATE MO. YR.	NAME	AVG. STY. HT.	AREA SQ. FT.	CONTENT CU. FT.	COST SQ. FT.	COST CU. FT.	CONTRACT PRICE	FINAL PRICE
1957	Building	24.4	206,500	5,038,500	$ 4.54	$.186	$ 938,538	
	Paved Area		167,500		$ .31	—	$ 52,377	
	R. R. Siding		2,025		$11.45	—	$ 23,210	
	Plbg., Htg., Ventlg. & Air Conditioning				$ .71	$.028	$ 144,807	
	Electrical				$ .41	$.016	$ 84,984	
	Sprinkler				$ .32	$.013	$ 67,184	
					$ 1.44	$.057	$ 296,975	
	Refrigeration				$ .48	$.022	$ 102,000	
	Insulated Cooler Rm.				$ .39	$.015	$ 79,418	
	TOTAL EQUIPMENT (BUILDING)				$ 2.31	$.037	$ 478,393	
	TOTAL BLDG. & EQUIPMENT				$ 6.85	$.280	$1,416,931	

1964 CONTRACT COSTS FOR NEW STEEL FRAME/140,000-SF ADDITION TO RICHMOND WAREHOUSE

	Amount	Sq. Ft.	Cu. Ft.
General	$742,694.00	6.69	.260
Heating & Plumbing	82,364.00	.74	.029
Fire Protection	52,092.00	.46	.018
Electrical	39,690.00	.35	.014
TOTALS	$916,840.00	8.24	.321

Sq. Ft. 110,912 without platform/Cu. Ft. 2,799,412 warehouse only

BEHAVIOR OF FIXED AND VARIABLE COSTS/IN OLD AND NEW WAREHOUSES

A. In Projected new warehouse

sales volume	fixed costs		variable costs		total costs	
	DOLLARS	%	DOLLARS	%	DOLLARS	%
$ 5,000,000	$30,000	0.60	$50,000	1.00	$80,000	1.60
6,000,000	30,000	0.50	60,000	1.00	90,000	1.50
7,000,000	30,000	0.43	70,000	1.00	100,000	1.43
8,000,000	30,000	0.38	80,000	1.00	110,000	1.38
9,000,000	30,000	0.33	90,000	1.00	120,000	1.33
10,000,000	30,000	0.30	100,000	1.00	130,000	1.30

B. In outmoded old warehouse

sales volume	fixed costs		variable costs		total costs	
$ 5,000,000	—*	—*	75,000	1.50	75,000	1.50
6,000,000	—	—	96,000	1.60	96,000	1.60
7,000,000	—	—	119,000	1.70	119,000	1.70
8,000,000	—	—	144,000	1.80	144,000	1.80
9,000,000	—	—	171,000	1.90	171,000	1.90
10,000,000	—	—	200,000	2.00	200,000	2.00

*None, or Negligible

Fig. 1 An example of how reduced variable costs resulted in lower total costs for a warehousing operation in spite of the rising cost of new construction. (*Building Design & Construction*, August, 1966.)

BID TABULATION

SIMPLE INDUSTRIAL BUILDING, PHILADELPHIA, PA., MARCH 13, 1961

Contractor A	Contractor B	Contractor C	Contractor D	Contractor E
Total General Construction Bid				
$438,000	$454,000	$459,640	$462,200	$466,500
Alternate Price For Increasing Height 2'-0" to a total of 22'-0"				
$ 8,900	$ 5,600	$ 6,000	$ 6,075	$ 6,000

A comparison of alternate prices received on a 1961, one-story structure illustrating the slight increase in cost in providing flexibility of two more feet in building height.

Fig. 2 Variation in contractors' bids on a project for which complete construction documents were available. Note slight increase in total cost for an increase of 2 feet in building height. (*Building Design & Construction*, January, 1966.)

tions, the estimate is not likely to approach an accuracy of more than plus or minus 5 percent, as illustrated in Fig. 2. In the early phases of the cost engineering analysis, with only the most general concept of the new or remodeled facility to work with, estimates will do well to stay in the range of plus or minus 20 to 30 percent. Thus, establishing the cost of a construction project is reduced to a sequential process in which an increasingly accurate figure is developed as project concepts move from the general to the particular. Figure 3 illustrates one approach to this process.

To differentiate among the various types of estimates, the American Association of Cost Engineers published these study definitions of the basic estimate types.

- Order of magnitude, ratio estimate—Variable accuracy, usually based on previous similar cost information, probable error over ±30%.
- Study estimate, factored estimate—Better than order of magnitude, accuracy insufficient for budgeting but a guide to further interest. Probable error up to ±30%.
- Preliminary estimate, budget authorization estimate, scope estimate—Data ample for estimate to be budgeted. Probably error ±20%.
- Definitive estimate, project control estimate—Considerable data available. Short of completed drawings and specifications. Probable error ±10%.
- Detailed estimate, firm estimate, contractor's estimate—Prepared from complete engineering specifications, drawings, and site surveys. Probable error ±5%.

These are known by other names as well, but essentially all estimates can be reduced to these categories. The kinds of information used, as well as other features of these estimate types, are summarized in Fig. 3.

APPROACHES TO THE PRELIMINARY ESTIMATE

In the early stages of analysis, a "ballpark" estimate is often adequate. A gross order of construction cost magnitude may be established by the following:

Cost per square foot For many buildings there are well-established historical records of cost per square foot. The "ranch style" one-story factory is a good example. The plant engineer may already have a set of historical data or else may refer to a number of publications such as those published by Dodge and Means. These are updated on an annual basis and usually provide multipliers for various geographic locations throughout the United States.

Cost per cubic foot While not as commonly used as cost per square foot, cost per cubic foot may offer a more valid estimating base for buildings with irregular roof configuration or other structural features which cause total cost to be more accurately reflected by a measure of cubic feet enclosed rather than square feet of floor plan.

Cost per unit of space provided or unit served Parking garages of specific types can be quite accurately costed on the basis of the numbers of cars to be served, and many industrial plants can be similarly costed on the basis of the number of work stations. Schools and hospitals can also be costed on the number of students or patients for which the facility is to provide. There are obvious parallels to be drawn between commercial, educational, and other types of buildings and certain industrial types.

Cost per unit of production The chemical industry, in particular, has had good success in developing rough estimates of the cost of new construction based on a cost per unit of production. The figures can be adjusted to include such variables as inflation rate, new production techniques, labor cost increases, and similar items. These cost-per-unit-of-production figures are, of course, subject to variation based on the size of the facility and must therefore be bracketed over specific ranges of production.

Interpolated cost When historical data are lacking or traditional rules of thumb do not seem to apply, costs may be approximated by simple linear interpolation based on a study of existing facilities. With the total cost figures for a group of facilities of varying production capacity established, rough estimates of the cost of a project with a specific capacity other than those known can be established by interpolation. With an adequate data base, such interpolations may be made on other than a linear basis by the application of more sophisticated mathematical techniques.

Cost based on published financial and operating data From such sources as the U.S. Department of Commerce and Dun & Bradstreet, financial and operating characteristics of a number of industries can be obtained. For example, for the stone, clay, and glass industry group, the average economic plant life is 15 years, the total assets per dollar

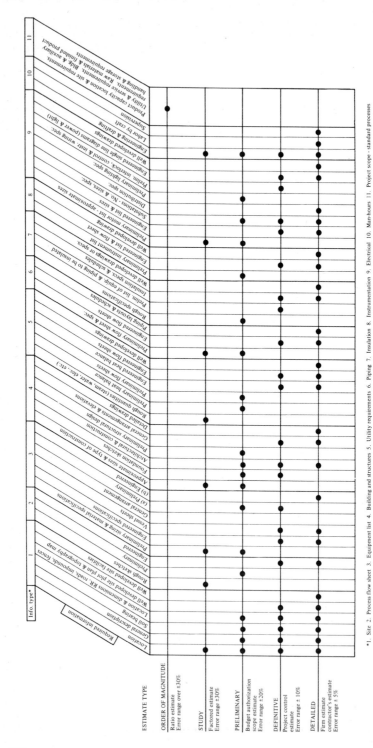

Fig. 3 Refinement of construction cost estimates as the design process progresses. (*Consulting Engineer*, April, 1970.)

*1. Site 2. Process flow sheet 3. Equipment list 4. Building and structures 5. Utility requirements 6. Piping 7. Insulation 8. Instrumentation 9. Electrical 10. Man-hours 11. Project scope - standard processes

of annual sales is $1, and the net worth per dollar of sales is $0.61. Combining this information with other details that are normally available will probably provide an adequate base for a construction cost estimate covering a plant with some specific annual output at a known current market price per unit of output.

There are other approaches to the costing problem which will also give a gross order of magnitude of construction cost for a specific industrial project. Some will at best be "gross," but others can be "fine-tuned" to varying degrees of accuracy with a little extra effort. However, in the preliminary phases of economic analysis, it is often wasted effort to try to refine what is intended to be only an educated guess.

REFINING THE ESTIMATE

Admittedly, it would be unwise to make any irrevocable decisions based on estimating techniques as precarious as those just outlined. However, if construction in the form of remodeling, plant addition, or new facilities still seems attractive, the plant engineer should go ahead with more refined estimating techniques. At this point, of course, there must be a further refinement of project concepts. In some industries it is conceivable that the investment in processing or production machinery far outweighs the cost of the enclosing structure itself. In this event, the cost of building construction may have negligible impact on the overall investment analysis. However, it is more than likely that the cost of the basic structure will remain a significant element in the engineering economy analysis.

If the latter situation prevails, it is necessary to begin to make some basic decisions about the structure. Is it to be purely utilitarian, with only minimum attention to esthetics? Or, are there social and economic reasons for emphasis on appearance? Either choice implies something about the structure—for example, cost per square foot of the enclosure system. If the site has been selected, a soils investigation is in order to determine foundation alternatives, e.g., slab on grade, grade beams, isolated spread footings, or possibly piling.

At this stage of the analysis, it is important to recognize Pareto's law—a concept developed in the eighteenth century by an economist who sought a general mathematical solution to the problems posed by economic systems. Loosely applied to the construction industry, this law implies that only 20 percent of the building systems making up a total structure will account for 80 percent of the cost—exclusive of sophisticated processing or production machinery. This concept is the basis of what the construction industry sometimes refers to as conceptual or parameter estimating.

Cost parameters are physical measures of those parts of a building's anatomy that are the major determinants of costs. For example, *Engineering News-Record* has been published reports on building parameters and their costs for almost 10 years. And, a number of architectural and engineering firms as well as contractors have maintained parameter-type cost data on various types of buildings for many years. The Austin Company, a design-build firm headquartered in Cleveland, has published data on a standard industrial-type building since 1913, as shown in Fig. 4.

A typical *Engineering News-Record* report includes the following data:

Type of building ....
Location.....................................
Construction start/complete..................
Type of owner ....
Frame..(Structural steel, reinforced concrete, etc.)
Exterior walls...............................(Concrete block, brick, metal, etc.)
Fire rating..................................(Class A, Type 1, etc.)

PARAMETER MEASURES

1. Number of floors excluding basement........
2. Number of floors including basement........
3. Basement plan area........................
4. Basement area, total ....
   Number of basement floors.................
5. Gross area supported (exclusive of slab on grade) ....

6. Face brick area.........................
7. Interior partitions.........................
8. Curtain wall, including glass ....
9. Net finished area ....
10. Other exterior masonry walls ....
11. Number of elevators ....
12. Storefront-type perimeter ....
13. Number of plumbing fixtures (sinks, toilets, etc.)
14. Parking area ....
15. Roof area ....

OTHER MEASURES

Story height, typical floor ....
Lobby area ....
Air conditioning (type of system) ....
Number of rooms ....

TRADE

	Code	Parameter cost Unit	Cost
General conditions and fee	5	sq ft	
Site work (clearing, drainage)			
Utilities (water, sewer, electric, gas)			
Roads, walks			
Landscaping			
Excavation	3	sq ft	
Foundation	3	sq ft	
Caissons, pilings	3		
Concrete arch or formed concrete	5	sq ft	
Exterior masonry	10	sq ft	
Etc.			

The parameter cost approach can be quite accurate in the hands of an experienced estimator, especially when it is backed up by good historical records covering particular building types. In addition to the published data that can be accumulated from sources such as *Engineering News-Record,* there are a number of cost consulting firms that maintain their own data banks—some with computer capability. For the plant engineer with limited resources available internally, these firms can provide early cost data for a modest fee. And many of them can carry on with more detailed cost estimates as the design decisions progress toward final working drawings and specifications.

Parameter cost estimating will generally bring results within the range of plus or minus 10 to 20 percent. However, on rare occasions, such estimates have actually been used by contractors to prepare final, lump-sum contract bids. This is, of course, a calculated risk that can only be chanced for familiar types of construction by extremely competent practitioners. In today's construction market, even the detailed takeoff from completed working drawings and specifications will seldom produce a group of competitive bids from contractors that will fall within a range of plus or minus 5 percent.

Thus, it is necessary to reevaluate all the economic goals factored into the engineering economy analysis after the conceptual or parameter estimate has been prepared. If the construction cost appears to be too high, consultation with competent designers and constructors may develop changes that will effectively reduce overall cost. Even if the parameter estimate appears to be low enough to warrant a particular construction project, however, decisions should not be allowed to become irrevocable until the project has at least gone through preliminary design drawings done by competent staff or independent architects and engineers. The usual design process goes through preliminary, development, working drawing, and final bid stages, and it is imperative that the cost estimate be updated at each of these stages.

THE FINAL COST ESTIMATE

The final cost of any construction project is, of course, not established until the construction is completed and all the bills are paid. However, in a competitive bidding situation based on completed working drawings and specifications, it is the low bidder who sets the closest estimate of total cost before construction gets underway. The low bid is often assumed to be the final cost figure, but in the real-life situation, this is seldom a valid assumption. Few projects are ever completed without "extras" which result from errors or omissions in the original design, unforeseen site conditions, or changing conditions in the marketplace that force the owner to depart from carefully planned original goals.

In fact, the low bid itself is often influenced by factors which are more often than not beyond the control of the plant engineer, management, or the design-construction team. In a period of rapid inflation, the plant engineer may be pressed to cut production costs for a particular product, only to find that the solution is plant expansion or remodeling that is itself the victim of inflated construction costs. Or a new product development

LONG AND SHORT TERM TRENDS IN FACTORY COSTS

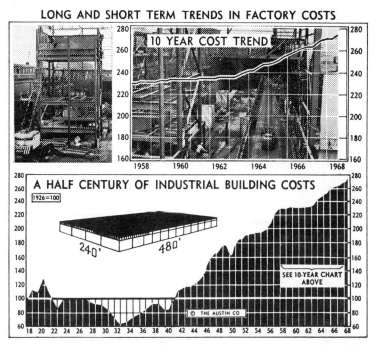

Fig. 4 The Austin Company has maintained this cost index for industrial buildings since 1913. The basic building was modified in 1962, at which time the size was changed from 100 by 200 feet to 240 by 480 feet, along with other details to reflect modern trends in construction. The base year is 1926-100, and the 1962 changes do not upset the validity of the base.

may be readied for production in a new plant that must go out for contractor bidding at the peak of the summer construction season. On the record, there is substantial evidence to indicate that midwinter bids are considerably lower than those made in midsummer.

In spite of these vagaries of the marketplace, there is no substitute for the detailed quantity takeoff from a completed set of working drawings and specifications for making an accurate estimate of construction costs. While it is true that this approach delays the start of construction until the designers have prepared the complete set of construction documents for the project, it is equally true that this approach is the only one that allows contractors to bid competitively on a reasonably common basis that is clearly understood by all. However, since each contractor is forced to make his own takeoff, there appears to be a considerable financial burden placed on the cost of construction by this duplication. In the British construction system, a professional quantity surveyor is paid by the owner to make a detailed takeoff of materials and quantities. This one-shot cost is clearly identified by the owner, who pays the fee, and the quantity surveyor takes professional responsibility for the accuracy of the figures. Unfortunately, American contractors have not been enthusiastic about this concept, although owner interest has led two British quantity survey firms to open American branches.

THE TIME VALUE OF CONSTRUCTION MONEY

In spite of the merits of having the contractor bid on a project with the complete set of construction documents in hand, the industry has long recognized that this approach tends to delay final project completion. In an era of high interest rates, this becomes a significant factor in raising construction costs. The owner suffers in two ways:

1. Large sums of money must be tied up—money allocated for construction progress payments that will draw little or no interest during the construction period.

2. The owner's return on investment is postponed until the project is completed and it can be put to its intended use.

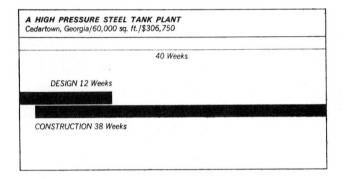

A HIGH PRESSURE STEEL TANK PLANT
Cedartown, Georgia/60,000 sq. ft./$306,750

40 Weeks

DESIGN 12 Weeks

CONSTRUCTION 38 Weeks

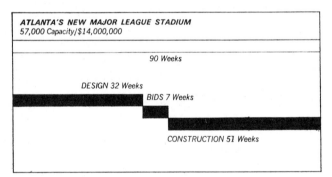

ATLANTA'S NEW MAJOR LEAGUE STADIUM
57,000 Capacity/$14,000,000

90 Weeks

DESIGN 32 Weeks

BIDS 7 Weeks

CONSTRUCTION 51 Weeks

Fig. 5 An illustration from Heery & Heery, Architects & Engineers, Atlanta Ga., showing the compression of time through use of simultaneous design and construction (*left*). (*Building Design & Construction,* March, 1966.)

Obviously, any reduction in the time span from project conception to completion is financially advantageous to the owner. To achieve this goal, many projects have been developed with design and construction underway concurrently. This approach is simply illustrated in Fig. 5, with the concurrent concept shown at the top, the conventional approach on the bottom. Note that the construction begins shortly after the design work gets underway, and the normal delay required for the receipt and analysis of competitive bids is allowed to meld with the design process in the concurrent concept.

The concurrency concept was used extensively for conversion of industrial plants to peacetime production during the post-World War II era and was revived in the early 1970s by the General Services Administration in an effort to speed up government procurement of badly needed building facilities. While this concept can reduce the time required to deliver a construction project, it tends to completely disrupt traditional industry relationships and often leaves the owner in the position of wondering just who is in charge of the project. This situation develops because as each design phase is completed, that portion of the project immediately goes out for competitive bidding. The contract for a segment of the work is awarded to the low bidder, and work begins on the site at once. Thus the owner and the designers must be prepared to make firm decisions and stick with them, for a change of mind now implies alteration or actual demolition of existing work rather than a simple erasure on a drawing. In addition, as the project progresses, there may be a substantial number of prime contractors on the site, all with direct contractual obligation to the owner. However, there is usually no general contractor in charge of coordinating the work of the several contractors.

For sophisticated owners with substantial in-house capability in design and construction management, the coordination problem may not be significant. However, when the owner is not prepared to provide the coordination services, numerous concepts have been advanced to replace the function of the missing general contractor. One of these involves assigning the individual contracts to a single contractor designated as the general contractor.

The most widely discussed and used idea in the early 1970s was construction management. Under this system, an individual or firm is retained to provide construction management services for a professional fee. The construction manager may either enter the picture when construction is about to begin or get involved early in the design stage via value engineering services and a continuous monitoring of costs. The construction manager is then well grounded in the designers' and owner's intent when actual management of construction is taken over.

The role of the construction manager has not yet been clearly defined, and the owner wishing to use the concept would do well to investigate carefully the contractual arrangements on those projects where success has been reported. Reactions of people involved in the construction industry are mixed, but enough successes have been reported to indicate that construction management will be around for some time.

There are numerous other arrangement available to the plant engineer faced with development of a construction project cost estimate and the ensuing construction. Among these are the design-build concept which places all responsibility for design and construction with a single firm. This approach usually involves concurrent design and construction, but its major attraction is the guaranteed "not to exceed" price. Design-build firms will often arrange to share any savings on the project with the owner; on most projects where goals are clearly defined, they will set a maximum cost figure. Some contractors and design firms have been able to compete with established design-build firms by putting together independent design and construction firms on a one-project basis. This type of consortium has been used successfully for a number of industrial projects, with considerable success reported in keeping costs at reasonable levels.

Fig. 6 Variation in structural cost due to change in bay size, from the Ballinger Company. (*Building Design & Construction,* January, 1966.)

INCREMENTAL COST FOR SLAB ON GROUND			
LOADS	THICKNESS	REINFORCING	INCREMENTAL COST
200 psf	5"	6 x 6 Mesh 6/6	
500 psf	6"	6 x 6 Mesh 6/6	+.08
750 psf	6"	2 Layers 6 x 6 Mesh 6/6	+.14
1500 psf	7"	2 Layers #4 12 EW	+.50
3000	9"	2 Layers #5 12 EW	+.85

Fig. 7 Incremental cost for variations in slab on ground, from the Ballinger Company. (*Building Design & Construction,* January, 1966.)

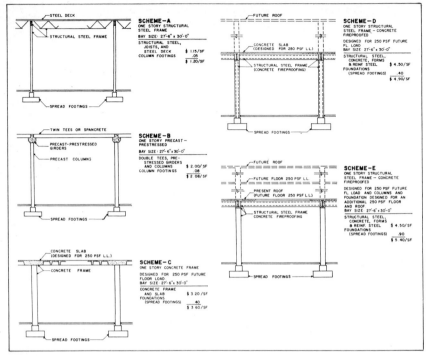

Fig. 8 Five schemes for industrial plant construction, from the Ballinger Company. (*Building Design & Construction*, January, 1966.)

CONSTRUCTION ALTERNATIVES

To the plant engineer involved in the development of a new production facility or the remodeling of an old one, there is a bewildering array of choices in the selection of basic structural, enclosure, and finish systems. In addition to well-established systems, there is a constant stream of new ideas which must be analyzed in the hope that they will provide alternatives at reasonable cost levels and higher standards of performance.

Figures 6 through 8 give some idea of the alternatives available for basic elements involved in the construction of an industrial building. The dollar values shown, which date from the mid-1960s, are no longer valid because of inflation, but the general cost relationships are still useful as a basis for comparison of the specific alternatives and as models for the type of current information the plant engineer should seek to develop for use in construction cost estimating and control.

Chapter 9

Quality Control in Maintenance

STEVE KOZICH
President, Quality Audit Company

INTRODUCTION

In order to appreciate quality control, one must first understand the science of quality technology. The results are proportional to its proper application.

Maintenance, on the other hand, is based on the value of the function being performed in relationship to the facility being maintained. To apply quality control to the maintenance function is to assure proper expenditure of funds for the total plant maintenance operations. So often, an organization takes its maintenance function for granted for two reasons: first, there is a lack of understanding and appreciation for the services and facilities being furnished; second, if the equipment is working, maintenance is not required. Then there is the problem of maintenance personnel who really are most content fighting "fires," where cost is not hard to sell, in lieu of establishing a preventive maintenance program.

An area where quality control is well established in maintenance and preventive maintenance is seen in commercial air transport. All airlines break each aircraft down into a separate maintenance control center and apply various measurements. Adjustments, and replacements are made on the basis of a statistical preventive program. In fact, airlines even exchange information among themselves; this may lengthen or shorten the frequency of measurement, adjustment, or replacement. It is not difficult to sell airline management on preventive maintenance. In fact, they are strong in the procurement phase, defining maintainability needs and quality control to the aircraft manufacturer. A quality control program starts in the purchase cycle. If the valve in a hotel were purchased to the same definition as the valve in an aircraft and the operational ecords were audited and maintained in the same way, the result would most likely be the same.

Quality control during the operational phase of a product's life cycle must be based on the design and test history of the product. In order to maintain a product, its design, intended use, and definition must be totally understood. History of performance and continuous measurement of the environment where the product is being operated are very important. A review of the original equipment manufacturer's manual will often identify environmental restrictions or those that will affect the product's life. Major factors in controlling operational reliability of equipment are time, temperature, vibration, and input power control. Each of these must be monitored at the proper frequency and necessary accuracy to control equipment wearout.

The *first element* of quality control is based on product definition, or—stated another way—a set of blueprints defining the product and its operational needs. Quality control requires assurance that the blueprints include each piece of the product and that the product or equipment meets the technical requirements. The *second element* of quality control is tied to the basic units of measurement such as time, temperature, length, mass, current, light, etc., and to process controls as related to pollution, painting, waste, and special facilities (these may include plating tanks, heat-treating ovens, and items of that nature). In manufacturing facilities, nondestructive testing (which includes x-ray, dye-check, and welding operations) may require special safety and drain considerations. Quality control requires special training to assure that measurements are traceable and accurate. In fact, there is no way to implement a quality control program without making measurements and there is nothing to measure until it is defined. The *third element* of quality control is based on risk and economics, which depends on statistical application. Working with statistical control charts develops a good record. In fact, the charts will highlight areas where dollars or man-hours available provide the greatest return.

DEFINITION OF FAILURE

The objectives of quality control in a maintenance program are to protect reliability. Reliability implies the absence of failures. It is appropriate, therefore, to consider a very generalized definition of failure. A failure is the presence of an unsatisfactory condition. Observers may differ on whether an event is a failure. An unsatisfactory condition to one observer may not be an unsatisfactory condition to another. Examples of unsatisfactory conditions that should be considered as failures (or they will quickly be determined as unsatisfactory in operation) are:

1. Inability of components or systems to function at all
2. Inability of components or systems to function within specified performance limits
3. Cracked or broken members
4. Dirty external surfaces or soiled interiors
5. Insufficient lubrication
6. Corrosion
7. Poor handling characteristics

In some cases, the time at which failure occurs is quite apparent. Some failures, for example, involve performance failure of a system. An airline flight crew is aware of the exact time at which a failure occurred because they are alert and they have planned the characteristics to monitor. Failure often occurs with a broken part, smoke, or leaking fluid—and such failure might often have been prevented if the primary condition had received the proper attention. In other words, the characteristics preventing failure must be identified, monitored, and maintained.

Quality control in a maintenance program must take into consideration each bolt, valve, switch, door, projector, or whatever is included in the facility. The objective is to assure proper operation of the total facility when it is required to perform. From operational experience, records, and facility audits, the established frequency of preventive maintenance is developed. Once the task is identified, based on a level of expected operation, a statistical plan will provide the economics.

The maintenance program itself can be considered to consist of a group or set of defined actions to be completed at specified intervals. These are the routine jobs associated with scheduled maintenance and the one-time jobs associated with modification of the facility, its systems, and its components. The maintenance program can also be considered as a set of actions which results either from the set of defined actions or from reports of obvious malfunctions of the facility, its systems, and its components.

The development of a scheduled maintenance program must be based on operation time, age, and the environment of operation. It must consider:

1. Which individual actions should be taken
2. How frequently these actions should be taken
3. What facilities are required to enable these actions to be taken
4. Which stations should have which tools to perform the action
5. Which actions should be accomplished concurrently in the interest of economy
6. Others peculiar to the program

The action in a maintenance program can often be performed by a single technician or professional worker; however, it must include each task to be accomplished and incorporate a record of:

1. Servicing
2. Inspection
3. Testing
4. Calibration
5. Repair
6. Replacement with new items
7. Replacement with overhauled items
8. Modification

Historical records of the events must be maintained.

A strong emphasis is placed upon time limitations as a means of reliability control and is based upon the curve shown in Fig. 1. This represents a functional relationship between reliability and age. The curve is frequently referred to as the "bathtub" curve.

The curve has three periods: an "infant mortality" period of relatively high failure tendency immediately after installation overhaul or manufacture; a normal operating period related to relatively low failure tendency; and a wearout period where the failure tendency increases with further increases in age. Using the example of tire wearout, infant mortality is the result of poor installation, improper training, or not having the proper equipment for installation. The normal operating period is governed by the miles traveled, load carried, and proper maintenance of tire air pressure. The wearout cycle is generally affected by the tire's usage during its operating cycle; however, if the vehicle is not operated often, the wearout period can be extended. Keeping the tires out of the sun is helpful this way because heat speeds the aging of rubber. Without proper storage, the tire will show little thread wear but will fail from aging. Good quality control records and definition of characteristics to be monitored would show temperature in storage to be more critical than miles traveled.

If this concept of the relationship between age and reliability is adequate and true, the

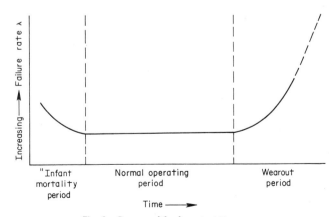

Fig. 1 Common life characteristic curve.

specific time of maintenance can be determined for each component. As a safety factor, the program can be implemented as follows:

1. Set a low initial maintenance time based upon design knowledge and related experience. Measure the proper characteristic.

2. Operate to this limitation until measurement of wear is associated with the maintenance frequency.

3. Increase the maintenance frequency by small increments and determine the failure rate associated with the new maintenance period.

4. Repeat these increases in time until the observed failure rate appears to increase.

5. Establish a maintenance frequency, with a safety factor, prior to any point of increase in failure rate.

This practice is a cautious exploration of the relationship between age and reliability. A second example may be to monitor the input power to a computer. Errors in data, storage, and component failures can be directly associated with power spikes, blackouts, or reduced power periods.

ANALYSIS OF TRADITIONAL MODEL

On analysis it is apparent that three of the conditions necessary for time limitations to be an effective means of reliability control would have become apparent. These conditions are as follows: (1) there must be some age at which the failure tendency shows a rapid increase; (2) sufficient units must survive to this age to enable a fixed time limit to have a real effect upon reliability; and (3) repaired units must have the same failure tendency as new units.

CURRENT TRENDS

The development and use of quality control techniques make clear that current maintenance alternatives include:

1. Component overhaul time control
2. Specific total time control of single-celled items
3. Periodic test and/or inspection
4. Reliability monitoring
5. Operations without scheduled maintenance

What must be accomplished is reduced emphasis on unit overhaul time control in favor of technical evaluation to meet a need. There is a bias related to experience, but new systems must be evaluated separately. A basic quality control program will improve the overall reliability of a complex system. However, with history of behavior, the program will change. There will be more specific components with specified repair cycles and there will be rapid increases in the repair-time limits. From this, there will be an increase in the number of life limitations upon single-celled items whose failures can have direct, adverse effects on operating costs. Once the program is implemented, there will be an increasing ratio of unscheduled to scheduled maintenance because scheduled maintenance has decreased. At first, large quantities of complex systems will be operating without preventive maintenance because maintenance people tend to call in the original manufacturer rather than learn about the equipment. However, the utilization of engineering action to develop preventive maintenance during early installations will provide cost savings by improving availability. From these cost savings there will be increasing utilization of engineering action, based upon experience obtained from malfunctions. This will improve reliability of the total complex.

A dramatic illustration of the effectiveness of planned preventive action will result from the records maintained. Those same records will become backup and justification of necessary expenditures. Remember, the value of records lies in the guidance they provide.

POSSIBLE FUTURE DEVELOPMENTS IN MAINTENANCE PROGRAMS

Increased failure effect analysis will more completely identify failure modes which have operational effects. Such identification may lead to redesign and elimination of the exposure to failure. Alternatively, it may lead to more effective development testing to determine the safe life for critical single cells or simple assemblies or to exploration of the life characteristics of a component. The way to fault-free operation is through better understanding of the facility.

The control of maintenance time should be related to the quality control records. Thus serviceability will improve. The combination of space, proper tools, and test facilities must be designed to support the total maintenance activity. These considerations will reduce repair and maintenance time.

The quality control records of equipment operation, repairs, and failures should result in the establishment of a preventive maintenance program and develop into a plan of progressive maintenance. This provides cost savings by continuing from a previous point or reducing the frequency of previous maintenance. When two or more similar systems are operated, a statistical maintenance plan can be developed by checking specific zones, or any one of the systems, to establish a preventive maintenance cycle by hour of operation, or time period, for all systems.

Chapter **10**

Comparative Statistics of Plant Engineering Operations *

LLOYD CALAWAY
and
LEWIS BUTTERY
Booner & Moore Associates, Inc.

INTRODUCTION

Good managers intuitively feel the need for indicators of the performance of their own functions or areas of responsibility as well as those of their subordinates. Since the control of performance must be preceded by measurement and comparison, most indicators are in the form of indexes. Most indexes are mathematical functions, usually ratios, of two or more quantitative or parametric measurements. Since data of this type are either not always routinely available or are of factors not amenable to direct measurement, the use of nonparametric determinations or estimates is sometimes necessary. A good example of a matter of management concern that is not directly measurable is the state of worker morale. Fortunately, indicators of this type are in the minority, and some type of direct or indirect measurement is usually possible.

The main problem confronting most managers is usually not a lack of data but of a rationale to enable them to establish a basis and determine the best indicator for each of the factors they wish to keep under surveillance.

The reasons for this are usually multiple and may include the following:

1. A myopic manager whose attention is focused too strongly on narrow internal departmental detail to the exclusion of a view of wider plant or company horizons

---

* The authors wish to acknowledge the help of Mr. Emery D. Carlson and Ing. A. Kuettner, whose critical review of this chapter was deeply appreciated.

2. A manager who is not aware of either the need for a particular index or of the basis used by superiors to judge the performance of the department

3. A manager who is either not aware of the existence of the information, or afraid to ask for it, or confronted with real difficulties in obtaining it routinely

4. A manager who has no basis for comparison or way to judge the adequacy of the controls he or she has devised or inherited

The objective of this chapter is to provide some relief for the last point. There are no easy cures for the other points, but most can be accomplished; in any event, the problem is more one of selection than one of invention. Another problem, though usually not as apparent, is finding a means of assuring that a set of indexes is adequate to represent all facets of the operation and to minimize distortion due to unbalanced emphasis on the various facets.

In the course of studies of the managements of numerous plants, the problem encountered most frequently is that managers are not making the best use of the information that is already being generated within the company. This is particularly evident within the plant engineering function. In this instance, it occurs most frequently as a failure to use information available at the total plant level or from an adjacent functions or departments such as production, operations, or whatever name is applied to the plant engineering department's best customer and reason for existence. The solution to this problem is outside the scope of this chapter, but this is a point each manager should check personally.

There are literally hundreds of indexes and indicators to choose from. One of the obstacles to selecting the best one for a specific purpose is the lack of a logical framework or classification method for all possible indicators. This may be provided by a model depicting the plant, the demands it generates, and the resources utilized for satisfaction of demands for service.

MODEL DEVELOPMENT

Considering the problem objectively, it would appear that there are only three major elements involved:

1. Plant (P): all manufacturing and support facilities at one site

2. Demand (D): sales orders, production schedules, work orders, and material requisitions

3. Resources (R): products, raw materials, utilities, personnel, mobile and shop equipment, tools, spare parts and supplies

These elements are closely coupled in a cause-and-effect-sense (see Fig. 1), but the linkages are necessarily elastic.

Since the resources (R) eventually operate on the Plant (P), a triangular model to make this a closed system is more appropriate. The springs are eliminated for convenience in diagraming. The linkages are now information flow paths with inherent variable time delays, and they may be identified by (as in Fig. 2) numbering in the same sequence as they normally occur. These are all feed-forward channels in a servomechanism sense.

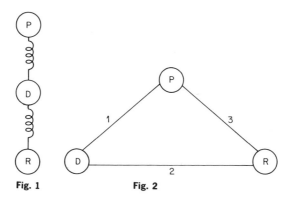

Fig. 1   Fig. 2

The opposite linkages are feedback channels and are also numbered in the same sequence as they normally operate (see Fig. 3).

This model will accommodate all information concerning a manufacturing or processing facility or plant. Its three main elements and six linkages may be used to classify origins of information or data and the relationships between the elements, but they require additional subdivision to be of practical value.

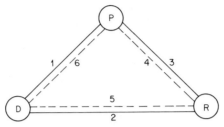

Fig. 3   Hierarchy of control indexes and sources of data for maintenance.

USEFUL SUBDIVISIONS

The next level of subdivision employed is that of type in a functional sense. Types that occur in a manufacturing plant include but may not be limited to three major functions:

1. Sales (S):   Same functional definition as defined by organ-
2. Production (P):   ization and actual operations
3. Plant Engineering (M):

Other types may be added if required, but the necessity has not been encountered in the application of the classification scheme to maintenance performance indicators.

The third level of subdivision found to be necessary is that of components of each of the types. Components are usually typified by their units of measurement. Those found useful in the formation of performance indicators and their units include:

1. Quantity (Q): number, weight, volume, etc.
2. Cost (C): dollars, cents, any other monetary unit
3. Time (T): minute, hour, day, week, month, quarters, years, etc.

INDEXES

Practically all indexes in use in the plant engineering area are composed of ratios of two or more of the individual measurements discussed earlier. Percentages and proportions

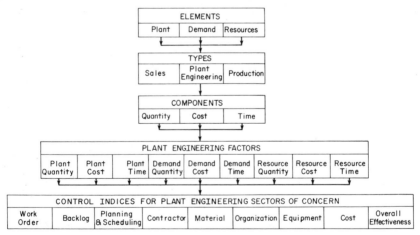

Fig. 4

would also be included in this definition.   An abbreviated hierarchy of control indexes and sources of data for plant engineering sectors of concern is depicted in Fig. 4.   The required indexes may be formed from individual measurements or data after giving due regard to the relationships between the major elements that are to be expressed.

STEPS IN DEVELOPING SETS OF INDICATORS

In selecting a set of performance indicators for routine reporting, the manager should consider each index separately and, upon its adoption, check to see that a balanced set has been adopted for each sector of concern.

Steps involved in selecting a particular index include answering the questions:
1. What do I want to control?
2. What index will indicate the performance?

After selecting the index, a target value of desired performance is needed for comparison.   These may be based on budgets, past history, future goals and objectives, or some other basis.   Target values selected should be checked for consistency between indexes within the set.

Sets of performance indicators should be established to give complete coverage of the plant engineering function in terms of elements, types, and components and sectors, as discussed previously.

Typical reports found to be useful in industry, composed of groups of performance indicators for various sectors of plant engineering management concern, are presented in Tables 1 through 9.

TABLE 1 Typical Performance Indicators—Sector: Work Order Control

No.	Index	Units	Comments
1	Cumulative work orders received / Number of days in the period	Number per day	One of the best indicators for anticipating a short-term change in the work load.
2	Cumulative work orders completed / Cumulative work orders received	Percent	Good indication of short-term balance between resources and demand; gaining on backlog or falling behind.
3	Cumulative work orders completed / Number of days in the period	Number per day	Indicates rate of work being accomplished.
4	Number of work orders in backlog	Number	A snapshot of backlog size on a given date. Provides a cross check on no. 2, but may be affected by laxity in closing work orders completed or awaiting late charges due to delayed invoices. No. 5 is better indication of backlog size.
5	Backlog work content, man-hours / 40 × number of workers available	Weeks	
6	Cumulative "emergency" work orders received / Cumulative work orders received	Percent	The analysis of work orders received by priority level gives a good indication of the time being allowed for scheduling of resources, whether the priority system is being abused, and how well the demand is balanced. No. 6 should be held to 10 to 20 percent and no. 7 should not exceed 15 percent.
7	Cumulative "urgent" work orders received / Cumulative work orders received	Percent	
8	Cumulative "routine" work orders received / Cumulative work orders received	Percent	
9	Cumulative "preventive" work orders received / Cumulative work orders received	Percent	
10	Cumulative "turnaround" work orders received / Cumulative work orders received	Percent	
11	Cumulative "preventive" work orders received / Cumulative "repair" work orders received	Percent	Used to monitor effectiveness of preventive maintenance effort.
12	Cumulative man-hours worked overtime / Cumulative man-hours worked straight time	Percent	Like no. 2, a good indication of balance between resources and demand.

TABLE 2 Typical Performance Indicators—Sector: Backlog Control

No.	Index	Units	Comments
1	$\dfrac{\text{Backlog work content, man-hours}}{40 \times \text{number of workers available}}$	Weeks	Same as no. 5 in work order control.
2	$\sqrt[n]{\text{Product of ages of all work orders}}$ where n = number of work orders in backlog	Days	The geometric mean is appropriate for expressing the mean of a highly skewed distribution with a zero origin.
3	Same as no. 2, but for priority level 1, etc.	Days	Comparison with no. 2 value gives good picture of reasons for delays in work completion.
4	Same as no. 2, but for skill "A" only, etc.	Days	
5	Same as no. 2, but for area "A" only, etc.	Days / Weeks	
6	$\dfrac{\text{Backlog work content, man-hours, skill "A," etc.}}{40 \times \text{number of skill "A," etc., workers available}}$	Weeks	Study of trends will detect if backlog is real or being maintained by craftsmen for a feeling of job security. Monitor for staffing levels
7	$\dfrac{\text{Active backlog work content, man-hours, skill "A," etc.}}{8 \times \text{number of skill "A," etc., workers available}}$	Days	Active backlog consists of work orders that could be done today if manpower available. 10 to 15 days is healthy, but varies by work load and craft.

TABLE 3 Typical Performance Indicators—Sector: Planning and Scheduling Control

No.	Index	Units	Comments
1	$\dfrac{\text{Actual time charged to scheduled work, man-hours}}{\text{Scheduled time for scheduled work, man-hours}}$	Percent	Good indication of quality of time estimates. These indexes should run close to 100 percent. Low results would indicate interruptions to the daily schedules or poor plans. High results, 120 percent or greater, are usually due to poor manpower estimates.
2	$\dfrac{\text{Scheduled time for scheduled work, man-hours}}{\text{Estimated time for scheduled work, man-hours}}$	Percent	
3	$\dfrac{\text{Actual time charged to scheduled work, man-hours}}{\text{Estimated time for scheduled work, man-hours}}$	Percent	
4	$\dfrac{\text{Unscheduled work, man-hours}}{\text{Scheduled work, man-hours}}$	Percent	Index indicates the quality of scheduling and how well the schedules are being followed.
5	$\dfrac{\text{Work scheduled, man-hours}}{\text{Time and workers available for scheduling, man-hours}}$	Percent	Indicates flexibility of craft lines and work procedures. Also indicative of manpower utilization and backlog. Should run about 95 percent.
6	$\dfrac{\text{Time and workers available for scheduling, man-hours}}{\text{Total work performed, man-hours}}$	Percent	Numerator is a forecast. Denominator is what actually happened. Indicative of how well the number of workers present each day is being forecast.
7	$\dfrac{\text{Emergency priority jobs worked on regular time, man-hours}}{\text{Total work performed, man-hours}}$	Percent	Used in conjunction with nos. 8 and 9, gives an indication of real emergency work needs vs. people abusing priority system to have non-emergency work done immediately.
8	$\dfrac{\text{Overtime for work during normal day shift, man-hours}}{\text{Total work performed, man-hours}}$	Percent	Indicates shift personnel working on days to handle work load in excess of day-worker capacity.
9	$\dfrac{\text{Total overtime worked, man-hours}}{\text{Total work performed, man-hours}}$	Percent	Optimum level usually ranges from 3 to 8 percent. "Lean and hungry" staffing levels may lead to 12 to 15 percent normal and economic. Over 15 percent leads to worker fatigue and should be avoided. Little or no overtime may indicate (a) poor planning and scheduling, (b) equipment abuse/neglect, (c) overstaffing, (d) management edict, or (e) lax supervision.

TABLE 4 Typical Performance Indicators—Sector: Contractor Control

No.	Index	Units	Comments
1	$\dfrac{\text{Number of contractor workers}}{\text{Total number of plant engineering workers}}$	Percent	Generally ranges about the 30 percent level for best results. Too few contractors may indicate overstaffing. Too many contract people may indicate too few company people to handle critical work, leads to a reduction of bargaining power and makes company vulnerable to contractor work stoppages.
2	$\dfrac{\text{Total contractor man-hours worked}}{\text{Total plant engineering man-hours worked}}$	Percent	No. 2 eliminates effect of absenteeism from no. 1.
3	$\dfrac{\text{Contract man-hours worked by craft}}{\text{Total man-hours worked by craft}}$	Percent	No. 3 indicates level of contract work by craft; ideal level varies by craft—lowest levels in shops, electrical and instrument, highest levels in field crafts.
4	$\dfrac{\text{Maximum man-hours demand by craft}}{\text{Base workload man-hours by craft}}$	Percent	No. 4 indicates the volatility of demand for a craft and should be compared to actual usage reflected by no. 3.
5	$\dfrac{\text{Contractor man-hours scheduled by craft}}{\text{Contractor man-hours worked by craft}}$	Percent	No. 5 indicates how effectively contractors are being utilized on planned work; the balance may be either emergency work or to avoid overtime by company people.
6	$\dfrac{\text{Contractor overtime man-hours by craft}}{\text{Contractor regular time man-hours by craft}}$	Percent	No. 6 indicated level of contractor overtime.
7	$\dfrac{\text{Contractor cost}}{\text{Contract man-hours worked}}$	Dollars per man-hour	No. 7 gives a cost per man-hour for estimating purposes and comparison with cost of company manpower; the difference between the two indicates the premium being paid to contractors for the privilege of adjusting staffing levels to immediate demand.

TABLE 5 Typical Performance Indicators—Sector: Material Control

No.	Index	Units	Comments
1	Requisitions filled from stock without delay / Total requisitions received	Percent	Nos. 1, 2, 3 and 4 measure service factor of materials supply function.
2	Requisitions not filled due to stockout / Total requisitions received	Percent	
3	No. of stocked-out items causing lost production / No. items not filled due to stockout	Percent	
4	Value of lost production due to stockouts / Value of scheduled production	Percent	
5	Value of maintenance material inventory / Value of facilities (replacement cost)	Percent	Nos. 5, 6, 7, 8, and 9 are indicative of the cost of providing the service reflected in nos. 1, 2, 3, and 4.
6	Value of spare parts inventory / Value of maintenance material inventory	Percent	The two groups must be balanced at a satisfactory level.
7	Cost of operation of materials supply / Value of materials issued	Percent	Indicates overhead charges applied to materials issues; will vary widely due to accounting practices.
8	Cost of operation of materials supply / Value of materials inventory	Percent	When the numerator of no. 8 includes the current interest rate applied to the value of the inventory, the ratio reflects the total inventory carrying cost; will average 25 to 30 percent per annum.
9	Value of materials issued / Value of materials inventory	Percent	No. 9 indicates the stock turnover rate or activity and average age of materials in inventory. General materials should have an average turnover of 3 to 4 times per year and are controlled by normal inventory control practices. Spare parts turnover should average about 2 years, the greater the turnover, the greater the risk of stockout, delayed repairs, and lost production; lower turnover produces inflated inventory levels.

TABLE 6 Typical Performance Indicators—Sector: Organization Control

No.	Index	Units	Comments
1	Average no. of plant engineering workers / Value of facilities (replacement cost)	Number per $1,000	Reflects staffing level and service demand relative to size of plant to be maintained.
2	Annual no. of plant engineering man-hours worked / Value of facilities (replacement value)	Man-hours per $1,000	
3	No. of plant engineering craftsmen / No. of plant engineering foremen	Percent	Will vary between 6/1 and 12/1. Proper level varies widely by craft.
4	No. of plant engineering craftsmen / No. of plant engineering supervisors (2d line)	Percent	Will vary between 20/1 and 40/1.
5	No. of plant engineering craftsmen / No. of planners and schedulers	Percent	Will vary between 20/1 and 40/1. One scheduler can normally handle the work of 2 to 4 planners.
6	No. of plant engineering craftsmen / No. of plant operators	Percent	Reflects relative rates of adoption of new technology.
7	Plant engineering payroll cost / Total plant engineering cost	Percent	Reflects balance between labor and material costs.
8	Plant engineering labor overhead cost / Plant engineering payroll cost	Percent	Reflects cost of special services with inflation and advancing age and seniority.
9	No. of new workers hired by craft / No. of workers terminating by craft	Percent	Level of replacement planned should consider vacation earned, retirements, resignations, average age, availability of replacements, apprentice training, work force utilization, workload demand, and contractor policy.
10	No. of instrument loops / No. of instrument workers	Number per man	Indicative of demand for maintenance services per available qualified craftsman.
11	No. of electric motors / No. of electricians	Number per man	
12	No. of rotating equipment items / No. of mechanics	Number per man	

TABLE 7 Typical Performance Indicators—Sector: Equipment Control

No.	Index	Units	Comments
1	$\dfrac{\text{Annual plant engineering cost by equipment type}}{\text{Replacement cost by equipment type}}$	Percent	Will reflect cost of plant engineering as function of equipment age and condition.
2	$\dfrac{\text{Failure repair man-hours by equipment type}}{\text{Total plant engineering man-hours by equipment type}}$	Percent	Gives indication of effectiveness of plant engineering efforts by equipment type or class.
3	$\dfrac{\text{Preventive maintenance man-hours by equipment type}}{\text{Total plant engineering man-hours by equipment type}}$	Percent	
4	$\dfrac{\text{Overhaul and turnaround man-hours by equipment type}}{\text{Total plant engineering man-hours by equipment type}}$	Percent	
5	$\dfrac{\text{Downtime caused by equipment type, hours}}{\text{Total plant downtime, hours}}$	Percent	
6	$\dfrac{\text{Total operating time by equipment type, hours}}{\text{Total number of failures by equipment type}}$	Hours per failure	Mean time between failures by equipment class.

TABLE 8 Typical Performance Indicators—Sector: Cost Control

No.	Index	Units	Comments
1	$\dfrac{\text{Plant engineering cost by product, dollars}}{\text{Total production by product, 1,000 lb}} \times 10$	Cents per pound	Portion of product manufacturing cost due to plant engineering. Also useful for utilities supplied internally.
2	$\dfrac{\text{Total plant engineering cost}}{\text{Facility value (replacement cost)}} \times 100$	Percent	Varies according to complexity of processes and severity of conditions; runs 2 to 3 percent for refineries, 4 to 5 percent for petrochemicals.
3	$\dfrac{\text{Direct plant engineering labor cost}}{\text{Direct plant engineering materials cost}} \times 100$	Percent	Reflects utilization of available man-hours and policy of "replace" vs. "repair" of equipment components.
4	$\dfrac{\text{Total man-hours worked}}{\text{Total man-hours paid}} \times 100$	Percent	Utilization of available man-hours on work orders.
5	$\dfrac{\text{Actual cost per work order}}{\text{Estimated cost per work order}} \times 100$	Percent	Variances in excess of $200 or 10 percent require explanation.
6	$\dfrac{\text{Actual total plant engineering cost}}{\text{Budgeted total plant engineering cost}} \times 100$	Percent	
7	$\dfrac{\text{Total labor cost (company and contract)}}{\text{Total man-hours worked}}$	Dollars per hour	Cost per man-hour of actual work on work orders.
8	$\dfrac{\text{Cost of planning and scheduling}}{\text{Total plant engineering labor cost}} \times 100$	Percent	Should range from 4 to 6 percent.
9	$\dfrac{\text{Cost of plant engineering supervision}}{\text{Total plant engineering labor cost}} \times 100$	Percent	Should range from 15 to 20 percent.
10	(Direct plant engineering cost) + (cost of downtime) + (cost of deferred work) = total cost due to plant engineering	Thousands of dollars per year	Should be balanced against service factor of facility to determine the optimum balance between the two.

TABLE 9 Typical Performance Indicators—Sector: Overall Performance

No.	Index	Units	Comments
1	$\dfrac{\text{Total costs due to plant engineering}}{\text{Total sales of plant production}}$	Costs per dollar	Numerator from no. 10, Table 8; indicates plant engineering costs from a director's viewpoint.
2	$\dfrac{\text{Value of lost production due to downtime}}{\text{Value of scheduled production}}$	Percent	Evaluates service factor slippage: runs 0.5 to 1.5 percent for most industries. High premium on a low value only if lost production could have been sold.
3	$\dfrac{\text{Total costs due to plant engineering}}{\text{Total after tax earnings}}$	Percent	Will range between 0.8 and 1.2 for most companies.
4	$\dfrac{\text{Total costs due to plant engineering}}{\text{Total conversion cost}}$	Percent	Total conversion cost is the total manufacturing cost less the cost of raw materials. Will vary widely from industry to industry, but is relatively constant for a given plant.

Chapter **11**

Computerized Work Sampling —A Valuable Tool

BARBARA H. YOUNG
Management Analyst

THE NEED FOR EFFICIENCY

In these days of spiraling costs and often limited personnel and matériel resources, it becomes increasingly important for managers to get the best possible utilization out of their plant engineering work forces.

This does not mean that personnel should be subjected to speedup tactics or undue pressure. This approach is usually self-defeating anyway. Instead, every effort should be made to determine what is causing delays or ineffective work methods and to do something positive to correct the problem. Inefficiency is frequently the result of inadequate training, poor supervision, awkward shop layout, or lack of tool, equipment, or transportation. Contrary to many a frustrated supervisor's suspicions, it is seldom caused by deliberate worker idleness.

WORK SAMPLING—A TOOL FOR MEASUREMENT

The tasks performed by plant engineering or maintenance personnel are often difficult to measure accurately. Maintenance work is not highly repetitive or production-type work, which can be counted as it comes off the production line. Instead, it often consists of small repair job, similar but not identical. On the other hand, the jobs may be long-cycle and nonrepetitive. The ideal tool for measuring or analyzing this sort of effort is work sampling, a widely used and proved study technique based on the laws of probability in which an observer makes observations at random times and records categories of productive and nonproductive effort of the personnel or equipment being studied.

Why Work Sampling?

There are, of course, many other techniques for measuring work. These include time study, standard data, predetermined time systems (such as Methods Time Measurement [MTM] and General Purpose Data [GPD]), historical estimates, and technical estimates. Some of these are quite detailed in application, extremely accurate, but costly to apply and maintain. Others are little more than historical averages—which, of course, include all past mistakes—or educated guesses. They are economical to be sure, but limited in value if good, workable standards are needed. Work sampling is a happy medium and for that reason is often selected as the most economical and practical means of approaching work measurement. Any degree of reliability and accuracy desired by the manager can be obtained by work sampling. It can be used for any number of people doing a multitude of jobs. This is a fairly good description of the plant engineering work force.

What Work Sampling Can Do

Work sampling is an excellent fact-finding tool and can be used to assist the manager in solving problems. Before a work sampling study is undertaken, a list of some of the things that are to be determined should be made. For example:

How much of the worker's time is really used productively?
Are the workers waiting around for tools or transportation?
Are top mechanics or journeymen performing routine cleanup tasks?
Is too much time being used to check out equipment?
Are workers waiting around for work assignments?

As a manager, you can probably think of a dozen other questionable areas that might be applicable to your own shop situation. A work sampling study can be designed to answer these and many other questions. It may well point out problem areas you did not even suspect existed. It lends itself well to determining the utilization of either personnel or machinery. However, it is not economical for studying a single operator. It can be applied intensively if the need for information is acute, or it can be applied over a long period of time. If the work being studied is cyclic in nature, however, care should be taken that a complete cycle is covered in the study. One other limitation of work sampling is that while it can tell you how much time is being expended to accomplish a particular job, it cannot tell you whether or not the best method is being used or if the person doing the job is working at optimal speed.

A COMPUTERIZED APPROACH TO WORK SAMPLING

In an effort to improve their own productivity, federal employees engaged in work measurement programs at the Marine Corps Base, Camp Pendleton, California, have devised and are using a computerized work sampling program in which an IBM Port-A-Punch is used to record observations on the spot. The punched cards are accumulated for a week and then processed through a System 360/50 computer program which prepares listings showing the total observations by day, by individual shop, and by branch, making all the calculations which would otherwise take so much valuable analyst or technician time. The computer is also used to prepare the random timetables used in conjunction with work sampling for each individual shop or area, eliminating the need for charts and tables and assuring absolute impartiality in the selection of observation times. Once programmed, the system is so simple to use that inexperienced personnel, with a minimum of training in observing and recording, can be utilized for the actual sampling, leaving the analyst or the manager free to analyze the results, determine necessary corrective measures, and take appropriate action.

Use of the IBM Port-A-Punch

The IBM Port-A-Punch, as indicated by the name, is a portable device into which a prepunched IBM card can be inserted. A stylus is then used to punch the cards, indicating various types of work categories according to whatever codes have been established. The Port-A-Punch shown in Fig. 1 has been marked off with tape to show the coding used in the work sampling program described above. The prepunched IBM cards allow for only 40 columns of data to be entered rather than the standard 80. Column 1 is used to indicate the shop or area being observed; codes 1 through 9 can be used for shop identification. The next three columns, 2 through 4, are used to indicate the sampling day, starting with 001 and continuing through 999. The computer correlates the sampling day with the calendar date, a helpful guide in cyclic-type work. The remaining 36 columns are used for the two-digit codes which designate the type of work and are

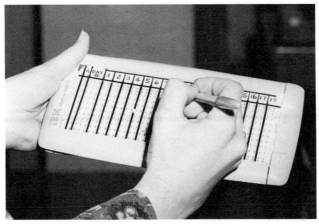

Fig. 1 The IBM Port-A-Punch.

called elements. The digits 10 through 99 can be used for element identification, although it is very seldom that more than 20 or 30 codes are needed to describe the activities in any one shop. Up to 18 observations can be entered on each card. It may be noted that neither the time of the observation or the identity of the operator is indicated in the coding. This information is not essential in determining the overall effectiveness of a shop.

SETTING UP A WORK SAMPLING STUDY

Before undertaking a work sampling study, the manager should establish goals and objectives. What really needs to be accomplished? For example, if the results are to be used for work measurement standards, certain steps must be taken that are not necessary if the study is to be used only as an investigative tool, i.e., a problem-solving device. To set standards, it will be necessary to select the work unit or units and devise an accurate and auditable method for counting them, both during and after the study. Also, a man-hour accounting system will be needed if there is not one already in operation. The total time of the study along with the number of units of work produced during that time will allow the analyst to determine the allowed time (standard) for the predetermined work units. The standard must also be leveled—i.e., the operators' performance compared to the concept of normal—and it must also include some allowance for personal time, fatigue, and unavoidable delays. A study may take from a week to several months.

Developing Work Element Codes

The work in each shop or area must be divided into categories of work and nonwork. These categories are sometimes called productive and nonproductive, with the nonproductive time divided into further groups of avoidable and unavoidable delays. Unavoidable delays usually consist of such things as obtaining tools, travel time, and other necessary actions which must be accomplished before the work can be done but that are not actually part of the production of a work unit. Avoidable delay is usually personal time, coffee and cigarette breaks, idle awaiting work, and similar delays which could be lessened or avoided. In some activities, avoidable delay is described as that which is within the control of the worker or supervisor and unavoidable delay is that which is not under the control of either. Every organization will most likely have its own preference for defining categories of work. The important thing is to clearly define them so that the observers will recognize and be able to code them accurately as they make their random observations.

Fig. 2 shows the results of a hypothetical work sampling study. In it the various categories of work and nonwork are separated into element groups in the following manner:

Code	Work category	Element
1	Paperwork	Productive
2	Machine work	Productive
3	Repair pumps	Productive
4	Issue tools	Productive
5	Overhead crane	Productive
6	Phone/callbox	Productive
20	Official talk	Nonproductive, unavoidable
21	Travel time	Nonproductive, unavoidable
22	On-job training	Nonproductive, unavoidable
23	Work assignment	Nonproductive, unavoidable
24	Obtain tools	Nonproductive, unavoidable
30	Personal	Nonproductive, avoidable
31	Idle	Nonproductive, avoidable
40	Leave	Absence
41	Training	Absence
42	Not observed	Absence

Fig. 2

When performing a work sampling study in an activity with several shops or sections, codes (which would not be applicable to any other area) may be assigned to identify jobs in one specific area. As many as 99 codes may be used to identify work categories, but in reality such a detailed breakdown is seldom necessary and makes analysis of the data collected unnecessarily difficult.

Briefing the Personnel

As noted before, work sampling can be used either to set standards or as a fact-finding tool. In either case, certain basic steps should be taken to ensure its success. One of the most important is to obtain the cooperation and participation of the employees who are to be covered in the study. The knowledge that their work is to be subjected to an intense investigation creates both uneasiness and awareness on their part. Every effort should be made to thoroughly brief all personnel on the purpose of the study and to reassure them that their jobs are not in jeopardy. Explain to them that they are to participate in setting their own standards if such is the case. Questions should be invited and answered fully and openly so that the project does not have an air of secrecy. Otherwise there will be a tendency to resent the observation, resulting in attempts to cover up problems, make work, work at a faster pace, or otherwise thwart the observers. Sometimes it is necessary to run a trial sampling period for a few days or a week until both the observers and the employees become accustomed to the routine.

USE OF COMPUTERIZED REPORTS

There are six different reports generated by the work sampling program, each designed to provide a slightly different look at the same data base. Managers will find these reports of varying interest depending upon the area of their concern. The shop supervisor will probably find that those showing daily and cumulative totals for one work area contain all the information that is needed. The division or branch manager, with several shops or sections to control, will be more interested in looking at the reports showing all areas.

Daily Totals by Work Area

The first report lists each separate element for a specific work area. At the top of each column is entered the sampling day number (e.g., day 11, day 12, etc.). Just below, the calendar date is shown (e.g., 7/15, 7/16, as applicable). The alert supervisor will soon be able to note trends occurring on certain days of the week. It is common, for example, to find leave showing up more often on Mondays and Fridays. Under each day's date is shown the number of observations for each category of work for that day. In the second column for each day is the percentage of the total observations for the day. If no observations were made on one day, the computer enters zeros for this skipped day so that the days of the week remain in the correct sequence. Since the sampling is done at random times, not always the same number of observations are made each day. At the bottom of the report the number of invalid codes detected and omitted are noted. The observer should be advised if there are errors, so that the coding procedure can be corrected.

Cumulative Totals by Work Area

Cumulative observations for the work elements in each area are gathered as each day's totals are added to the previous day's. This report will show where trends are beginning to develop upward or downward. A supervisor—noting that machine work tends to go down and personal time tends to go up toward the end of the week—might want to spend a little more time in the work area during those times.

Daily and Cumulative Totals by Element Groupings

The daily and cumulative totals and percentages of daily observations by element grouping are shown. This provides a quick overview of work and nonwork when a detailed report is unnecessary. It also indicates what level of accuracy has been reached in this particular work area. If several shops are being covered in the study and the desired accuracy is reached in one before it is in the others, sampling can be discontinued in that one area.

Daily Totals for All Areas by Element Groupings

Daily observation totals for all shops or areas in a study are shown. A listing of this type would only be of interest to a branch or division manager. In some instances comparisons can be made between the different areas, but keeping in mind that the number of personnel and type of work accomplished in each shop will cause variations. Of more concern would be the fluctuation in the productive time from one day to the next, an indication that perhaps the workload is not distributed as evenly throughout the week as it might be.

Cumulative Totals for All Areas by Element Groupings

The final report produced by the work sampling program is shown in Table 1 and is the cumulative result of all observations. The daily cumulative percentages tend to round off the daily fluctuations into a more normal curve. Following the first subtotal across the page, it can be noted that productive time, which started at 68.5 percent on Monday, has dropped to 66.5 percent by Friday. This is a tendency which is seen in many activities. On the other hand, personal and idle time—or nonproductive, avoidable—has crept up a little each day, from 8.4 percent at the beginning of the week to 10.5 percent toward the end. At the bottom of the report, the accuracy of the data for the entire study is computed for the manager's benefit. As a general rule, an accuracy of ±10 percent at the 95 percent confidence limit would be needed in order to set engineered standards. If the study is being used for information and guidance only, a much lower accuracy could be tolerated.

CONCLUDING THE STUDY

When the collection of data has reached the level of accuracy needed by management, the work sampling can be stopped. Again, at the conclusion of the investigation, it is

TABLE 1 Port-A-Punch Sampling Program, Cumulative Totals by Element Groupings—Totals for All Areas*

Element group	Day: 11 Date: 7/15 Samples	%	Day: 12 Date: 7/16 Samples	%	Day: 13 Date: 7/17 Samples	%	Day: 14 Date: 7/18 Samples	%	Day: 15 Date: 7/19 Samples	%
Productive										
Area 1	133	9.0	133	9.0	144	8.8	167	9.3	173	9.0
Area 2	91	6.1	91	6.1	99	6.1	113	6.3	120	6.3
Area 3	149	10.0	149	10.0	167	10.2	182	10.1	196	10.2
Area 4	120	8.1	120	8.1	128	7.8	142	7.9	154	8.0
Area 5	188	12.7	188	12.7	202	12.4	221	12.3	231	12.1
Area 6	337	22.7	337	22.7	357	21.9	373	20.7	400	20.9
Subtotal	1,018	68.5	1,018	68.5	1,097	67.2	1,198	66.6	1,274	66.5
Nonproductive unavoidable										
Area 1	33	2.2	33	2.2	36	2.2	38	2.1	43	2.2
Area 2	14	0.9	14	0.9	15	0.9	18	1.0	18	0.9
Area 3	39	2.6	39	2.6	41	2.5	46	2.6	48	2.5
Area 4	18	1.2	18	1.2	20	1.2	21	1.2	24	1.3
Area 5	28	1.9	28	1.9	31	1.9	33	1.8	34	1.8
Area 6	42	2.8	42	2.8	43	2.6	46	2.6	50	2.6
Subtotal	174	11.7	174	11.7	186	11.4	202	11.2	217	11.3
Nonproductive avoidable										
Area 1	25	1.7	25	1.7	27	1.7	35	1.9	36	1.9
Area 2	25	1.7	25	1.7	30	1.8	39	2.2	40	2.1
Area 3	19	1.3	19	1.3	23	1.4	30	1.7	33	1.7
Area 4	11	0.7	11	0.7	16	1.0	19	1.1	22	1.1
Area 5	17	1.1	17	1.1	28	1.7	32	1.8	34	1.8
Area 6	28	1.9	28	1.9	33	2.0	34	1.9	37	1.9
Subtotal	125	8.4	125	8.4	157	9.6	189	10.5	202	10.5
Absence										
Area 1	25	1.7	25	1.7	33	2.0	36	2.0	36	1.9
Area 2	42	2.8	42	2.8	46	2.8	47	2.6	51	2.7
Area 3	5	0.3	5	0.3	5	0.3	10	0.6	11	0.6
Area 4	14	0.9	14	0.9	14	0.9	14	0.8	14	0.7
Area 5	62	4.2	62	4.2	71	4.4	80	4.4	87	4.5
Area 6	21	1.4	21	1.4	23	1.4	24	1.3	25	1.3
Subtotal	169	11.4	169	11.4	192	11.8	211	11.7	224	11.7
Grand total	1,486	100.0	1,486	100.0	1,632	100.0	1,800	100.0	1,917	100.0

*Accuracy of the latest cumulative results above:
1. Within ±13.3 percent for 95 percent confidence limits
2. Within ±8.7 percent for 80 percent confidence limits

a good idea to notify affected personnel, brief them on the results or anticipated results of the study, and thank them for their participation and cooperation. Later on, if changes are made in procedures or working places, they will be more ready to accept the changes if they can see that the knowledge was a result of their own observed actions.

Analysis of Data

Analysis of the performance of any shop and the isolation of possible problem areas requires a thorough knowledge of the area being studied, even with all the reports generated by this program. What appears to be a major deviation to an outsider may have some perfectly legitimate explanation when viewed through the eyes of the foreman or supervisor. So give them a chance to see the results of the study before jumping to conclusions. The reports will be a valuable tool and can give the manager an insight into the workload that could never be obtained otherwise.

Follow-up of Study Results

It is a rare shop indeed where some area for improvement cannot be discovered, and a good manager will take whatever corrective action is necessary to make these improvements. A dollar savings is not always realized, but improved working conditions and employee morale are worthwhile goals too. If the study points out high production or other good management indicators, do not hesitate to bring these to the attention of the foreman and shop personnel. It will enhance the value of the study and give it more validity in their estimation. If standards are developed, a chart showing weekly or monthly progress is usually prepared for each shop. These charts can be used to adjust workloads and/or personnel as needed. In conclusion, it must be remembered that work sampling is just a tool, not a complete solution. It can never replace good management procedures, but it can help the manager see what needs to be done. As managers of a large slice of the labor force and the operating budget, the plant engineers of today need all the help they can get.

REFERENCES

1. Ralph M. Barnes: *Motion and Time Study—Design and Measurement of Work,* 6th ed., Wiley, New York, 1968.
2. *Defense Integrated Management Engineering System in the Marine Corps,* Department of the Navy, MCO P5220.8A, November 30, 1971.

Section 9

Personnel Administration

Chapter **1**

The Job Description

MORRIS GEWIRTZ
Consultant

IMPORTANCE AND USES

One of the cardinal principles of good management calls for the assignment of clear-cut responsibilities to all personnel of the company. A simple way of accomplishing this is to prepare a written statement of the duties each employee is required to perform. Such a statement is called a position or job description. Although a distinction is sometimes made between white-collar and blue-collar work by applying the term "position description" to the former and the term "job description" to the latter, the terms are often used interchangeably. Most well-managed companies today use some form of job description for various levels of work, including managerial positions.

The importance of the job description can hardly be overemphasized. It is a significant element of the system used to determine the compensation structure. Clearly stating what the job calls for in the way of duties and qualification requirements makes it possible to retain the equal pay for equal work concept. This concept is strengthened when different levels of job difficulty are associated with appropriate levels of grade, salary, or wages. The job description helps set a policy of comparability for similar work. This assures the employee equity with his counterparts in the rest of the organization and minimizes the problems associated with placing and retaining personnel in the positions most suitable for their talents, experience, and training.

Providing a written record of the assignment of duties and responsibilities enables supervisors to keep closer control of their organization and gives them a convenient basis for a check on employee performance. Higher quality of performance by individuals within the grade assigned to the job can be rewarded by salary step increases approved through an incentive award program.

Job descriptions have additional valuable attributes. Their use in clearly delineating work is of primary importance. They are a significant aid in identifying overlapping duties, gaps in responsibilities, or ambiguous delegations of authority. They provide useful information for improving work methods, designing or redesigning organizational units, eliminating excessive layering of supervision, and identifying too narrow spans of control.

By using a coding and numbering system, positions can be identified and grouped in ways that will serve as a basis for statistical information. Personnel data derived from these statistics will be found useful in budget and manpower forecasting. If the size of the manpower force is large enough, this type of data can be computerized for ease of handling and analysis.

Job descriptions have other potential values that, if taken advantage of, can foster good management in a company. For example, they can help the training department determine the type of training programs needed by the employee. The supervisor can use the job description in explaining their jobs to new employees. Top management can promote clarity, uniformity of understanding, and generally minimize communication breakdowns by circulating job descriptions around to departments where mutual knowledge of each other's responsibilities is necessary.

WHO SHOULD PREPARE THE JOB DESCRIPTION?

Depending on the circumstances at the time the description is needed, it should be prepared by the person best qualified to prepare it. For example, if a new organizational unit is being developed, the duties of each job must be projected or anticipated. This can be done by the individual who will head up the unit or, if no one has been assigned as yet, by the staff specialist who is helping to formulate the structure and staffing of the unit. Experience has shown that maximum effectiveness in the use of job descriptions to further total management objectives can be achieved best by a close working relationship among operating officials, personnel specialists, and organization analysts. For this reason it is often advisable to work with a team—consisting of the personnel or classification specialist, the manpower or organization analyst, and the supervisor or executive in charge—in developing the description. In some cases, especially when dealing with blue-collar jobs, it may be desirable to include a union representative.

If an organizational unit has been in existence for some time, the duties and responsibilities have probably changed from what the original job description may have said. In this case it is usually best to let the employee rewrite his or her own description to bring it up to date. Of course, the immediate supervisor and at least the next higher supervisor should review the description, correct it if necessary, and approve it.

PREPARING THE JOB DESCRIPTION

To ensure the success of the program for preparing job descriptions, management, especially the immediate supervisor, must be involved throughout the process. The individual supervisor is the one who can best interpret the job both to the personnel department and to the employee. This dual role as chief negotiator with the personnel department and as management's representative to employees places the supervisor in a position to make a major contribution to a successful, smooth-working program. Involving the supervisor begins with a training plan that will delineate the basic elements of a job description and show how to prepare one. The training plan should cover the procedures for gathering the facts about a job; writing them down; processing the package through the employee, management echelons, and the personnel department; and —finally—how to maintain the job description on a current basis.

ELEMENTS OF THE JOB DESCRIPTION

Keeping in mind that the job description states the current duties and responsibilities assigned or delegated to one person in a specific organizational unit, the following elements should comprise the body of the description:

1. The title of the position
2. The introduction
3. Major duties and responsibilities
4. Position controls
5. Qualification requirements.

TITLING THE POSITION

One advantage of a job description program is that it encourages the development and use of uniform titles for the same jobs. The manager must realize that job titles are used in personnel, budgeting, manpower, and payroll operations, among others, and that they therefore should be standard for similar positions. This does not mean that organizational or informal titles cannot be used for internal purposes. Individualized titles very often provide useful status symbols that improve morale and help retain technical and executive personnel. It is therefore important to emphasize that flexibility should be allowed in titling positions. Official documents and permanent records should carry the standard title of the position; but in correspondence, organization charts, and at professional meetings, the more descriptive title can be used. For example, "Maintenance Engineer" may be the correct standard title for an employee, but if this individual is a senior person guiding the work of junior engineers or technicians, "Maintenance Projects Leader" may be more appropriate.

If the incumbent will be responsible for a workload carried out primarily through a subordinate staff of three or more employees dealing with the substantive work of the unit, the position should be designated as supervisory. In this case, the standard title might be "Supervisory Maintenance Engineer," but the organizational title could be "Director, Maintenance Division."

Titles should be brief and meaningful. Brevity is important to reduce the administrative work in typing, filling in of forms, and other processes where titles of positions appear. The job itself should be readily identifiable from the title, so that operating and staff personnel outside the unit can derive the information they need for their purposes.

INTRODUCTORY STATEMENT OF THE POSITION DESCRIPTION

The introductory paragraph should locate the position in the organizational unit to which it is assigned and can include a brief statement of the mission of the unit. For example, "This position is that of electrical engineer, and is located in the Engineering Division of the Maintenance Department. The division is responsible for preparing plans and specifications for repair and maintenance projects." A brief statement of the position content is also useful in this paragraph. For example, "The incumbent is responsible for dealing with complex electrical engineering projects and acts as a specialist in this area."

MAJOR DUTIES AND RESPONSIBILITIES

Since the job description should not be excessively long (one or two pages would be a good rule of thumb), it is well to select only the major duties for listing. These are the ones that occupy most of the incumbent's time and determine the qualifications needed to perform the job. The position was originally established to carry out these tasks because they were expected to recur regularly. Major duties generally are performed in a continuous, uninterrupted manner, but even if a task is not characterized in this manner, it should be included as a major duty if it lasts over a long period of time, and if it recurs repeatedly even though unpredictably. As a rule of thumb, a task that takes about 10 percent of the incumbent's time would probably be a major duty.

Many positions, especially those in professional and technical fields, have varying combinations of major and minor duties and may be complex in their relationships and characteristics. Any attempt to define in detail all these variations would lead to an overly long write-up and would obscure the elements of the job that are significant to the manager, the employee, and the personnel department. In these cases, it is important to select with discretion those major duties which adequately define the position.

POSITION CONTROLS

The extent of authority delegated to a position and the scope of responsibility inherent in the duties of the position can be indicated by the amount of supervision received by the incumbent from superiors or exercised by him or her over others. The sample job descriptions below show one way to express these relationships. In this paragraph, a brief statement of what sources of information the incumbent has available can be included. These provide guidelines and indicate the difficulties, if any, the incumbent would face in developing solutions or originating policy to solve the problem at hand.

QUALIFICATION REQUIREMENTS

The qualification requirements that should be outlined in the job description are the basic skills and knowledges the incumbent should have at the time he or she enters the job. These may include not only professional attainments, such as degrees and specialized experience, but also personal characteristics that help to assure successful performance once the employee is hired. It is important that the qualification requirements be consistent with the standards used for grading the position during the job evaluation process. Here it is well to point out once more the value of team effort in developing a job description program, so that staff personnel from manpower and organization can coordinate their efforts with those from classification and job grading.

KEEPING JOB DESCRIPTIONS CURRENT

Since the job description or job sheet, as it is sometimes called, is management's statement of what duties and responsibilities it wishes an employee to have, and since this becomes the official record on which the employee's pay is based, it is important to keep the description current. It is a fact of organization life that assignments to an individual change, sometimes by direct management action and sometimes by the impact of the person on the job. It occasionally happens that an individual in a job will change its scope through dint of personal effort. By imagination, resourcefulness, aggressiveness, or industriousness, the employee expands his or her responsibilities, attracts more authority, invents new ways to do the job, and finally justifies a rewrite of the position. On the other hand, the wrong person in a job can reduce its effectiveness and have a negative impact on its functions.

If changes are minor or affect only one or two duties, a simple pen-and-ink change or a brief paragraph amending the description may be sufficient. Use of this amendment process is preferable, especially if the change is not likely to affect the grade or pay of the position. To ensure that there is no such effect, all such changes should be cleared through the classification and grading system.

The best way to ensure that job descriptions are current is to establish a system of periodic annual reviews of each position. During such reviews, a simple card form can be given to each employee to fill in, indicating whether he or she considers the description of the job to be accurate or not. The immediate supervisor should review the employee's entry, and the two should discuss it together if necessary, so that the need for change may be affirmed or denied. The card can then be used as a basis for further action or as part of a data bank for the next year's review.

In some companies management policy may encourage the grouping of positions into categories to indicate the kind of action desired on each position. For example, category A may mean that the position is current and requires no action. Category B may mean that the position should be changed but cannot be at this time for budgetary or other management reasons. Category C may indicate that the position is not current but should not be changed until the incumbent leaves. Finally, in Category D would be those positions that are so seriously out of date that delay in updating them cannot be tolerated, regardless of the consequences.

Sometimes when an employee is working under a job description, the supervisor may ask him or her to do something that is not listed in the job sheet. The employee may react by saying, "You can't ask me to do that. It's not in my JD." This is a mistaken attitude on the part of the employee. The job description is not intended to be a straitjacket. Management has the prerogative to readjust work assignments to meet current needs. However, discretion must be used to prevent degradation of the employee in terms of professional status, grade level, or pay. The employee should accept reasonable changes in his or her duties and responsibilities and should follow established procedures for updating the job description if the changes are significant enough. Of course, if the changes affect pay and grade adversely, the employee should have access to an appeals procedure to ensure fair treatment and to verify that management's needs support the adverse action, rather than being the result of arbitrary or capricious decisions.

Sample Job Description for Professional Employee

1. Introduction This position is that of an electrical engineer located in the Maintenance Engineering Branch of the Facilities Management Division. The branch provides engineering services and technical assistance in interpreting objectives, policies, and functions of the company's Facilities Management Program. The incumbent of this position is responsible for the execution of complex electrical engineering maintenance projects and acts as a specialist in this field.

2. Major duties and responsibilities *a.* Plans, coordinates, and executes electrical engineering investigations of special projects and engineering service requests involving electrical control failures, facilities electrical distributions, terminals, air conditioning, lighting, and sound systems.

b. Reviews and validates electrical engineering aspects of projects to ensure proper description, justification, cost estimate, and proposed engineering solution.

c. Conducts research and engineering studies to develop electrical maintenance standards in support of company maintenance problems.

d. Serves as an electrical engineering specialist in reviewing plans and specifications for new construction, repair, and maintenance projects.

e. Serves as training group leader for training programs on electrical equipment operation and maintenance.

3. Controls over position The incumbent is under the supervision of the manager of the Maintenance Engineering Branch. The incumbent is responsible for the professional adequacy of the work since it is not reviewed during progress. Only highly controversial matters are discussed with the supervisor. Final results are judged on the basis of project accomplishments and adherence to policy.

4. Qualifications required The position requires the services of a graduate electrical engineer. The incumbent must have a comprehensive knowledge of electrical systems and equipment, be tactful, and be capable of fluent self-expression both orally and in writing.

Sample Job Description for Administrative Employee

1. Introduction This position is that of secretary to the director of the Facilities Management Division, one of three divisions in the Works Engineering Department. The division provides overall direction for the company's maintenance management program for its physical facilities. The incumbent is the personal secretary to the director and also provides stenographic and typing services to key personnel in the division.

2. Major duties and responsibilities *a.* Performs secretarial duties for the director of the division, including taking telephone messages, scheduling appointments and conferences, arranging travel itineraries, composing letters and memoranda, and performing other administrative duties.

b. Takes and transcribes technical and difficult dictation on all phases of maintenance management.

c. Takes, transcribes, and edits minutes of staff conferences to cover highlights of subjects discussed and decisions reached.

d. Receives all incoming and outgoing correspondence for the division. Routes incoming mail to branch managers for action or to division director for prior review. Ensures that outgoing mail complies with division and company policy on form, language and grammatical structure, accuracy of address, and similar items.

e. Requisitions and controls division office supplies.

3. Controls over position The incumbent is under the supervision of the director of the Facilities Management Division but performs the usual day-to-day duties without receiving specific instructions from the supervisor. Assignments from other personnel are usually given with brief oral or written instructions, such as possible sources of data, and a general idea as to the desired presentation of the material. The incumbent uses discretion and ingenuity in deciding the best way to complete the assignment, using as guides the company correspondence manual and generally accepted practice as set forth in secretarial handbooks.

4. Qualifications required Incumbent must be a qualified stenographer and have superior skill in taking down verbatim discussions at conferences. It is important that the incumbent be able to exercise the utmost tact and discretion in making personal contacts by phone or otherwise and in dealing with information considered confidential. Incumbent must have good appearance and be well spoken.

Sample Job Description for Blue-Collar Employee

1. Introduction This position is that of carpenter, leader in the carpentry shop of the Facilities Repair Division. The shop is responsible for building, repairing, altering, and installing wooden articles and structures for the physical facilities of the company. The incumbent is a journeyman carpenter and provides guidance and direction to a number of junior or apprentice carpenters.

2. Major duties and responsibilities *a.* Constructs and installs framework, rafters, interior and exterior wall trim, floors, windows, wood foundations, shelves, and similar structures.

b. Plans the installation of beams, shingles, and clapboards from blueprints, drawings, and oral instructions.

c. Determines work sequence, materials, and tools to be used.

d. Directs junior or apprentice carpenters in measuring and cutting materials to required lengths and in completing the installation.

3. Controls over position The incumbent is under the supervision of the chief carpenter in the carpentry shop and receives instructions orally or through written work orders. The incumbent determines the types of materials and tools needed and works without higher-level assistance except on the most complicated projects. The supervisor checks completed work for compliance with accepted trade standards, which serve as a guide for the incumbent's independent judgments and decisions.

4. Qualifications required The incumbent must be a qualified journeyman carpenter, knowledgeable and skillful in the use of accepted methods and techniques of the trade. Ability to plan and compute arcs, tangents, and circles using advanced shop mathematics is essential. Incumbent will be required to read and interpret blueprints, sketches, building codes, and similar material and must be physically fit, able to work under unpleasant conditions both inside and out, and be able to lift heavy objects weighing up to 50 pounds.

Chapter 2

Compensation

ARTHUR R. LANEY
Consultant

INTRODUCTION

One of management's most challenging problems is employee compensation. What *is* "a fair day's pay for a fair day's work?" How *can* workers be convinced that they are being adequately remunerated for the efforts they put forth on the job?

The answer to both questions is the same—we don't know for sure.

All that any organization can do is to try—with the imperfect means at its disposal—to compensate employees in such a way as to attract and hold the number and kind it needs in order to accomplish its objectives.

As is so often the case in personnel activities, the place to start is with job descriptions. Each job must be properly analyzed and, from the ensuing job descriptions, specifications for performing the jobs must be written in terms of such common job factors as responsibility, skill, mental effort, physical effort, and working conditions.

Such job specifications provide the basis of performing the two fundamental tasks of wage and salary administration; namely (1) compensating the workers in the plant fairly in relation to each other and (2) pricing jobs appropriately in relation to what other employers in the same locality or industry are paying.

With respect to the latter, the first place to seek relevant information is the government —both state and national. State employment offices know what employees whom they have helped place in various towns and cities are receiving for a wide range of jobs. This information is readily available from them upon request.

At the federal level, the Department of Labor, through its Bureau of Labor Statistics, publishes annual surveys of wages and salaries not only on a nationwide basis but also for many localities. Such information is free to participating companies, and others may obtain it at nominal cost. Get on their mailing list.

Many employers also rely upon their own comparative wage surveys to determine what others are paying. This is done on a locality or industry basis or both. (If the plant is unionized, the union will probably make its own survey and, in collective bargaining over wages, cite other employers who are paying higher wages for jobs similar to those included in the negotiations.)

The normal procedure is for the plant engineer (or the personnel manager, if any) first to determine which organizations in its labor market area and/or industry are likely to have the kinds of jobs for which comparative wage information is desired. These are key jobs related to the nature of the enterprise.

SURVEY FORM						
Company _____ Date _____						
Classifications	Rate min.	Range max.	No. of empl.	Actual hourly rates		
				low	high	ave.
Building repairman						
Bldg. maint. man						
General carpenter						
Carpenter "A"						
Carpenter "B"						
Electrician "A"						
Electrician "B"						
Electrician "C"						
General plumber						
Plumber "A"						
Remarks:_____						

Fig. 1 Sample survey form.

It is then advisable to telephone or write each such organization to learn (1) if it indeed does have such jobs and (2) if it is willing to exchange compensation information concerning them.

In the case of affirmative answers to these two questions, a survey form is mailed to each cooperating employer. Attached to it is a description of each job listed.

The job descriptions are essential because job titles by themselves are often misleading. The actual duties entailed may differ so much from plant to plant that without a full description of each job, it is impossible to determine which ones are actually comparable.

A sample survey form is shown in Fig. 1 and descriptions for the first two jobs listed thereon are listed below.

BUILDING REPAIRMAN

The building repairman classification requires that the employee shall be able to perform all the duties prescribed for building maintenance man and in addition shall be capable of and regularly engaged in the following:

Replacing pumps, motors, belts, couplings, valves and packings

Replacing parts on equipment such as gasoline pumps, power doors, and automatic car washers

Adjusting and repairing automatic doors, dampers, air handlers, incinerators, portable lifts, pumps, and expelsor system

Adjusting controls on heating and cooling equipment

Repairing doors and building hardware

Making minor repairs on boilers and related equipment

Preparing boilers and air tanks for inspection by city authorities

Changing oil in stationery compressors and engines

Minor cutting and heating using acetylene torch

Prerequisites   Must satisfactorily perform the work in this classification for a total of 90 days.

BUILDING MAINTENANCE MAN

The building maintenance man classification requires that an employee shall be capable of and regularly engaged in the following:

Doing minor repair work on roofs and drywalls, piping leaks on small lines, appliance cords, fences, sewers, and trenches

Painting, patching, and sanding on structures, furniture, and equipment

Replacing windows up to 3 x 6 feet

Replacing floor, ceiling, and wall tile; furniture parts; hardware on doors, cabinets, and lockers; water valve packings, washer gaskets, light switches, fuses, filters, strainers, and appliance cords

Checking motor couplings and bearings, oiling and greasing motors and pumps

Setting thermostats and diffusers and resetting circuit breakers

Driving company cars and trucks, up to and including 1-ton pickup trucks, and operating power equipment such as fork-lift trucks, snowplows, salt spreaders, tractors, power sweepers, and power lawn mowers

Installing and replacing thermo-protective pipe covering

Prerequisites   An employee must possess a low-pressure boiler operator's license issued by the city.   The license is to be obtained on company time and to be paid for by the company.   Employee must satisfactorily perform the work in this classification for 90 days.

FINANCIAL CONSIDERATIONS

Finding out what others are paying is helpful, of course, but it is only an initial step. Ability to pay is also a vital factor.   If the company is losing money or not earning what management considers to be an adequate return on investment, it may be reluctant or unable to meet wage levels set by other firms.

In collective bargaining sessions, management may justifiably have to take the position that it cannot afford to offer wages comparable to those paid by firms with better earnings. It may seek union cooperation in reducing costs or raising productivity, so that earnings may improve to a point where the plant *can* afford the higher rates demanded by the union.

Of course, management must avoid the temptation to "cry wolf."   If it had insisted during negotiations that an increase of 25 cents per hour would be financially disastrous but was ultimately obliged to settle for this in order to head off a strike, and if it subsequently continued to earn satisfactory profits, the union would not take such dire forecasts seriously the next time wages were negotiated.

In addition, the National Labor Relations Board has held that if you plead inability to pay during wage negotiations, you then have to permit the union to examine your books in order to prove the validity of your claim.   Most companies are reluctant to do this.

A better position to take may be that you do not want to get out of line with area wages. Or you may be justified in insisting that you need to see some increased productivity before you can afford to pay the wages the union is demanding.   If the union response is that productivity *has* gone up, management can say "show us."

Another argument against what you consider to be a too-high wage demand is that if it is granted, your customers will have to pay more for your product or services.   This, in turn, could lead customers who are part of the local labor force to seek pay increases from *their* firms, with an end result of more inflation and no gain in real wages from the increased pay rate.

OTHER CONSIDERATIONS

Increases in the cost of living are frequently cited by employees, organized or otherwise, as calling for offsetting boosts in wages. Some companies have negotiated cost-of-living clauses in their labor contracts so that changes in the Consumer Price Index, as compiled and published by the U.S. Bureau of Labor Statistics, are automatically converted into changes in wages.

This procedure has its advantages as well as its drawbacks. It is popular with employees in a rising market; but when the Index turns the other way and wages are reduced, so is employee morale. Then, too, should the practice become widespread, the result is inflation feeding upon itself. First the Index goes up, then wages are raised, calling for price hikes. This causes the Index to climb again, followed by another wage increase. And on and on.

For this reason among others, the practice of carrying a wage reopening clause in a contract that runs for 2 or more years has become an alternative means of dealing with inflation. Thus the company gets the union to accept a smaller immediate wage increase than it has been demanding and, at a specified future date during the life of the contract, it is agreed that the matter of wages will again be negotiated and most likely will result in an additional increase.

From a management point of view, the principal disadvantage of wage reopening clauses is that on the second round of negotiations only wages are considered. This deprives management of the advantage of being able to offer some improvement in fringe benefits—such as another holiday or a boost in insurance benefits, for example—as a substitute for a higher increase in wages than the company feels that it can afford. (Frequently an improvement in a certain fringe benefit has greater employee appeal than a more costly increase in pay.)

One way in which management can occasionally offset the disadvantage of bargaining on a wage reopening clause is to make the further hike in wages contingent upon a change in work rules or the discontinuance of an antiquated practice which has degenerated into featherbedding. Thus management benefits from a reduction in costs and/or a gain in productivity in return for the higher wages.

With regard to fringe benefits, it is important that management keep employees aware of the value of their "hidden paycheck." In the past decade, the cost to the company of vacations, sickness benefits, holidays, pensions, and other fringe benefits has increased substantially. What management is buying here is a more stable work force—mainly in the form of reduced turnover—since many benefits increase with seniority.

Unfortunately, these costly benefits tend to be taken for granted by workers and are not generally found to have any appreciable influence upon motivation or productivity. Perhaps this is because they relate to off-the-job behavior such as holidays, sickness, vacations, and retirement. Thus there should be a continuous program of periodic reminders to employees as to the cost of their fringe benefits to the company, which is perhaps best expressed in terms of hours of actual work.

The thing to stress here is that the plant's ability to continue to pay, say, 40 cents worth in fringe benefits for every dollar an employee earns working on the job, is dependent upon the kind of job performance which keeps other costs down and productivity up.

PRICING JOBS FAIRLY IN RELATION TO OTHER JOBS

Regardless of how a plant's general wage level compares with what other employers are paying for similar jobs, unless the workers *within* the plant feel that their jobs are priced fairly in relation to each other, there will be acute employee resentment.

This fact is underscored in a majority opinion of the National War Labor Board* over three decades ago:

> There is no single factor in the whole field of labor relations that does more to break down morale, create individual dissatisfaction, encourage absenteeism and hamper production than obviously

---

* National War Labor Board, *War Labor Board Reports*, vol. 6, 1943.

unjust inequalities in the wage rates paid to different individuals in the same labor group within the same plant.

Yet, in the absence of an appropriate and systematic procedure to keep such inequalities to a minimum, a plant's wage and salary relationships are more than likely to be lopsided, haphazard, and perhaps unduly influenced by a "squeaking wheel gets the oil" philosophy.

Fortunately, as is true of many other phases of personnel administration, there *is* a better way. In this case it is a procedure known as *job evaluation,* and usually entails the use of either the "point method" or the other widely practiced method, "factor comparison." Technical details of the two methods are readily available from reference books devoted to this subject.

In brief, the point method calls for each job to be evaluated on 11 characteristics, using a five-degree scale. There are three *skill* characteristics—education, experience, and initiative and ingenuity; two in the *effort* category—physical demand and mental or visual demand; plus four *responsibility* and two *job conditions* factors.

The factor comparison method compares each job in the plant with every other job in terms of just five factors; namely, skill, responsibility, physical effort, mental effort, and working conditions.

Since proper employee compensation is a major management responsibility and job evaluation is a highly technical speciality in the field of personnel administration, the way to launch such an undertaking is to engage the services of a competent outside consulting firm.

The individual consultant they assign to you (probably on a one-day-a-week basis) will doubtless make preliminary recommendations that include the following:

1. *Let your employees know about this project in advance.*

If you have a union, discuss the matter with its officers before making a general announcement of any kind. Some companies use a joint management-union job evaluation committee. You may wish to discuss the pros and cons of this with your consultant. One major drawback, from the union's point of view, is that after the jobs have been evaluated, a number of them will be shown to be overpaid in relation to other jobs. And the fact that the union committee members participated in arriving at this judgment can be a political liability to the union. For this reason the union may prefer that management do the evaluating, with the union reserving the right to take any individual job evaluations with which it disagrees through the regular grievance procedure.

2. From a wide range of past experience in the jobs to be evaluated, *select from your own personnel a job evaluation committee.*

The consultant will train the committee so that it can make the initial plantwide job evaluation and maintain the system once it has been established. Thus, as new jobs are created or as previously evaluated ones are materially changed, the committee can make additional evaluations to keep the system up to date.

3. *Designate a capable employee to work with the consultant and to be trained to become your plant staff specialist in wage and salary administration.*

During the installation of a job evaluation system, the outside consultant normally serves as nonvoting chairman of the committee and the plant's "specialist-in-training" serves as its secretary.

After all the necessary preliminary steps have been taken, the actual evaluation work begins and centers upon two simultaneous projects: (1) training the committee in the art of job evaluation and (2) selecting and training one or more job analysts to produce proper descriptions of all jobs to be evaluated.

The method used to train the committee may vary with the consultant. One fairly common procedure is to supply each committee member with a work manual describing the job evaluation method to be used (usually either the point method or factor comparison) and the specific procedures to be followed in the evaluation of each job.

Prior to the availability of plant job descriptions, the committee can practice by evaluating jobs which have already been evaluated in other plants, using descriptions supplied by the consultant.

Of course the committee members do not know how the practice jobs have already been evaluated in the company from which the descriptions were obtained. Thus, prior to the committee meeting, each member will independently evaluate each job for which he or she has received a description and turn the evaluations over to the secretary. The latter will summarize these data, and the meeting will be devoted to discussing the differences in evaluations between the individual members. These differences should be reconciled so that at least a consensus is reached. Then it may be seen how the neophyte committee's evaluations compare with those of the experienced committee in the other plant from which the training materials were obtained.

As the plant's own job descriptions are developed and approved for evaluation purposes, they will be fed into the committee, and the practice jobs used for "learning by doing" will be discarded.

After all the plant jobs have been evaluated, two important wage curves may be plotted—a "going-rate" curve and a "plant-rate" curve. The going-rate curve shows how the committee's evaluation of a wide range of key jobs compares with the rates of pay for corresponding jobs in the labor market or industry. The latter information can be obtained from comparative wage surveys. Any jobs which are found to be appreciably out of line with the market should be reevaluated unless the difference is justified by conditions peculiar to the particular plant.

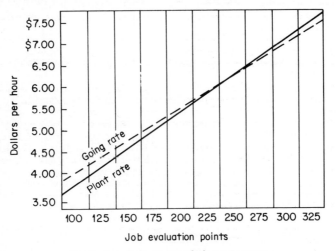

Fig. 2 Going-rate curve and plant-rate curve.

Both the going-rate curve and the plant-rate curve can be plotted on the same graph, as illustrated in Fig. 2.

On the graph shown in Fig. 2, the plant-rate curve is represented by the unbroken line and the labor market (going-rate) curve by the other line. What this particular example shows is that the plant is paying less than the going rate for the lower-paid jobs and a little more than the going rate for its highest-paid jobs. This may have resulted from the influence of other considerations such as the economic condition of the plant, supply and demand factors in the local labor market, or contract negotiations. Or it may have come from bias on the part of the job evaluation committee and, if this is the case, the out-of-line jobs should be reevaluated before the findings are communicated throughout the plant.

PROS AND CONS OF JOB EVALUATION

Although quantitative job evaluation is the best system yet devised for pricing jobs fairly in relation to each other, it does not provide an absolute guarantee that no inequity can exist. It is based on human judgment and, for that reason, it cannot claim perfection. What it can do is *minimize* the possibility of errors in setting job pay rates. (If the plant is unionized or if, even in the absence of a union, it has a formal grievance procedure, job evaluation strengthens management's hand in justifying rates paid for any job which may be the subject of a grievance.)

Then too, there is the problem presented by jobs which are found, as a result of the job evaluation, to be overpaid in relation to the others. Although the rates on *under*paid jobs are raised to bring them in line with the results of the evaluation, it is not recommended personnel administration practice to reduce the rates on the overpaid ones.

What many companies do is to "red circle" these rates. This means that the people who are already in the overpaid jobs get only general increases in the future; as they are reassigned, retire, resign, or die, they are replaced by employees whose pay rates are kept in accordance with the evaluated price of the job.

Another method is to freeze the rate on an overpriced job until the rates of the other jobs catch up with what the proper differentials should be. In either eventuality, it is only a matter of time until all jobs are properly priced in relation to each other.

RELATED CONSIDERATIONS

After the systematic evaluation is completed and the jobs are ranked in order of the amount of compensation that is regarded as being correct, they should be classified into grades.

Grade one will include all jobs with similar evaluations which fall at the lowest end of the pay scale. Grade two will be made up of the next-lowest-paid group of jobs; on up to grades seven, eight, or higher at the top of the scale.

The starting rate for each grade should be between 5 and 10 percent below the evaluated rate for the jobs in that grade, and the pay range should run from the starting rate to between 5 and 10 percent above the evaluated rate.

The rate ranges for the various grades should overlap, so that the starting rate for, say, grade four is below the top rate on the range for grade three. This is proper because an experienced employee in the next-lower-grade job is likely to be more valuable to the plant than a worker hired from the outside for the adjacent higher-grade job. However, if an employee already on the rolls is *promoted* to a higher-grade job, he or she should not receive the starting rate but the rate on the new job which is just above his or her present rate.

One precaution must be taken in promoting employees from their present grade to the next higher one. If the employee is within about a month of receiving a raise in his or her present grade, the promotion should be deferred until after the raise. The employee would then be promoted to the higher grade and receive the pay rate which is one step above his or her current rate. If for any reason the promotion cannot be delayed, a suitable adjustment in the rate for the higher-grade job should be made, so that the employee will not start in the new grade at the same rate as that which would have applied to the old job in another 3 or 4 weeks.

Once a rate range has been established for each grade, it can be divided into pay-increase steps. If the plant is not unionized, the raises are usually given on a merit basis, with a person who is only doing an average day's work not being raised any higher than the middle of the range; i.e., the evaluated price of the job. Better performers can be raised up to but not beyond the top of the rate range.

Unions are likely to insist upon automatic increases based solely upon length of service in a grade. A constructive compromise, if management can negotiate it, is to settle for automatic increases up to the middle of the rate range, with the top half of the range being reserved to reward special merit. Thus an industrious and efficient junior employee can ultimately receive greater compensation than a worker with longer service in the same grade who only does enough to get by.

COMPENSATION AND MOTIVATION

Management has traditionally regarded compensation as a means of motivating better employee job performance. The belief is that if you pay people more, they will work harder. Recent findings by behavioral scientists, notably Herzberg,* have proved that such a belief is generally erroneous.

Compensation is more likely to be a cause of dissatisfaction—and the highest-paid

* Frederick Herzberg, *Work and the Nature of Man,* World Publishing, Cleveland, 1966.

workers are not necessarily the most productive. Herzberg classified pay as a "hygiene" factor, meaning that, like plumbing, it only becomes a major preoccupation when it is felt to be inadequate.

A person may be temporarily motivated to work harder if he or she is striving for a merit increase. Once he gets it, however, there is no guarantee that the extra effort will continue to be expended. What *is* virtually certain is that regardless of the rate of compensation the worker will, in time, become dissatisfied with it and unhappy until another raise is granted.

This is where enlightened *performance appraisal* can make an important contribution. Today's competent supervisor makes it a regular practice to sit down with each employee so that both may plan how job performance might be improved and the worker's value to the plant enhanced.

COMPENSATION DOS AND DONT'S FOR PLANT ENGINEERS

DO	DON'T
• Get on the mailing list of the Department of Labor's Bureau of Labor statistics, so you will be kept informed of what comparative wage information is currently available.	• Overlook your state employment office as a source of information as to what other employers in your locality are paying for the performance of jobs similiar to those in your plant.
• Attach position descriptions to each wage survey form that you send out to a cooperating employer.	• Fail to develop and to keep current position descriptions for each job in your plant, including management positions.
• Attempt to tie financial concessions made in wage negotiations to receiving in return a pledge of union cooperation in lowering costs and/or improving job performance.	• Plead inability to afford the cost of union demands in wage negotiations unless you are willing to let the union examine your books.
• Engage the services of a competent consultant to help you install a systematic job evaluation program to keep your job rates in proper alignment with each other.	• Fail to keep your employees informed as to the ever-increasing value of their "hidden paycheck," namely, fringe benefits.
• Make management development *your* continuing concern and set an example which will encourage all supervisors to base their leadership style on "Theory Y" assumptions about people	• Let your "squeaking wheels get the oil" as far as pay raises are concerned. Tie them to measurable improvements in job performance.
	• Rely upon pay raises or larger fringe benefits to motivate workers. These "hygiene" factors merely tend to minimize job dissatisfaction.

The supervisor will encourage the worker to *plan his or her own* personal development and growth on the job; to set personal objectives as well; as the means for gauging the results of all this. The supervisor's role is that of coach and facilitator rather than critic. The discussions are informal but continuing; they are held whenever a need of any kind arises.

And when the supervisor feels that the employee has made significant progress, the supervisor can provide—in addition to recognition and appreciation—whatever financial rewards may be available in the form of pay raises and possible promotions.

The workers' jobs are "enriched" in the sense that now they are not only *doing* a certain task or tasks but they are participating with their supervisor in the *planning* and the *evaluative* processes related to these jobs.

There are now impressive and objective research findings demonstrating that *employee motivation is a function of the job itself*—the kind of tasks assigned to the workers. If their duties are such that they feel they are doing something meaningful and worthwhile, if they gain some kind of recognition for their accomplishments—along with a day-by-day sense of growth and progress—they will be self-motivated.

Plant engineers are fortunate in that they supervise workers who can usually see the outcome of their efforts in terms of tangible results. This in itself, however, is not enough to assure adequate motivation.

What must be added to this is the sort of supervision which recognizes accomplishments, fosters an acceptance of responsibility, and enables workers to maximize the growth of whatever inherent talents they may possess.

Such a leadership style is based on "Theory Y" assumptions, as described in McGregor's classic *The Human Side of Enterprise*.* All plant engineers should upgrade their own management skills by becoming familiar with and practicing this better way to manage.

* McGraw-Hill, New York, 1960.

Chapter 3

Disciplinary Actions

HERBERT R. BROWN
Consultant

BACKGROUND

All discipline involves behavioral change in response to rewards and punishments, including the punishment of wrongdoers.

Discipline is essential to all organizational activity if the organization is to achieve its agreed-upon goals. Members of the organization must reasonably comply with the codes of behavior established by organization leaders. Workers and managers must control their individual wants and needs to cooperate for the common good. If the individuals comprising an organization do not adhere to standards of conduct, behavior, ethics, and practices as codified and-in some unionized organizations-as contractually established, the organization faces disruption, loss of goal attainment, and eventual collapse. Business organizations without policies, rules, and processes cannot function. Companies must recognize that skill in establishing and maintaining positive discipline is an important qualification for supervisors. Some supervisors have the technique of developing a healthy, integrated, willing compliance among workers. Others must resort to fear and punishment, and still others have abrogated their responsibility and take no more notice of violations of company rules than they absolutely must as a matter of self-preservation and as pressure from thier supervisors requires.

The employees' observance of and compliance with organizational standards is maintained by discipline. Disciplinary action is taken by the organization against an employee who fails to meet the standards established.

The purpose of discipline is therefore to encourage employees to behave sensibly at work. Just as we have laws in society to preserve order and to protect lives and property, so we have rules and regulations in companies. They are essentially designed for the same purpose as well as to meet the companies' objectives of survival, profits, service, and social responsibility. Employees recognize this need, and therefore few would want to abolish company rules.

APPROACHES TO DISCIPLINE

Applying the dictionary definitions to discipline, there are basically two approaches. *The first is constructive, educative, and positive.* A manager using this approach believes in the dignity of employees, recognizes potentiality, listens, and is responsive to employee input.

Positive discipline requires that type of leadership which develops a willing compliance with the rules and regulations of the organization. The aim is to help, not to be vindictive or to "get" someone.

Positive discipline must ensure that all employees are aware of the requirements of their jobs, the rules and regulations governing the conduct of their relationships to and within the company, and what management expects of them. In creating a climate for positive discipline, management seeks to develop a sense of personal responsibility and self-discipline in its employees. Such development must start with an orientation of the new employee. Management delegates this responsibility to the supervisor or to the personnel department, and it is the responsibility of the delegatee to explain what work performance is expected and what help is available when necessary. The orientation should include such items as attendance, hours of work, punctuality, whom to notify when justifiably late or absent, cooperation, codes of behavior, standards of morality and honesty, and safety precautions where these are essential. This aspect of orientation comprises the "givens," that is, what the employee is expected to give and to do in return for the "getums," his salary, fringes, opportunities, and other direct and indirect renumeration and benefits received from the company. Many managers now believe that good performance depends in great measure on the degree to which employees voluntarily carry out instructions and abide by rules. The key to this belief is the term "voluntary." Accordingly, effective discipline is a by-product of positive and intelligent leadership and willing cooperation by employees within the policies and rules established. The strongest basis for discipline is voluntary self-discipline. If all employees at all times could be expected to perform well and within accepted and necessary codes of conduct, there would be no need for disciplinary action. If all managers could be expected to be exemplary, consistent, and reasonable in imposing penalties or corrective discipline, there would be no reason for appeal procedures.

To achieve constructive discipline, a manager must set an example. If a company rule prohibits wearing finger jewelry in production areas where moving parts may produce finger injury, it would be difficult to enforce the rule if the manager of this area persisted in wearing a ring. Similarly, managers and executives visiting "no smoking" areas cannot hope to enforce this rule if they do not comply with it. Hours of work and tardiness is yet another example of an area where the supervisor must set the example. Despite the possible acceptance by the company of a manager's right to some deviation from established hours of work, a supervisor who is tardy at the beginning of the work shift or who abuses the time allowed for lunch periods will have difficulty in enforcing these rules.

The second approach to discipline is negative. Negative discipline is the style of leadership that rules through fear and punishment. This style was typical in industry prior to the growth of unions, which was encouraged by the Wagner Act of 1935. The typical approach was to keep employees in line by the threat of punishment. The psychological effect—a state of insecurity and hostility—was in part responsible for the enormous growth of unions. The power of the boss to impose penalties and to threaten individuals who did not respond as expected was almost absolute.

A basic difficulty with negative discipline is that it achieves nothing but fear and hostility. It usually produces only the minimum performance necessary to avoid punishment. This style of leadership depends on making an example of violators. Our crime statistics demonstrate that punishment, regardless of its severity, is no deterrent. Employees or citizens who violate the rules or the laws usually do not plan far enough ahead to take the possible consequences into account. Their concern is fulfillment of immediate wants. In the long run, management through fear can have only limited success. Despite the arguments against this negative approach to discipline, there are and will be circumstances when supervisors must use the full force of their power and authority. There are certainly instances when some employees will respond only to "tough" supervision.

ADMINISTERING THE DISCIPLINARY ACTION PROGRAM

In administering a disciplinary action program, management must be constantly aware of the two objectives of preserving the interests of the organization as a whole and protecting the rights of all employees. The objective of preserving the interests of the organization includes the rights, obligations, and authority of the various managerial levels to impose discipline. Unless sound policies are established and orderly procedures followed, there is certainly the possibility that management will consider a given situation only in terms of its own needs at the moment rather than in terms of the needs of the employee as well as the organization. There is the danger that expediency of the moment may prevail over the long-term and future considerations.

PRINCIPLES, POLICIES, AND PROCEDURES

It is the responsibility of the management to achieve a healthy state of discipline throughout the organization. Top management must indicate what kind of behavior it expects from employees and how it hopes to accomplish this. Presumably, the objective is to establish positive, constructive discipline through good leadership and training of employees. In pursuing this goal, the following should be kept in mind.

1. To the extent possible, rules should be developed or modified cooperatively with employee representatives. If employees participate in formulation, they will be more apt to follow the rules subsequently established. In nonunion companies prior to the establishment of a rule, management might communicate its intent and reasons and request comment. It is important for management to remember the two objectives-organizational interest and rights of all employees-when considering the adoption of a rule. Management should not establish a rule to cover all employees because of negligence or misbehavior on the part of a small minority of employees. In such instances, management might recognize that a cohesive, loyal work group will generally support a good supervisor's disciplinary efforts. If there are one or two members of the group producing too much "horseplay" too frequently, if they are on the wrong side of the tardiness line, shaving their performance just enough to be annoying but not enough for disciplinary action, or if they are generally performing or behaving a shade below the acceptable standards, the cohesive group might do more to bring these few up to standard than the supervisor could do. Certainly the establishment or modification of a rule to govern these few might have far more damaging effects than the hoped for correction it was intended to achieve.

2. All rules should be periodically reviewed to ensure that they are reasonable, current, and appropriate to changes in the organization and that they recognize changes in societal mores.

3. All rules may not apply equally or equitably to all employees of the organization. Plant production area rules may have to differ from rules affecting office areas and office employees. Working conditions, differences in required hours, shifts, company policy, and contract provisions may require different rules.

4. Variations in rules may be acceptable and, in fact, required. Variations in enforcement cannot be allowed. Exceptions to enforcement should only be permitted under unusual circumstances, when the exigencies of a situation demonstrate bona fide evidence that it would be an advantage to both the employee and the organization that an exception should be made. Rules that are enforced fairly, evenly, in an orderly way, without malice and with intent to provide equity, are productive of greater respect for management. Those that are overlooked, half-heartedly enforced, or enforced to provide examples produce a disbelief in thier purpose, a lack of respect for management, and hostility because employees do not know where they stand.

5. Obviously rules should be published and widely communicated. Penalties and procedures for enforcement should be equally as well published and communicated as

are the rules. Employees have the right to know what to expect, and managers should know that employees know what is expected of them.

6. During the development of a rule and its subsequent establishment and implementation, it is most important to ensure that another rule or phase of company policy, or some contract provision or legal aspect, does not produce a conflict between the rule and another policy, principle, or procedure. Should this happen, management should not take the position of letting the rule stand as a face-saving measure and then not enforce it. The negative consequences are far too great. In such a situation, management should quickly abolish or modify the rule.

7. Data on rule violations and the penalties given should continually be maintained. Periodic analysis indicating excessive violations of certain rules requires investigation to determine the reasons. It might be necessary to modify the rule, the area, or the training program in order to correct the circumstances leading to the excess.

8. Problem employees and chronic rule breakers must be expected. Special attention will have to be provided in these cases.

9. Appeal and review procedures should be carefully and precisely defined for all disciplinary actions taken, published, and communicated to all employees.

10. Top management must decide on a policy position with regard to the supervisor's role. Since most appeal procedures provide for a multilevel appeal process, the supervisor's decision-the first appeal level-is usually appealed if his decision or the penalty imposed does not satisfy the union or employee. Some companies may take the position that since the supervisor is imposing the penalty, the appeal, if any, should not be to him but to the supervisor's superior. In other instances, company position may be to allow the supervisor to issue oral and written warnings. Penalties that have adverse action effects may be taken only after consultation with higher authority. In either instance, the supervisor is placed in the awkward position of being bypassed and losing authority and possibly control of his people.

11. If supervisors are to impose penalties, there should be sufficient range in the penalty provided for the specific offense to allow latitude and discretion when circumstances warrant. This may appear to contradict uniform application of penalties, but in fact it strengthens supervision, and wise application will produce fewer supportable grievances.

12. Penalties should be graduated, with heavier penalties imposed after the first or second offense.

13. Some consideration should be given to time periods and penalties. Violations of rules or the same rule in a short period should be considered differently than, for example, two violations occurring 10 years apart.

14. Management must ensure that supervisors are fully and completely trained in every aspect of disciplinary action.

GRADUATED OR PROGRESSIVE PENALTIES

Disciplinary penalties in industry have become fairly well standardized. They are usually graduated or progressive and typically follow an ascending order of severity, the first infraction producing the lightest penalty and each succeeding infraction a heavier one. Examples are as follows:

1. An oral warning not made a part of the employment record
2. An oral warning with a notation of same in the employment record
3. A written warning noted in the employment record
4. Withholding an anticipated increase in salary
5. Suspension without pay from the job, ranging from a day to several weeks
6. Discharge

CLASSES OF DIFFICULT EMPLOYEES

Gluecke* believes that difficult employees may be grouped into three classes:

1. Those whose personal problems off the job (alcoholism, drugs, family relationships) begin to affect job productivity

* Walter F. Gluecke, *Personnel, A Diagnostic Approach*, Business Publications, Inc., Dallas, Tex., 1974.

2. Those who violate laws while on the job by such behavior as stealing from the organization or its employees and physical abuse of employees or property

3. Those whose quality or quantity of work is unsatisfactory due to lack of ability, training, or job motivation

Class 1 behavior has increased, and an NICB Report (1969) indicates that a generally successful program includes a conference between employee and supervisor covering four points:

1. The supervisor documents the effects at work of the employee's problem.

2. The supervisor offers to help.

3. The supervisor requires that the employee participate in a rehabilitation program (alcoholism, drugs).

4. The supervisor notifies the employee that nonparticipation may mean loss of job.

Class 2 behavior is normally dealt with by security departments and usually results in termination and/or prosecution of the employee.

Class 3 behavior may be caused by deficiencies in the employee's intelligence and job knowledge, by lack of work motivation, or by the work organization itself. Steinmetz* suggests the following ways, in order of precedence, to handle the marginal worker.

1. Preventative approach. This emphasizes analysis to make sure that the match between employee and job is right.

2. Thereapeutic approach. When the preventative approach does not apply, counseling employees about the fact that they are effective and how they might improve is in order.

3. Self-improvement approach. Here the technique is for the supervisor to document the ineffectiveness of the employee and then encourage the employee to design a self-improvement program. This puts the emphasis where it belongs, on the employee's improving his or her performance with supervisor's counsel and help.

4. Punitive approach. When steps 1, 2, and 3 do not work, corrective discipline is the last resort. This will vary from minor penalty to discharge.

TWO TYPES OF OFFENSES

The concept of what constitutes an offense will vary from company to company based on its history and customs, the processes used, the legal and safety requirements, and the mores of the communities within which it operates. Generally, offenses may be grouped into minor and major categories, with a longer, gradually increased severity for the former group and a shorter gradation and far more severe penalties applied to the latter group. Moderate offenses are usually among the following:

Tardiness
Unexcused absence
Failure to report injury
Leaving job without approval
Loafing
Gambling
Fighting
Horseplay which could produce injury or damage to property, particularly in safety areas
Selling or canvassing on company property without approval
Sleeping on the job
Smoking in prohibited areas
Failure to obey safety rules
Being intoxicated while on job
Clock-punching someone else's card or signing off for someone else
Concealing defective work
Below standard performance
Major offenses are usually such things as:
Willful damage or destruction of company property
Insubordination
Immoral or indecent conduct

* Lawrence, Steinmetz, *Managing the Marginal and Unsatisfactory Performer,* Addison-Wesley, Reading, Mass., 1969.

Stealing
Carrying concealed weapons
Promotion of gambling on company property
Attacking another with intent to seriously injure or kill
Willful falsification of company records
Penalties for major offenses can be a discharge for a first offense.

DEMOTIONS AND FINES

Sometimes a demotion is used as a penalty. However, it should rarely be used. The question of demotion usually arises when performance is questioned. If an employee is not performing because of a lack of ability or capacity, he or she could be reassigned to a less complex or less demanding job at the same or lower pay. However, this is really not a disciplinary action and should not be treated as such. If it is determined that he or she is capable of doing the job but is deliberately not doing so, this is a proper disciplinary consideration. In such an instance, the employee's behavior might be the result of a personality clash and a transfer might be the answer. If his or her attitude toward the job is negative, a demotion will hardly correct this. Corrective, positive dicipline may be the answer.

Withholding an anticipated increase in salary may be a penalty. This could be imposed and made subject to behavioral change evidencing no further infractions. Such a penalty might be imposed subject to revocation at the end of 1 to 6 months, depending on the severity of the rule infraction.

Fines are rarely imposed in industry. The legal and implementational aspects can become far too complex to operate efficiently, since it would probably involve a deduction from the paycheck. The practice is common in professional team sports, but here again history and precedent provide for the acceptance of this form of disciplinary action.

Discharge

Discharge is the ultimate penalty in industrial disciplinary action. It may be the only feasible course of action available to management when an employee's behavior is so bad as to endanger other employees or the effective operation of the business. Lester R. Bittel reports "that a study of 4,174 discharge cases showed that 62.4 percent were for the personal shortcomings of the employees themselves. Underlying personal characteristics that came up most were carelessness, noncooperation, laziness, dishonesty, lack of initiative, lateness and lack of effort."*

A Bureau of National Affairs labor arbitration report analyzing discipline arbitration cases involving 1,055 discharges for a 14-year period, from 1942 to 1956, revealed that management was too prone to fire without sufficient justification. Management's decision was upheld in only 41 percent of the cases and was reversed or modified in 59 percent. Despite increased awareness on the part of management of the added protection given to workers as the result of recent legislation (the Civil Rights Act of 1964 and the Age in Discrimination in Employment Act of 1967), the increasing strength of unions, and the growth of behavioral science in management philosophy, the number of awards granted in cases going to arbitration rose to 3,954 in 1973. The discharge and disciplinary action case remains the single longest issue in arbitration cases, 1,302 in 1973.†

An aspect of the question of discharge is the consideration management should give to off-job criminal offenses. In the absence of a union, management has free rein to determine its position. In many organized companies, such discharges have gone to arbitration. Generally, arbitrators have tended to uphold management's decision to discharge when the off-job criminal offense leads to the opinion that the presence of the person on the job would adversely affect the employer's business, would disrupt relations with fellow employees, and might possibly endanger other employees. Arbitrators will look at the total circumstance, including the individuals's past record with the company and previous convictions as well as the nature of the job.

* L. R. Bittel, *What Every Supervisor Should Know*, 3d ed., McGraw-Hill, New York, 1974.
† Federal Mediation and Conciliation Service 25th Annual Report 1972 and addenda for 1973, Bureau of National Affairs, Washington, D.C., 1973.

OTHER DISCIPLINARY SYSTEMS

In addition to the accepted hierarchical disciplinary system administered by the supervisor and used in most nonunion companies, there are other discipline and appeal systems, such as the following:

1. Peer disciplinary systems are designed to use independent or related peers to assess behavior and recommend changes. One method is to have a jury of peers to adjudicate. This is used in professional situations in law or medicine. It is being sought in educational institutions. Another is to have student disciplinary boards as judges of discipline in colleges and universities.

2. Quasijudicial systems involve independent outside persons to adjudicate cases. Examples may be the use of ombudsmen, who are similar to arbitrators in union situations, or the use of a board of neutral outsiders from the community.

3. Modified hierarchical systems that provide regular appeal channels but exlcude the supervisor. One method is to have the personnel department conciliate and assess. Another is to have top executives from departments other than the immediate one hear all the facts and judge the action taken or to be taken.

4. Several other methods may be used, such as these:

   a. A formal shop committee. A group selected by employees hear and adjudicate cases.

   b. A floating committee. Management members at least two levels above the case and employees selected by each department on a rotating basis hear and adjudge disputes.

   c. Company grievance committee. Management members selected by top managers and a management member selected by the grievant hear and judge disputes.

CONCLUSIONS

Most deviant or difficult employees' problems probably have multiple causes. Employers need to concentrate on trying to modify the effect of these problems by rehabilitation and counseling, particularly when the causes are drugs or alcoholism.

Rules are more likely to obeyed if employees participate in the formulation and updating.

The best methods of behavior change are those that are relatively positive and less punitive. Only when all else fails should termination be used.

The larger the organization, the more likely it is to need to supplement the hierarchical justice system with other methods.

REFERENCES

1. D. R. Hampton, C. E. Summer, and R. A. Webber: *Organizational Behavior and the Practice of Management*, Scott, Foresman, Glenview, Ill., 1973.
2. Dale S. Beach: *Personnel*, Macmillan, New York, 1970.
3. W. F. Dowling and L. R. Sayles: *How Managers Motivate*, McGraw-Hill, New York, 1971.
4. H. Koontz and C. J. O'Donnell: *Essentials of Management*, McGraw-Hill, New York, 1972.
5. Richard I. Henderson and Waine W. Suojanen: *The Operating Manager*, Prentice-Hall, Englewood Cliffs, N.J.
6. G. S. Watkins, P. A. Dodd, W. L. McNaughton and P. Prasown: *The Management of Personnel and Labor Relations*, McGraw-Hill,
7. Clayton Resser: *Management*, Scott, Foresman, Glenview, Ill.,
8. Lester R. Bittel: *What Every Supervisor Should Know*, 3d ed., McGraw-Hill, New York, 1974.
9. Keith Davis: *Human Behavior at Work*, McGraw-Hill, New York, 1972.
10. U.S. Department of Agriculture: *Guides for Supervisors*, October 1969.
11. P. Pigors and C. A. Myers: *Personnel Administration*, McGraw-Hill, New York, 1973.
12. *The Federal Mediation and Conciliation Service 25th Annual Report 1972 and 1973 addenda*, Bureau of National Affairs, Washington, D.C., 1973.
13. Walter F. Gluecke: *Personnel*, Business Publications, Inc., Dallas, Tex., 1974.
14. Lawrence Steinmetz: *Managing the Marginal and Unsatisfactory Performer*, Addison-Wesley, Reading, Mass., 1969.

Chapter 4

Grievances and Adverse Action Appeals

CARL T. SIEG
Consultant

GRIEVANCES

A grievance is an expressed complaint or dissatisfaction about one or more conditions affecting an employee or group of employees. Generally it is caused by something felt to be unfair, unsafe, or otherwise detrimental to the employee(s) personally. Employees can and do file grievances about such things as:

Poor lighting
Lack of safety devices and equipment
Lack of parking facilities
Loss of promotion
Assignment of overtime work
Dirty rest rooms
Uncomfortable working conditions
Ignoring complaints and breaking promises (by the supervisor)

Management must consider two important factors; first, how to prevent to the extent possible the occurrence of any condition which could lead to a grievance and, second, how to establish and use a system for handling grievances quickly, fairly, and as informally as possible.

POLICY

The company's policy on the expression of a grievance should be in written form. If the employees are unionized, this usually is spelled out in the contract management has with the union. In any event, the written policy should be made available to all members of management, all union officials, and all employees. As a minimum, it should cover the following:

    1. Definition of a grievance

    2. If applicable, those subjects or matters not covered by the procedure (for example, conditions not within the control of the company, such as those imposed by law or a regulatory agency)

    3. Who may file a grievance

    4. The right of the aggrieved to be represented—either by a fellow employee or by a union representative; the right of the union to represent members of the unit it represents

    5. Time limits within which a grievance must be submitted after the occurrence of the event or condition leading to it

    6. To whom and how the grievance should be presented

    7. Time limits within which the supervisor or other manager must act on the grievance

    8. Who is responsible for taking any necessary corrective action

    9. The fact that employees may file grievances without fear of reprisal, interference, coercion, or discrimination

PROCEDURE

The procedures used in handling grievances may vary from employer to employer and in accordance with any contract management may have with a union. The basic concepts, however, are fairly consistent.

INFORMAL PROCEDURE

The most economical way to resolve a grievance is to have it worked out on an informal basis *between the employee and the immediate supervisor.* Resolution at this level strengthens supervisor-employee relations; strengthens the supervisor's position in the management hierarchy; and eliminates the need for costly, formal procedures involving higher levels of management, staff offices, or arbitrators.

Under an informal procedure, the aggrieved employee preferably presents his or her grievance to the supervisor orally, although it may be in writing. The supervisor checks into the validity of the grievance to determine whether or not the alleged unsatisfactory condition does in fact exist. Where it is determined that the complaint is not valid, the supervisor meets with the employee and/or the employee's representative to reach a mutually acceptable understanding about the situation. If the complaint is valid, the supervisor tries to resolve the problem as quickly as possible. If the solution requires help, the supervisor should be free to check with other members of management and appropriate staff offices as needed to seek a satisfactory solution.

The supervisor should be required to make a decision, whether favorable or otherwise, and give it to the aggrieved within a specified period of time. Normally this is from 2 to 5 days.

FORMAL PROCEDURE

When the employee or the union is not satisfied by the action of the supervisor or the supervisor has not responded within the specified time limit, the grievance is submitted formally, in writing. Depending on company policy or the contract with the union, the written grievance is submitted either to the second level of supervision or to a designated staff office. It is submitted within a specified time limit, usually 5 days, which starts with the expiration of the time allowed to handle the initial complaint or receipt of an unacceptable answer by the employee. The employee may request that he or she be represented or accompanied by another employee or by a union representative if the shop is organized. In the latter case, the union will have a right to represent the employee or to participate in the grievance éven if the employee does not request such representation.

Again, a time limit should be set within which management must act on the complaint. Normally this should be not more than 5 days.

If the employee or the union is not satisfied with the response obtained at this level, the grievance is submitted in writing to the chief executive of the company, who makes a decision. If the employee is still not satisfied and it is a union shop, the union may ask for arbitration. If it is a nonunion shop, the employee may decide to seek relief in a court of law.

HANDLING GRIEVANCES

Whether the grievance is submitted by the employee, a coworker, a union representative, or a combination of these, the supervisor should use guidelines such as the following:

Treat the employee fairly and with courtesy.

Treat a union representative as an equal even though he or she may report to you. Remember that when such a person is doing official union business, his or her status is the same as the supervisor's.

Listen, listen, listen. By doing so the supervisor gains more information and the nuances have a better chance of surfacing.

Hold onto your temper. Be businesslike—not argumentative.

Control the discussion and ask the type of questions which will get to the real nature of the grievance as quickly as possible.

Determine early in the discussion whether the complaint involves an alleged violation of the union-management contract. If so, get a clear understanding of the section or article involved.

If it can be determined that the complaint involves subject matter not covered under the grievance procedure, the discussion should be limited to that point.

If the supervisor is unsure of the applicability of the grievance procedure or the portion of the contract involved, he or she should remember that an immediate answer is not required. The supervisor should explain that an answer will be developed within the specified time limit and use the time to get help from other levels of management or from appropriate staff offices.

The supervisor makes all efforts to see all sides of the problem and to find out exactly what the employee or union wants.

The meeting should be adjourned to a later date for such reasons as to give the supervisor time to give the problem more thought, to allow time for the supervisor to get more facts, to allow a cooling off period if tempers start to wear.

Any settlement offered should be based only on facts and should conform with company policy as well as the terms of the union contract.

If the supervisor was wrong, it is well for him or her to admit it and to take steps to prevent a recurrence.

The supervisor must remember that the goal is to settle the grievance at the supervisory level if this can be done without adverse effect on the company's interests.

APPEALS

An appeal is a written request by an employee for reconsideration of a management decision to take an action which is adverse to him or her, such as a suspension or a discharge. Where the employees are represented by a union, appeals normally will be handled under the negotiated grievance procedure. In government agencies at all levels, however, they often are separate procedures because of various legal requirements.

HIERARCHY OF ACTIONS

The major goal of a "disciplinary program" should be that of correcting an employee who errs rather than simply inflicting a penalty. Thus the general practice is to have a hierarchy of actions which the supervisor follows in correcting an employee. The usual pattern is this:

For a first offense of minor proportions or one of obvious inadvertence, the supervisor has an *informal talk* with the employee. This is held in private with the supervisor pointing out the error to the employee and explaining why it is serious, how it could have been avoided, and why it is important that it not be repeated. Finally, the supervisor encourages the employee to do better.

If there is a later offense or a repeat of the first one and unless the error is so serious as to warrant the use of one of the actions described below, the supervisor *counsels* the employee. In the counseling process, the supervisor again talks privately and informally to the employee. This time, however, the supervisor explains that the employee is being counseled. The error is explained as well as its seriousness; the supervisor points out how it could have been avoided and how to avoid it in the future; finally, the possible result of future errors are pointed out. Again, the employee is encouraged to do better.

The third level of action is the issuance of a *letter of warning.* This specifies the offense, recalls any previous discussions or counseling sessions between the supervisor and the employee, and advises what the employee must—or must not—do to avoid more formal disciplinary action.

A *letter of reprimand* is the first level of formal disciplinary action. It differs from a letter of warning by advising the employee that a reprimand is being made and that a copy of the letter is being placed in his or her personnel file. Since issuance of such a letter could lessen the employee's chances for future promotion, its issuance is an action which usually can be appealed by the employee.

Suspension without pay, or *layoff,* is the first level of formal discipline that affects the employee's pay. Depending on the seriousness of the offense committed, the employee may be suspended for as little as 30 minutes or for as long as 90 days or more. Suspensions without pay are appealable. They also are an undesirable form of discipline because they "punish" management as well as the employee. During the suspension, management must frequently hire a temporary replacement, use overtime, shift another employee temporarily to cover the vacant job, or leave the work undone.

Discharge is the most severe penalty management can impose. It should be used only when it is obvious that other actions did not correct the employee or when the offenses involved are such that any other form of discipline would be inequitable.

PROCEDURES

Because actions which are adverse to the employee are serious and can have lasting effects, there are certain procedures that are usually followed in taking a formal disciplinary action. If the employees are represented by a union, these procedures will be set forth in the contract negotiated by management and the union. If the employer is a government agency, the procedures will comply with applicable legislation.

The letter of reprimand advises the employee of the offense committed and why it was considered an offense; it outlines previous informal corrective actions taken by the supervisor; it states that a copy of the letter is being placed in the employee's personnel file and that he or she has a right to reply to the letter of reprimand; and finally, it spells out the procedure to be followed in making a reply, the time limit for the reply, whether it may be made orally or in writing or both, and to whom it should be made. If the employees are organized, it will also explain the employee's right to be represented by the union and the union's right to become involved.

Usually a suspension without pay is preceded by a written notice to the employee of the intent to place him or her on suspension. Depending on company policy, applicable legislation, or the terms of the union contract, this advance notice will vary from a few days to as much as 30 days. This notice of intent specifies the offense which led to the proposed suspension, why it was considered an offense, previous efforts at corrective action, the number of days of suspension proposed, the date and time on which the suspension starts, and the date and time on which it ends. The notice also includes all of the other information regarding the rights to representation and reply which is contained in the letter of reprimand.

The notice of intent to discharge is handled in the same manner as for a suspension, but it also specifies the date and time of the proposed separation from the payroll.

EMPLOYEE'S REPLY

The right to reply gives the employee a final opportunity—before management decides to take the action—to give his or her side of the story, to point out why the proposed action should not be taken or why it is too harsh. If the employee replies to the written notice, the supervisor and other management personnel concerned must review the rebuttals and claims set forth in a careful and objective manner. Often it will claim that the employee is being used as an example or that custom and practice have made acceptable the behavior which led to the proposed adverse action. In such cases management must be thorough in its review and consider seriously the effect the proposed action could have on employee-management relations as well as labor relations.

At this time, too, the supervisor should look for causes of maladjustment that may have contributed to the employee's behavior. (Ideally, the supervisor would look for such causes before initiating the adverse action.) Some of the causes of maladjustment that are frequently overlooked are:

Lack of aptitude for the job

Intelligence above or below that required by the job

Emotional disturbances

Physical limitations

Personal problems

If it is found that one or more of these conditions has contributed to the problem, the supervisor should obtain help from the personnel and other staff offices in trying to resolve the situation in a way that will be best for both the employee and the employer.

After considering the employee's reply, the supervisor takes any one of the following actions:

Determines that the proposed action was unwarranted. In this case the supervisor notifies the employee that the action has been canceled, giving the reasons for this decision.

Determines that the proposed action is too severe and decides on a lesser penalty. This decision is given to the employee in writing, usually as an amendment to the initial proposal.

Determines that the action initially proposed should be taken. This, too, is communicated to the employee in writing. The notice of decision includes a restatement of the offense, the penalty being imposed, and the effective date of same. It also explains the consideration given to the employee's reply as well as the reasons for the decision to impose the proposed action. Depending on company policy, applicable legislation, or any contract with a union, an additional right of appeal may be granted. If that is done, this letter advises of that right and states the time limit for filing such an appeal, whether the right to representation is granted, how the appeal is to be made, and to whom.

HANDLING OF THE APPEAL

An appeal of an adverse action is filed with a level of management above that of the initiating supervisor, with the personnel office, or with some other designated staff office. It is a request for adjudication of the matter—an objective review by a third party. Because of the flavor of adjudication, the reviewing officials(s) must go to great lengths to assure thoroughness and objectivity.

Appeals may be based either on the merits of the case or on allegations of procedural error. Depending on the employer's policy, the provisions of a union contract, or applicable legislation, the employee also may have the right to a hearing before an impartial panel. Regardless of the basis for the appeal, the adjudicating office should conduct a thorough review of the causes of the action being appealed and the justness of the penalty being imposed.

Investigation and documentation   This process calls for a complete review of the record by the adjudicator and may include one or more of the following actions to assure that all pertinent data is obtained and considered:

Interview privately and separately each person who actually saw what took place.

Obtain detailed and complete statements from persons with pertinent, firsthand information.

Examine pertinent records and note facts that have a bearing on the case. Reconcile conflicting statements where possible.

CONSIDERING THE FACTS

After completing the fact-finding investigation—and the hearing, if one is held—the adjudicating office or the hearing panel considers all the facts developed. In addition, before coming to a decision, it may consider such information as the following:

The seriousness of the infraction in relation to the severity of the penalty being imposed. Is the penalty too severe? Is it equitable? Is it designed to correct rather than to punish?

The nature and the effect of the misconduct involved. Here precedent may have some effect. The action taken by management may be the same as that taken against another employee for the same or a like offense. But similar offenses may not have the same effect, especially if committed by persons at different levels within the organization. For example, serious misconduct by a middle-level manager might have a far greater adverse effect than similar misconduct by a rank-and-file employee.

The employee's work record should again be considered. Is this the first offense? If so, is the severity of the penalty warranted? Is the employee's record otherwise good? Is the employee a habitual offender? Does the action fit the circumstances?

Did the employee know the rules? Communications are notorious for their failure to communicate! How were the rules communicated to the employee? By whom? When? Was there an effort made to assure that they were received and understood?

Consider whether there were any mitigating circumstances which contributed to the bahavior, such as personal, marital, or health problems.

After considering all the facts, the adjudicating office or the hearing panel makes its decision, which is communicated to the employee in writing. There are various choices: uphold the action taken by management, return the action to the initiating supervisor for further consideration, set aside the penalty in its entirety, reduce the penalty to something less severe, or determine that that employee did commit the offense but set aside the penalty for various reasons.

PROCEDURAL ERROR VS. MERITS OF THE CASE

When an employee appeals an adverse action on the merits of the case, he or she feels that the action taken by management was basically wrong or uncalled for. In short, the employee contends that there was not merit to management's action. In these situations, the adjudicating office or hearing panel must dig into all the facts, precedents, and practices as discussed above. If they find that the action should be taken, the employee and/or the employee's representative may still take the case to arbitration if the shop is unionized. If the shop is nonunion, the employee or the employee's representative may seek relief in the courts. History has shown that in these cases, the arbitrator or the court is as thorough or even more so than is suggested above for the adjudicating office. It behooves management at all levels to be certain that the case did have merit.

Many cases are won by employees, or, if you prefer, lost by management on the basis of procedural error. All union contracts will spell out in detail the procedures to be followed by management in initiating and taking an adverse action against an employee. In other cases management has set the procedure to be followed. When an employee files an appeal based on procedural error, it is incumbent on the adjudicating office to review all steps taken by management in comparison with the applicable procedural requirements for each step of the process. Any time an error is discovered, the adjudicator can take one of two courses of action: return the case to the initiating supervisor with a suggestion that the action be rescinded or find against management and determine that the action should be canceled. In either case, the supervisor is usually free to reinstitute the action and, one hopes, to follow the correct procedures. Failure of the adjudicating office to take one of these actions will assuredly lead either to arbitration or a court case. In either instance, management's chances of winning are very, very remote.

Chapter **5**

Separations and Reductions in Force

ROBERT S. MACH
The Sherwin-Williams Company

INTRODUCTION

There are four major types of employee separations: resignations, retirements, discharges (for cause), and reductions in force. Two of these, resignations and retirements, are employee-initiated and consequently present minimal problems to line/staff management, with the exception of turnover and/or replacement costs. On the other hand, discharges and reductions in force are company-initiated actions and, if handled improperly by management, may lead to serious problems among the remaining work force. In any type of separation, either employee-initiated or company-initiated, the line/staff manager must keep in mind two considerations: (1) the emotional content and impact of the separation on the departing employee and on the remaining work force and (2) the continuation of normal operations. Leaving an organization, particularly in the case of an employee who resigns or retires, is a highly personal and emotional event. Forced separations such as discharges and reductions are frequently extremely emotional events, and the employees involved tend to be somewhat irrational in their analysis of the situation. This, coupled with the impact on the remaining work force, suggests that each employer develop, publish and utilize organized, objective, consistent, and equitable separation plan. While the circumstances under which an employee is separated will determine how each case is handled, a formal plan will serve as a base or starting point for the line/staff manager to begin the separation process. Even in organizations of considerable size and complexity, the separation plan need not be lengthy or verbose. However, it should summarize the company's policies, priorities, and procedures regarding employee separations. This chapter will present an overview of salaried employee separations—the legal considerations, the separation procedure itself, and a more in-depth look at the four major types of separations.

SEPARATION PROCEDURE

As stated previously, the specific circumstances will determine how each separation is handled. However, there are several factors that are common to almost all employee separations with the possible exception of retirements. The final days of employment for most employees about to be separated are generally filled with mixed emotions and many unanswered questions. It is vital that the line/staff manager treat the employee openly and fairly in order to obtain information from the individual and to permit the employee to make the separation in a positive manner. All principals in the separation—the immediate supervisor, the department head, and the personnel representative—should be thoroughly familiar with all facts pertaining to the separation, including actual separation date, conditions or circumstances of the separation, company commitments or obligations, wage/salary entitlements, vacation entitlement, etc. This should minimize the confusion and simplify the procedure. The foundation of the separation procedure (retirement excepted) is the exit interview.

Exit Interview

The exit interview, generally between the employee and the personnel representative, should ideally take place a day or two before the actual date of separation. This interview should be conducted in a conference room or private office, preferably away from the employee's immediate work area. In an employee-initiated separation—resignation—the objective of the exit interview is to determine the employee's reasons for leaving and his or her general evaluation of the supervisor, the department, and the organization. In other words, this interview allows the employee to express previously hidden feelings concerning this decision to leave the company. In addition, the exit interview offers an excellent opportunity to complete any required paperwork and to discuss any company benefits that might apply to the separating employee. In a company-initiated separation—discharge and/or reduction—the main objective of the exit interview is to inform the employee of the separation and to allow him or her to release any built up emotions regarding the situation.   Conducting an efficient and effective exit interview requires much preparation, skill, and practice. The following topics and/or questions are typical for an exit interview:

1. Name and address of new employer.
2. Position and responsibilities of new job.
3. Specifically, why are you leaving the company?
4. What does the new employer offer that is superior?
5. Was your position with our company correctly defined when you were hired? If not, explain.
6. What did you like most/least about your job here?
7. Did you receive satisfactory training while with us? If not, explain what could be improved.
8. How would you rate your immediate supervisor? (technical competence, managerial skill, etc.)
9. If you had the responsibility to run your department here, what would you do differently?
10. Identify any other comments about any aspect of the company, its policies, or its personnel.
11. Conflict of Interest considerations.

At some time near the end of the interview, the person conducting the interview should discuss in detail the company benefits that may apply to the separating employee. These include such topics as:

1. Pay entitlement
2. Vacation entitlement
3. Unemployment Compensation benefits
4. Social Security benefits
5. Return of company property
6. Health care coverage
7. Group life insurance
8. Pension rights
9. Tuition Aid Programs
10. Stock/savings programs
11. Savings bonds
12. Company credit union accounts
13. Conflict of Interest

Each applicable area should be thoroughly discussed and all questions should be answered if possible. If signatures are required for any of the above topics, the exit interview is an excellent time to obtain them. On occasion, a separating employee, particularly a discharge or resignation, will inquire about his or her future reference status with the company. In order to avoid conflict, it is suggested that this subject be evaluated and a decision made prior to the exit interview. The decision should be communicated to the departing employee in a straightforward, clear, concise manner so that the individual has no doubts regarding it. Be prepared to answer all questions on this subject.

Conflict of Interest

Most organizations, particularly those who engage in any type of research and development, have conflict-of-interest policies and guidelines that relate to such matters as financial holdings, acceptance of gifts and/or donations, personal gain or wealth, stock transactions, real estate, patents, proprietary information, etc. At the time of separation, it is advisable to identify any potential problems in this area so that the employee fully understands both the ethical and legal grounds of this subject. Normally, the personnel representative and/or the legal staff will provide specific guidance to the line/staff manager regarding conflict of interest. In discussing this with the separating employee, be sure he or she thoroughly understands the meaning and interpretation of possible conflict of interest. This approach may prevent unneeded embarassment to both the individual and the organization.

Pay in Lieu of Notice

In most employee-initiated separations, the departing employee is expected to work a reasonable period of time after giving notice to the company of his or her intention to leave. The exact amount of time generally varies according to position, length of service, and company policy; however 2 weeks is generally considered minimum for most situations. On the other hand, in a company-initiated separation, or due to the negative impact of a separation on the remaining work force, or due to the confidential nature of the work being performed, the company may elect to separate the employee immediately in order to minimize conflict. In such cases the company generally provides pay in lieu of notice. As indicated above, the amount of pay is determined by position, length of service, and company policy. In that each separation is different, the responsibility for the equitable and consistent administration of pay in lieu of notice rests with line/staff management. The situation, the people involved, and the company's policies must be carefully weighed and analyzed to arrive at a sound decision.

Consideration of the Remaining Work Force

In any separation such as discharge or reduction in force, the line/staff manager should make a concerted effort to minimize or neutralize the impact of the separation on the remaining work force. This is done to maintain continuity in the operation and to preserve the efficiency of the work atmosphere or environment. There are several methods of accomplishing this goal; however, in far too many instances, the manager tends to underestimate the importance of this topic. As a result, little or nothing gets done. The remaining employees, on the other hand, particularly when a discharge or reduction affects one of their coworkers, have many unanswered questions and will lean toward rumor and the grapevine if management does not provide the answers. Perhaps one of the most effective ways in which to handle this situation is to discuss the subject with the remaining employees in department meetings. The line/staff manager should assemble the group and openly discuss the subject. On a discharge, the manager should explain the situation in as much detail as possible. Remember, if the separated employee was a poor performer, his or her coworkers probably realized this fact long before management; on a reduction in force, the manager should identify the cause(s) for the reduction (realignment, poor sales, lack of work, etc.), the alternatives for a solution, and finally the decision made and its rationale. In addition, the method used to determine who is separated (seniority, position, etc.) should be made clear to all involved. For this reason it is imperative that any separation or reduction be handled equitably and consistently. After stating the situation, the line/staff manager should open the meeting to questions and answers. Responses to all questions should emphasize the positive aspects of the situation and should show the concern management has for the employees. If the manager can convey the fact that the company does, in fact, care for the welfare of its employees and that it (the company) has and will continue to do so, the employees involved tend to become much more understanding toward this type of situation.

RETIREMENT

Retirement—thought of by many as a time of health, happiness, and relaxation—can be and often is a period of emotional conflict, failing health, and frustration to the employee. As a form of separation, retirement and its consequences command attention from line/staff management, particularly the problems inherent in retirement, the needs of retirees, and, finally, the methods that may minimize the impact of impending retirement. Several major factors contribute to an enjoyable retirement: good health, financial security, voluntary retirement, and a positive attitude by the retiree. Conversely, poor health, financial worries, forced retirement, and poor attitude contribute to a negative outlook on retirement. Specifically, retirement is a transition period where an individual changes roles—that is, he or she moves from a work-centered role to a role of idleness. Over the years, research into the subject of retirement and retirement living has indicated that the most successful and enjoyable retirement usually stems from careful planning prior to the actual event.

Perhaps the most effective and beneficial way in which to assist employees about to retire is to establish a preretirement counseling program and a postretirement activity program for the retirees and their wives and families. Remembering that the success of retirement depends primarily on employee attitudes about retirement and on the need for planning, the preretirement counseling program should focus on the needs of the older employee:

1. Financial planning
2. Health care
3. Life insurance
4. Social activity
5. Job opportunities after retirement

The preretirement counseling program should ideally begin several years before the actual retirement date for an employee. The meetings may be conducted as groups if there are a sufficient numbers of employees to be retired; however, as the retirement day approaches, individual or one-on-one sessions should be scheduled to allow the retiree to voice any personal problems. If the group method is used, the initial meeting should be an informal get-acquainted session with the focus on retirement in general. Follow-up meetings, either group or individual, should deal primarily with specific topics such as:

1. Financial planning—pension plan, social security, banking, etc.
2. Health care—government programs, company plans, community programs, etc.
3. Life insurance
4. Legal matters—wills, powers of attorney, taxes, etc.
5. Social activity—clubs, organizations, community activities, company activities, etc.
6. Postretirement employment

An important point regarding the counseling sessions: they are intended to provide counseling only. Facts, data, and alternatives should be presented to the individual, but under no circumstances should a company representative make a recommendation on a personal matter. The company's obligation is to ensure that the employee has the necessary information to make personal decisions regarding retirement. In order to reinforce the topics covered in the meetings, it is sometimes appropriate to distribute written pamphlets or handouts that contain the subject matter of the meetings. The preretirement counseling program is normally conducted by the personnel representative; however, the line/staff manager may assume this responsibility in the absence of an in-house specialist.

As retirement draws near, the line/staff manager should complete several activities to recognize the years of long service and the upcoming retirement.

1. Recognize the retiree in the company publication and in community newspapers
2. Visit socially with the retiree (luncheon, dinner, etc.) and assure the individual that he or she is welcome to visit the organization and is entitled to any special company benefits (discounts, publications, clubs, etc.)

Postretirement programs primarily involve keeping in touch with the retiree and keeping him or her informed of company activities and events. This is generally done via the company publication; however, in its absence a letter or bulletin may suffice.

RESIGNATION

With the possible exception of retirement, the largest number of separations from an organization are employee-initiated. People leave an employer for a wide variety of reasons: to accept a better position with another firm, to return to school, to attend to personal problems, to relocate, for the sake of advancement, because of dissatisfaction, frustration, and/or conflict; etc. The line/staff manager should know both why the employee is leaving and, if possible, the reasons why the employee made the decision to leave. If the employee is leaving for a better job, to return to school, or to relocate, the impact is not detrimental to the organization. However, if a sizable number of employees are leaving the company for personal reasons or because of dissatisfaction, etc., then it is possible and probable that a serious internal problem exists in the department involved or in the company as a whole. The manager, once aware of a potential problem, should utilize the exit interview procedure to identify the source and causes of the problem, whether this involves company policies, operating procedures, safety requirements (or the lack of them), personnel, or whatever. Remember, turnover costs in today's economy can, if unchecked, be a significant drain on the net earnings of an organization. A separating employee, particularly one who quits in frustration and anger, will undoubtedly present a one-sided picture of the problem. On the other hand, if several separating employees indicate similar problems, the situation obviously warrants investigation.

As indicated earlier, an employee who quits or resign is expected to work a reasonable period of time after the date of notice of intent to leave the organization. In some instances this does not happen; rather, the employee announces his or her resignation one day and is gone the next. While this tactic often causes confusion and concern in the organization, it can be managed to have minimal impact, particularly if the company has a separation plan in effect.

An employee who quits is generally not entitled to any form of severance or separation pay, although he or she may be paid up through the last day worked. As an exception, the manager may decide to give the employee pay in lieu of notice. In this case the separating employee would receive a specified amount of pay for time not actually worked. Depending on the type of vacation plan in effect at the time the employee leaves, he or she (the employee) may or may not qualify to be paid for any unused vacation. It is the responsibility of the line/staff manager to ensure that the separating employee is fully compensated for all hours worked and for vacation to which he or she is entitled. The employee should be given an exit interview, either by the personnel representative or the manager, and all company benefits and policies should be explained in detail to the employee. The key here is the exit interview—every employee who leaves an organization should be given an interview and all topics should be discussed thoroughly, regardless of whether the employee gives a day's notice or a month's notice. By following this procedure, the line/staff manager ensures that the company's interests are protected and that the employee has been treated equitably.

DISCHARGE

On occasion, the line/staff manager is confronted with an employee who must be discharged or terminated from the organization. The following types of actions are generally considered serious enough to warrant discharge:

1. Theft of company property
2. Fraud
3. Insubordination
4. Sabotage
5. Assault on supervisor or fellow employee
6. Using, selling, or being under the influence of alcohol and/or drugs; possession of alcohol and/or drugs
7. Possession and/or use of a weapon
8. Sustained poor work performance

As in any separation, each case should be evaluated on individual basis; however, if the facts indicate that a discharge is necessary, the company has no specific obligation to the employee, regardless of years of service or level of responsibility. Specifically, the employee, if discharged, may lose his or her rights to such benefits as vacation entitlement, pay in lieu of notice, separation pay, pension, etc. Once again, the facts of each situation dictate the company's obligation to the employee. In regard to the discharge action itself, the line/staff manager must ensure that the punishment fits the offense. The following questions are appropriate in a discharge case:

1. Are all the facts known and are they accurate?
2. Are the facts direct or circumstantial?
3. Was the offense deliberate or were there mitigating circumstances?
4. Were the correct procedures followed by management?
5. Is the discharge consistent with similar cases involving violation of this particular company rule?
6. What is the employee's disciplinary record?
7. Is the decision to discharge fair and impartial?

This type of questioning and reasoning should take place prior to initiating the discharge procedure.

When the decision has been made to terminate an employee, the matter should be handled in complete confidence. Only the immediate supervisor and appropriate management personnel should be made aware of the decision. In order to avoid embarassment to the employee and to the line/staff manager, the actual discharge should take place away from the employee's work area, preferably in a conference room. It is recommended that two representatives of management be present, along with the employee to be discharged. The tone of the conversation should be straightforward and to the point. The employee must be told he or she is being separated and must be given the reasons. Although it is extremely difficult to look a person in the eye, particularly a friend or associate, and explain that his or her services are no longer required, in most cases this is the only effective way in which to convey the message. Too often the manager will beat around the bush, creating confusion and misinterpretation and leaving the employee in limbo. Once the employee has been told, be prepared for varied responses, from anger to tears. Remember that the shock of this event will trigger numerous defense mechanisms within the employee and consequently rational explanations may fall on deaf ears. There is little the line/staff manager can do or say to minimize the impact; therefore the best approach is simply to state the decision and explain the reasoning behind it. It is good practice to let the employee release his or her frustration and anger; however this too must be controlled and managed. Finally, because of the emotional impact of the discharge, it is sometimes wise to have the discharge meeting late on a Friday afternoon. This tactic minimizes the embarassment of the employee in the eyes of peers and it allows him or her to leave the organization without fanfare. It also allows the employee to clean out his or her desk, locker, etc., without having to face fellow employees and friends. This arrangement is also beneficial to the remaining work force in that they are not put in the position of having to face the discharged employee. As soon as practical after the discharge, the line/staff manager should communicate the necessary facts to the remaining work force so that they will not be in the dark as to what happened to one of their coworkers.

REDUCTIONS IN FORCE

A reduction in force, or layoff, of salaried personnel is generally a difficult situation for the line/staff manager, primarily because the employee(s) are not being terminated for cause but rather for lack of work. As such, in most cases a reduction is not a direct attack to an individual's performance and therefore the situation is often not as emotionally charged as is a discharge. While it is still difficult to explain to an employee that his or her job has been eliminated, the atmosphere in a reduction is one of assisting the employee find suitable employment, either internally or externally, and at the same time letting the employee know that his or her performance and ability are not suspect. Reductions in force are triggered by a variety of reasons; however, the primary cause is financial, in the form of job elimination, company or department reorganization, cost reduction programs, etc. The objective of handling a reduction is to minimize the impact of the reduction, both socially and operationally.

Depending on the type of operation, the number of personnel, and the staff involved, a reduction in force may be handled individually by the line/staff manager or by a group of managers. Assuming a final decision has authorized a reduction in force, one very effective method of determining who should be laid off is to establish an evaluation committee composed of personnel representative(s), line/staff management, and the immediate supervisor(s) in the department involved in the reduction. The makeup of the committee serves a dual role: first, it ensures objectivity and equity in handling the reduction and, second, it brings together both line and staff management in the decision-making process. The primary objective of the committee is to establish the criteria to be used in making a decision to reduce the operating force and then to decide which employees will be transferred, reorganized, and/or laid off. Prior to beginning any serious deliberation regarding reductions, it is necessary that all members of the evaluating committee thoroughly understand and agree upon both why the reduction is being made and the criteria to be considered. Typical criteria in a reduction are:

1. Performance
2. Length of company service
3. Employee skills and abilities
4. Level of responsibility.
5. Combination of above

Through experience, many organizations have found that in the final analysis, length of company service, with certain limitations, is a safe and effective criterion upon which to base reduction decisions. First, if service length is utilized, required special skills and high-potential employees are usually exempted from the reduction procedure for obvious reasons. Second, if a short-service employee is laid off, the impact is not as severe compared to laying off a long-service employee. In addition, the social cost is not as high and the amount of severance pay is minimal. Normally, when length of service is utilized to place employees within the organization, a long-service employee would replace a short-service employee. Since this is a management decision, the long-service employees do not have the option of choosing where they want to go in the company. The needs of the organization and the people involved dictate who goes where.

The evaluation committee should decide what criteria are applicable to the local operating conditions, consistent with Equal Employment Opportunity requirements. Prior to beginning a discussion of specifics in the reduction, the following data on the employees involved in the reduction are considered to be minimum:

1. Name
2. Age
3. Position—level
4. Previous positions
5. Length of service
6. Performance history
7. Salary history
8. Special skills and abilities

With these data in hand, it is the responsibility of the committee to weigh the facts and decide which employees will be retained in the organization (transfer, demotion, promotion, etc.) and which employees will be laid off. If the committee decides to retain personnel and place them internally within the organization, these employees should be considered for positions of equal or greater responsibility if possible. A lateral move would not normally warrant a change in salary, whereas a promotion would. On the other hand, if an employee does not qualify for an equal or greater position, then a demotion with a corresponding reduction in salary is appropriate. As a part of this process, the evaluation committee also has the responsibility to define the time period and the geographic location(s) to be considered in the decision, in addition to identifying by whom, how, where, and when the employees involved are to be informed of the decision.

Once a decision has been made to place an employee internally, the immediate supervisor and the line/staff manager should have a confidential meeting with the employee in order to explain that his or her job was eliminated and to give the reasons for the elimination. The discussion should be open and straightforward, focusing on the facts. The employee should be advised that the company will attempt to place him or her internally in a suitable job; however, the supervisor and manager must be careful to avoid raising false hopes. In addition, the time limitations and all options in the case should be explained. Once the counseling session is completed, immediate action to place the employee should begin.

If the evaluation committee decides a particular employee cannot be placed internally, then it is the responsibility of the immediate supervisor and the line/staff manager to inform the employee of the decision. Using the format indicated in the previous paragraph, the employee should be told why he or she is being separated and that internal placement is not possible because of the criteria defined by the evaluation committee. The situation should be thoroughly explained so there is no doubt in the employee's mind regarding the separation. If the decision to separate the employee is based on poor performance, then the exit interview procedure should be initiated. If the decision is based on lack of work, seniority, etc., then the company has an obligation to assist the employee in finding suitable external employment. There are several ways of assisting an employee find employment; however, a one-on-one counseling session is extremely effective. Topics could include:

1. Preparation of letters of inquiry and résumés
2. How and where to look for a job:
   a. Newspaper classified ads
   b. Professional and trade publications
   c. Employment agencies—state and private
   d. College placement annual
   e. Federal, state, and local government agencies
   f. Friends, associates, and business contacts
3. Unemployment compensation benefits
4. Other—agencies to be notified of the situation:
   a. Banks
   b. Creditors—finance companies, mortgage company, credit card accounts, etc.
   c. Landlord
   d. Insurance agents
5. Company benefits

An effective method of reinforcing the counseling session is to prepare a written pamphlet or brochure that identifies these considerations to the employee. This gives him or her a basis on which to begin the search for employment. Finally, as in separation, the departing employee must be given an exit interview.

The last concern in a reduction in force is the impact on the remaining work force. Ideally, the group should be assembled and the situation and reasoning should be explained in as much detail as is required to convey the point. All employees should be given the opportunity to ask questions and, in turn, line/staff management should answer them openly and honestly. The manager should be aware of dissatisfaction and take positive steps to deal with any potential problems.

Chapter **6**

Job Enrichment in the Plant Engineering and Maintenance Department

ERIC M. BERGTRAUN
Manager, Plant Engineering and Maintenance, National Semiconductor Corporation

INTRODUCTION

In the past, efforts to improve motivation and job satisfaction have been concentrated mainly on areas peripheral to work: pay, benefits, company policy and administration, relation with supervisors, working relations, interpersonal relationships, security, and so on. More recently, plant engineers have joined many other managers in realizing that the most important factor of all may be the work itself and the challenge and opportunity for growth it provides.

When we examine industry, we discover that people are probably the most underutilized resource. There is an enormous waste of human resources in many manufacturing departments, including plant engineering and maintenance.

In this chapter, six points in the movement to eliminate waste of human resources through the introduction of job enrichment are discussed:

    1. The job itself   3. Responsibility   5. Advancement
    2. Achievement   4. Growth   6. Recognition

A good manager can easily develop a job enrichment program.

JOB ENRICHMENT

Engineering and maintenance, as practiced by the plant engineer, are part of the overall work of managing. Plant engineers also provide support to other functions of manufacturing management.

Companies and corporations are very concerned about rising costs in their plant engineering departments. They strongly support work management that develops its own successful program of motivation as an important opportunity to stem the rising costs of engineering, operating, and maintaining facilities.

Job enrichment—making jobs more appealing and satisfying—can be an extremely powerful motivational force in the plant engineering and maintenance department. Although not a panacea for all industrial ills, it is a good tool to improve overall management.

Much has been written about motivation, but the motivation to work is still the most neglected factor in American industry. Too many plant engineers still think that money is the best—and a suprising number will say the only—people motivator. Some of today's managers are using finesse in approaching the motivation problem by advocating various types of incentive programs. A number of companies are successfully using the work-team approach, in which teams know their assignments, choose their own hours, schedule their own overtime, and arrange most major details of their jobs. With this approach, companies are introducing incentive programs in which groups are rewarded, rather than individuals only.

Plant engineering managers must recognize that today's employees are motivated most by the work itself and by the way management attempts to make that work more meaningful and rewarding. A recent survey showed that group participation approaches are winning increased acceptance as the way to improve productivity, create job satisfaction, and resolve labor-management problems.

It is unreasonable to assume that maintenance personnel will work harder just to help their companies—most people work only because they must support their families, hobbies, and general way of life. Most successful companies subscribe to the theory that work habits can be greatly improved by enriching the job itself. Workers want a challenge. Pay, benefits and good working conditions, while important, are not as crucial in motivating people as the challenge of the job itself. A recent Department of Health, Education, and Welfare report on work in America states that jobs should be enhanced not only out of corporate self-interest but also for humanitarian interest—to improve society. The report states that aggression, alcoholism and drug abuse, mental depression, and physical illness have been linked by researchers to dissatisfaction with work.

Experiments have proved that maintenance people are more productive and more satisfied with their work when their jobs are enriched. They enjoy working in a more professional atmosphere with adequate facilities, the right tools, and a more active voice in their jobs. They have a greater sense of achievement and a better chance for rapid advancement when they are given greater responsibility and training. Enriched jobs make for an atmosphere of growth and bring recognition as well. Enriched jobs provide the means of satisfying the motivation seekers and achievers in the maintenance department.

The person who can make all this possible, with only a little support from management, is the manager of plant engineering. Who will gain from job enrichment? The company, of course. Their profits will improve because of significant increases in performance due to job satisfaction, which will spread from the plant engineering department to the other service organizations and operating departments. The manager of plant engineering responsible for the upturn will find that his own job is enriched also. The employees in the plant engineering department responding to this program will enjoy more stimulating and challenging jobs.

But in reality, how many management people are seriously concerned about job enrichment in the plant engineering and maintenance departments? Management is usually concerned about the performance in the maintenance department. Complaints are often heard about the high cost of maintenance, the ever-increasing cost of maintenance labor and material. The "experts" lecture about more effective maintenance organizations and the need for better training, planning, job scheduling, estimating, work measurement, labor performance analysis, controls, indexes, reports, energy savings, communications, and so on.

It is true that many of these needs exist. The psychology of motivation is tremendously complex. The most important item, though, is the motivation to work. This can best be achieved by enriching the job itself.

The time is long gone when managers could use fear or punishment to control people. Those were the days of negative motivation or, as Professor Herzberg calls it, the "KITA"* approach. This KITA—the externally imposed attempt by managers to "install a generator" in the employee—has been demonstrated to be a total failure. Herzberg found that the absence of such hygiene factors as good supervisor-employee relations and liberal fringe benefits can make a worker unhappy, but their presence will not want to make him or her work harder. Essentially meaningless changes in the tasks that engineers and workers are assigned to do have not accomplished the desired objective either. The only way to motivate employees is to provide challenging work for which they can assume responsibility in a professional environment. Herzberg found that many things that were formerly considered motivators do not motivate, although lack of them will produce dissatisfaction. Some of these are:

Benefits
Salary
Security
Company policy and administration
Relations with supervision
Working conditions
Interpersonal relationships

Herzberg discovered that the presence of these factors will only make it a little easier for people to tolerate their work. The essential ingredient is still missing: a long-range satisfier. This missing factor can be supplied by giving the employee such work motivators as:

Achievement
Recognition
Appreciation of work itself
Responsibility
Advancement
Growth in competence

Lester R. Bittle of Academy Hall, Inc., of Strasburg, Virginia, wrote in a recent article in *Mechanical Engineering:*

> The behavioral people have convincingly demonstrated that true motivation exists in the very nature of the Work Itself. They have irrefutably documented the motivational power of those elements which are characteristic of managed work. These are the ingredients which can be engineered into the work itself by a creative and thoughtful management. And these elements are typically expressed as opportunities and freedoms rather than as restrictions and repressions. They include in particular, the following:
>
> 1. Free access to all information that is needed to do the work well.
> 2. An opportunity to set one's own production goals, to choose one's own production methods, and to determine one's own working pace.
> 3. An opportunity to achieve something that is worthwhile to others and meaningful to one's self.
> 4. Recognition by others for one's achievements.
> 5. An opportunity to interact with others, in particular with one's supervisors, without fear of recrimination.
> 6. An opportunity to exert self-control and to exercise self-discipline.
>
> Not all of these factors can be attained purely by predesign, of course. They must be put into place daily by the managers who share these responsibilities. But many of the problems of Work Management do respond readily to engineering forethought. When taken one at a time, sound resolutions are not only technically feasible, they are already on-stream in many organizations.

Plant engineers, especially those who are primarily concerned about motivating employees in the maintenance department, can learn a lot from the industrial hygienists and will be able to apply many of their theories and findings. One of the prime responsibilities of a manager in plant maintenance is to do everything possible to make the

* "Kick In The Afterburner."

maintenance man like his job. In the concept of effective worker motivation, what it means to like a job is shown by a description of the attitude of satisfied employees, who:

Do not hate to go to work
Are not bored by their work
Actually look forward to an interesting workday
Like the facility they work in
Have the right tools to perform good work
Are reasonably satisfied with their compensation
Are proud of their company's achievements
Want to be part of their company's growth
Respect their supervisors
Have a chance for advancement
Get recognition for doing a good job

Quite a few factors must be considered by the plant engineer when a job enrichment program is being prepared. The plant engineer must be aware of the motivation problem and can gain an understanding of job enrichment through extensive study. Patience will be necessary, because new habits must be established, and it will take a long time to make some of the necessary changes.

What does all this mean to our companies? A smoothly running plant engineering and maintenance department, one that employs motivated workers, is a very important factor in the successful operation of our businesses and in profitability. Since profits are the single most important factor in the operation of any business, we had better take a very good look at how plant engineers and maintenance managers can enrich jobs in their organizations.

SIX AREAS OF EFFECTIVE WORKER MOTIVATION

The six areas of effective worker motivation are:

1. The job itself   4. Growth
2. Achievement   5. Advancement
3. Responsibility   6. Recognition

These six area areas of potential work satisfaction improvement deserve special consideration by the plant engineer, who is responsible for the maintenance or in-house construction activity within the plant engineering department. Following is some advice to the managers who want to apply these six areas of potential work satisfaction improvement to their programs:

The Job Itself

Organization You must plan the activities of maintenance and construction carefully. Workers perform best when their daily routine work is precisely outlined. They want tools and material available when needed and a clear description of their work. You must tell them exactly what is expected of them. Your workers will be motivated when they know exactly what their job is and what you want them to do. You must give them orders that are concise, clear, and easy to understand. You must tell them who makes the decisions and who is available for further instructions and answers to their questions. You should tell them how long each job can take and how they should report job completion.

Delegation of authority Provide each worker with a direct supervisor. Always use your established supervisory or management chain of authority when you give an order. Employee morale suffers when personnel other than the immediate supervisor give orders.

Establishment of priorities You must insist that job priorities be established. Workers should not be pulled off half-finished jobs and reassigned. Only in extreme emergencies should they be ordered to other work.

Providing help on menial jobs You should assign helpers and laborers to do menial work. But often, large maintenance operations employ no laborers. Supervisors on these jobs are usually proud that their people do all jobs—furniture moving, digging ditches, aligning machinery, and testing electronic control circuitry. These supervisors fail to understand that trained craftsmen resent being expected to do laborers' work routinely.

Maintainable facilities The plant engineer must think about maintenance when the facility is being designed or when equipment is being ordered. Too often, when maintenance needs are not considered, machines and facilities are practically impossible to maintain.

Adequate maintenance and construction shops   The greatest motivator of any worker is a well-designed, environmentally controlled, well-illuminated shop that has modern tools and a supply of spare parts and material adequate to handle most emergencies. If a shop is located in a corner of a boiler room, in a noisy machine room, or in a cluttered storage and construction area—or if it is dimly lit and without adequate tools, supplies, or spare parts—the usual result will be a department of unmotivated workers, excessive turnover among employees, high maintenance and construction costs, and many costly breakdowns. You must also insist on good housekeeping and safety habits. Orderly and clean shops provide pleasant workplaces. No one likes to work in a place where everything is dirty and disorganized.

You must always consider the health and personal welfare of your workers. In providing a strong safety program that meets all OSHA requirements, you must set the personal example.

Achievement

Motivate every employee to feel personally important. Personnel are highly motivated by feelings of achievement. For example, completing an assigned task successfully instills the desire to do the next job even better. Employees enjoy working on complex and interesting machinery and being responsible for their own particular segment of work.

Workers enjoy learning about new technology necessary for today's modern job. When they receive good training in doing the job well, they have a real feeling of achievement. Workers know that their jobs have to be done in a predetermined time. They expect you to make the studies and indexes available to them and are willing to accept the fact that the work has to be completed in the estimated and allocated time.

All this should not restrict their mobility and ingenuity in search for better methods. You should make it possible for employees to manage their own work as much as possible and you should give them time to explore new methods and procedures to do a better job.

Within the plant engineering department, the construction and maintenance sections have a tremendous impact on the profit-and-loss statement of any company. Most every company runs cost-saving programs, but many forget the very important point that workers should be allowed to share fully in these programs.

Responsibility

Many companies have achieved excellent results by making maintenance departments responsible for their work efforts—setting them up as cost centers. Similarly, it is desirable that you make individual workers responsible for specific areas. The workers are then responsible for the maintenance, housekeeping, safety, breakdown of machinery, security, and so on, in their specific areas. You can try to break out the cost of their efforts and compare this with budget figures.

You should detail exactly what you expect from each individual in the effort to achieve overall department objectives. When expected individual contributions are known, each worker will be motivated to attempt to give what is demanded.

Growth

The success of any company depends on its growth. Management and workers grow with the company. If you provide your workers with an enriching job, one that satisfies their human needs on the job, you are offering them an atmosphere of working toward their personal growth and fulfillment.

Smart maintenance managers will use company growth to enrich their departments. They will promote from within the department when they have to add a foreman or leadman. A progressive company has permanent training programs to prepare workers for promotions.

Your training programs must go beyond the necessary technical education—workers must learn more about the business their company is in. Such programs can be started with the help of other company employees or by involving corporate staff activities. Here is an example of a "one hour a week" training program, that can be organized by you, involving company personnel:

Plant manager   Explaining the nature of the corporation. What part does the plant play? Need for profits. What are profits? Effect of inflation on profits, compensation, and organization.

Marketing manager   What does it take to sell the company's product? How can we impress the customers visiting the facility? What is customer satisfaction?

Product manager   What makes the company's product successful? Uses for our products. What are our critical production machines? What causes product defects?

Plant engineer   Theory of machine operation. How to select sizes of pipes and electrical conductors. How to troubleshoot. Importance of avoiding utility interruptions.

Safety engineer   Common industrial accidents and their prevention. OSHA regulations, electrical codes, city codes.

Accountant   What is a profit-and-loss statement? How does the maintenance dollar affect profits? What is depreciation?

Purchasing agent   What is needed to handle a purchase order? How much money can be saved by eliminating crash purchasing? What is needed for good bidding? Why do we develop new vendors?

Storekeeper   Explanation of the stores catalogue. What should be stocked in the storeroom? How can maintenance and construction prevent stockouts?

Custodian   What makes the janitor's life miserable? How can the janitor help the maintenance worker?

Security manager   Why the need for company security? How can the security and maintenance departments work together better?

Personnel manager   How best to explain fringe benefits and insurance. How does the plant environment affect the moral and productivity of a company?

Company nurse   A starter course in first aid. Instructions in how to report an accident.

In addition to these suggested courses, you should be able to arrange for lectures and demonstrations by equipment manufacturers and maintenance product suppliers. Such a well-rounded "continuous" training program will ensure growth in your organization.

The well-informed employee is a more effective employee. This holds true not only for the worker but also for the manager. You should broaden your professional and technical knowledge at all times. Take advantage of every opportunity to learn more about your managing job and be able to give a good technical example to your workers. You've got to know your business. This is the most important factor to gain the respect and confidence of your employees.

Advancement

If responsibility and growth are handled properly, individual advancement will occur naturally. A department that delegates responsibilities to its workers and prepares them for growth through meaningful training will be able to advance workers, both within the department and by transfers to other growing departments in the company. A growing company will always have open positions in its maintenance department. As trained maintenance people move into lead positions, chances for advancement will open up for helpers and apprentices. Some of the senior people will get a chance to get into maintenance management positions; others can get into plant or product engineering; jobs for production foremen will open up also. It often happens that well-trained maintenance people move into inspector and safety jobs. Some get a chance to become maintenance managers in a new plant or division. When this is part of the overall company program and happens regularly, it becomes an important factor in the job enrichment program of the plant maintenance and construction departments.

Recognition

The programs mentioned will automatically result in recognition. In a well-organized company, recognition is practiced daily by the entire management team. Some of management's tools are:

1. Company newsletters and bulletins that provide recognition for many employees
2. Recognition presentations and dinners for employees having five, ten, fifteen, or more years of service with the company
3. Recognition for perfect attendance
4. Quarterly or semiannual dinners for departments and company management representatives
5. Competitive awards for safety, housekeeping, suggestions, and cost savings

6. Company recognition of promotions and also of employees' outside interest achievements

7. Company recognition for completed training programs by individuals or teams

8. Top management interest in its employees-shown by visits to shops, introduction of new managers, etc., by top managers

Of course, in maintenance or plant engineering, where the employees are often reprimanded by just about everybody for doing or not doing something, any kind word or gesture will enrich the jobs.

This should start with the management team in plant engineering—they must set an example. They must make the workers feel important to themselves by making them important parts of the organization.

CONCLUSION

The six points that have been covered at length can enrich jobs in the maintenance and construction department and they can also be applied to all other areas and departments in the plant engineering organization.

The job chart (Fig. 1) laying out motivation needs and maintenance needs, published

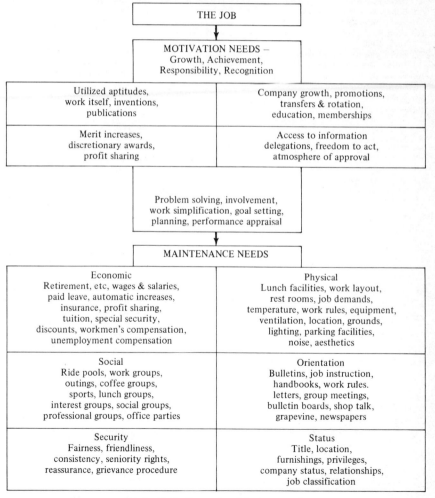

Fig. 1 Motivation and maintenance needs.

in *Plant Engineering Magazine* of July 11, 1974, shows clearly that these needs can be easily applied to all sections of the plant engineering organization.

Job enrichment, monetary compensation, job security, and good supervision are the tools needed to build an effective plant engineering organization.

Plant engineers often shrug off problems in their departments by lamenting: "Management does not give me their support; they do not want to spend the money." Often this is just an excuse for their own nonperformance.

Good managers of plant engineering organizations can develop, introduce, and practice their own job enrichment programs. The good results of such a program should be visible at once. When the manager of plant engineering can show these results off to management it should elicit their support to go further. It is really up to each plant engineering manager to develop and sell such a program personally.

REFERENCES

1. C. Argyris: *Integrating the Individual and the Organization,* Wiley, New York, 1964.
2. Henry M. Boettinger: *Moving Mountains,* Macmillan, New York, 1969.
3. Keith Davis: *Human Relations at Work,* McGraw-Hill, New York, 1962.
4. Peter F. Drucker: *The Effective Executive,* Harper & Row, New York, 1967.
5. Robert N. Ford: *Motivation through the Work Itself,* American Management Association, New York, 1969.
6. Fred K. Foulkes: *Creating More Meaningful Work,* American Management Association, New York, 1969.
7. Saul Gellerman: *Management by Motivation,* American Management Association, New York, 1968. "Motivation and Productivity," American Management Association, New York, 1963.
8. Frederick Herzberg: *The Motivation to Work,* Wiley, New York, 1967. *Work and the Nature of Man,* World Publishing, Cleveland, 1966.
9. Rensis Likert: *The Human Organization,* McGraw-Hill, New York, 1967.
10. John Maher: *New Perspectives in Job Enrichment,* Van Nostrand-Reinhold, New York, 1971.
11. Scott Myers: *Every Employee a Manager,* McGraw-Hill, New York, 1955.
12. E. T. Newbrough: *Effective Maintenance Management,* McGraw-Hill, New York, 1967.
13. Norman R. F. Maier: *Psychology in Industry,* Houghton Mifflin, Boston, 1955.
14. William Van Dersal: *The Successful Supervisor,* Harper & Row, New York, 1974.
15. James K. Van Fleet: *How to Use the Dynamics of Motivation,* Parker Publishing Co., West Nyack, N.Y. 1967.
16. Victor H. Vroom: *Work and Motivation,* Wiley, New York, 1964.
17. W. F. Whyte: *Money and Motivation,* Harper & Row, New York, 1955.

Chapter **7**

Labor-Management Relations

HERBERT R. BROWN
CONSULTANT

INDIVIDUAL DIFFERENCES AND THE ORGANIZATION

We live in an age of change; change is a partner to stress, and stress affects individuals differently. Dynamic organizations are targets of change; they are subject to it and seek it. Individuals make up organizations and individuals are, therefore, subject to organizational stress. The greater the difference between individuals, the more likely it is that there will be a greater variance in the results of stress.

Individuals are products of environment and heredity. They bring to their jobs their personal beliefs, prejudices, family upbringing, training, education, identification with friends and groups, aspirations, expectations, church orientation, likes, dislikes, myths, illnesses, physical characteristics, genetic tendencies, and all other conditions and attributes that make them unique human beings. These differences, when they do not work toward a cooperative relationship with organizational objectives, may produce suspicion, resentment, and open conflict between individual and organization. When these differences are allied in a sincere cooperative relationship with organizational objectives, the individual human beings with their individual differences may unite to produce higher morale, increased productivity, and greater organizational strength.

The individual differences among workers require a constant effort by management toward a cooperative endeavor. Fortunately there are common denominators among workers as well as between workers and management. For example, workers may belong to the same union, club, or organization. Workers are employed by the company and expect to work, to be paid, to be treated with dignity, to be given opportunity, and—to varying degrees and under different time phases—workers expect recognition and reward for achievement. Managers, as employees, expect very much the same.

A worker expects to be efficiently supervised. A manager aspires to supervise efficiently. A major element in labor-management relations is the perception vs. the reality of supervisory efficiency. The worker's perception of the quality of the supervision received and the manager's perception of the quality of the supervision provided, rather than the reality in each instance, usually produces a gap and creates the need to strive for the worker-organization cooperative venture essential to the worker's expectations and the organization's strength and growth.

UNION OBJECTIVES AND BEHAVIOR

As a manager representing your company and, possibly, a negotiator with your union, it is necessary for you to understand the union's objectives and behavior in order to deal with it effectively. First, unions seek to advance the interest of their members. In this sense they are no different from the American Legion, the Chamber of Commerce, or any other membership association. There is a basic thrust to achieve a better life for the membership. This includes a higher standard of living, financial and income protection, job rights and job protection, opportunity for advancement, more leisure time, and various forms of insurance and retirement benefits. Some unions have broader social goals advocating broader educational opportunity, better housing, equal employment opportunities, increased participation by government in health and medical insurance, additional protective labor legislation, and other social benefits.

Unions have social and fraternal goals to provide their members with a sense of belonging to and identifying with the union. These goals are implemented through banquets, lunches, picnics, and union meetings. To some workers, the union has the same status as the corporation does to executives.

Unions use two principal means of accomplishing their goals, and union behavior is directly related to these means. The main union effort is made through the collective bargaining process. The union, serving as representative of employees with employers, negotiates agreements. Collective bargaining includes the subsequent day-to-day contract administration, and this covers enforcement of the agreement. Enforcement might include informal discussions relative to interpretation of the agreement, usually to forestall a grievance and, possibly, an arbitration case. Enforcement also includes the formal grievance that, if not settled to the satisfaction of both parties, may go to arbitration. Unions also become involved in collective action resulting in strikes or picketing. A second form of behavior, influencing government legislation, takes the form of lobbying, campaigning to elect friends of labor to public office, and disseminating of information to mold and sway public opinion through direct use of the media.

The behavior of a craft union is essentially different from that of an industrial union. Craft unions—as exemplified by those in the building trades (carpenters, plumbers, electricians, bricklayers, and so on)—concentrate on control over jobs. Since it is their belief that jobs in these skill areas are few, they seek to protect both job rights and skill areas. This is done by controlling apprenticeship numbers; opposition to technological advances that will reduce the level of skill needed and thus reduce pay or jobs; obtaining rules that require licensed craftsmen, such as plumbers and electricians, before a job is approved by the municipality; establishing hiring halls, requiring high initiation fees, and, for example, insisting on long apprenticeship periods (3 to 5 years) before journeyman status is granted. They also establish a work pace that limits output (e.g., in the case of bricklayers). Most craft unions have a membership that is skilled and in short supply, hence difficult to replace. Thus, should they call a strike, all they need do is post few pickets explaining the strike. Employers are unable to replace the striking craftsmen and other unions accustomed to dealing with the company will not cross the picket line. Hence the company will probably significantly diminish its productivity or shut down. Strikes by most craft unions tend to be peaceful.

Industrial unions must behave differently to be effective. Rather than artificially restricting membership, industrial unions acquire strength and power by increasing their numbers. They seek to encourage all workers in the factory to belong. This would include unskilled, semiskilled, skilled, and white-collar employees. Fees and dues are usually low to encourage membership, and the effort is to promote solidarity among all who work for the company or industry. The United Automobile Workers is an example of an industrial union whose strike behavior is different. An industrial union that has been recognized as the bargaining agent in a factory attempts total and complete action by all its members. In most factories, semiskilled workers predominate. These skill levels are more easily replaceable should management decide to keep the factory open during a strike. In a strike situation, management can either shut down and wait out the union, counting on the fact that the company's economic holding power is greater; or the company can aggressively push a back-to-work movement, hiring replacements for the striking workers. The industrial union usually resorts to mass picketing to prevent strikebreakers from crossing picket lines. This usually results in violence. Mass picketing is outlawed by the Taft-Hartley Act and local police usually attempt to prevent such union action. The industrial union is inevitably faced with the dilemma of needing to take mass action and not being allowed to do so. An industrial union must have almost full support and complete membership of all factory workers to be successful. The industrial union seeks more union security and control of job changes—such as promotion, transfer, and layoff based on seniority—attempting thereby to eliminate favoritism. Industrial unions want a union shop. This requires workers to join the union within 30 days of employment. This provision becomes necessary to protect the union membership, because factory turnover among semiskilled labor is typically high. Without the union-shop provision, union membership and thereby its strength is constantly being eroded.

WHY WORKERS JOIN UNIONS

As company representatives, managers should know why the employees they supervise —and other workers as well—are attracted to and join unions. Unionization is a process arising from the workers' feeling that belonging to the union will aid in the achievement of goals or conditions to which most workers aspire.

In general, unionization is largely an indication of discontent, and the joining of unions and subsequent commitment to union objectives is an attempt on the worker's part to fulfill a variety of needs that are not being met in the work situation. These are the typical needs for security, belonging, esteem, integration in the group, and self-actualization. Union membership has at least partially served to meet these needs. A desire to improve wages and fringe benefits may be primary, but it is only one reason for joining. Workers wish to obtain the society and respect of others. The worker finds the union providing a social structure that may not be present otherwise. The worker is also subject to the social pressures brought by fellow employees, finding that failure to join the union may lead to ostracism both within the plant and under social conditions outside the plant. It is important to note that a large proportion of new union members are required to join unions as a provision of the union shop. However, the number of decertification elections are remarkably low; thus it appears that acceptance and continuance in the union is voluntary. The union can also provide a worker with a sense of security, a sense of status, a feeling of independence in relation to his employer, and the satisfaction of identifying with a group. Even in a well-managed company that pays good wages and has good working conditions, union membership may have an appeal because it frees the worker from a sense of complete dependency on the employer. This has the effect, claims management, of a leveling off, so that individual initiative is stifled and the productivity level is geared to the average worker. The union position is usually that uniform treatment eliminates cliques, factional grouping, and special treatment accorded to "management's fair-haired boys or management pets" among the union membership.

Despite these restrictions and attempts to eliminate individual differences, unions have certain advantages that are recognized by some managements, and these include improved personnel policies and practices. The presence of the union requires management to consider and reduce favoritism. It also requires that management consider more fully workers' needs. Faults in personnel policy will be noted by union officials and changes will be recommended or demanded.

THE UNIONIZATION PROCESS

The initiative for organizing workers may come from the employees themselves, from a union already representing some of the employees of the company, or from a union representing workers elsewhere. Typically, union organization starts with an aggressive campaign. The first steps may be relatively quiet. Workers are contacted at their homes, at eating places, or at amusement places, and a good deal of soliciting takes place. In some instances, contacts may be attempted on the job, although this is not likely in plants. It does occur in stores, however. Any and every management action that is questionable will be used against management. The solicitation is at all levels, including the emotional, social, economic, and physical. The effort is to sell the prospective buyers—the workers—on the idea that by joining the union they will have better, more productive, better-paying, healthier lives, with a voice in those management decisions that affect their present and future conditions of employment, fringes, and opportunities for better and more challenging jobs. They will belong to the group that will recognize them for their real worth, who will fight for them when they are wronged, who will protect them, who will ensure that their rights are always recognized, and who will strive to improve not only their conditions but also those of their friends, fellow workers, and families. Every sales pitch is considered and used as may be appropriate. The workers cannot remain neutral. They are moved into a position where they are made to believe that they are either for the union or against their fellow workers. Rational and logical arguments for unionism are a part of the sales kit, but the emotional arguments are basic and major.

The initial effort on the part of the union organization is to sign up 30 percent or more of the employees in the particular bargaining unit sought. At this point the regional office of the National Labor Relations Board will be petitioned to supervise an election. During the organizing drive, management is subject to a number of legal constraints. Under Taft-Hartley (Labor-Management Relations Act), the following constraints apply:

Management or employers may not interfere with employees in the exercise of their rights to organize a union or to refrain from union activity.

Employers may not dominate or interfere with the formation or administration of a union.

Employers may not discriminate against any employee for union activity.

Employers may not discriminate against employees for filing an unfair labor practice charge or for testifying in an National Labor Relations Board, (NLRB) hearing.

There ar further legal constraints against employers resulting from the provisions of Landrum-Griffin, the Labor-Management Reporting and Disclosure Act:

Employers must file reports with the Secretary of Labor as to expenditures for outside labor relations consultants, the influencing of employees in the exercise of their rights, and the obtaining of information about the progress of organization.

Money payments or things of value between management and union officials seeking to organize is illegal.

Under the free speech provision of Taft-Hartley, however, management has every right to communicate with employees regarding the organizing drive and to attempt to dissuade the workers from joining as long as threats are not used or rewards offered for not joining the union.

There is an almost universal tendency on the part of management to resist unionization. For example, when union organizers working for the AFL-CIO wanted to form an organizers' union called Field Representatives Federation, union officials refused recognition. The case went to NLRB for decision, and the FRF won recognition. There are other cases involving union and company managements resisting unionization. Once the threat to egos and the defensive behavior is past, management resistance in this day and age is not too strong.

Management must know that there are legal constraints against unions during the negotiation process. These include the following:

Unions may not coerce workers in their right to refrain from union activity.

A union may not strike against an employer to compel that employer to bargain with that union when another union has already been certified as representative of the employees of the employer.

No election may be held within a bargaining unit when a valid election has been held within the previous 12 months.

A union must submit certain information to the NLRB about its internal affairs before an election is requested.

The Landrum-Griffin Act provides additional restraints on the union, including these:

Picketing for organizational purposes must be followed by an election within 30 days. If the election goes against the union, there can be no picketing for 12 months.

Picketing is illegal when the employer has lawfully recognized another union.

Picketing to stop deliveries or to cause other employees to withhold their services is illegal.

IMPACT OF UNIONIZATION ON ORGANIZATIONAL PROCESS

During the unionization process, managers are restricted in what they can do and say regarding the union drive. The compensation process affecting the bargaining unit practically ceases. Management should not grant pay increases or promotions to any of the personnel within the unit or change fringe benefits in any way lest this be interpreted as coercion or interference with the organizing drive. Should the union win the election and become certified, collective bargaining follows. The labor agreement now governs and any unilateral management action can only be taken in areas not covered by the agreement.

THE BARGAINING UNIT

Besides supervising the election, the NLRB also determines the appropriateness of the bargaining unit should there be a dispute on this matter. This is very important and can influence the results of an election. If a particular group of employees is known to be strongly pro-union, it is to management's advantage to attempt to have them excluded from the unit. Management's position could be that these employees, or some of them, are in different functional areas, are part of management, would provide a heterogenous group with different background and job requirements, are classified differently, have historically been treated differently, etc., and that inclusion would not only produce undue hardship in administration but violate long standing and accepted classification, administrative, and work relationships. Similarly, the inclusion of a group of anti-union employees might swing the election so that the organizing drive fails. Thus, the determination of the bargaining unit is an important management strategy.

THE BARGAINING RELATIONSHIP

There are numerous studies that define and identify numerous types of bargaining relationships, the background leading to this relationship, and the behavior accompanying and following the relationship. In general, the more familiar and frequently observed types are as follows:

Open conflict This occurs when management does not accept the union regardless of certification and deals with it on a minimal basis. Management statements or implications may be that the union does not really represent the thinking and attitudes of the majority of employees; that union officials lie, misrepresent, are inaccurate, and take advantage of management's benevolence. Such a management position will not be too effective after a union has been certified. Legal difficulties may arise; strong pro-union employees may become so aggressive and disruptive that continuance of organizational effectiveness and productivity is seriously threatened.

Containment This is an "armed truce" relationship, based on the premise that management and union objectives are too far apart for reconciliation and are inherently in conflict. This is a usual type of relationship. The company deals with the union as required by law, accepting legal constraints. Every effort is made to contain union power and to retain the rights of management.

Accommodation In this relationship both union and management recognize some common goals and work together by sharing information and using problem-solving techniques to achieve solutions to bargaining problems. This will probably result in a minimum of conflict, but there may be some undesirable effects. If accomodation is one-sided, with management agreeing to union requests, then few solutions actually occur. The Studebaker Company is the classic example of a most harmonious relationship. Excess manpower and ever-increasing production costs resulting from unilateral accommodation were major factors in forcing Studebaker out of the automobile business.*

Cooperation   This involves an extension of the bargaining relationship beyond the contract itself. There is a formal plan for consultation and action on problems previously handled by management alone. It emerges because of a major problem facing the company, the industry, or the area. An example would be the problems resulting from automation.

Deal   There is one other relationship that has existed in the past and which probably will continue to exist in some areas. This is the type in which management makes certain special arrangements with the union leaders, usually without membership knowledge or approval. Union leaders may agree to forego an expected wage increase for a checkoff system. This type of bargaining relationship usually does not remain stable. Membership may resent the contract, the practices during the campaign may cause hostility to persist long after settlement, or a change of union leadership or of management may require a more effective approach to evolve. In some instances, a company may have a policy of containment but may on occasion work with the union on an accommodation basis; in a specific instance, both may arrive at a deal to bypass state safety laws. Or because the company is in a precarious financial position and jobs are scarce, a deal may ‑be entered into to reduce previous union gains to protect jobs and help the company through a difficult competitive period.

The typical bargaining in the negotiation process may be diagramed somewhat as follows:

A	Union initial demand	Bargaining field	Management initial position
B	Union retreat position	narrows	Management give
C	Union expectations	until	Management requirements
D	Final positions	s	Final position
		e	
		t	
		t	
		l	
		e	
		m	
		e	
		n	
		t	

The difference between A and D and the extent of movement between A and D is the amount which each side has given in any collective bargaining situation. When great victories are proclaimed by management or by the union, that side has perceived that the distance it has traveled from A to D is less than the distance traveled or given by the other party.

PREPARATION FOR BARGAINING

It has been a typical practice for the unions to present a series of demands to which management would react. Too often management would await these demands before considering its own needs. Of recent years, it has become common practice for management to spend considerable time and effort preparing for negotiations, and management has even taken the initiative in presenting its demands to the union. Companies use survey data in their geographical areas to consider changes in wages and fringe benefits. If there are sections of an existing contract that represents particular sources of trouble, grievance and arbitration awards are studied. Supervisors are questioned for suggested changes. The negotiating team should be thoroughly briefed on the company's financial

---

* R. W. Walton and R. B. McKersie, *A Behavioral Theory of Labor Negotiations,* McGraw-Hill, New York, 1965.

position, on the costs of changes in wages and fringes, and—to the extent possible—on union power in the company.

Unions will also do their homework and have much of the same information and a rationalized position for their demands.

If you are to represent the company, you must be prepared with a variety of information. For a new negotiation or a renegotiation, you should know:

How well has present policy or the present agreement worked?

What do competing companies and unions do about wages and working conditions?

What has happened to the cost of living?

What recent changes in economic conditions have affected the company?

Other information a company representative should have includes the following:

What is the present personnel policy of the company? How will anticipated changes resulting from union demands conflict with this policy?

What are the legal limitations and the effect of national and state laws on wages, hours, and overtime?

What is bargainable and what is illegal under the law?

What are the laws in your state with which you must be familiar, such as state workmen's compensation, unemployment compensation, and the effect of these on layoff procedures and severance pay?

You will also need statistical data on the number, type, sex, and age of employees; their seniority, ethnic, and minority status; and their classification, wage rate, rate range per classification, and distribution within classifications. You will need to know the number of promotions made, reclassifications granted, other pay systems used, and pay given under these systems. Information on existing employee benefits and their cost to employee and to the company must be available. You will need to have available the vacation policy, sick time granted, holidays, time off, special hazards, peculiarity of working conditions, seasonal employment, incentive pay, and more.

You may be requested to furnish this information to the union and, under Taft-Hartley, you are required to do so. You may also be requested to supply information on the company's business as it may affect wages and fringes, and you are required to do so.

It is essential that your preparation be thorough. Once you have been presented with union demands, you will need to compute cost data relative to each request and to review pertinent data from other competing companies in order to determine your relative position and the nature of your counterproposals.

Who pays for the time taken up by union negotiations if bargaining is held during working hours? The answer to this question will vary from company to company. In many plants, employee representatives are given time off for the purpose of bargaining and are paid the amount they would have earned during the working day. If the bargaining sessions extend over the normal work period, the participants are not paid overtime. In other companies, when employee representatives leave the plant to participate in multiplant bargaining, they do not lose seniority; they may or may not be paid by the company, if they are not, their compensation is usually made up by the union.

THE NEGOTIATION PROCESS

Once the union has been certified as the exclusive bargaining agent for the employees, management and the union are required by the Taft-Hartley Act to bargain with each other over wages, hours, and other conditions of employment. Traditional collective bargaining is not unlike the bargaining that goes on in an open-air marketplace or between a used car salesman and a buyer. There is a give and take, and any final agreement is less than either party would like. However, collective bargaining has become incredibly complex, not only because both parties wield power but also because unions are moving toward participation in decision making, training and development, and community relations. Further, the complexities of certain fringes such as insurance plans, retirement plans, and incentive plans affect other contracts with insurance companies or investment companies—contracts that, because of the labor agreement, that may require renegotiation.

The process of striving to obtain what you believe you should have and of attempting to keep what you do not believe the other party should have is both rough and delicate, a time of decision and controlled vacillation, a polarization of position as well as a temporization of a previous position. It is also a time when there is great temptation to wheel and deal. From a managerial viewpoint, the bargaining process must also be considered a part of conflict management. It is at the conference table that conflict issues are brought into focus. The following are some suggestions that members of the negotiating team should consider:

1. Be certain that the union representatives and/or employee representatives are in fact the representatives delegated to represent the employees in the bargaining unit. The delegation should be in the form of a written letter to management naming by name and position the persons representing the workers. This authorization should be on letterhead stationary, if possible, and signed by the known union officials.

2. Union representatives should be introduced as such and introductions of management's representatives should be made at the same time.

3. Insofar as possible, the atmosphere and attitude should be friendly and cordial. Hostility and negativism will produce a similar reaction. This does not mean a "hail fellow well met," slap-on-the-back boisterousness but rather a pleasant, businesslike approach that would be typical of any buy-sell activity where the parties are friendly and determined to conclude the bargaining in a manner satisfactory to both.

4. Listen to all arguments presented. You can always say no. Once you do say no, however, it will be difficult to retreat should this become necessary.

5. Give all members of the other team their opportunity to state their position. This will identify the strength of a position and show who is the particular proponent.

6. Know as much as you can about the backgrounds of the parties with whom you are bargaining. This may clue you on the relative strength of an initial request.

7. Do not attempt to restrict or limit the discussion to the issue. Let the conversation wander on occasion. This may provide you with additional information.

8. Do not permit a polarization of position. This will lead to stalemate. Attempt to continually identify the problems and to suggest solutions. Keep the conversation going.

9. Discussion of the facts may lead from one problem to another. Be ready to move along this line rather than attempting to block further discussion on items that seem to move off the central issue.

10. Be certain that each issue raised is clearly defined. Schedule discussion of each issue on the basis of the facts presented.

11. Insofar as possible, avoid including in the contract specific company regulations and an overabundance of procedural detail. The contract can and should make reference to job sheets, other contracts with insurance carriers, company regulations outside the scope of the agreement, or other areas which are mutually agreed upon.

12. The bargaining group—the actual negotiators—should be limited in number. The smaller the group, the fewer the interactions on matters unrelated to the issues. On the other hand, a group that is too small will reduce the necessary exchange and may be charged with not adequately representing the parties. The actual size of the group is always subject to argument. Depending on the size of the company, the number represented, the number of issues, and the relationship existing between management and the union, suggested size should probably be between 6 and 12.

13. The length of bargaining sessions must be considered in terms of fatigue and attitude. Most sessions should probably not extend beyond 3 hours, with suitable breaks for food, rest, and review of the discussions. All-day and all-night sessions are sometimes held in emergency bargaining. Even in these situations, fatigue might produce faulty judgment and possibly a polarization of position. Fatigue might also cause improper settlement, which will only produce subsequent problems.

14. The results of the agreement may have an impact on the public or the consumer. Both union and management must place the public interest, if there is one, in proper perspective and should consider public and consumer rights in reaching a settlement.

15. The collective bargaining process should be an educational experience and should provide management with additional information on employee attitudes toward existing policy. It should also give management the opportunity to explain to the union leaders—and thereby to the employees they represent—the economic problems and the complex operating problems with which management is faced.

16. Collective bargaining must be perceived as a means of identifying the best

possible solution to a problem rather than acquiring as much and giving as little as possible. The effort must be to solve rather than to compromise.

17. Both union and management must strive to be certain that all national and state laws applicable to collective bargaining and to settlements are rigorously adhered to.

18. Leadership on the part of both parties must be present, recognized, and respected.

19. Arguments range pro and con on who should do the talking during negotiations. If all discussion comes from the chief negotiator, crosscurrents and cross issues will find minimal expression and any internal disagreements within the bargaining team will not surface. This approach would present a solid, uniform, and unanimous position, creating an impression of the strength and unanimity. On the other hand, such an approach would forego much useful interaction which might help to identify and resolve some of the problems underlying a given issue. It might be advisable to try both approaches, depending on the issue under discussion.

IMPACT OF THE UNION UPON MANAGEMENT

After a union has won recognition as the bargaining representative, management will find that its relation to unionized employees and the way it handles its employment relationships is considerably changed.

Every union-management agreement places a restriction that did not previously exist on management's freedom of action. Every improvement in the agreement, from the union viewpoint, secures more for the workers and/or increasingly limits management's right to act unilaterally. This restriction of freedom affects on management in various ways. Individual dealings with workers over wage changes, hours of work, and the conditions of work are no longer possible. A shop steward is present and the first-line manager must be sure that the agreement is not violated. For example, if a worker is asked to perform certain jobs that appear to call for a higher-level skill, the worker and the union may demand a higher classification. If sales decline and the work force must be reduced, the layoff may affect the most competent because the layoff will probably affect those with the least seniority. If a new fringe is being considered for installation, the union will have to be consulted. Promotion may not go to the most competent but to the worker with the greatest seniority. Initially, the effect of these restrictions may be a reduction in efficiency. Another effect of the union is the union pressure for uniform treatment for its constituency.

ADMINISTERING THE CONTRACT

The contract is the base as well as the guide governing day-to-day union-management, worker-supervisor relationships. You must be aware that the contract will not eliminate conflict, nor will it establish policy or procedure for all activity either for the present or the future. It is not uncommon for many companies that are newly organized by a union to give the union more than the contract requires. This is an effort to reduce conflict and to maintain friendly relations. As the bargaining relationship matures, management's tendency is to reassert its rights under the contract and to insist on stricter enforcement of the contract. Many companies enjoy informal cooperation between management and union representatives. In some instances, these informal cooperative arrangements lead to private agreements to ignore certain contract provisions or not to require enforcement. These agreements may be helpful on a short-term basis, but the long-term result may be continuing union pressure for more informal concessions, resulting in increased production costs, decreased production, or poor quality. Further, concessions and continuing informal agreements become precedential in grievance cases leading to arbitration, and they may well be the determining factor in the grievance or arbitration decision. In addition, continuing concessions may become demands when new contracts are negotiated. Eventually, as management and union personnel change, continued administration of the contract may become unnecessarily complex.

Under more formal procedures, supervisors are requested to notify management of provisions of the contract that are causing difficulty so that they may be modified by agreement or may be changed through subsequent negotiation. If management takes unilateral action with respect to its interpretation of a contract provision, the union may file a protest through the grievance procedure. It should be noted that grievance machinery is sometimes used as a means of communication to improve the day-to-day operation under the contract. A review of grievances by J. H. McGuckin ("Grist for the Arbitrator's Mill," *Labor Law Journal*, 1971) indicates that most grievances are filed in disputes involving discipline rather than on contract interpretation.

As a rule of thumb, upon conclusion of bargaining and a new contract, both parties should:

1. Enjoy and show a spirit of cooperation and goodwill.
2. Issue instructions on behavior under the new contract, orient supervisors to its provisions as soon as possible, and live up to each provision strictly.
3. Observe scrupulously every commitment that is made.
4. Recognize that union representatives and managers have the appropriately delegated labor relations responsibility and avoid undercutting or bypassing this responsibility center.
5. Avoid paternalistic or gloating behavior during or after the negotiation.
6. Behavioral science research has repeatedly advised of the importance of recognizing and attempting to meet human needs. To the extent possible, collective bargaining must emphasize settlement results, laying stress on motivation and productivity. Otherwise, from a managerial viewpoint, the "givens" will not balance the "gettums," and either company strength or labor-management relations will deteriorate as a result.

TO THE MANAGER

The effect of labor relations is usually dichotomous. Both single-plant and multiplant companies tend to centralize the labor relations function in a single personnel or labor relations office empowered to make decisions in labor matters. Corporate industrial relations officers negotiate the agreement, formulate policy, and play a key role in administering the agreement. Plant industrial relations personnel and plant managers have limited authority under these conditions. The decision-making authority is frequently taken away from the first-line supervisor when there is a union. Additionally, the union often does not accept the word or decision of first-line supervisors when a centralized labor relations office is established and upper levels of management are involved in labor matters. The result is that the first-line supervisor is bypassed, thus undermining the supervisor's authority. In the long run, a company will develop better labor-management relations and better procedures in the day-to-day operations if first-line supervisors are helped and trained to do a better job instead of indirectly or directly being bypassed. Many companies have found it advantageous to establish supervisory and managerial training programs to ensure a complete understanding of the agreement and to enhance, where possible, managerial leadership.

The result of individual differences among workers and managers, the dynamics of organizational behavior, the effects of external forces, and the effects of change occurring through time practically guarantee that there can be no simple bromide or equation that can be universally applied to produce a happy, motivated, productive, and loyal employee. Effective managers must reconsider the use of the "law of effect"; they must practice the management principles of planning, organizing, coordinating, and controlling that have been researched and documented; and they must apply a perceptive quality to subordinate needs. Managers must extend their efforts to integrate these needs with those of the organization to provide the cooperative relationship essential to the well-being of the organization and the employee.

Section 10

Safeguarding the Facility

Chapter 1

Plant Protection and Security

RICHARD J. HEALY
Head, Security Department, The Aerospace Corporation

INTRODUCTION

Security in most modern, progressive organizations is now commonly recognized as an essential management element. This has not always been true, because protection against nonbusiness losses in the past has often been relegated to a minor role in the management structure, with any effort made to protect the assets of the organization usually limited to the use of watchmen or guards. However, progressive top-management representatives in industrial, business, governmental, and institutional organizations currently realize that an effective, complete assets protection program is an essential ingredient in the management of the modern, complex enterprise.

THE POTENTIAL HAZARDS

Events of the 1960s had a great influence on the changing attitude toward the protection of assets because of the increasing size, frequency, and the cost impact of all forms of losses. The increase in crime—176 percent in the 1960s—was certainly a contributing influence (Fig. 1). The pervasive image of strife and violence that developed in the form of bomb threats and riots was another.

One striking example of the cost of crime involves property loss, now estimated to be 16 billion dollars each year in the United States. Also, white-collar crime—embezzlement, bribes, and kickbacks—has apparently become a way of life.* Experts warn that although the Equity Funding and Spiro Agnew incidents made headlines in 1973, such cases are only the tip of the iceberg, and that undetected losses amounting to billions of dollars each year are passed on to the consumer in the form of price increases. Kickbacks alone, it is estimated, exceed 5 billion dollars a year, with practically all of this amount being passed on to consumers. Further, it is estimated that 15 percent of the cost of all goods and services goes to pay for dishonesty.

New hazards have also been developing in recent years because of constantly improving technology. Widespread utilization of the computer, which has been described as an uncontrolled giant brain, has made many organizations vulnerable to severe damage or serious losses because security for the computer and information being processed is

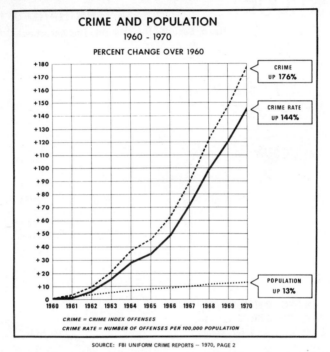

CRIME AND POPULATION
1960 - 1970
PERCENT CHANGE OVER 1960

CRIME UP **176%**

CRIME RATE UP **144%**

POPULATION UP **13%**

CRIME = CRIME INDEX OFFENSES
CRIME RATE = NUMBER OF OFFENSES PER 100,000 POPULATION

SOURCE: FBI UNIFORM CRIME REPORTS — 1970, PAGE 2

Fig. 1 The increase of crime in the 1960s—176 percent.

often not provided. As a computer operation is seemingly complex, many management representatives have assumed that it defies manipulation or misuse. This has appropriately been designated "computer mystique" (Fig. 2). The computer has already been responsible for a number of large reported losses and it has been predicted that many losses, not yet discovered, will result in many future "horror stories."

Another hazard resulting from the evolution of technology is the loss of valuable information because of industrial espionage. This risk seems to be increasing because the race to develop and market new products and services in recent years has resulted in increasingly larger expenditures for research and development. It has been estimated that the bill for research may reach 31 billion dollars in the United States in 1973 (Fig. 3). Peter F. Drucker—an international authority, business consultant, writer, and lecturer—is reported to have said that 50 percent of the gross national product will be related to the acquisition and dissemination of knowledge by 1980. The cost of espionage is not currently known and probably will never be estimated with any accuracy, because the objective of the successful industrial spy is to obtain information of value without letting the victim know that a theft has occurred. However, experts speculate that losses resulting from industrial espionage in the United States are now as much as 5 billion

---

* "Kickbacks as a Way of Life," *U.S. News and World Report*, October 29, 1973, p. 38.

dollars annually. Although it has been stated that business or industrial organizations that do not have any information of value are not competitive, the Watergate scandal clearly demonstrated that an organization does not necessarily have to be engaged in business or commerce to have information of value. Every organization, regardless of size or type, has data that require protection.

Fig. 2 "Computer mystique."

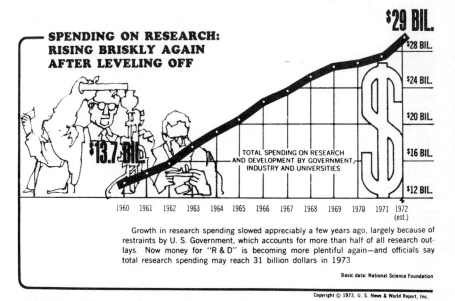

Fig. 3 The cost of research in the United States. (Chart reprinted from *U.S. News & World Report,* Jan. 22, 1973; U.S. News & World Report, Inc., Washington, D.C., 20037.)

SOME COMMON HAZARDS

PEOPLE PROBLEMS

THEFT OF ASSETS

PILFERAGE	EMBEZZLEMENT
FRAUD	INDUSTRIAL ESPIONAGE
RECORDS MANIPULATION	SHOPLIFTING
FORGERY	ROBBERY AND HIJACKING

PERSONNEL PROBLEMS

GAMBLING	ABSENTEEISM
LOANSHARKING	MISREPRESENTATION
DISAFFECTION	NARCOTICS
DISTURBED PERSONS	ANTISOCIAL BEHAVIOR

SABOTAGE AND MALICIOUS DESTRUCTION

INCENDIARY FIRE   BOMBS AND BOMB THREATS
LABOR VIOLENCE   CIVIL DISTURBANCE
VANDALISM

CONFLICTS OF INTERESTS

EMPLOYEES WITH THEIR OWN BUSINESSES
EMPLOYEES WORKING FOR COMPETITORS
KICKBACK SITUATIONS

DISASTER SITUATIONS

INDUSTRIAL EMERGENCY

EXPLOSION	FIRE
STRUCTURAL COLLAPSE	RADIATION INCIDENT
MAJOR ACCIDENT	HAZARDOUS MATERIAL INCIDENT

ENVIRONMENTALLY CAUSED

TORNADO	HURRICANE
EARTHQUAKE	FLOOD

WAR OR NUCLEAR ATTACK

Fig. 4 Some common hazards that may threaten an organization.

In addition to the threats to assets already discussed, another asset more priceless than any mentioned—employees—must be protected. As a result, awareness of the need to have a plan to cope with emergency situations is now commonly regarded as an essential element in any security plan. The fire toll is now 12,000 American lives annually, while it is estimated that more than 11 billion dollars in resources are wasted each year.† Also, about 43 percent of businesses struck by fire are unable to resume operation or are out of business within 6 months. Floods in some years cause more than 1 billion dollars in damage. In 1972, hurricane Agnes alone caused 2.2 billion dollars damage.‡

The definition of security might be examined and related to the needs of the modern day facility. According to Webster, security is "Freedom from exposure to danger, protection, safety or a place of safety." Applying this definition to present-day security needs, the threats or hazards faced by most organizations might be divided into two general categories (1) people problems including crime, such as dishonesty, and espionage and (2) problems not involving people, such as environmentally caused emergencies (Fig. 4).

PREVENTION—THE KEY

The most successful protection programs are those designed to avoid the types of risks that have been discussed. The organization that does not design controls to prevent losses but plans to deal with them after they occur is risking business suicide; because once a loss happens, it may be so great the enterprise is forced to close its doors. For example, the organization that depends mainly on arrest and prosecution to deter dishonesty may find that there are individuals who will be tempted when they realize preventive controls are ineffective or do not exist. Such individuals may decide to take a calculated risk and siphon off large amounts of funds or goods. If they are successful over a sufficient period of time, the organization may be bankrupt or be at the brink of insolvency by the time the losses are discovered.

Another argument in favor of prevention is the fact that once an incident occurs, it is difficult or virtually impossible to recover anything. Legal recourse, of course, is always available to the damaged enterprise. However, legal actions are not only costly but often ineffective. In cases of embezzlement, for instance, the embezzler, by the time of discovery, usually has disposed of all the funds that have been obtained, and so that

† *America Burning,* The Report of the National Commission on Fire Prevention, Washington, D.C., 1973, p. 1.
‡ *Newsweek,* August 12, 1972, p. 72.

restitution is impossible. Criminal prosecution, of course, is always possible, but it will be no compensation to the victimized organization to know that the individual who caused the damage has been jailed.

Loss of profit is another factor that must be included when avoidance or prevention is considered. It has been said that profit represents funds that are not wasted. As the types of losses already discussed can be classed as wasted assets, such losses must be subtracted from the profits in the case of business organizations, and they will result in increasing operating costs for other types of enterprises such as insititution and non profit organizations. For example, the business enterprise that prevents a hundred-dollar theft will realize a hundred-dollar increase in net profit. If the business earns a net profit of 2 percent, a hundred-dollar-theft loss means that sales must be increased by $5,000 to compensate for that loss.

Some hazards cannot be completely avoided. Examples are hurricanes, tornadoes, and earthquakes. However, losses can be mitigated or controlled if a plan has been developed, as a part of the assets protection program, to deal with such situations.

VULNERABILITY ANALYSIS

An analysis of the hazards faced by an organization is the first step in designing an assets protection program. This is frequently not done, and an organization experiencing losses will often attempt to solve the problem by adopting countermeasures, such as hiring a guard force, without understanding clearly where the losses are occurring. Therefore a complete vulnerability analysis of the organization must be conducted, so that the actual risks the organization may face can be neutralized by adopting appropriate preventive measures.

For example, the facility might not have a computer installation on the premises. Because of this, it might be concluded that loss of computer information would not be one of the risks faced by the enterprise. However, many organizations utilize computer service bureaus. Information being sent to a service bureau might be vulnerable if the service bureau does not have an adequate protection program. The same vulnerability exists, of course, when any information or material is sent to a subcontractor or vendor with an inadequate program to protect the material. An effective vulnerability analysis should uncover such risks.

Losses occur for three basic reasons: (1) vulnerabilities are not recognized, (2) countermeasures adopted are ineffective, (3) vulnerabilities change. The value of an assets protection program depends, not only upon the appropriateness of the countermeasures but also upon their relevance to the vulnerabilities faced by the organization. In designing countermeasures, then, the kinds of risks threatening the assets of the organization, the probability of those threats becoming actual events, and the actual impact or effect on the assets must all be considered.

When the analysis of the impact on the assets of the enterprise is being made, indirect losses as well as direct losses must be included. Both involve loss of assets and income. Potential direct losses such as money, negotiable instruments, property, and information can ordinarily be more easily cataloged than indirect losses. Examples of indirect losses are reputation, goodwill, morale of employees, and market.

Insurance may be regarded at the main factor in loss protection in some organizations. However, enlightened managements in progressive organizations are now more interested in developing complete protection programs to prevent losses rather than attempting to buy insurance to cover all risks highlighted during a vulnerability analysis. Although it might be found during a risk analysis that a large number of losses are or could be covered by insurance, it will usually be found that it is not possible to obtain sufficient coverage to protect against all the kinds of losses threatening an enterprise. Insurance coverage should generally be utilized for protection against hazards that cannot otherwise be avoided through the use of preventive techniques or controls. Potentially catastrophic risks often are, and generally should be, included in insurance coverage.

An effective vulnerability analysis usually cannot be conducted as a casual task by someone not familiar with the techniques involved or knowledgeable about countermeasures that are available to neutralize the potential threats to the enterprise. A proper analysis should ordinarily be done by an experienced security professional with the special skills to understand all the exposures present in an enterprise.

For instance, an analysis by an inexperienced individual of a working area containing cash or negotiable instruments in large quantities might result in a listing of only the physical threats, with the result that the protection provided for the area would be limited to physical security countermeasures such as identification badges, keys, locks, safes, etc. A professional threat analysis would include not only physical risks but also an analysis of procedures and the responsibility being assumed by supervisors as well as employees to ensure that the required security practices are adequate and are being followed. In summary, a complete analysis of all possible risks includes those that are obvious as well as those that are intangible.

Qualified, professional, skilled consultants are available for the organization that does not have competent in-house professional security personnel to perform a vulnerability analysis in an effective manner. If such consultants are utilized, the result will usually be that, because of their broad knowledge of the protection field, a more effective program at less cost is developed.

A word of caution. There are some security companies (offering hardware or guard service) that will propose to conduct a security survey at no cost. The objective of such a company may be self-serving, because this technique is often utilized to sell the hardware or service being offered. Also, the individual or the company representatives offering the survey will usually have knowledge only of the product or service being marketed and will not have the background or be professionally qualified to make a complete objective analysis. As a result, there is good reason to be suspicious of such proposed surveys, because they may be worth exactly what they cost—nothing.

COUNTERMEASURES

After the completion of a vulnerability analysis, the next step in the development of an assets protection program is the selection of appropriate preventive measures. A broad range of countermeasures are required to obtain effective security in most organizations. Some examples of the necessary protective controls are guards; electronic systems; fire, documents, emergency, and property controls; etc. (Fig. 5.)

Countermeasures can be placed into three general categories—procedures, people, and hardware. The proper use of appropriate countermeasures is important, because the result will be better protection at the least cost.

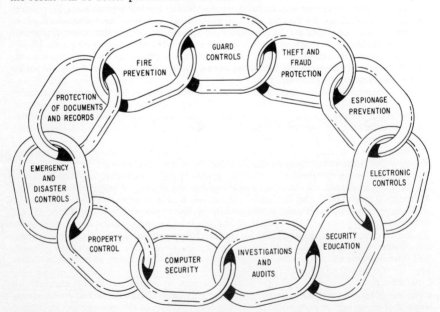

Fig. 5 Some examples of protective controls that must be interrelated to ensure an effective security program.

Procedures

Basic in any assets protection program are policies and practices, because through these the program is defined and the requirements to be followed by everyone in the enterprise are outlined and defined. For example, an essential ingredient in this area is the adoption of appropriate policy statements and practices providing for the screening of applicants. The screening process should include sufficient background checks to ensure that those being hired are of good character and are trustworthy. Unless this is done, there is a good possibility that individuals who are untrustworthy or unstable may be brought into the organization, with the result that the assets of the organization are made vulnerable. Consequently, with such threats present within the organization, it will be more difficult or perhaps even impossible to protect the assets through the use of internal controls.

Procedures and practices to be followed by all employees must be developed. A program of education should also be designed to acquaint all employees with the security requirements they will be expected to follow. The instructions can be given in meetings with employees, through the organization newspaper, and with bulletins, posters, etc. Disciplinary action to be taken when practices are not followed must also be defined and explained as a part of the education program.

The procedural aspects of the program can also be utilized to reduce security costs. Rather than expect members of the security organization, such as guards, to perform all of the security functions in the enterprise, some responsibility for security can be assigned to supervisors. Members of the security organization can then be assigned the responsibility of conducting inspections and checks to ensure that the responsibilities delegated to others are being discharged. As a result, fewer personnel will be needed in the protection organization, with a consequent reduction in personnel costs.

People

The proper planning of the second category of countermeasures, people, is particularly important from the standpoint of cost reduction, because manpower is normally the most expensive item in any protection program. For example, the average cost of one guard in the United States is more than $8,000 a year. This average cost includes both contract and in-house guards, and if the enterprise maintains its own guard force, the cost will be a great deal more.

Guards are often utilized to control entrances. This is a costly use of personnel because an entrance must usually remain open for more than one shift, which means that the number of guards needed will be increased according to the amount of time an entrance must remain open. For example, if an entrance is to remain open 24 hours a day, 7 days a week, the average number of guards required is 4.5 It can readily be seen that the cost of guards can be a significant item in a security budget and that, if possible, other means of controls should be adopted (Fig. 6). Also, the costs generated by guards must continue during the life of the facility if adequate safeguards are to be maintained.

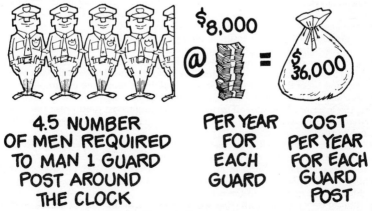

4.5 NUMBER OF MEN REQUIRED TO MAN 1 GUARD POST AROUND THE CLOCK

PER YEAR FOR EACH GUARD

COST PER YEAR FOR EACH GUARD POST

Fig. 6 The cost of one guard post.

Some organizations have attempted to reduce their costs by paying less to the guards they hire. This has a tendency to compound the problem, for the guards are then less efficient and less effective. Consequently, the hazards become greater when the enterprise attempts to reduce costs in this way.

Hardware

The proper use of hardware in a facility can result in an improvement in protection; at the same time, impressive cost savings can be realized through a reduction in personnel (that is, without the hardware, more people would be needed). Hardware includes items such as fences and other barriers, lights, locks, doors, gates, turnstiles, safes, vaults or other special security constructions, and electronic controls.

Three lines of defense Hardware may be utilized very effectively to establish protection in depth. Three lines of defense can ordinarily be established with hardware for the protection of a facility.

The edge of the property may be designated as the first line of defense; the exterior walls of the building constitute the second line; and the third line runs within the buildings. Large facilities with property and parking on the exterior of buildings will normally require all three lines of defense. Smaller facilities without surrounding property may require only the latter two.

Hardware items at the first line of defense might include barriers, gates, lights, and alarms which would be installed to discourage trespass. Barriers at the first line of defense may be divided into two types—natural and structural. Natural barriers are rivers, lakes, streams, cliffs, canyons, or other terrain difficult to traverse. Structural barriers are such items as fences or walls.

Use of hardware items at the second line of defense is more important than at the first line because they will be utilized to prevent entrance into buildings. Protection at this point should include the roof, basement, and sides of each building to be secured. Experts warn that any opening of 96 square inches or more which is less than 18 feet above the ground must be secured.

As a result, hardware should be utilized, wherever possible, for protection of doors, windows, and other openings such as manholes, grates that lead to basements, elevator shafts, openings for ventilating equipment, and skylights.

When personnel entrances must be controlled, hardware items can also be utilized to reduce to a minimum the number of access points required at the second line of defense.

Generally, control of personnel entrances is required for two reasons: first, to prevent those who should not have access from entering the facility and, second, to control thefts. If guards are used for control, the cost will increase proportionally with additional entrances. In addition, the more entrances there are, the more difficult the control becomes. Of course, it is much easier to concentrate on the control of one entrance and to put all security controls on it than it is to control a number of entrances.

One technique for eliminating personnel entrances is to interconnect buildings on a site, so that a group of buildings can be treated as one unit in planning entrance controls. For example, barriers such as block walls or chain-link fencing can be used to interconnect buildings. Then, instead of having a separate entrance for each building on the site, one or two openings might be provided for the entire site.

Other methods of interconnecting buildings can also be considered. For example, attractive, well-lighted underground interconnecting links could be utilized. Anyone entering the interior of the facility would then have free access to all the buildings through the underground links. Buildings can also be connected by walkways or bridges. This technique is commonly used to connect buildings above the ground-floor level.

Barriers, such as fencing, should also be used so that vehicles are prevented from entering the interior of the site. If service vehicles and trucks must enter the inner area, a security-controlled gate should be provided. This gate should be locked and controlled when not in use.

Hardware barriers may also be used at the second line of defense to protect areas utilized for the disposal of scrap or trash. If a provision is not made for controls for such areas and the material is stored in an uncontrolled area, an individual who has stolen something and has placed it in the trash or scrap will find it easy to pick it up during the night or when no one is in the area.

Examples of items of hardware that would be useful at the second line of defense are fencing or other barriers, locks, lights, electronic detectors, closed-circuit television, bars for windows and other openings, etc.

If the hardware at the third line of defense is properly planned, an intruder who has penetrated the first two lines will not find any material or information of value readily available. The value and the importance of the items to be protected will determine the type of controls necessary here. A few examples of items and areas to be considered for protection are cashier offices or other areas containing significant sums of money; laboratories or research areas vulnerable to industrial espionage because new products or designs are being developed there; areas containing negotiable instruments such as checks, drafts, and airline tickets; accounts receivable and other vital company records; and classified material if the company is a government contractor.

If negotiable instruments or other valuables are removed surreptitiously, the loss may not be recognized for some time. Then, when the loss is finally discovered, it may be impossible to determine who committed the theft and when it happened.

Therefore the type of protection selected for these areas should at least offer security against surreptitious entry. Otherwise, an intruder might gain access to material, copy it or remove it, and yet leave no indication that the area has been entered. And if valued proprietary information is copied or reproduced, the results could be damaging, for a competitor could use the information with great success, and the victim company would not even know the information had been taken. A common key lock will not provide protection against surreptitious entry.

At the third line of defense, hardware items that would be useful include locks, safes, vaults, alarm detectors, lights, etc.

Electronic Controls

Electronic controls are also hardware items that can be utilized to improve protection and at the same time reduce costs. As electronic controls are only one hardware element, they cannot by themselves be relied upon to give protection but should be integrated with the other hardware items already discussed, so that each will act as a check upon the others through some form of operational dependence. For example, even if intruders penetrated all the hardware items at the three lines of defense, and effective electronic system inside the third line of defense should announce their presence.

"Electronics" and "automation" have become magic words in the missile and space age. Unfortunately, their use in recent years has generally been limited to the installation of devices and components to solve specific security problems. A lack of understanding of the effectiveness as well as the general potential uses of electronic devices has no doubt been one factor in their limited use for security. Probably a most significant reason for the lack of use of automation or electronic techniques is that their use has not been approached as a system problem. Often, electronic devices are installed on a piecemeal basis to meet needs as they develop. The installation and the design is also often done by electricians, and a hodgepodge of equipment and devices then usually results. Consequently, the use of electronics should be treated as an engineering task with all elements tied together into a complete system.

Detectors A broad range of reliable security and fire protection detectors are manufactured and marketed by a number of companies. The effectiveness, efficiency, and dependability of the devices produced by the leading manufacturers can be considered good. In general, electronic devices are used to detect abnormal conditions. The capacities of detectors can be compared to the senses of a person, but they are more reliable—if, that is, they are properly installed. For example, the detector never sleeps and is alert 24 hours a day, 7 days a week, but a person may not be alert all the time because of fatigue, an emotional problem, or any number of other factors.

When utilized for security and fire protection, a detector is actually functioning as a machine and is performing a machine task. Therefore it is a mistake to attempt to make a person react like a machine when electronic devices may be more cost-effective and better suited to certain security and fire protection tasks than are the human senses. Each device is usually designed to detect a single phenomenon and, for that reason, each situation must be analyzed to determine the type of device or devices that will be most efficient. No one device will be adaptable to every location and environment. Also, more than one type of device may be required in a particular situation to give coverage for all the items that need to be monitored or protected.

Closed-circuit television   One of the most widely accepted electronic techniques for the reduction of personnel in recent years is the use of closed-circuit television. With closed-circuit television, the capability of a guard at a post or at a control center can be extended so that multiple entrances can be controlled. Guards that would be needed to control the entrances being monitored with television can then be eliminated, with a resulting reduction in labor costs.

The minicomputer   Another electronic technique that will also result in the elimination of manpower is the minicomputer. With a minicomputer it is possible to design a system in such a way that all electronic protection is interfaced with the computer and controlled by it. All routine tasks can then be programmed so that they are performed by the computer, while protection personnel can be assigned nonroutine tasks which require human intellect or judgment.

A broad range of tasks can be planned into such a computer-controlled system. In addition to performing the normal security functions—such as access control, alarm supervision, etc.—a minicomputer control system can, by expansion, perform other functions as well. For example, utility alarm supervision, process control monitoring, and time and attendance reporting might be added (Fig. 7).

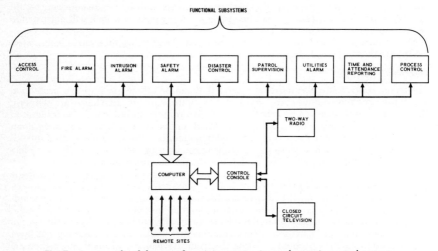

Fig. 7   An example of the use of a minicomputer in an electronic control system.

The minicomputer is a digital machine that is smaller in size and less costly than its counterpart, the larger, all-purpose machine that has been in use for many years. It weighs 50 to 100 pounds and, unlike the larger machine, has no special air-conditioning or voltage requirements. A complete installation consists of a minicomputer, input and output devices, a data storage device if necessary, and software.

Although the cost of a basic minicomputer is in the 10,000-dollar range, additional data storage may be necessary. In that case the cost of the machine would have to be increased to cover the amount of additional memory required. Basic software or programming for the operation of the minicomputer is usually furnished by the manufacturer. However, any additional application software must be furnished by the purchaser. This may also increase the cost of the installation.

The minicomputer and access control   If a minicomputer is used to control personnel at entrances and within a facility, essentially all the manpower required for this type of control can be eliminated. This can be particularly beneficial from a cost-reduction standpoint. Earlier in this chapter it was pointed out that closed-circuit television can be utilized to reduce personnel costs. However, this technique can usually be used only during low-traffic periods due to the fact that an individual at a remote location must make an identification of each individual and take action to either deny or allow access. A computer-controlled access system does not have this limitation, because a computer is able to process data and respond in microseconds. As there is no significant time delay in a computer identification and response, as there is with closed-circuit television, there is virtually no limit to the number of people that a computer can handle in such an installation. (This, of course, assumes that the computer memory has been properly sized and that the system has been designed and engineered to accommodate the traffic that is to be handled.) As a result, when a computer is used for access control, it is possible to eliminate more personnel than with closed-circuit television, because the computer can be used as the access controller at all times.

In addition to reduction of costs, another benefit is possible with a properly designed computer-controlled access system. This benefit—more positive identification and control of personnel—stems from the fact that the human error factor, which is always present in every control system requiring identification by a human being, is eliminated.

A positive physical control of personnel at access points would be a basic requirement in the system design, since the minicomputer would be acting as the control mechanism and substituting for manpower ordinarily used for controlling access. One method of accomplishing an effective control would be to utilize a "man trap" or double-door booth arrangement.

In order to have a positive identification of those at access points, coded cards and card readers inside of all booths might be utilized. Each of those who were authorized to have access would be issued a card containing an invisible code which would be unique to each individual. To gain access, an individual would place the card in a reader at an access point. The computer memory would be searched, and if it had been programmed to allow the individual to have access at that control point, the computer would automatically unlock the door.

The identification could be further sophisticated by the addition of a remembered code which would be issued to each individual. A 10-digit keyboard might be added to the card reader and connected to the computer. Each individual desiring access would then be required to punch in his or her remembered code—perhaps three or four digits—which would also be unique to each individual. If the combination of the remembered code and the coded card met the programmed requirements for the individual requesting access in the computer memory, the computer would take the necessary action to allow access. The identification media combination just described would ensure positive identification of the card and code and would generally be more effective than depending on guards or other personnel to identify individuals through the use of badges or the like.

The booth or "man trap" arrangement previously mentioned to physically control access might be designed so that an individual desiring entrance would enter the first door, which would then lock behind him. The inside or second door would also be locked and would remain locked until the individual had satisfactorily accessed the computer memory with the appropriate identification. The computer would then allow access by unlocking the inner door, keeping the outer door locked until the individual had completed the entrance procedure.

A wire communication link between the booth and the control center would also be desirable, so that an individual in the booth and the control center operator could enter into a conversation when necessary. Also, a closed-circuit TV camera might be installed in each booth, not for the purpose of identification but so the control center operator would be able to observe the booth on a monitor in case of an alarm or other problem. Also, sensors could be installed in the booth so that the control center operator would be alerted to an attempted penetration.

Two or more individuals entering the booth after one individual had properly identified himself could, of course, be a problem. To counteract this, a load cell might be installed in the floor of the booth so that each person entering would be weighed. This would not be an identification feature and hence the weight of each individual, within 15 or 20 pounds, would be programmed into the computer. If more than one individual entered the booth, this fact would be recognized by the computer because of the excess weight. However, the 15 or 20 pounds excess weight allowed in the computer memory would compensate for a heavy briefcase or package the individual might be carrying. A turnstile might be used instead of the booth. All the control components described in the discussion of the booth could also be incorporated into the design of a turnstile.

As previously mentioned, an appropriately sized and programmed minicomputer would not cause any delay at the access points because it would respond immediately to the proper identification signals. However, an average time of about 7 seconds would be required to process each individual through an entrance point. An analysis of traffic through each access point would be necessary to determine the number of booths and turnstiles that would be required at each location. Each facility would be required to relate the amount of traffic at each access point to the amount of queuing time individuals could be expected to accept. The number of booths or turnstiles required at each entrance would then be determined.

Those exiting could also be processed out by the computer. Then it would be necessary to design the booths and turnstiles so that they could be adjusted to control traffic in either direction—in or out. During the time heavy traffic was entering, the majority of booths and turnstiles could be programmed to accommodate this need. During heavy exit traffic, the majority could be reversed to accommodate those leaving. The identification routine for those leaving could also be simplified. For example, although both a card and remembered code might be required for entrance, only one—the card or code—might be utilized to activate the computer memory so that the doors in a booth or a turnstile would unlock.

REFERENCES

As it is impossible to cover the entire field of plant protection and security in a single chapter, the following texts written by the author are suggested for those who desire to obtain more data on the subject matter discussed above:
1. Richard J. Healy: *Design for Security,* Wiley, New York, 1968.
2. Richard J. Healy: *Disaster Planning,* Wiley, New York, 1969.
3. Richard J. Healy and Timothy J. Walsh: *Industrial Security Management,* American Management Association, New York, 1971.
4. Richard J. Healy and Timothy J. Walsh: *Protecting Your Business against Espionage,* American Management Association, New York, 1973.
5. Timothy J. Walsh and Richard J. Healy: *Protection of Assets Manual,* Insurors Press, Santa Monica, Calif., 1973.

Chapter **2**

Safety

WILLIAM R. MILLER
Manager, Corporate Safety Programs, Goodyear Tire & Rubber Company

INTRODUCTION

The 1970 Occupational Safety and Health Act has added a new dimension to business and industry—that of enforcing a safe workplace for employees. An approach to establishing and maintaining control of this new dimension should be no different from controls on other functions, such as production, personnel, engineering, finance, etc.

Safety Management Objectives

Vital to any business function is an effective cost-control program—in safety, a program that allows for specific budgeting for injury cost and, equally important, specific accountability for injuries. This method assumes that employee injury costs should be controlled just as any other production costs, since they increase operating overhead, as do the expenses of raw material, parts, and labor.

The High Costs of Accidents

This is not a cold, inhuman approach to safety. There is a direct correlation between cost and human suffering. An accident that causes a great deal of pain and suffering will also generate high cost and loss of productivity. Thus, elimination of high-cost accidents will not only save money but also make the workplace safer and minimize the possibility of accidents that generate suffering.

THE WORKPLACE AS A SYSTEM

A systems approach must be established to provide current measurements of conditions relating to problems in safety. The feedback from this system must be comprehensible and relevant. It must also be flexible and provide outputs that are understandable by the one who is expected to make the system work—the supervisor. For large, multiplant companies, the computer is a very useful tool in providing output data from an effective safety system.

MONITORING WORKPLACE ACTIVITY

The design of the system must give cognizance to factors that are not controllable. Performance or goal setting becomes the key to optimizing an acceptable safety program, using systems theory in controlling. Section 5 of OSHA states:

> *(a)* Each employer—
> (1) shall furnish to each of his employees employment and a place of employment which are free from recognized hazards that are causing or are likely to cause death or serious physical harm to his employees;
> (2) shall comply with occupational safety and health standards promulgated under this Act.
> *(b)* Each employee shall comply with occupational safety and health standards and all rules, regulations, and orders issued pursuant to this Act which are applicable to his own actions and conduct.

It has been estimated that these requirements will affect the lives of almost 60 million employees and 4½ million companies. There is no escape for any company doing business that is affected by interstate commerce.

QUANTIFYING SAFETY PERFORMANCE

Recently, some companies began to look at safety and health in a very positive manner—the philosophy being that of maximizing manpower availability. This is in direct contrast to the general philosophy of the past—to prevent accidents. An accident or illness reduces the availability of the victim's labor, which in turn reduces productivity and increases the overhead cost (medical staff, compensation, support employees). Thus, increasing available manpower increases productivity and reduces overhead. This approach to safety and health is good business management philosophy.

It is a fact that in good business management today, the costs of employee injuries must be handled and controlled like any other production costs, because occupational injuries and fatalities increase a company's operating costs, as do the expenses of raw materials, parts, and labor.

In general, production costs are controlled by:
1. *Budgeting.* Setting up a budget based on a cost that is expected and accepted.
2. *Costing.* Calculating, recording, and allocating current cost for the guidance of management.
3. *Accountability.* Holding the supervisor of each company unit accountable when the cost of a unit exceeds its budget.

There are certain problems that must be recognized, however, when a company starts to apply these principles to the control of injury costs. One of the most serious problems encountered is the difficulty of determining the cost of severe injuries on a current time basis. A systems analysis approach will improve our ability to predict and control these costs accurately. Severe injuries usually account for 50 percent or more of a company's total injury cost. Yet the individual loss from this type of injury often cannot be fully determined until years have passed. This is why historical safety data is so important.

Another problem lies in the fact that compensation benefits—a basic part of injury cost—vary widely from state to state. It is, therefore, unjust to compare the performance of a plant supervisor in a high-cost state with that of a supervisor in a low-cost state if actual injury costs are used as the basis for comparison.

The cost of a fatality can also be influenced by the number of the victim's dependents. Here again, the supervisor has no control over dependency matters; yet the supervisor will be heavily penalized when actual costs are compared if the victim happened to have a number of dependents.

In my opinion, there are two motivators for action in safety:

1. *Cost.* To the company, employee, and employee's family
2. Federal standards (safety and health)

Data Collection

The federal law added a health dimension that requires some pure research before appropriate standards can be developed and promulgated. The recordkeeping provisions of the act are designed so that information will be accumulated—information specific enough to provide some answers—along with research that will be done by the Department of Health, Education, and Welfare. Companies should take advantage of

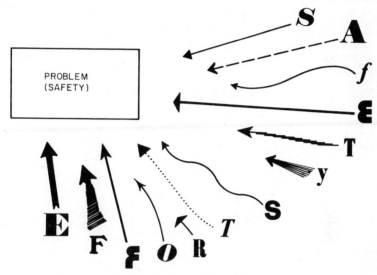

Fig. 1   Usual approach to safety.

this opportunity to examine or reexamine their criteria in the areas of safety and health. Some real advantages and answers can be derived on a company basis long before the federal government gets the answers. To accomplish this, a completely new analytical approach must be taken. This new approach can and should incorporate the *cost* approach previously mentioned, in addition to an approach that meets federal requirements. It should be a systems analysis approach to safety, an approach that represents progressive management philosophy in almost all other areas. This approach permits current evaluations, so that criteria can be changed frequently if necessary.

Applying systems analysis to safety.   How does systems analysis or systems theory apply to safety in terms of cost and federal standards? How can this theory or approach be used in focusing management's attention on the area of safety? But most important, how can this approach be used by safety engineers to design efficient safety programs to meet an ever-changing environment?

First, there is the approach to safety most have taken in the past (see Fig. 1). A problem is identified and action is taken. The action is taken, in most cases, on a very limited amount of real information. In all other industrial disciplines—personnel, production, engineering, finance, sales, industrial relations—there are technical publications, case studies, or research data to assist in problem solving. This is not true in the field of safety. This is why the Federal Occupational Safety and Health Act of 1970 is a labor-oriented bill. Management had no real documentation as to the real problems in safety. The causes of most accidents are not the unsafe conditions as shown by safety committee minutes and labor-management safety inspection reports. Examine them and you will find such things as light bulbs that need replacing, oil spills on floors, window glass broken, etc. None will show that the greater percentage of accidents are the result of unsafe acts of employees. Consequently, records evaluations indicate that the major causes of accidents are hazardous workplaces provided by management. Only a systems approach will permit future investigations to identify the real causes of accidents in plants.

A system is defined as an arrangement, set, or collection of things connected in such a manner as to form an entity or whole. Looking at safety in this manner puts it in the same perspective as any other control system such as maintenance control, quality control, production control, engineering control, etc.

How will a systems approach to safety permit examination of the working environment? There are controllable and uncontrollable inputs to the working environment (see Fig. 2). These, in combination or singularly, can result in an accident.

These are some uncontrollable inputs: age of employee, experience on job (particularly in union shop), sex, finances, attitude toward work, attitude toward management, family or home environment.

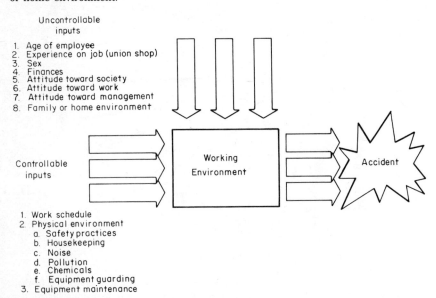

Uncontrollable
inputs

1. Age of employee
2. Experience on job (union shop)
3. Sex
4. Finances
5. Attitude toward society
6. Attitude toward work
7. Attitude toward management
8. Family or home environment

Controllable
inputs

Working
Environment

Accident

1. Work schedule
2. Physical environment
  a. Safety practices
  b. Housekeeping
  c. Noise
  d. Pollution
  e. Chemicals
  f. Equipment guarding
3. Equipment maintenance

Fig. 2 The accident process.

These are some controllable inputs: work schedule, physical environment (safety practices, housekeeping, noise, pollution, chemicals, and equipment guarding), and equipment maintenance.

The interrelationship of controllable and uncontrollable factors may be shown graphically as in Fig. 3.

Teaching safe behavior.   With these two factors kept in mind, safety problems can be considered from another point of view. Management has permitted over the years a concentration of efforts on the physical environment. Yet the volumes of safety data that plants have collected over the years indicate that unsafe conditions are the problem. The real problem in safety is people committing *unsafe acts*. The real job in safety is monitoring development of proper attitudes. This is not easy. How does systems analysis help in this area? The supervisor is the key.

A supervisor teaches each employee what the company expects regarding work schedules, quality of work, quantity of work, company policies and procedures, and safety practices and procedures. Safety, the supervisor feels, is the responsibility of the safety engineer or other members of the safety department. It is not. It is the supervisor's responsibility to train the employee in safe work practices and to insist on compliance, just as in matters of absenteeism, quality and quantity of work, and other company policies and procedures.

The safety engineer can provide some assistance and guidance in approach, but this individual's main responsibility is *measuring* and evaluating safety performance, just as

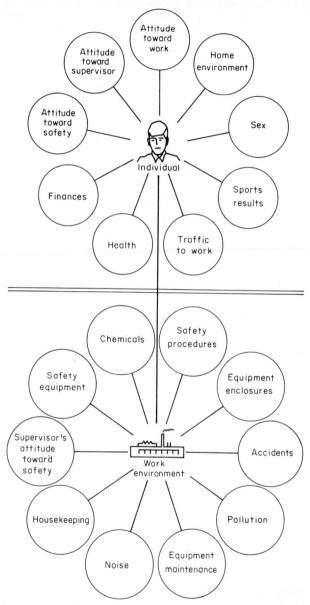

Fig. 3   Interrelationships of factors.

quality control monitors quality, production control monitors production, and finance monitors cost.   Quality control has standards or specifications on the basis of which comparisons can be made.   Production has tickets or orders to meet, sales has quotas to meet, finance has market data for guidance.   The standards are not frequency or severity, because these terms mean different things to the few people who really know what they mean.

Measuring safety on the basis of cost puts it into language the janitor as well as the board chairman can understand. Peter Drucker, in his book *The Effective Executive,** states that there are two important criteria in being effective: *Making a contribution and making an effective decision.* If a contribution is defined as the utilization of available resources or knowledge, and an effective decision as one that involves follow-up or feedback, then it is possible to develop an effective safety system as shown in Fig. 4.

What does this figure show?

1. Develop criteria for measuring safety performance. As suggested previously, the criteria should depend on terms that everyone understands—cost, lost time, etc. (something other than "frequency" and "severity"). The federal law requires that occupational injuries or illnesses be reported in three categories—fatalities, lost-time cases, and nonfatal cases without lost time. These, in combination or by themselves, become yardsticks for measuring safety performance.

2. Measure the criteria to determine whether the performance goal is being met. In measuring, you will probably find that there are problems that require immediate

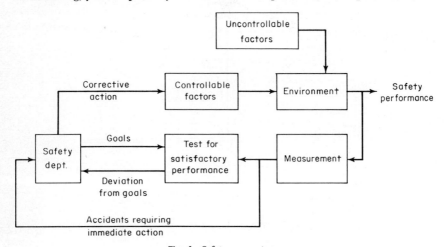

Fig. 4 Safety as a system.

action and those that will take longer. The more time-consuming ones usually involve feasibility studies and budgeting.

3. The problem areas are identified by the safety department, which recommends corrective action to be taken; so safety becomes a self-correcting system. It is similar to the operation of your furnace—you set the thermostat for the set point, and the thermostat reacts by setting the necessary parts of the furnace in motion to bring the temperature up to the set point (goal). But, what happens if you meet your goals? This is an indication that your goals are set too low.

Use of a Computer

Until now, utilization of a computer has not been mentioned, because use of a computer should be determined by the quantity of data to be processed. Large companies cannot, in my opinion, process data and keep current for decision making without use of a computer.

Figure 5 shows where the computer fits into the safety control system. The information that most of us have on safety is in files and in such a state that its effective use is almost impossible. Therefore the computer, with very minimal effort, can be used in analyzing and storing information for instant recall for decision making. It is recognized that there are many problems to be solved in developing sound safety programs. One

* Peter Drucker, *The Effective Executive,* Harper and Row, New York, 1974.

of the severe problems is inadequate data and lack of proper and immediate analysis of the limited data we do have in our files (see Fig. 6).

Using a computer permits provision to each plant, on a regular basis, an analysis of the accident experience over the measured period—monthly, quarterly, etc.

Information for research and program planning can be obtained because it is stored in the computer. Information from the accident report or source document includes age, part of body involved, location (plant), equipment or processes, sex, time on job, repeaters, supervisor's injury record, cost, medical history, and chemical exposures.

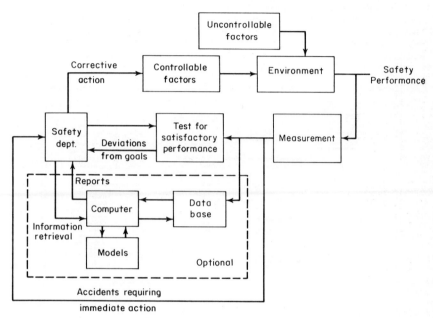

Fig. 5 Safety management system.

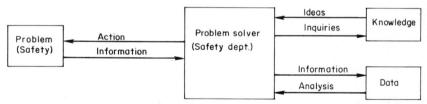

Fig. 6 Safety data base.

Therefore the source document beomes the most important and significant tool in defining various occupational hazards, including safety or health. To do this, most companies will need to redesign the document, commonly referred to as a *report-of-injury form*. The criteria for this form can be taken from the reporting requirement of the Occupational Safety and Health Act of 1970.

Figure 7 is an example of a source document that meets a company's requirements and also OSHA requirements. The company requirements are more strenuous than federal requirements. Detailed examination of this document shows that it includes all information required for determining and defining all occupational safety and health hazards.

EFFECTIVE CORRECTIVE ACTION

Problem Identification

Adequate data will identify many problem areas. It is the manager's job to select the major problem areas that will maximize manpower availability and minimize costs incurred by accidents. It is also the manager's responsibility to find alternate solutions for these problems. Next, the manager has to recommend to management those solutions

THE GOODYEAR TIRE AND RUBBER COMPANY
REPORT OF INJURY

CASE NO.

EMPLOYE NAME — LAST, FIRST, MIDDLE			PLANT LOCATION — CITY & STATE		
SOCIAL SECURITY NO. (1-9) — —	AGE	SEX ☐ 1-MALE ☐ 2-FEMALE	PLANT NO. (10-11)	DEPARTMENT NO. (12-15)	SHIFT NO.
HOME ADDRESS — STREET, CITY, STATE				DATE OF INJURY (16-21)	TIME OF INJURY
HOME PHONE NO.	C.C. NO.	CONTINUOUS SERVICE — MO. & YR.		DATE & TIME REPORTED TO MEDICAL DEPT.	
PRESENT JOB	JOB INJURED ON — TIME ON THIS JOB			LOC. OF ACCIDENT - ON OR OFF CO. PREMISES?	

CAUSE OF INJURY
ENTER APPROPRIATE CODE NUMBER HERE → (22-23)

Struck by Object
01 Hand Tool or machine in use
02 Falling or flying object
03 Tipping, sliding or rolling object
04 Object handled by other person
09 Other

Strain
11 In lifting
12 In using tool or machine
13 In pushing or pulling
14 In holding or carrying
15 In reaching

Fall or Slip
21 On same level
22 To or from different levels (stairs, docks, ramps, platforms, scaffolds, ladders, etc.)
23 Slip (not fall)
29 Other falls (escalators, etc.)

Striking Against Object
31 Objects being handled
32 Stepping on sharp objects
33 Stationary objects
34 Moving parts of machine

Caught In, On, or Between
41 Machine or machine parts
42 Other mechanical apparatus
43 Object being handled and other object
49 Other

Contact with Temperature Extremes
51 Steam or hot fluids
52 Welding flash
53 Fire or flame
54 Hot or molten metal
59 Other (frostbite, sunstroke, heat exhaustion, freezing, etc.)

Inhalation, Absorption, Swallowing
61 Absorption or other skin contact with substance
62 Breathing gases, vapors, fumes, dusts
63 Swallowing substance
70 Contact with Electric Current
80 Foreign Body in Eye

Miscellaneous
91 Accident involving moving motor vehicle (tow motor, lift truck)
92 Explosion or flareback
99 Other

PART OF BODY VS. TYPE OF INJURY

24	25	26	27	28	29	30	31	32	33	34	35

Enter letter for part of body in even-numbered square, followed by letter for type of injury in adjacent odd-numbered square.

Part of Body		Type of Injury
A—Head	M—Knee	A—Laceration
B—Ears	N—Ankle	B—Contusion
C—Eyes	O—Feet	C—Strain-sprain
D—Neck	P—Toes	D—Abrasion
E—Shoulder	Q—Chest	E—Burn-thermal
F—Arms	R—Abdomen	F—Burn-chemical
G—Elbow	S—Groin	G—Foreign body
H—Wrist	T—Back Cervical	H—Puncture Wound
I—Hands	U—Back Dorsal	I—Fracture
J—Fingers	V—Back Lumbo-Sacral	J—Dislocation
K—Hip	W—Pelvis	K—Hernia
L—Leg	X—Other	L—Amputation
		M—Electric Shock
		O—Other

NAME OF EQUIPMENT, MATERIAL OR PROCESS INVOLVED (36-58) ____________

A. CIRCLE ONE: (59)
1. Injury
2. Skin disorders or diseases
3. Dust diseases of the lungs (pneumoconioses)
4. Respiratory conditions due to toxic agents
5. Poisoning (systemic effects of toxic materials)
6. Disorders due to physical agents (other than toxic materials)
7. Disorders due to repeated trauma
8. All other illnesses

B. Extent of injury or illness (60) (Check only one)
[1] FATALITY
[2] LOST TIME
[3] OTHER REPORTABLE

C. If an illness, complete the following:
Diagnosis 1. ____________
Agent (61-80) 1. ____________

PHYSICIAN NAME - ADDRESS	HOSPITAL NAME - ADDRESS

HISTORY
To Be Completed By Employe
PLEASE PRINT

BRIEF DESCRIPTION OF ACCIDENT & INJURY, MENTION CIRCUMSTANCES BEFORE, DURING & IMMEDIATELY FOLLOWING CLAIMED ACCIDENT

SUPERVISOR'S NAME	NAME OF WITNESS TO ACCIDENT	EMPLOYE SIGNATURE	DATE SIGNED

MEDICAL DEPARTMENT

Fig. 7 Data collection form.

which will return the greatest benefit to the company for the cost to implement the solutions. Finally, the manager must follow up the solution implementation.

Data collected from source documents should be sorted in at least two ways. The first should be by work area—for example, by department. This sort quickly identifies areas that have the highest probability or occurrence of accidents. The second sort identifies common problems throughout the entire report area or plant.

From these two groupings, a major problem area and a major type or cause of injury can be chosen. The following should be considered in identifying these two major problems: number of accidents, costs of accidents, number of accidents per person, number of accidents per man-hour, number of days lost, and number of safety grievances.

Determining Solutions

There are two approaches to analyzing safety problems: the top-down approach and the bottom-up approach.

The top-down approach considers a problem. The problem, is then divided into three components: man, machine, and environment. Under each component are listed those

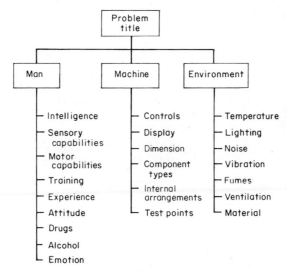

Fig. 8 Top-down approach.

EQUIPMENT ANALYSIS

Component	Failure or error mode	Effects on:		Hazard severity	Frequency	Detection methods	Recommendations or remarks
		Other components	Total system				

Fig. 9 Equipment analysis.

items that will contribute to the problem. Some items to be considered are shown in Fig. 8. A summary analysis is made to describe the probability of the problem occurring, the extent of damage, method and time of problem detection, reaction time available, action after the problem has occurred, and recommendations to prevent the problem from occurring or to minimize the extent of damage.

There are two bottom-up approaches, one for equipment and one for the job or person interfacing with equipment. The method is to consider the failure and its effect on each component in the equipment or each step that a person takes. Sample forms are shown in Figs. 9 and 10.

Solution Selection

The top-down and bottom-up approaches will generate many possible solutions. Selection of the solutions to be implemented should be made by considering each solution with respect to effectiveness in reducing costs and maximizing manpower availability, cost to implement, the severity of the problem, the frequency or probability of its occurrence, management acceptance (consideration of company policies), and labor acceptance (consideration of union practices).

OVERVIEW OF FEDERAL REQUIREMENTS

The Occupational Safety and Health Act (OSHA) of 1970, a law which went into effect on April 28, 1971, provides guidelines for improving safety and health in the workplace. By requiring industry to comply, the act establishes a common reference base. This should lift safety and health to a higher plateau throughout American industry.

The act provides for the formulation of standards by the Department of Labor governing the conditions, practices, means, methods, operations, or processes used by employers in the conduct of their businesses. Where specific standards are not applicable, the employer is held to a high degree of care for employee safety by what Congress has

JOB HAZARD ANALYSIS

Job steps or tasks	Environment or machinery involved	Name of hazard	Hazard description	Hazard severity	Recommendations

Fig. 10   Job hazard analysis.

conceived to be every employer's "general duty" to safeguard employees by maintaining a safe workplace.

The constitutional right of due process is preserved. An employer aggrieved by punitive action taken by the Department of Labor has the right to question that action before the Occupational Safety and Health Review Commission, an independent administrative body, and its courts.

The act has an even broader reach. The need for vast research in occupational safety and health, funded by the federal government, is recognized, and the development of reliable statistics on industrial hazards, to be processed through a central bureau, is an important requirement of the act. Employers are involved. All except those with fewer than eight employees must maintain records of industrial accidents. They may be called upon to participate in statistical surveys to be conducted by the Bureau of Labor statistics.

When Congress passed the act, it preempted the field of legislation on occupational safety and health. No state law inconsistent with the terms of the act could thereafter be enforced. This result comes about through operation of the constitutional doctrine of the supremacy of federal law.

The act contains provisions inviting the states to step in and take over all or any part of the responsibility of administering and enforcing the occupational safety and health laws applicable to employment within their state. This invitation is a difficult one for the states to refuse, since Congress made it attractive by the offer of substantial grants of money available, both to cover the states' cost of developing the plan under which it will administer its safety and health laws and to defray a large part of the costs of administering the plan over the years.

OSHA will not be phased out as the states step in and enforce their own safety and health standards under OSHA-approved state plans.

OSHA must continue to maintain vigilance to the end that the state standards are enforced with the same effectiveness as OSHA standards are enforced.

The act specifies certain conditions which state plans must meet before they can be approved by the Secretary of Labor. Once these conditions or criteria have been met, and the Secretary will make that determination, he is bound to approve the plan.

Labor does not favor turning over the enforcement of safety and health standards to the states. Its experience with state enforcement in previous years was such as to leave it with the conviction that once the states reassume jurisdiction over enforcement, it will become lax and and the promise of federal legislation will be lost. Labor can be expected to insist upon strict enforcement by state personnel or to make a quick call for OSHA intervention.

Management and business should oppose institution of state plans because of the possibility of lack of uniformity in standards. This should be of great importance to large companies operating in more than one state.

The Occupational Safety and Health Act, in its effort to provide complete protection for the employee, adopted national consensus standards, established federal standards, and established proporietary standards.

The principal sources of the national consensus standards are the American National Standards Institute (ANSI) and the National Fire Protection Association (NFPA).

Index